Reservoir Simulation

Calvin C. Mattax
Editor
Reservoir Div. Manager
Exxon Production Research Co. (retired)

Robert L. Dalton
Editor
Training Div. Manager
Exxon Production Research Co.

First Printing
Henry L. Doherty Memorial Fund of AIME
Society of Petroleum Engineers

Richardson, TX
1990

Dedication

To the late L.W. Welch Jr., whose interest in advancing the science of reservoir engineering was a constant source of inspiration.

ISBN 1-55563-028-6

SPE Monograph Series

The Monograph Series of the Society of Petroleum Engineers was established in 1965 by action of the SPE Board of Directors. The Series is intended to provide authoritative, up-to-date treatment of the fundamental principles and state of the art in selected fields of technology. The Series is directed by the Society's Monograph Committee. A committee member designated as Monograph Editor provides technical evaluation with the aid of the Review Committee. Below is a listing of those who have been most closely involved with the preparation of this monograph.

Monograph Review Committee

George J. Hirasaki, Shell Development Co., Monograph Editor
George E. Slater, OGCI-Software
Pang T. Woo, Technology Consultants Inc.

Monograph Committee (1989)

John L. Gidley, John L. Gidley & Assocs. Inc., Chairman
Glenn P. Coker, Amoco Corp.
Satish K. Kalra, Arco Oil & Gas Co.
Medhat M. Kamal, Arco Oil & Gas Co.
Charles E. Konen, Amoco Production Co.
Raymond E. Roesner, Atlas Wireline Services
David R. Underdown, Arco Oil & Gas Co.
Robert R. Wood, Shell Western E&P Inc.

Authors

All the authors are either current or former employees of Exxon Production Research Co. (EPR).

Perry Cockerham, Jim Hutfilz, and Vic Hvolboll are members of the senior staff in the Reservoir Div. at EPR.

Tom Boberg, Hugh Jacks, and Ed Woods are advisers in the Reservoir Div. at EPR.

Bob Rossen is a supervisor in the Reservoir Div. at EPR.

Jerry Hillestad is a Reservoir Engineering Manager at Esso Australia Ltd.

Bob Dalton is manager of the Training Div. at EPR.

Bill Watts is a supervisor in the Production Operations Div. at EPR.

Cal Mattax and Don Peaceman, retired from EPR, are independent consultants.

Joe Richardson, retired from EPR, is a consultant at J.G. Richardson Consultants Inc.

Jack Bobek, retired from EPR, is an annuitant.

Alan Weiser works in the Mathematical Sciences Dept. at Rice U.

Acknowledgments

This monograph is the work of many people in addition to the authors. We gratefully acknowledge their assistance. Exxon Production Research Co. (EPR) was generous in its encouragement and support of this monograph. Susan Bielstein edited the first drafts of many chapters and coordinated preparation of all illustrations. Kimberly Taylor Herrick, Richard Hall, and other members of EPR's Training Div. read much of the manuscript and made many useful suggestions. Judy McCann, Debbie Pool, Linda Scott, and Jean Steen typed the many "final" versions of the manuscript. Their patience is especially appreciated. Carolyn Mattax assisted with the final editing. The SPE Monograph review committee spent many hours reviewing drafts of the manuscript. Their constructive comments contributed greatly to the clarity, accuracy, and relevance of material in this monograph. And finally, many thanks to our wives for their support of this endeavor.

Contents

Chapter 1
Introduction and Overview

Numerical reservoir simulators are used widely, primarily because they can solve problems that cannot be solved in any other way. Simulation is the only way to describe quantitatively the flow of multiple phases in a heterogeneous reservoir having a production schedule determined not only by the properties of the reservoir, but also by market demand, investment strategy, and government regulations.

The potential of simulation was recognized in the late 1940's and early 1950's by a number of companies. Their commitment of effort both to fundamental research on numerical analysis and to development of practical methods for using available computers resulted in crude, but nonetheless useful, simulators by the mid 1950's.

The principal application of early simulators was in studies of reservoirs that were large enough to justify costly studies. The need at that time was for detailed performance predictions to be used in intermediate- and long-term planning. Simulation successfully met that need in most cases and, as a result, became established as an important management tool for most large reservoirs.

The reliability of modern simulators and the ready availability of computers suggest that simulation is practical for use on all sizes of reservoirs for day-to-day decision-making as well as for planning. Simulation is still not used extensively for smaller reservoirs, however, and is not used routinely in daily operations even on larger reservoirs. If it is to reach its potential, simulation must become a tool that is used confidently by a large number of reservoir engineers. The primary objective of this monograph is to encourage use of simulation by providing reservoir engineers who have limited simulation experience with a compilation of information drawn from the experience of long-term simulation users.

A second objective of this monograph is to describe simulation in an understandable, credible manner so that the reader who is not a reservoir engineer can understand its usefulness as well as its limitations. Because the reservoir engineer normally recommends actions but is not the final decision-making authority, he must persuade others of the wisdom of his recommendations. This demands that others have faith in the tools he uses.

1.1 Audience

The audience for the monograph includes (1) those who use simulators, (2) potential users with little or no background in numerical analysis or simulation who may need help in getting started, (3) nonusers involved in reservoir management who must understand simulation well enough to judge its usefulness and the validity of simulation results, (4) higher-level managers, government officials, arbiters, and others who need to know enough about simulation to appreciate both its usefulness and limitations, and (5) simulator developers who may need additional insight into the practicalities of simulator usage.

1.2 Organization

1.2.1 Introduction to Simulation. The first two chapters of the monograph are particularly pertinent for engineers who are inexperienced in simulation and for managers and other nonusers. Chap. 1 summarizes the most important incentives for using simulation, cites examples from the literature that demonstrate its usefulness, and outlines the various activities involved in conducting a simulation project. Chap. 2 presents qualitative explanations of simulation concepts. The objective of this chapter is to provide the background needed for further study by beginning users and to supply nonusers with enough information to participate in discussion and evaluation of reservoir-performance simulation.

1.2.2 Model Design. Chaps. 3 and 4 are intended for those who are involved in reservoir description, reservoir simulation, and reservoir management. Chap. 3 discusses the design phase of reservoir modeling and addresses the level of complexity needed in a simulation study. It also covers the representation of reservoir rock and fluid properties and the manner in which wells, surface facilities, and the reservoir are coupled. Chap. 4 discusses the selection of data and the assignment of rock and fluid properties to locations in the reservoir model.

1.2.3 Model Construction and Testing. Chaps. 5 through 8 should be useful to all but the most experienced simulator users. Chaps. 5 and 6 discuss factors and decisions that affect the accuracy, reliability, and cost of simulation, and the options that must be considered in selecting solution methods. Chap. 7 describes comprehensive well-management routines that are used to tailor models to specific reservoirs, surface facilities, operating strategies, and externally imposed constraints. Chap. 8 discusses a number of ways to develop a better reservoir description by adjusting properties of a reservoir model until the model can "duplicate" actual reservoir history. This process of "history matching" is the most reliable way to fine-tune and to test the quality of a model. A successful history match normally is a prerequisite for confident use of a model to predict future reservoir performance.

1.2.4 Forecasting Performance. Chap. 9 discusses the prediction of future reservoir performance and the evaluation of the reliability of predictions. The chapter describes procedures and plans for running prediction cases, requirements for input data, concepts involved in making a smooth transition from history to predictions, and checks of the quality of results.

1.2.5 Editing Simulator Input and Output. Chap. 10 lists types of edits commonly used to reduce simulation input and output to summaries that can be easily understood, analyzed, and communicated to others.

1.2.6 Simulation of Special Processes. Chap. 11 discusses the status of simulators for the more complex processes involved in enhanced oil recovery (EOR). Although much remains to be done to develop adequate simulators for many EOR processes, current simulators support and assist engineering judgment and provide information that is useful in the design and operation of EOR projects. In most cases, simulation is an indispensable tool for detailed analysis of the performance of an EOR project.

1.2.7. Appendices. Appendix A should be valuable to inexperienced users. It discusses hand-calculation methods that can be used to check the reasonableness of simulation answers to many reservoir mechanics problems. Appendices B and C are geared toward readers who need to delve more deeply into the mathematics of simulation. Appendix D discusses regression techniques that are sometimes useful in history matching a reservoir model.

1.3 Incentives for Reservoir Simulation

As mentioned earlier, reservoir simulators are used primarily because they can solve problems that cannot be solved in any other way. However, the usefulness of numerical models extends beyond solving difficult problems; even on simple problems, simulation is often the best solution method because it may be faster, cheaper, or more reliable than other methods.

This is not to say, of course, that numerical simulation is always the best method of analysis for a particular reservoir engineering problem. Analysis methods that supplement and sometimes compete with numerical reservoir simulation include well testing, field observation, laboratory tests, field pilot tests, simple mathematical analyses, and extrapolation from the performance of other reservoirs. Problems should be solved by the simplest and least costly method that will yield an adequate answer. Reservoir engineers should always first determine the proper level of simplification and then select the appropriate method of analysis to avoid technical "overkill."[1-3]

Two kinds of simulators predate numerical reservoir simulators: electric analog models and scaled physical (fluid-flow) models. Electric analogs are outmoded now, because any problem they will solve can be handled more efficiently by a numerical simulator. At one time, scaled physical models had a variety of applications. Now, however, physical models are more expensive, more time-consuming, and less flexible than numerical simulators. Fluid-flow models are now used only in a narrow spectrum of special tests that are often ancillary to numerical simulator studies. Physical models, however, remain one of the best tools for developing insight into the physical processes governing reservoir mechanics.

The final selection of an analysis method must be based not only on the proper level of simplification but also on cost, time, and acceptability. Over the years, the trend for time and cost requirements for simulator studies has been downward. For other kinds of analysis, time requirements have changed little and costs have increased at about the same rate as manpower costs. Because these trends are expected to continue, the time and cost factors will favor the use of simulators in an increasing percentage of reservoir studies.

The business incentives for virtually all current applications of reservoir simulation fall into one or more of the following categories: economics; credibility and reliability; decision-making; arbitration and unitization; performance monitoring; nonelective studies resulting from safety, environmental, or regulatory concerns; and communications and personnel utilization.

1.3.1 Economics. Typically, the main incentive for reservoir simulation is increased profitability through better reservoir management. A realistic reservoir model can be an effective tool for developing plans for new fields, for estimating facility needs (platforms, compression, etc.), and for evaluating plans to improve well productivity, to increase or to accelerate production, to reduce operating costs, and to improve ultimate recovery.

Formal assessment of cost-effectiveness is not needed for most simulator studies. The magnitude of the economic incentive obviously is related to the overall cost of developing and producing reserves. For a very small reservoir with low costs, the difference in profit between the best depletion scheme and other reasonable schemes may not be enough to pay for a complicated reservoir study. On the other hand, if reserves are very large or development and operating costs are high, expensive studies that could increase recovery or reduce expenditures by even a small percentage would be cost-effective.

A frequent criticism of simulation is that "reservoir engineers simulate reservoirs they cannot adequately describe." Interestingly, though, one of the most fruitful applications of simulators is in predevelopment and early development studies that test the sensitivity of reservoir performance and development strategy to variations in reservoir properties within a range of possible values. Sometimes such studies can quantify the economic risk associated with poor reservoir description. Sensitivity studies typically involve variations in horizontal and vertical permeability, relative permeability, capillary pressure, aquifer size, and extent and location of barriers such as tar mats, sealing faults, and shale stringers.

1.3.2 Credibility and Reliability. Credibility and reliability, which are related and sometimes indistinguishable, are often the key incentives for using a reservoir simulator. When a program is known to be mathematically reliable, calculations can be represented as unbiased. When discussing results generated by such a program, one can focus on the quality of the input data. If a relationship with a third party (government agency, partner, etc.) is important, the credibility a simulator can lend to a study is sometimes the deciding factor in determining whether simulation should be used.

1.3.3 Decision-Making. Numerical simulation is an excellent tool for predicting the potential consequences of reservoir-management decisions. While no single prediction may be accurate, the *differences* in predicted performance generated by simulations of alternative operating strategies normally will be directionally correct. Of more importance, such differences can be fully explained by analyzing predicted pressures, saturations, and individual well performance. Hence, decisions can be made rationally, with experience and good judgment compensating for lack of hard information.

1.3.4 Arbitration and Unitization. Simulation is used frequently by individual parties involved in equity negotiations to evaluate the impact of various compromise positions on the possible eventual distribution of recoverable reserves. It is seldom a dominant negotiating tool, because agreement must be reached on other matters—e.g., reservoir description and depletion plans—before results of simulation will be accepted. Simulation, however, has been used extensively in many of the major equity negotiations reported publicly in recent years.

1.3.5 Performance Monitoring. When flow in a reservoir is relatively complex, it may be difficult to evaluate the quality of reservoir management without a surveillance model. If the model is kept current by including all new geologic and seismic data and by updating history matches, it can serve as a standard by which to judge actual performance and as a routine source of information on probable future performance.

1.3.6 Nonelective Studies. In a small percentage of simulator studies, the main incentive springs from safety concerns, environmental issues, or government regulations and requests. These studies are usually nonelective—they must be executed to comply with laws or with the policies of the producing organization.

1.3.7 Communications and Personnel Utilization. In this category are a number of incentives for using simulators that cannot be directly quantified because their value depends on how effectively simulators are used and on the level of confidence people have in the results. One way of expressing these incentives is to list the benefits that individuals and specific groups may obtain from simulation. When prudently used, reservoir simulation can offer (1) the *engineer* a fast, mathematically precise, comprehensive method of reservoir analysis; (2) the *manager* thorough reservoir studies that can include adequate comparisons of alternative operating plans; (3) the *inexperienced engineer* an effective training tool; (4) the *third party* (government, co-owner, royalty owner, etc.) an understandable, credible, systematic reservoir analysis, including operating constraints that are specified in detail; and (5) the *operating company* a tool that enhances the efficiency of reservoir management teams.

1.4 Examples of Beneficial Applications of Numerical Reservoir Simulators

An abundance of literature describes reservoir studies in which simulation was the deciding factor in reaching a desired goal—whether that goal was to increase profits or to solve a problem unrelated to economics. A few typical studies are summarized in the following paragraphs. See Refs. 1, 2, and 4 for other general discussions of simulator usage.

1.4.1 Simulation of Conventional Processes With "Black-Oil" Simulators. "Black-oil" simulators, which were the first type developed, are still the most frequently used. These simulators can model the flow of water, oil, and gas, and can account for pressure-dependent solubility of gas in oil, but they cannot model changes in oil or gas composition. When modern black-oil simulators are used properly, the user can be confident that the calculations will give realistic answers if the input data are complete and reasonably accurate. Early versions of these simulators did not warrant such confidence, but current black-oil simulators are usually so reliable that they are sometimes used to verify new analytic methods. Bremer *et al.*[5] used a two-dimensional (2D) radial simulator model to help verify a new analytic method for interpreting certain kinds of well tests.

1.4.2 Applications of Full-Field Models. Black-oil simulations having the greatest economic incentives model entire reservoirs or major segments of reservoirs. Such models can be applied profitably to many kinds of studies, such as flank and pattern water injection, gas injection, competitive and unitized operation, lease-line migration, and location and timing of development wells. They can also be used to study well patterns and spacing, completion intervals, producing rates, infill drilling, gas-lift timing, and other operating options.

Staggs and Herbeck[2] present a typical example of the use of history-matching simulations with an areal model to obtain a more accurate reservoir description. In their example, a producing reservoir contained several faults that were potential barriers to fluid movement. A 2D areal-model study proved that the faults were nonsealing by showing that the pressure/production history could be duplicated only if good communication existed across fault lines. Without the insight provided by simulation, unnecessary wells probably would have been drilled to ensure drainage of all areas of the reservoir.

Economics, credibility, and timing were all important incentives for the Blackjack Creek simulation study.[6] Because this deep (15,700-ft [4785-m]) reservoir contained a sour crude that could not be produced until a processing plant was constructed, time was available for planning the operating strategy and completing a unitization agreement. Simulations indicated that pressure could be maintained with seven peripheral water-injection wells and that ultimate waterflood oil recovery would be 40 million STB [6.4×10^6 stock-tank m^3]—twice the anticipated primary recovery. Although pressure would have been maintained even in the absence of a simulator study, the study provided a rapid means of analysis, defined an operating scheme that seemed to be near optimum, and used a form of analysis acceptable to the other leaseholders in the field.

Simulations with areal models of the Lake Barre field in Louisiana indicated that profits could be increased considerably if an existing nitrogen injection project were expanded.[7] Simulations of the Virginia Hills Boundary Lake "A" pool in Canada prevented an expensive mistake in the modification of surface fluid-handling equipment.[8] Economics and credibility were the main incentives for simulating performance of the Jay-Little Escambia Creek[9] fields in Florida and Alabama. After reviewing the benefits of pressure maintenance indicated by simulation, the field operators approved a unitization agreement in March 1974, and water injection started the same month.

A study of the very-low-permeability Appalachian Devonian shale reservoir in Ohio[10] demonstrates the flexibility of simulators. A simulator was adapted to include a dual-porosity feature that handled both free reservoir gas and gas adsorbed on the shale. Simulation of the desorption process was important because this process greatly influenced the producing potential.

Other examples of particular interest include Tapis, an offshore field east of Malaysia,[11] and the Sadlerochit reservoir of Alaska's Prudhoe Bay Field.[12]

1.4.3 Cross-Sectional and Cylindrical Models. Cross-sectional and cylindrical (sometimes called single-well, radial, or *r-z*) models are used to simulate segments of a reservoir. The models are commonly used to generate input for areal models.

Radial models were used in studies of the Prudhoe Bay field, where coning at individual wells has a significant effect on overall reservoir behavior.[13] A three-dimensional radial simulator capable of modeling manmade fractures was used to study low-permeability gas production in the Carthage (Cotton Valley) field.[14] One reservoir-behavior problem that is frequently probed with both single-well and cross-sectional models is the effect of rate on ultimate recovery.[15-17] The usual finding of such studies has been that, if reservoir pressure is properly maintained, changes in producing rates seldom, if ever, influence ultimate recovery.

1.4.4 Special-Purpose Simulators. After the appearance of black-oil simulators, other programs were developed to solve problems that were mathematically more difficult than black-oil problems. Simulators are available to model compositional, thermal, and chemical processes; they are applied most frequently in studies of EOR projects.

Compositional simulators can model performance of volatile-oil and gas-condensate reservoirs in which phase compositions vary widely with pressure. A typical use is optimization of gas cycling in a gas cap or a gas-condensate reservoir. A good example of the profitable use of a compositional simulator is a study of the Anschutz Ranch East Unit in Utah and Wyoming.[18]

Thermal-process simulators can model steam cycling and steamflooding. Typical steam-project simulations include those of the Mount Poso field in California[19] and a group of heavy-oil reservoirs near the Cold Lake field in Canada.[20]

Chemical-process simulators have been developed for polymer injection, surfactant flooding, and flooding with alkaline solutions. These oil-displacement methods involve complex fluid property changes and chemical reactions, and there is still some question as to the accuracy with which these processes can be simulated.[21,22]

See Chap. 11 for more comments on the simulation of special processes.

1.5 Planning a Simulation Study

A comprehensive study may take a year or more to complete and, for a time, may place intense demands on computer hardware and skilled personnel. Less-comprehensive studies require fewer resources but usually must be conducted under severe time constraints. Both types of studies should follow clear, practical plans to ensure that they supply the correct information to the reservoir management team in appropriate detail and, above all, in time to be used effectively.

Most studies involve essentially the same kinds of activities, although the distribution of effort among the activities will vary from project to project. Fig. 1.1 charts the most significant activities; timing and duration shown are for the first comprehensive study of a field or for a major update of a previous reservoir study. Sec. 1.5 was written with studies of this type in mind.

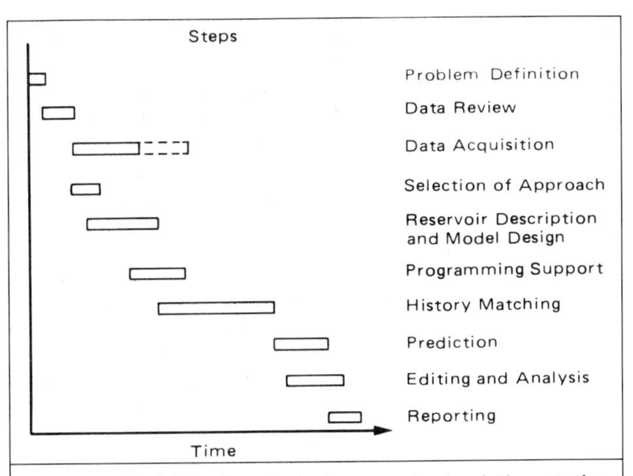

Fig. 1.1—Activities in a typical reservoir simulation study.

1.5.1 Problem Definition. The first step in conducting a study is to define the reservoir performance problem and the associated operating problem. To do this, one must gather enough information about the reservoir and its operating environment to identify what performance projections are needed, when they will be needed, and how they can contribute to reservoir management. At this stage, it is useful to be a member of the reservoir management team or to communicate directly with the team.

As soon as adequate background data have been assimilated, practical objectives for the study should be defined clearly and concisely. Many decisions that must be made as work progresses will follow naturally if care is taken to develop realistic objectives. Although this phase of the project is relatively short, it can have a major impact on the efficiency with which a project is conducted.

Once the objectives and scope of a study are clear, a preliminary analysis of the reservoir fluid mechanics should be conducted. The analysis may be available from earlier evaluations, or it may involve hand calculations, small simulation models, or simply a review of the performance of other reservoirs that appear to be similar in appropriate respects to the reservoir under study. The purpose of the analysis is to identify the principal depletion mechanisms and to recognize the factors that will dominate reservoir performance (e.g., coning, gravity, heterogeneity). The analysis should be thorough enough to permit the study objectives to be restated in terms of reservoir mechanics.

It should then be possible to determine the level of complexity needed in the reservoir model, to start designing the model, and to identify data needed to construct it.

1.5.2 Data Review. Data needed to construct a reservoir model are discussed in Chap. 4. Data usually must be reviewed and reorganized once they have been collected because they will have been obtained for a number of loosely related reasons and normally will not have been screened or organized well enough to be of immediate use. Because a detailed data review may be time-consuming and tedious, effort should be carefully focused. The review should be as extensive as necessary but designed to avoid needless work.

Review of the available data will almost always reveal gaps and inconsistencies that need to be resolved. This may entail considerable thought and effort. Sometimes it will be necessary to decide whether there are enough data and whether the quality of the data is adequate to construct a reservoir model with sufficient accuracy to meet the objectives of the study. If available data, modified and supplemented by experience and good judgment, are inadequate, the objectives must be scaled down or reoriented, or additional data must be collected. Keep in mind, however, that many objectives can be met even with poor data by evaluation of the sensitivity of reservoir performance to reservoir description or other parameters over a range of values believed to encompass the actual values.

If additional data must be collected, data requirements should be prioritized and collection should be timed to meet the schedules of each project phase. Refer to Chap. 4 and Fig. 1.1 for relative timing of data needs.

1.5.3 Selecting the Study Approach. Having defined the fluid-mechanics problems, one must decide what simulation models are most suitable for solving them. It is not always necessary or desirable to attempt to model the entire reservoir. In studies of coning, cusping, or severe underrunning, for example, individual well, cross-sectional or segment models should be used. Most often, one should use a combination of models that may include fine-grid, detailed models to analyze flow near wells or in selected parts of the reservoir and full-field models to study overall reservoir performance.

Factors that influence the approach to a study include (1) availability of simulators that can adequately solve the reservoir-mechanics problems, (2) programming changes that must be made to the simulator to model wells and facilities, (3) the type and number of simulator runs needed to meet study objectives, (4) calendar time, manpower, computing, and financial resources available for the study, (5) the need for special editing capabilities, and (6) availability of peripheral resources needed to complete the study on time.

1.5.4 Model Design. The design of a simulation model will be influenced by the type of process to be modeled, the difficulty of the fluid-mechanics problem, the objectives of the study, the quality of the reservoir-description data, time and budget constraints, and the level of credibility needed to ensure acceptance of the study results.[23-25]

As previously mentioned, the most common simulators are immiscible, black-oil programs that use tabular fluid-property data and conventional relative permeability functions. The simulation of some processes requires use of a special-purpose simulator, often supported by peripheral programs to predict such factors as wellbore heat loss or hydrocarbon phase behavior.

Time or cost constraints frequently impose compromises on the type of simulator to use and on the design of the reservoir model. The number of gridblocks and the detail included in the treatment of individual wells are perhaps the two most common areas for compromise. The engineer will have to determine, within the framework of the study objectives, the level of sophistication really needed to solve the problem.

1.5.5 Programming Support. After the appropriate simulator has been chosen and the model(s) designed, it is usually necessary to tailor parts of the program specifically to the problem at hand. The most common modifications deal with management of wells and editing of results.

Well-management programs can help to automate simulation by using logic that translates field operating conditions and constraints into mathematical boundary conditions for the simulator. A comprehensive well management routine can incorporate enough logic and operating guidelines to make most of the major decisions needed to simulate reservoir management realistically. The routine should be no more complicated than necessary, of course. In some cases, it is necessary only to specify well rates or sandface pressures; most simulators will have these options available. At other times, the management routine must calculate and account for constraints imposed by surface facilities, wellbore and flowline hydraulics, artificial lift, production targets, and regulatory or contractual obligations. Occasionally, it may be necessary to couple a multiphase-flow pipeline simulator to the reservoir simulator so that backpressure from production and injection facilities is imposed on the reservoir model at all times during the simulation.[26] It is common practice to include logic in the well-management routine for adding, shutting in, or working over wells.

In general, the more complicated aspects of a well-management routine will be required only during the prediction phase of the simulation study. During the history-matching phase, well rates supplied to the simulator will be fixed by historical production and injection, and well boundary conditions will most often be individual fluid rates. Hence, history matching can begin and the model can be "fine-tuned" while the comprehensive well management routine is being programmed.

An editing package can summarize simulation results in a clear, readable format—in both tabular and graphic displays. Some of the output available from a typical editing package includes (1) production and injection summaries by well, area, or field, (2) well status reports (wells drilled, wells worked over, and wells shut in), (3) saturation and pressure contour maps, (4) PV-weighted average pressure by area, and (5) recovery efficiency by area.

The time spent in defining requirements for editing and display, in evaluating available programs, and in programming additional edit routines usually will be recouped by reducing the time it takes to analyze results.

1.5.6 History Matching. After a reservoir model has been constructed, it must be tested to determine whether it can duplicate field behavior. Generally, the reservoir description used in the model is validated by running the simulator with historical production and injection data and comparing calculated pressures and fluid movements with actual reservoir performance. A more severe test is to have the simulator compute the past performance of individual wells, as well as historical pressures and fluid movements. The data used in history matching will vary with the scope of the study, but usually will include reservoir pressure and production data. The history-matching process may be a simple one involving only aquifer parameters, or it may be a complex procedure involving both the reservoir and the aquifer.

Model input parameters must be adjusted until an acceptable match between the model and the field is obtained. Keep in mind when adjusting reservoir parameters during history matching that the intent is to describe the real reservoir as accurately as possible with the data available. Typically, one adjusts (1) reservoir permeability to match field pressure gradients, (2) the permeability and areal extent of shales or other low-permeability zones to match vertical fluid movement, (3) relative permeability/saturation relationships to match dynamic saturation distributions and pressure gradients, and (4) aquifer size, porosity, thickness, and permeability to match the amount and distribution of natural water influx.

If no performance history exists, this phase of the project cannot be conducted, of course. Under these circumstances, predictions should be qualified appropriately.

Chap. 8 covers the history-matching procedure in detail.

1.5.7 Predicting Performance and Analyzing Results. Once an acceptable history match has been obtained, the model can be used to predict the future performance of the field and to achieve the objectives established for the study. The types of performance predictions that may be generated by a prediction run include (1) oil production rates, (2) WOR and GOR performance, (3) well and well workover requirements, (4) reservoir pressure performance, (5) positions of fluid fronts, (6) recovery efficiencies by area, (7) general information concerning facility requirements (e.g., timing of gas lift, water handling, and low-pressure separation), and (8) estimates of ultimate recovery.

One of the most difficult aspects of making predictions is evaluating results of the computer runs. Because reservoir simulators can generate hundreds of thousands of lines of output, care must be taken to concentrate on the results that are needed to meet the goals of the simulation study.

The accuracy of performance predictions obviously will depend on the characteristics of the model and on the accuracy and completeness of the reservoir description. It is important, therefore, to spend some time estimating the quality of the simulation to determine whether it is adequate for its intended use.

1.5.8 Reporting. The final step in a simulation study is to assemble results and conclusions in a clear, concise report. The format used for reporting can range from a brief interoffice memorandum for a small study to a multivolume report complete with color displays for a full-field study. Regardless of the style and size of the report, it should state the objectives of the study, describe the model used, and present the results and conclusions in a context appropriate to the specific study.

References

1. Coats, K.H.: "Use and Misuse of Reservoir Simulation Models," *JPT* (Nov. 1969) 1391–98.
2. Staggs, H.M. and Herbeck, E.F.: "Reservoir Simulation Models—An Engineering Overview," *JPT* (Dec. 1971) 1428–36.
3. Richardson, J.G. and Blackwell, R.J.: "Use of Simple Mathematical Models for Predicting Reservoir Behavior," *JPT* (Sept. 1971) 1145–54; *Trans.*, AIME, **251**.
4. Coats, K.H.: "Reservoir Simulation: State of the Art," *JPT* (Aug. 1982) 1633–42.
5. Bremer, R.E., Winston, H., and Vela, S.: "Analytical Model for Vertical Interference Tests Across Low-Permeability Zones," *SPEJ* (June 1985) 407–18.
6. Burwell, R.B. and Hadlow, R.E.: "Reservoir Management of the Blackjack Creek Field," paper SPE 6195 presented at the 1976 SPE Annual Technical Conference and Exhibition, New Orleans, Oct. 3–6.
7. Haag, J.W.: "Analysis and Design of a Deep Reservoir, High Volume Nitrogen Injection Project in the R-1 Sand, Lake Barre Field," paper SPE 10159 presented at the 1981 SPE Annual Technical Conference and Exhibition, San Antonio, Oct. 5–7.
8. Serra, J.W. and Wilson, R.C.: "Reservoir Simulation Studies Reveal Key to Maximizing Waterflood Oil Recovery, Virginia Hills Beaverhill Lake 'A' Pool," paper CIM 7617 presented at the 1976 Annual Technical Meeting of the Petroleum Soc. of CIM, Calgary, June 7–11.
9. Shirer, J.A., Ainsworth, W.J., and White, R.W.: "Selection of a Waterflood Pattern for the Jay-Little Escambia Creek Fields," paper SPE 4978 presented at the 1974 SPE Annual Meeting, Houston, Oct. 6–9.
10. Horton, A.I., Mercer, J.C., and Sawyer, W.K.: "Infill Drilling for Shale Gas Development: A Field Case Study," paper SPE 11182 presented at the 1982 SPE Annual Technical Conference and Exhibition, New Orleans, Sept. 26–29.
11. Loveless, D.E., Goh, S.T., and Heacock, D.W.: "Exploration, Development, and Reservoir Engineering Studies for the Tapis Field Offshore Peninsular Malaysia," *JPT* (June 1983) 1051–60.
12. Killough, J.E. *et al.*: "The Prudhoe Bay Field: Simulation of a Complex Reservoir," paper SPE 10023 presented at the 1982 Intl. Petroleum Exhibition and Technical Symposium, Beijing, March 19–22.
13. Addington, D.V.: "An Approach to Gas-Coning Correlations for a Large Grid Cell Reservoir Simulator," *JPT* (Nov. 1981) 2267–74.
14. Meehan, D.N. and Pennington, B.F.: "Numerical Simulation Results in the Carthage Cotton Valley Field," *JPT* (Jan. 1982) 189–98.
15. Lee, J.E. *et al.*: "The Effect of Rate on Recovery for Canadian Carbonate Reservoirs," paper SPE 5128 presented at the 1974 SPE Annual Meeting, Houston, Oct. 6–9.
16. Beveridge, S.B. *et al.*: "A Study of the Sensitivity of Oil Recovery to Production Rate," paper SPE 5129 presented at the 1974 SPE Annual Meeting, Houston, Oct. 6–9.
17. Chambers, B., Karra, S., and Mortimer, L.: "Use of Type Curve Analysis in Predicting the Behavior of a Water-Drive Reservoir," *J. Cdn. Pet. Tech.* (Jan.–March 1980) 54–60.
18. Kleinsteiber, S.W., Wendschlag, D.D., and Calvin, J.W.: "Development of a Plan-of-Depletion in a Rich Gas Condensate Reservoir: Anschutz Ranch East Unit, Summit County, Utah, Uinta County, Wyoming," paper SPE 12042 presented at the 1983 SPE Annual Technical Conference and Exhibition, San Francisco, Oct. 5–8.
19. O'Dell, P.M. and Rogers, W.L.: "Use of Numerical Simulation to Improve Thermal Recovery Performance in the Mount Poso Field, California," paper SPE 7078 presented at the 1978 SPE Symposium on Improved Methods for Oil Recovery, Tulsa, April 16–19.
20. Bowen, W.B. and Patel, C.: "Use of a Numerical Simulator as an Aid to the Optimization of Steam Stimulation in a Typical 15°API Heavy Oil Reservoir," paper CIM 82-33-38 presented at the 1982 Annual Technical Meeting of the Petroleum Soc. of CIM, Calgary, June 6–9.
21. Khatib, A.K.: "Discussion of Reservoir Simulation: State of the Art," *JPT* (June 1983) 1176.
22. Coats, K.H.: "Author's Reply to Discussion of Reservoir Simulation: State of the Art," *JPT* (June 1983) 1176.
23. Richardson, J.G. *et al.*: "The Effect of Small, Discontinuous Shales on Oil Recovery," *JPT* (Nov. 1978) 1531–37.
24. Lutes, J.L. *et al.*: "Accelerated Blowdown of a Strong Water-Drive Gas Reservoir," *JPT* (Dec. 1977) 1533–38.
25. Graham, M.F. and Smart, G.T.: "Reservoir Simulator Employing a Fine-Grid Model Nested in a Coarse-Grid Model," paper SPE 9372 presented at the 1980 SPE Annual Technical Conference and Exhibition, Dallas, Sept. 21–24.
26. Emanuel, A.S. and Ranney, J.C.: "Studies of Offshore Reservoir With an Interfaced Reservoir/Piping Network Simulator," *JPT* (March 1981) 399–406.

Chapter 2
Modeling Concepts

It is not essential to have a working knowledge of numerical analysis to use reservoir simulators effectively and confidently. It is necessary, however, to understand some of the basic concepts of reservoir modeling if one is to exercise judgment in selecting an appropriate simulator, in choosing between available options, and in controlling the quality of simulation results. Almost without exception, the concepts involved are simple and easy to understand even though their mathematical representation may be complex. The intent of this chapter is to explain the concepts pictorially and qualitatively; more rigorous treatments are presented or referenced in later chapters.

2.1 The Concept of Gridblocks and Timesteps

In general, the partial differential equations that describe fluid flow in reservoirs cannot be solved analytically. They can be solved numerically, however, by replacing the differential equations with difference equations. Implicit in a difference equation is *discretization*—the subdivision of distance and time into definite, specified increments. In other words, to use difference equations it is necessary to treat the reservoir as if it were composed of discrete volume elements and to compute changes in conditions within each volume element over each of many discrete time intervals. The conceptual reservoir volume elements are most frequently referred to as *gridblocks;* the time intervals are called *timesteps.*

Although subdivision of the reservoir is an abstraction, it is qualitatively correct to visualize gridblocks as well-stirred tanks with permeable sides. To extend this analogy, visualize the contents of a gridblock as uniformly distributed within the block, and the rates at which fluids flow in or out as determined by permeabilities of the sides of the block and the pressure differences between adjacent gridblocks. In essence, the mathematical problem is reduced to a calculation of flow between adjacent gridblocks.

Fig. 2.1 illustrates the stirred-tank analog for a model in which fluid flow is restricted to one dimension (1D). Observe that in this analog, the ratio and/or compositions of fluids flowing from one tank to the next are determined by the contents of the upstream tank. We will consider some significant implications of this aspect of the model later.

As implied by the well-stirred tank analog, properties within a gridblock do not vary with location within the block; indeed, locations within a block are not defined.* For example, at any particular time, a block has only a single value of each phase saturation and any property that is saturation-dependent (e.g., capillary pressure and relative permeability). To represent variations in reservoir properties, the properties of gridblocks must differ from block to block. Thus, there may be abrupt changes in properties from one gridblock to the next. The abruptness with which a property changes between neighboring blocks is, to an extent, a function of gridblock size.

*Conceptually, locations within gridblocks may have meaning. For example, techniques that use some form of *point-tracking* indirectly define locations within a gridblock and may assign saturations or concentrations to those locations. Also, a calculated pressure may be thought of as being applicable at a specific point within a gridblock.

The precision with which a reservoir can be described in a model and the accuracy with which the flow of reservoir fluids can be calculated will depend on the number of gridblocks used in the model. In practice, the number of blocks will be limited principally by the cost of calculations and the time available to prepare input data and to interpret results. As a consequence, the size and complexity of a reservoir model must be considered carefully. The model should contain enough blocks (and dimensions) to simulate the reservoir and its behavior adequately, but within that constraint the model should be as small and simple as possible.

Fig. 2.2 illustrates a few of the many types of models that are needed in reservoir simulation. Specific applications of several of these models are discussed in other chapters.

As previously stated, the life of a reservoir must also be discretized or divided into time increments. A simulator computes changes in a reservoir (flow, pressure, etc.) over each of many finite time increments. Conditions are defined only at the beginning and end of a time interval; nothing is defined at any intermediate time "within" a time interval. Consequently, conditions within a reservoir and, more specifically, within each gridblock, may change abruptly from one timestep to the next. Usually, timesteps are chosen to be small enough to limit the sizes of these abrupt changes to acceptable levels. In general, the accuracy with which reservoir behavior can be calculated will be influenced by the lengths of the timesteps.

2.2 Consequences of Discretization

To illustrate the consequences of using gridblocks to model a reservoir, we will move one step beyond the stirred-tank analog of Fig. 2.1 and introduce a 1D, four-gridblock simulator model of a hypothetical two-well reservoir that is being waterflooded. Fig. 2.3 shows a plan view of the reservoir, a sketch of the grid system for the model, and plots of the water saturation distribution in the reservoir and in the model relatively early in the waterflood. Note that in the reservoir the water saturation is a smooth function of distance, but in the model there is an abrupt drop in water saturation between Blocks 1 and 2 and again between Blocks 2 and 3. A similar plot of pressure in the model would also show a "stair-step" distribution, whereas a plot of actual reservoir pressure would be a continuous smooth curve.

Lack of definition within a single gridblock and the abrupt changes in saturation and pressure between blocks create several problems that must be recognized and accommodated. A few of these will be discussed in the following paragraphs.

2.2.1 Representation of Wells. The pressure and saturation assigned to a gridblock represent values for the entire volume of reservoir encompassed by the block. Because each gridblock usually models an area of many acres, gridblock saturations and pressures will not be representative of saturations and pressures at the sandface of a flowing well. To translate block pressures to well pressures and to assign rates and distributions of injection or production,

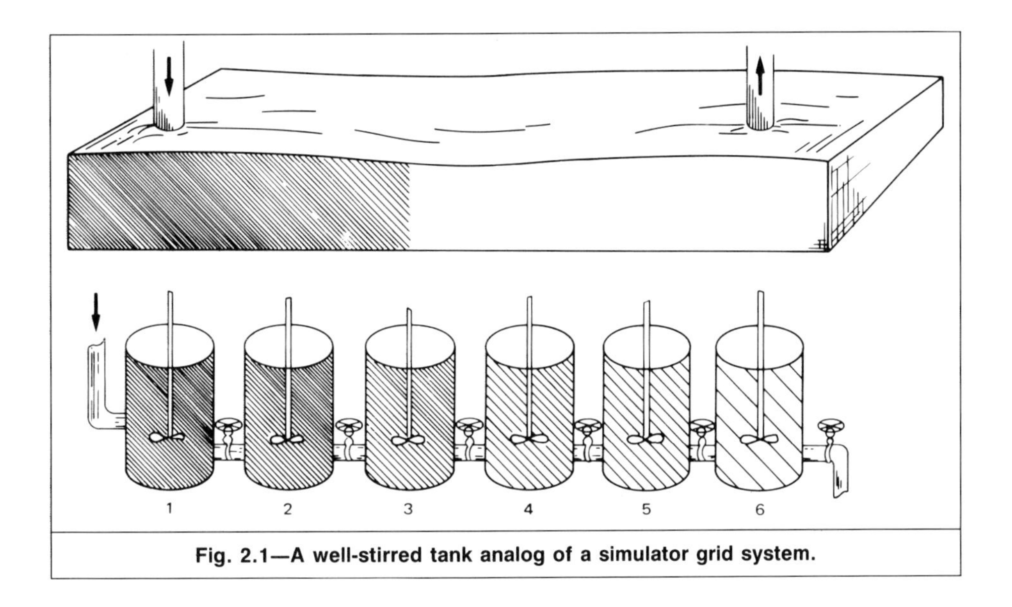

Fig. 2.1—A well-stirred tank analog of a simulator grid system.

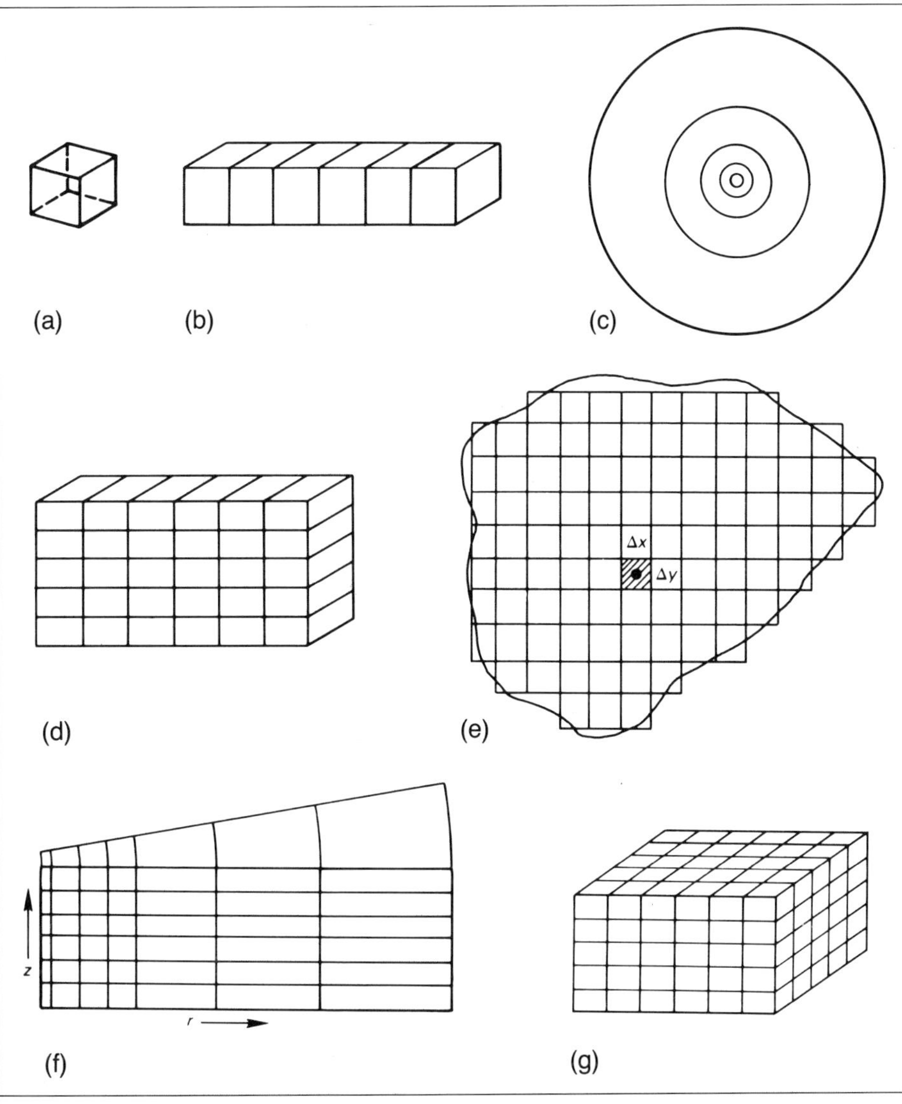

Fig. 2.2—Typical models used in reservoir simulation: (a) tank, (b) 1D, (c) 1D radial, (d) cross-sectional, (e) areal, (f) radial cross-sectional, and (g) 3D.

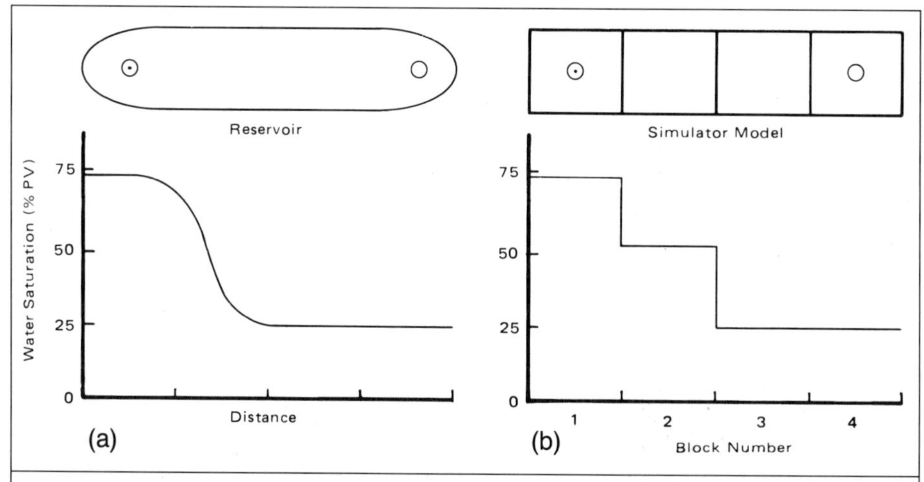

Fig. 2.3—A four-gridblock waterflood model: (a) hypothetical reservoir and its water-saturation distribution at a certain time in the waterflood and (b) four-gridblock model and simulated water-saturation distribution.

data from an external source are necessary. The external source is frequently a separate well model designed specifically to have gridding fine enough to model near-wellbore behavior. Well performance calculated in the well model is then correlated to conditions in the appropriate gridblock of the reservoir model through well functions. See Sec. 2.4.1; also see Chap. 7.

2.2.2 Mobility Weighting. To calculate the flow of water and oil from block to block in our example waterflood, we must assign oil and water mobilities applicable to flow across the hypothetical boundaries between blocks. But the mobility of a phase is a function of saturation, and we have shown that saturations in two adjacent blocks may differ significantly. This leads to the question of what saturation to use in defining mobilities for flow between the two blocks. Clearly, no single value of water saturation, and hence no single value of water or oil mobility, can adequately describe flow behavior over the wide range of saturations that may exist in the regions of the reservoir represented by two adjacent gridblocks. But in a simulator, we must use a single value of mobility each time we calculate the rate of flow of a phase between two gridblocks.

A rational deduction might be to use an average of the mobilities in the two blocks, but we know from experience that this approach—called 50/50 weighting—seldom is best. Indeed, we know of no generally applicable best method for selecting the best value of mobility. There are currently four methods to consider.

(1) *Upstream weighting,* in which mobility to be used in computing flow between two adjacent blocks is determined entirely by the mobility in the upstream block (Block 1 for flow between Blocks 1 and 2 in the four-block waterflood model).

(2) *Downstream weighting,* in which mobility is determined entirely by mobility in the downstream block.

(3) *Mixed weighting,* in which some combination of mobilities in upstream and downstream blocks is used.

(4) *Extrapolation or interpolation methods,* such as two-point upstream weighting, in which mobilities (or saturations) in one or more neighboring gridblocks are used to develop an estimate of mobilities at the interface of two gridblocks.

Other considerations being equal, Methods 1 and 4 are most reliable. (See Chaps. 6 and 7 and Appendix C for more detail.) All the methods except Method 2, however, involve upstream weighting, which leads to numerical dispersion. (Method 2 involves 100% downstream weighting, which is almost never used because it cannot account for flow into a downstream block in which the fluid is immobile initially.)

2.2.3 Numerical Dispersion. Numerical dispersion is an artifact of current numerical analysis techniques that can cause severe distortions in simulations of processes in which relatively rapid saturation changes occur. Such changes are common in many types of reservoir displacements. To illustrate the problem, we will again use the four-block waterflood model and consider flow between Blocks 2 and 3 and Blocks 3 and 4 under conditions represented by Fig. 2.3. Blocks 3 and 4 have not yet been invaded by water, and in those blocks water will have little or no mobility. Water saturation in Block 2 is well above the initial low saturation and water will have considerable mobility in this block. If full upstream mobility weighting (Method 1) is used, the mobility in Block 2 will define the mobility to be used in calculating flow from Block 2 to Block 3. Thus, in the next timestep, some water will flow into Block 3 because water is mobile in Block 2. Water flowing into Block 3 will increase the water saturation and cause water to become mobile in this block. As a result, water will flow from Block 3 to Block 4 in the subsequent timestep. In other words, in this simulation at least some water will move forward one gridblock each timestep, regardless of the length of the timestep. In the four-block model illustrated here, calculations with upstream weighting will move some water into the producing-well gridblock within four timesteps.

There is no satisfactory way to eliminate numerical dispersion completely in a simulation. There are, however, a number of techniques for reducing dispersion. Use of a large number of gridblocks usually will reduce dispersion to an acceptable level. This approach is not practical for many studies because the number of gridblocks in the model is limited by cost and time constraints. Chap. 5 discusses alternative approaches for reducing numerical dispersion.

2.2.4 Grid Orientation Effects. In multidimensional models, numerical dispersion leads to an interesting and sometimes troublesome phenomenon in which calculated performance is influenced by the orientation of the grid relative to the locations of injection and production wells. The grid orientation effect is usually not important except in simulations in which the displacing phase is much more mobile than the displaced phase (as in steamfloods of heavy oil).

Fig. 2.4 illustrates the problem. It is a sketch of part of the grid system of a model for simulating steam injection into a viscous oil reservoir. This part of the model contains one production well and two steam injection wells, Wells A and B.

In the simulator, steam from Well A will move in a direct path to the producer. However, steam from Well B must zigzag on its way to the producer. Not only is the flow path from Well B longer, but steam from Well B will "see" more oil than the steam from Well A. So, in addition to arriving later, steam from Well B will appear to sweep the reservoir more efficiently than steam from Well A. If the grid were rotated 45° [0.8 rad], the performances calculated for the two wells would be reversed.

The problem is more complex than the discussion so far implies. Pressures as well as saturations are distorted by grid orientation. Use of a large number of gridblocks, which normally should control dispersion, will reduce but not eliminate the effect of grid orientation. Fortunately, the effect is unimportant in most simulations of water/oil displacement. Grid orientation can be important in some gas/oil simulations, however, and at times can pose a serious problem in the simulation of steamflooding or miscible-gas displacements. Chap. 5 discusses the grid orientation effect in more detail and comments on approaches to minimize its impact.

2.3 Explicit and Implicit Functions

We have discussed a few consequences of the discontinuities in saturation and pressure that exist at interfaces between gridblocks in a reservoir model. Similarly, saturations and pressures are discontinuous in time; reservoir conditions are defined only at the end of each timestep. To illustrate, Fig. 2.5 compares actual with calculated water-saturation buildup over time in a region of the hypothetical reservoir represented by the second gridblock of the four-block waterflood model.

During Timestep 3, water saturation in the second gridblock increased by about 10% PV. Properties that are functions of saturation, such as mobility and capillary pressure, will have changed significantly over this timestep. In the "real" reservoir, during the time modeled by Timestep 3, these functions will have assumed many values. Obviously, no single value of each of these functions is correct for the entire time represented by Timestep 3. In the simulator, however, a single value for each saturation-dependent variable must be used to describe conditions over the entire timestep.

As with mobility weighting, there is no single "best" method for selecting values to use during a timestep for all the saturation-dependent functions that change with time during a simulation. A number of procedures can be used, but, in essence, all the procedures are variations of the following three.

1. *Explicit* procedures use values of saturation known at the beginning of a timestep. These saturations are known from the previous timestep calculations (e.g., the end of Timestep 2 is the beginning of Timestep 3).

2. *Implicit* procedures use mobility and capillary pressure calculated as functions of saturation at the end of the timestep. The values are not known until the calculations for the timestep have been completed.

3. *Semi-implicit* procedures use estimates of mobility and capillary pressure developed by assuming that the functions will be straight-line functions of saturation during a timestep. The saturations are not solved for independently, so the procedure is still at least partially implicit.

2.3.1 Comparison of Explicit, Semi-Implicit and Implicit Procedures. To illustrate use of the three procedures, we will calculate the change in water saturation in Gridblock 1 (the injection-well block) that occurred in the four-gridblock waterflood model during the first few timesteps after water injection began. In the discussion, a superscript n refers to the immediately preceding timestep and $n+1$ refers to the timestep about to be taken.

Flow out of the block will be oil initially. Soon, however, both water and oil will flow out of Block 1, with the WOR increasing as the displacement proceeds. The only flow into Gridblock 1 is water from the injection well. As a consequence, the saturation change in the block during a timestep will be completely determined by the fraction of oil in the fluid flowing out of Gridblock 1 into

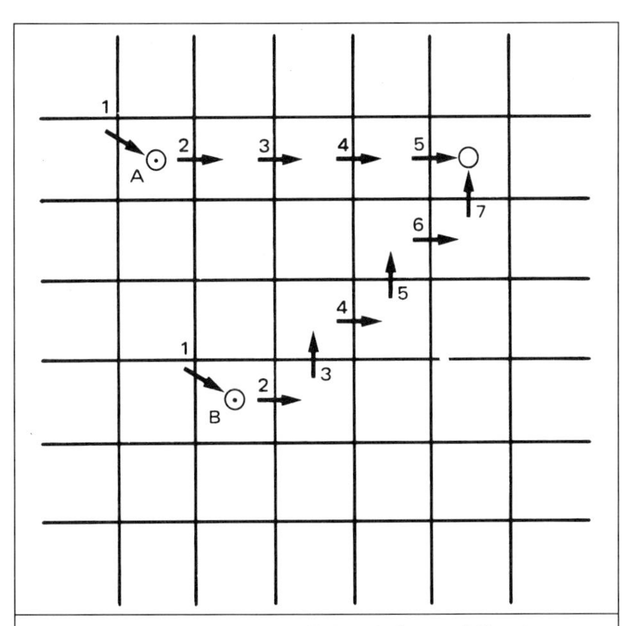

Fig. 2.4—Flow paths for parallel and diagonal flow in a rectangular grid system.

Gridblock 2 during the timestep, the length of the timestep, and the total rate of flow of fluids from Block 1 to Block 2. In equation form, the saturation change in Block 1 during Timestep $n+1$, for example, is

$$\Delta S_o=(S_o^{n+1}-S_o^n)=-(S_w^{n+1}-S_w^n)=-q\Delta t f_o, \quad \text{(2.1)}$$

where

S^n, S^{n+1} = saturations at beginning and end of timestep, respectively,
q = flow rate of fluids out of Block 1,
Δt = duration of timestep, and
f_o = fraction of oil in fluids flowing out of Block 1.

Note that q is expressed in PV's per unit time and that the negative sign implies flow out of Block 1.

Explicit, semi-implicit, and implicit procedures differ in the way they evaluate f_o. To simplify the illustration and to make the computations easy for the reader to duplicate, we make the following assumptions.

1. Mobility weighting is fully upstream; thus, all saturation functions are those of Gridblock 1.

2. The fraction of oil flowing can be expressed analytically as a function of water saturation.

2.3.1.1 Explicit Procedure. In an explicit procedure, f_o for calculation of flow during a timestep is a function of the saturations in the block at the beginning of the timestep:

$$f_o=f_o^n. \quad \text{(2.2)}$$

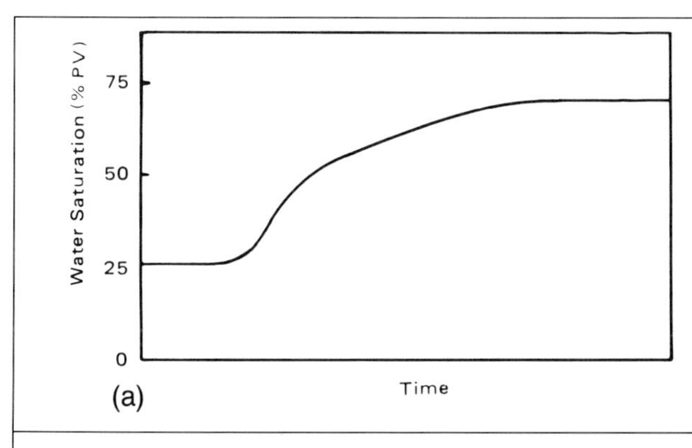

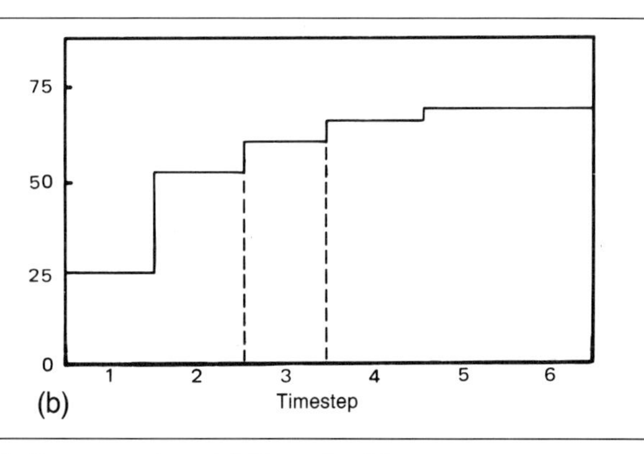

Fig. 2.5—Comparison of saturation vs. time (a) in the reservoir and (b) in a simulator.

TABLE 2.1—WATER SATURATION IN GRIDBLOCK 1 AFTER 50 DAYS OF INJECTION

Timestep Size (days)	Water Saturation (% PV)		
	Explicit	Semi-Implicit	Implicit
0.01	56.57180	56.56648	56.56647
0.1	56.58438	56.55182	56.55182
1	56.73216	56.40623	56.40656
10	58.33037	54.98752	55.03735
25	62.50000	52.63948	53.00287
50	75.00000	50.00000	50.00000

Eq. 2.1 becomes

$$(S_w^{n+1}-S_w^n)=q\Delta t f_o^n, \quad (2.3)$$

where f_o^n is known from the previous timestep. Hence, all terms except S_w^{n+1} are known, so S_w^{n+1} can be calculated directly.

2.3.1.2 Semi-Implicit Procedure. f_o in a semi-implicit procedure is estimated by linear extrapolation from the known value, f_o^n, to the end of the timestep:

$$f_o=f_o^n+\frac{\partial f_o}{\partial S_w}(S_w^{n+1}-S_w^n). \quad (2.4)$$

Eq. 2.1 becomes

$$(S_w^{n+1}-S_w^n)=q\Delta t\left[f_o^n+\frac{\partial f_o}{\partial S_w}(S_w^{n+1}-S_w^n)\right]. \quad (2.5)$$

The question here is where to take the slope $\partial f_o/\partial S_w$. The approach used in the simplest formulation of the procedure is to estimate the saturation change that will occur during the timestep and to use the average value of the slope over that saturation range. (We will mention one way to estimate the saturation change in Sec. 2.3.1.4.) In this way, the slope can be estimated at the beginning of the timestep with no information on the eventual value of S_w^{n+1}. Note that the semi-implicit procedure introduces an additional term in S_w^{n+1}, but because the coefficient $f_o^n+\partial f_o/\partial S_w$ is defined, not much work is added to the computation.

2.3.1.3 Fully Implicit Procedure. In a fully implicit procedure, the fraction of oil in the fluids leaving the block is evaluated at the end of the timestep:

$$f_o=f_o^{n+1}. \quad (2.6)$$

Eq. 2.1 becomes

$$S_w^{n+1}-S_w^n=q\Delta t f_o^{n+1}. \quad (2.7)$$

In this instance, f_o^{n+1} is a function of saturations at the end of Timestep $n+1$ and cannot be computed independently of S_w^{n+1}.

2.3.1.4 Comparison of Solutions. A few more conditions must be specified before the performance of Gridblock 1 can be computed.

1. The PV of the block is 10,000 bbl [1590 m^3].
2. The water injection rate is 100 B/D [16 m^3/d]. On a PV basis, this is a high input rate (0.01 PV/D) and offers a moderate challenge to the solution method.
3. *

$$f_o=\frac{1}{1+\left(\dfrac{S_w-0.25}{0.75-S_w}\right)^{2.5}}.$$

*In deriving the expression for f_o, it was assumed that water and oil viscosities are equal and that phase mobilities are simple exponential functions of the individual phase saturations minus the respective irreducible saturations. It was further assumed that the irreducible water saturation and the irreducible oil saturation are both 0.25 PV. An arbitrary value of 2.5 was chosen as the exponent.

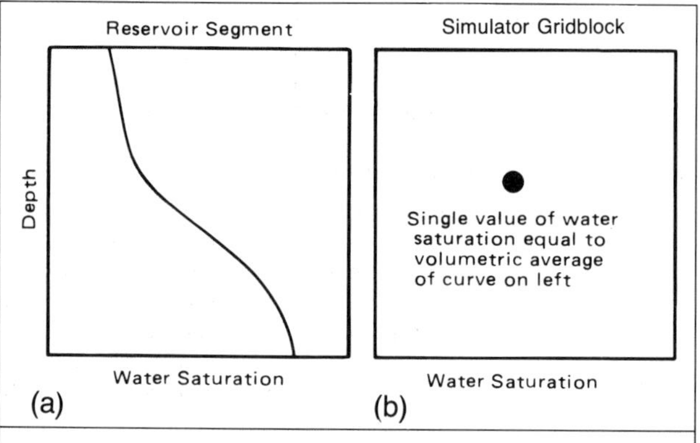

Fig. 2.6—Vertical saturation distribution in a reservoir segment is modeled as a single value in a gridblock.

4. The initial water saturation is 0.25 PV.

The water saturation in Gridblock 1 after 50 days of injection was computed by each of the three procedures with timesteps of 0.01, 0.1, 1, 10, 25, and 50 days.

The computation procedures were as follows.

1. *Explicit procedure.* f_o^n was calculated with the known value of S_w^n, and Eq. 2.3 was solved directly for S_w^{n+1}.
2. *Semi-implicit procedure.* At the start of each timestep, the change in saturation to be expected during the timestep was estimated with the explicit procedure. This estimate was used in calculating the average slope of $\partial f_o/\partial S_w$. Eq. 2.5 was then solved for S_w^{n+1}.
3. *Implicit procedure.* An iterative method (see Sec. 2.7) was used to solve Eq. 2.7. S_w^{n+1} was first estimated with the explicit procedure. Then f_o^{n+1} at S_w^{n+1} was calculated. f_o^{n+1} was used to compute a new estimate for S_w^{n+1}. The procedure was repeated until S_w^{n+1} did not change between iterations—i.e., until the solution "converged." This "point relaxation" method was satisfactory for timesteps of 10 days or less but modification of the procedure was needed for larger timesteps. Refer to Sec. 6.7.2.1 in Chap. 6 for a discussion of modifications to enhance convergence.

Results of the computations are summarized in Table 2.1. When small timesteps were used, the three procedures gave nearly identical answers. With larger timesteps, the explicit procedure overestimated the saturation change, whereas the semi-implicit and implicit procedures underestimated the saturation change in the gridblock. The semi-implicit and implicit procedures gave comparable answers for all timestep sizes, but even these methods gave results that varied with the size of the timestep used in the computation. (Note that the best measure of the length of a timestep is PV's of flow rather than days. In this problem, 10 days is a large timestep.) As discussed in Chap. 5, a number of constraints usually are imposed during a calculation to control the size of a timestep.

The data presented in Table 2.1 do not make the point, but in a semi-implicit computation the saturation change* over which the slopes of the saturation functions are taken can affect the quality of the answer. The reader may wish to verify the validity of this statement by computing the performance of the gridblock with the semi-implicit procedure using two different estimated saturation changes at each timestep when calculating $\partial f_o/\partial S_w$.

2.4 Treatment of Vertical Saturation and Pressure Distributions

A gridblock has a specified thickness in addition to its areal dimensions. But once again consistent with the stirred-tank analogy, vertical variations in fluid distribution, pressure, and rock properties cannot be defined directly within a single gridblock. Fig. 2.6 illustrates the problem for a gridblock representing part of the water/oil transition zone in a two-dimensional (2D) areal model. In the reser-

*The saturation change used to calculate $\partial f_o/\partial S_w$ is usually referred to as a "chord length" for reasons that are evident from graphic construction of the slope.

voir, oil saturation is high in the upper part of the zone and oil mobility will be high in this part of the zone. Similarly, water mobility will be high in the lower part of the zone. By contrast, water saturation in the model gridblock is defined by a single average value that does not distinguish between the upper and lower parts of the zone. To model flow behavior with reasonable accuracy, the simulator must assign to the gridblock mobility functions that properly account for the actual mobilities of fluids associated with this specific distribution of fluids at this specific average saturation.

Of course, the zone could be modeled accurately with a three-dimensional (3D) model having enough thin gridblocks to define the vertical saturation distribution. There is an alternative, however. In many reservoir models, a thick block can be made to behave as if it were constructed of many thin blocks by using a revised set of saturation functions (relative permeability and capillary pressure). As discussed below, the functions are derived in a manner that accounts for flow through a number of hypothetical layers, each with its own fluid saturation, thickness, and permeability. The contribution of each hypothetical layer to oil and water mobility is calculated. The total mobility is the sum of the mobilities of all the layers. The resultant total mobility for each phase is a "permeability-thickness weighted-average" mobility for one specific distribution of saturation and one value of average saturation defining conditions in one part of the reservoir at one specific time. Repeating the calculation for the full range of saturation distributions expected in a specific part of the reservoir will produce a set of mobility functions. The set of values thus derived is called a "pseudofunction."

For pseudofunctions to be satisfactory, it is essential that correct saturation distributions be used in deriving them. There are two sets of conditions to consider.

1. In the most general case, conditions are dynamic, and viscous, gravity, and capillary forces all influence the vertical saturation distribution.

2. In many instances, satisfactory pseudofunctions can be developed by assuming equilibrium conditions, in which gravity and capillarity control the vertical saturation distribution.

To develop pseudofunctions for dynamic conditions, the vertical distribution of saturation and permeability must be modeled. The type of model most often used for this purpose is a 2D cross-sectional model with adequate vertical grid definition. The cross-sectional model must be designed to simulate the principal directions of flow, so several different models may be needed. The validity of a particular set of dynamic pseudofunctions can be established by using the functions in a 1D model to simulate the performance of the cross-sectional model.

If the reservoir behaves as though capillary and gravity forces are in equilibrium, then vertical equilibrium pseudofunctions can be calculated analytically by vertical integration of the relative permeability and capillary pressure curves for different positions of the transition zone as it moves through the gridblock.

See Chaps. 3 and 5 for more detailed discussion.

2.4.1 Well Functions. It is clear from the preceding discussion that lack of vertical definition within a single gridblock makes it impossible to simulate directly the performance of a well in a 2D areal model in which the well is represented by one gridblock. A single gridblock obviously cannot model a partial completion and a single layer of blocks cannot model water or gas coning. These limitations can be removed by use of "well functions," which are pseudofunctions derived from finely gridded simulator models of individual wells or well types. Well functions relate fluid mobilities near the wellbore to gridblock saturations. The model used to derive well functions must properly represent the completion interval, near-wellbore reservoir properties, and the mechanics of multiphase flow into the well (whether by cusping, coning, or stratified flow). In other words, pseudofunctions assigned to a well must represent the producing mechanism and the geometric distribution of saturations that can be expected in the neighborhood of the well. This means that a separate set of well pseudofunctions may be needed for each completion or recompletion.

2.4.2 Gas Re-Solution. Within a gridblock, the solution GOR is normally expressed as a function of pressure. This will be accurate for constant or declining pressure, because on a reservoir time scale the establishment of an equilibrium saturation distribution during gas evolution is effectively instantaneous. Once a significant free gas phase is established, however, some gas will segregate and will not remain in intimate contact with the oil in which it was previously dissolved. If pressure then rises, equilibrium will not necessarily be re-established "instantaneously." Because the areal and vertical distribution of the free gas within a single gridblock is not defined, a reservoir model cannot rigorously calculate the amount of gas that should redissolve. If re-solution is thought to be important, either thinner and sometimes areally smaller gridblocks must be used or the process must first be studied in an external fine-grid model and the results imposed on the simulator through modified relationships between solution GOR and pressure.

2.5 History Matching

Reservoirs are so complex that no practical amount of reservoir description data can supply the detail needed to predict future performance with complete confidence and accuracy. The validity of the reservoir description data used in a model can be evaluated, however, by calculating the past performance of the reservoir and comparing calculated and actual performances. This process of *history matching* will disclose weaknesses in the reservoir data base that can be strengthened by altering the reservoir model until it accurately predicts past performance. Used this way, a simulator can be a powerful reservoir description tool—provided the data changes and additions are consistent with the known reservoir data base.

In general, the data that are matched are pressure, WOR, GOR, gas/water ratio, fluid contact movement, water and gas arrival times, and fluid saturations measured in cores, well logs, and chemical tracer tests.

History matching can be time-consuming, expensive, and frustrating, primarily because reservoir performance can be complex, responding to numerous interactions that, as a whole, may be difficult to comprehend. As a consequence, there has been considerable research on programs for inverse simulation or automatic history matching. The programs are rarely used, however, because for most studies automatic history matching is less efficient than manual matching.

Although the primary objective of history matching is improvement of the reservoir model, results of the work may contribute to one or more secondary objectives. For example, history matching will contribute to an understanding of the current distribution and movement of reservoir fluids and will supply a rational basis for reservoir description, including oil and gas in place, in parts of the reservoir where there are no data. A well-matched model that is kept up to date may also be an excellent aid in reservoir surveillance.

2.6 Well Management

In addition to the well functions mentioned earlier, a reservoir simulator must contain a program that translates production/injection data and desired field operating conditions and constraints into controls for the reservoir model. Such programs are called *well-management routines.* A well-management routine sets well rates or pressures, implements operating policies, and satisfies operating constraints at the levels of producing interval, well, well group, reservoir, and field.

In its simplest form, a well-management routine assigns specified rates or pressures to individual producing blocks in the simulator at specified times. This simplified form is often referred to as a "rate routine." More-sophisticated routines may also make and execute decisions that simulate many of the operating decisions required to manage the actual reservoir. For example, a well-management routine may drill, work over, or recomplete wells, calculate well and flowline hydraulics, install artificial lift, control gas or water rates, maintain production targets, and direct reinjection of gas or water. The routine may also impose production constraints that in practice could result from such external controls as production agreements, operating guidelines, or statutory rules.

2.7 Solution Methods

The solution of the flow equations consumes a large part of the computing effort in a typical simulation. As a consequence, selecting an effective equation-solving method for a particular problem can be an important step in managing the cost and controlling the difficulty of a study. Most simulators provide two or more methods for solving the equations and allow the user to select the method that is most appropriate for his problem.

Solution methods are either *direct* or *iterative.* In a direct method, unknowns are eliminated one by one until the equations are solved. Except for possible round-off error, the solutions are exact. The basis of an iterative method is the development of an "approximate" solution to the system of equations. The approximation is replaced systematically until the answers "converge" to within a specified tolerance of the "correct" answers.

Some form of direct solution—the method we normally use to solve small sets of simultaneous equations by hand—is included in most simulators. The method is usually an appropriate choice for small- to intermediate-size models. Answers are accurate and no user intervention is required. With models having a large number of gridblocks, however, direct solution may be impractical because the number of computations and the requirements for number storage during the computations may become excessive. The meaning of "large" here is influenced by the type of problem being solved and by the characteristics of the computing software and hardware.

Most simulators also contain one or more iterative methods for solving the equations. Computing effort for a single iteration of an iterative method may be only a small fraction of that required for direct solution. But an additional factor must be considered: the number of iterations required before convergence criteria are met. Without using the iterative method on the specific problem being solved, it may not be possible to estimate the number of iterations needed for a solution. An additional complication of some iterative methods is the need to select iteration parameters that are used to speed up convergence. The values of the parameters usually are influenced by the characteristics of the particular problem being solved.

For any particular study, the choice of a solution method may not be clear. A few guidelines are given in Chap. 6. In general, some experimentation with the reservoir model may be needed before the most appropriate method can be selected.

Nomenclature

f_o = fraction of oil in fluids flowing into or out of a block
q = flow rate of fluids
r = radial axis of a radial model or distance from center to a point in a radial model
S_o = oil saturation
S_w = water saturation
Δt = length of timestep
$\Delta x, \Delta y$ = gridblock dimension in a horizontal plane or in a plane parallel to formation bedding
z = coordinate in vertical direction or in a direction orthogonal to bedding plane

Superscripts

$n+1$ = timestep to be taken next
n = immediately preceding timestep

Chapter 3
Designing the Reservoir Model

This chapter specifically addresses the following design issues: the selection of the number of space dimensions, representation of the reservoir rock and fluids, and coupling of the wells and the reservoir. The discussion is geared primarily toward model design as it pertains to the simulation of conventional recovery processes. For convenience, many of the examples deal with water/oil displacements, but the concepts apply equally well to gas/oil and gas/water displacements. Much of the discussion also applies to model design for EOR processes, which is covered in more depth in Chap. 11.

It is usually best to design the simplest model that will simulate the displacement process with sufficient realism to allow proper decisions to be made regarding reservoir development and operation. Although study results may be more understandable and believable if more complexity is included than is needed to solve the problem, the added intricacy will almost always increase the cost of the study.

Model design is influenced by the following factors: (1) type and complexity of the problem (i.e., system geometry, rock heterogeneity, types of fluids present, and type of depletion process being considered); (2) quality of answer needed for reservoir-management decisions; (3) time available to complete the reservoir study; (4) economic factors; (5) availability and quality of data (note, however, that complex models may be needed even in the absence of certain types of data to test whether an investment decision should be especially sensitive to the values of certain reservoir properties); and (6) capabilities of the reservoir simulator and characteristics of available computers.

The following simplified checklist outlines the sequence of decisions involved in constructing a reservoir model.

3.1 Checklist for Model Design

1. Define the objectives of the study and the problems to be solved. Make clear statements of which predictions are to be made and why.
2. Become familiar with all available data. Note any missing data that are essential to solve the problem (Chaps. 1 and 4).
3. Considering all the available data, select the model configuration [one-dimensional (1D), two-dimensional (2D), or three-dimensional (3D)] that will best represent the fluid dynamics of the reservoir.
4. Simplify the model configuration as much as practical (e.g., determine whether pseudo-relative permeability or capillary pressure treatment is justified). This usually requires testing all assumptions that are made for the sake of simplification.
5. Consider the eventual use of the model and evaluate whether additional complexity may be needed to establish credibility.
6. Select the gridblock dimensions (Chap. 5).
7. Select the fluid (PVT) model.
8. Select the number of phases.
9. Define the initial conditions.
10. Define how wells will be treated in the simulator. (Are well functions needed?)
11. Define the capabilities needed in the well management routines.
12. Define whether black-oil, compositional, miscible, or thermal treatment is needed.
13. Select the simulator.
14. Design ancillary models to verify assumptions and to provide input to the primary model.

3.2 Selecting the Number of Dimensions

One of the first steps in designing a model is to decide on the number of space dimensions needed to represent the geometry of the physical system and, simultaneously, to determine which simplifications are justified. Both external and internal geometries must be considered. External geometry includes the field or aquifer limits (or an element of symmetry) and the top and bottom of the reservoir or aquifer (including faults). Internal geometry comprises the areal and vertical extent of individual permeability units and nonpay zones that are important to the solution of the problem and to the definition of the well geometry (e.g., well diameter, completion interval, and presence of hydraulic fractures emanating from the well).

The types of models to be considered are listed below in order of increasing cost, difficulty, and time incurred in their use. As will become apparent later, there can be exceptions to the order. For example, a simple 3D model of a reservoir segment may be less costly than a complex 2D areal model of an entire reservoir.

The types of models are

(1) tank models (zero dimension),
(2) 1D models,
(3) 2D areal (x,y; r,θ; curvilinear) models,
(4) 2D cross-sectional (x,z) or radial (r,z) models,
(5) multilayer (stacks of 2D areal) models, and
(6) 3D models.

3.2.1 Tank Models. The tank model, described in such reservoir engineering textbooks as Craft and Hawkins',[1] is most useful when rapid answers are needed and average reservoir pressure behavior is deemed the only important factor in making operating or investment decisions. Pressure gradients in the reservoir should be small or else their impact should not be considered significant. Use of a tank model simply involves a classic, hand-calculation method. The calculation can be made more easily and reliably, however, with unsteady-state, material-balance computer programs. Many such programs are available.

A standard tank model sometimes can be modified to accommodate special situations. Lutes *et al.*[2] used a tank model to study accelerated blowdown of a strong waterdrive gas reservoir. The model was modified to account for the expansion of gas trapped in water-invaded regions and its subsequent migration to the gas zone.

3.2.2 1D Models. 1D models can seldom be used for fieldwide reservoir studies because they cannot model areal and vertical sweep. For example, 1D models usually cannot calculate realistic displacement efficiencies in invaded regions because they cannot represent gravity effects perpendicular to the direction of flow.

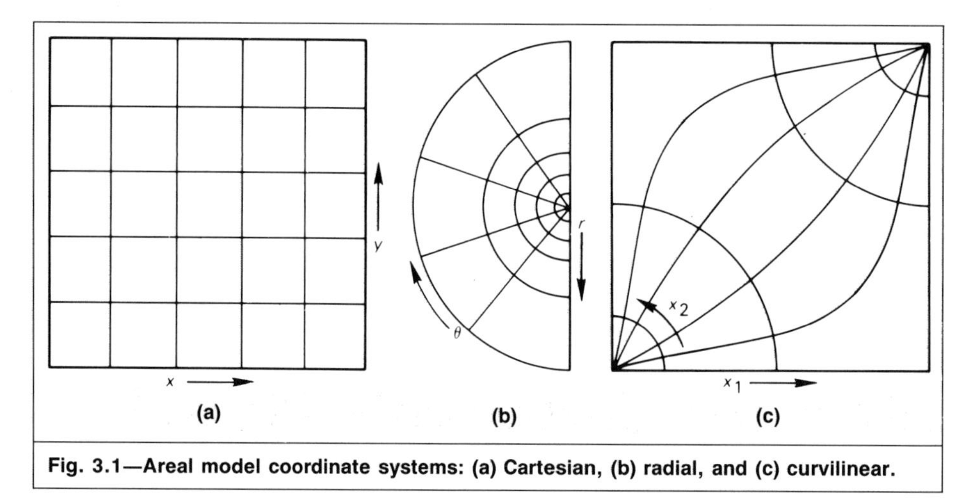

Fig. 3.1—Areal model coordinate systems: (a) Cartesian, (b) radial, and (c) curvilinear.

However, 1D models can be used effectively to investigate the sensitivity of reservoir performance to variations in reservoir parameters. These sensitivity studies can provide valuable insight when the engineer is history matching larger, more complex models. Hirasaki[3] used a 1D model to study the sensitivity of oil recovery to changes in displaceable oil volume, mobility ratio, permeability level, and shape of the relative permeability curves.

1D models are also helpful in evaluating the influence of heterogeneity in the direction of flow. Huppler[4] used this type of model to define the influence of heterogeneity on laboratory waterfloods. McCulloch *et al.*[5] found that natural depletion and crestal gas-injection behavior for a high-relief (reef) reservoir could be predicted reliably using a 1D vertical model.

In another example, Fussell[6] used a 1D radial model to study the influence of condensed liquids near the wellbore on the productivity of gas-condensate wells as pressure declined below the dewpoint.

3.2.3 2D Areal Models. 2D areal models are the most commonly used models in reservoir studies. They are used when areal flow patterns dominate reservoir performance. For example, areal models normally would be used when an optimal waterflood pattern is selected or the influence of areal heterogeneity on reservoir behavior is evaluated.

2D areal models are frequently used for studies of entire reservoirs. Objectives of such full-field studies usually include forecasts of oil, gas, and water production rates and of requirements for wells and surface facilities. Objectives might also include optimization of such factors as well locations, distribution of injection and withdrawal, and timing for installation of artificial lift or for modification of surface facilities. This type of study is also used to estimate ultimate recovery and to determine the influence of alternative depletion methods, production targets, and operating strategies on ultimate recovery.

Most 2D areal model studies use pseudofunctions to account for vertical flow of fluids (Sec. 3.3). Although pseudofunctions have their limitations, they frequently allow the third, vertical dimension to be represented adequately in 2D areal models. Pseudofunctions are not needed in areal models of thin reservoirs that are not highly stratified.

Areal models normally use Cartesian (x,y) coordinate systems (Fig. 3.1a), but there are some applications for which a radial (r,θ) or curvilinear coordinate system is more suitable (Figs. 3.1b and 3.1c). The latter two systems provide better definition near wells than do x-y areal models. In certain cases, curvilinear coordinates may reduce the number of gridblocks needed in areal or 3D models.[7,8]

Miller and Clements[9] described a 2D water/oil areal model that was used to study the mechanism involved in killing a blowout by injecting water into a nearby relief well (Fig. 3.2). The areal model calculated the time required for injected water to reach the blowout well and the increase in water cut after breakthrough (Fig. 3.3). Wellbore hydraulics was considered, so oil and water production rates, bottomhole and surface flowing pressures at the injector, and flowing bottomhole pressures at the blowout well were also determined.

Shirer *et al.*[10] used a 2D, water/oil areal model to select the optimal waterflood pattern for the Jay-Little Escambia Creek fields in northwest Florida and southern Alabama. They selected the 2D areal model because it provided detailed, reasonably accurate predictions of waterflood performance in a relatively short period of time. Cross-sectional models were constructed to determine the effects of reservoir stratification in different areas of the field. Pseudorelative permeability curves calculated from the cross-sectional model results were verified with a 1D simulator that modeled the average properties of each column of the cross section. 2D areal models of part, and later all, of the field were developed to evaluate the performance of four waterflood patterns for various oper-

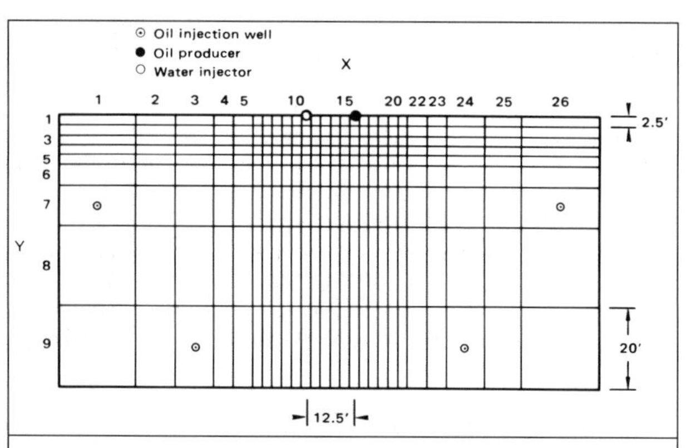

Fig. 3.2—Gridding used for well blowout studies.[9]

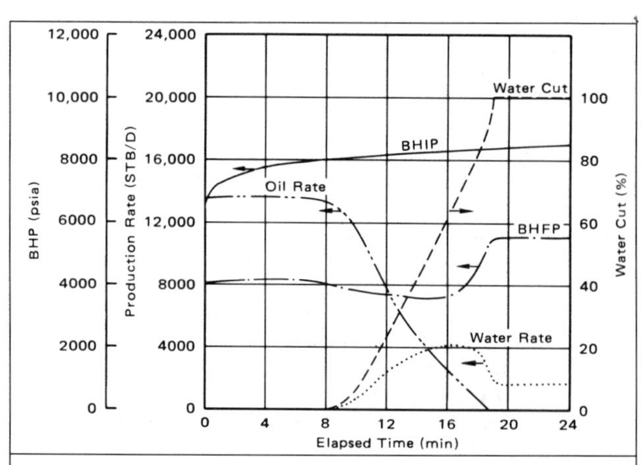

Fig. 3.3—Calculated behavior of relief and blowout wells.[9]

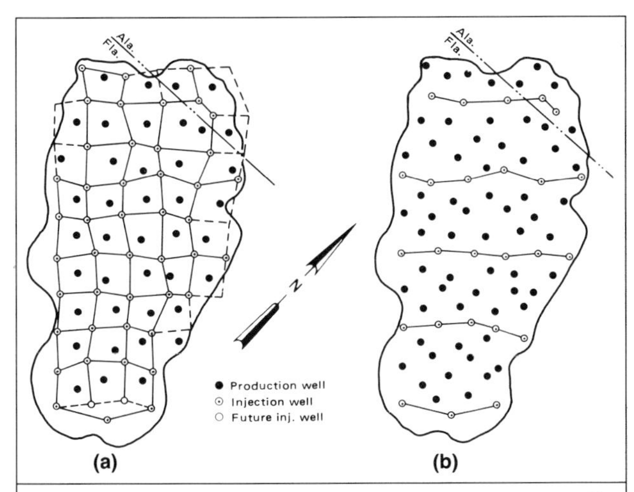

Fig. 3.4—Jay-Little Escambia Creek waterflood patterns[10]: (a) five-spot pattern, and (b) 3 : 1 linedrive pattern.

ating conditions. A peripheral pattern, two repeating patterns (five spot and 3 : 1 line drive), and a combination pattern were evaluated (Figs. 3.4 and 3.5). The model showed that the highest oil recovery and economic potential were realized with the 3 : 1 staggered linedrive pattern, which was ultimately used in field development. After the 2D areal model study had been completed, a 3D model of the field was constructed. The 3D model confirmed that the reservoir could be flooded as a single unit and that selective flooding of individual members was not necessary for optimal recovery.

Morse and Von Gonten[11] used 2D, single-phase models to study vertically fractured wells from the start of production until flow was stabilized. Productivity data were calculated for a wide range of fracture lengths, reservoir conditions, and fluid properties. Fig. 3.6 illustrates the type of grid used in the study. Note the fine definition used near the edge or end of the fracture.

Henderson *et al.*[12] used a 2D areal model to determine the optimal placement of wells in a gas-storage reservoir. They also used the model to evaluate the influence of withdrawal distribution on end-of-season gas availability.

3.2.4 2D Cross-Sectional and Radial Models. 2D cross-sectional and radial models are used primarily (1) to develop well functions or pseudofunctions for use in 2D areal or 3D models; (2) to simulate peripheral water injection, crestal gas injection, or other processes in which frontal velocities toward producers are largely uniform; and (3) to evaluate well behavior when vertical effects dominate performance, as in gas or water coning.

Cross-sectional models can be used to evaluate the interaction of gravity, capillary, and viscous forces and the resultant effect on vertical sweep and displacement efficiencies. If areal sweep efficiency is an important consideration, this kind of model cannot be used directly to estimate overall field performance.

2D radial models (r,z) can be used to represent converging or diverging flow in a radially symmetrical region of a reservoir.

Weaver[13] used a 2D, three-phase, cross-sectional model to study the performance of the Borregos R-5 (south) reservoir during production by gas-cap expansion and, later, by downstructure water injection. The objectives of the study were to define the ultimate effect of gas invasion on oil recovery during primary production and to evaluate the impact of wide vertical variations in permeability on oil recovery (Figs. 3.7 through 3.9). These questions were readily answered with a 2D cross-sectional model that could represent permeability stratification and three-phase relative permeability relationships. A 3D model was not chosen because the areal movements of gas and water were not important issues. Computing costs and study time would have been much greater if a 3D model had been used.

Kingston and Niko[14] discussed use of 2D cross-sectional models to compare displacement characteristics of injected water and gas in the Brent and Statfjord reservoirs of the Brent field. The studies were conducted as part of the development planning for this large, North Sea oil field. 2D cross-sectional models are typically used

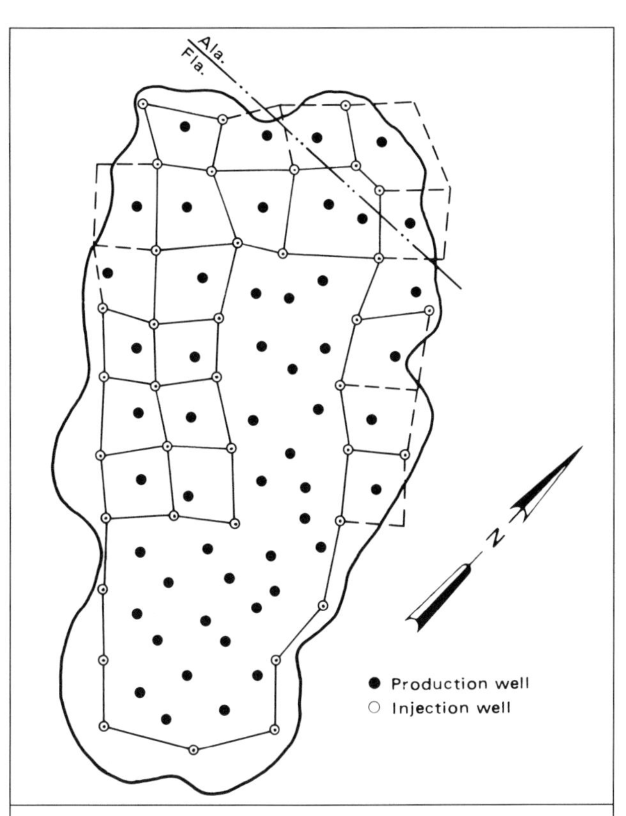

Fig. 3.5—Combination pattern for Jay-Little Escambia Creek.[10]

in development planning studies because they provide valuable insight into displacement mechanisms.

Cross-sectional models are also used often in studies of miscible processes to evaluate the influence of gravity and heterogeneity on displacement efficiency and sweep efficiency. Dicharry *et al.*[15] reviewed cross-sectional model studies that compared the relative merits of (1) continuous CO_2 slug injection followed by water and (2) the water-alternating-gas process for the SACROC unit, Kelly-Snyder field. Results from the cross-sectional model were compared with those from a multilayer streamtube model.

DesBrisay *et al.*[16] used a cross-sectional model to match performance of a combination miscible-gas/bottomwater displacement program for the Intisar "D" field, a carbonate reef. The matched model was then used to predict future performance of an ongoing high-pressure-gas, miscible-displacement process. Earlier model

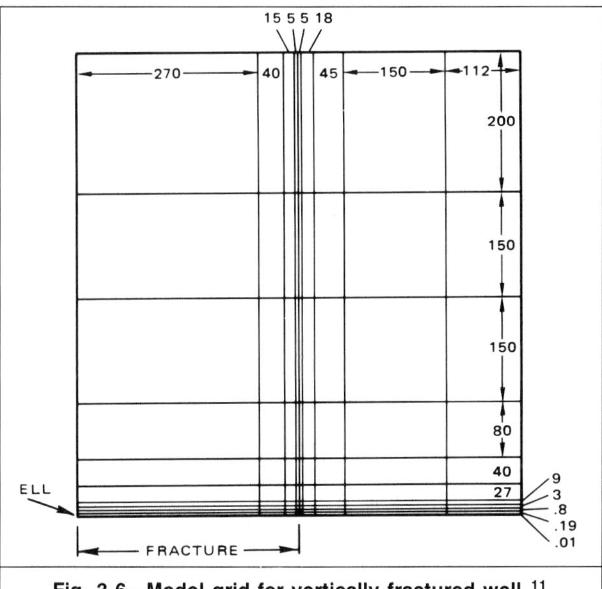

Fig. 3.6—Model grid for vertically fractured well.[11]

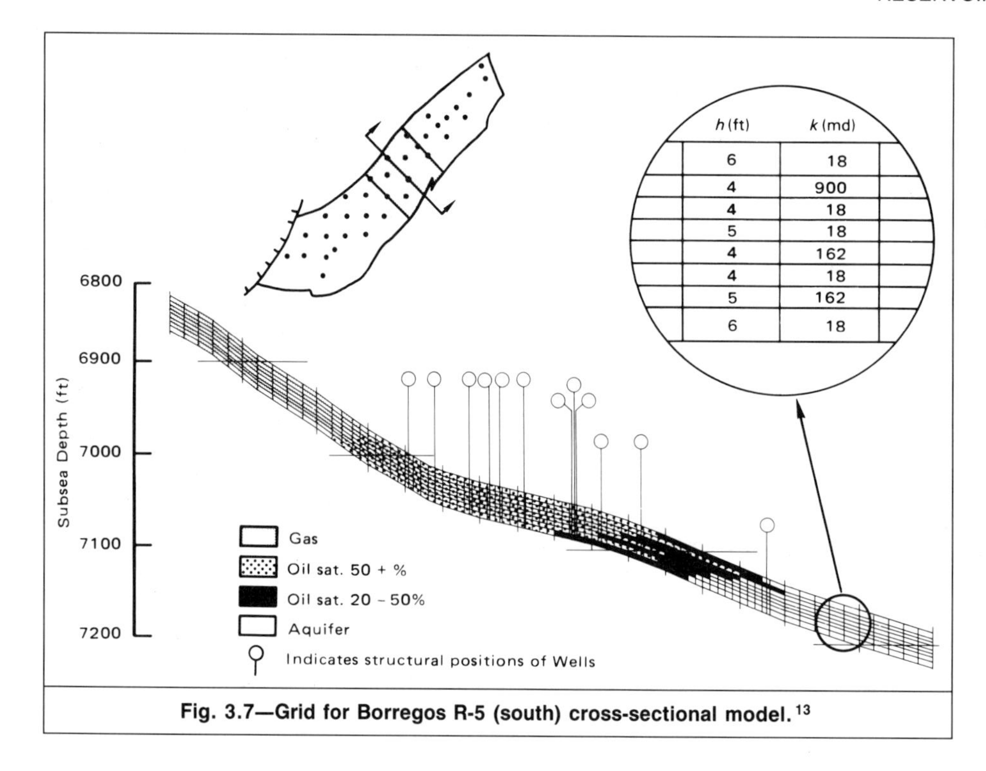

Fig. 3.7—Grid for Borregos R-5 (south) cross-sectional model.[13]

work had concluded that a 3D model was not needed to match field behavior, because vertical displacement was more significant than lateral displacement in this field.

Reitzel and Callow[17] constructed a cross-sectional model having detailed reservoir description to analyze performance of the Golden Spike D3-A field (Figs. 3.10 and 3.11). This limestone reef reservoir was depleted initially by fluid expansion followed by gas injection. Subsequently, a liquefied petroleum gas bank was injected to create a vertical, gravity-controlled, miscible-bank process. The cross-sectional model quantified the influence of reservoir heterogeneity on the miscible-bank process (Figs. 3.12 and 3.13). The size, number, and location of barriers within the reef severely affected the miscible-displacement process.

Cross-sectional models can help justify simplifications in models of entire fields or large segments of a field. For example, Richardson *et al.*[18] present a method for determining the effect of small, discontinuous shales on oil recovery—particularly during gas-drive operations, when high oil recovery depends on effective oil drainage by gravity. They used 2D, gas/oil cross-sectional models to determine effective vertical permeabilities in an anisotropic system in which performance, as measured by recovery efficiency, is equivalent to that of a system containing discontinuous shale barriers.

Jacks *et al.*[19] describe how 2D cross-sectional models can be used to develop dynamic pseudo-relative-permeability functions for use in 2D areal models of an entire field. The approach allows less-expensive 2D models to be substituted for 3D models. Applications of pseudo-relative-permeability functions are discussed in more detail in Sec. 3.3.

2D radial (r,z) models are especially useful in studies of the behavior of wells in bottomwater-drive reservoirs, gas-cap-drive reservoirs, or reservoirs having a thin oil column overlain by gas and underlain by water. For these types of reservoirs, selection of ini-

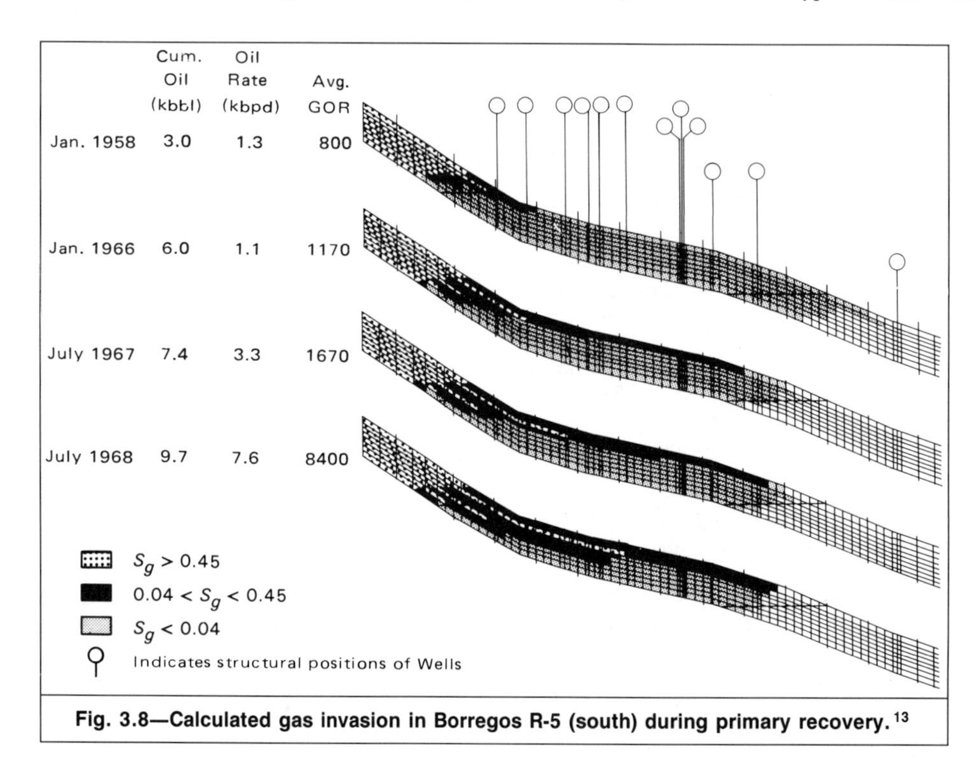

Fig. 3.8—Calculated gas invasion in Borregos R-5 (south) during primary recovery.[13]

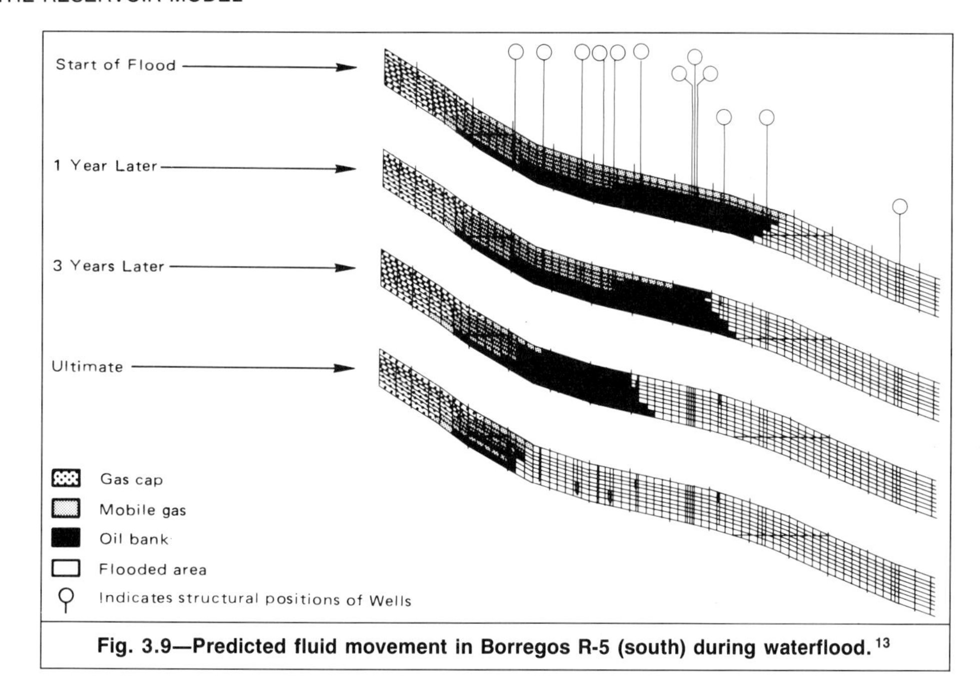

Fig. 3.9—Predicted fluid movement in Borregos R-5 (south) during waterflood.[13]

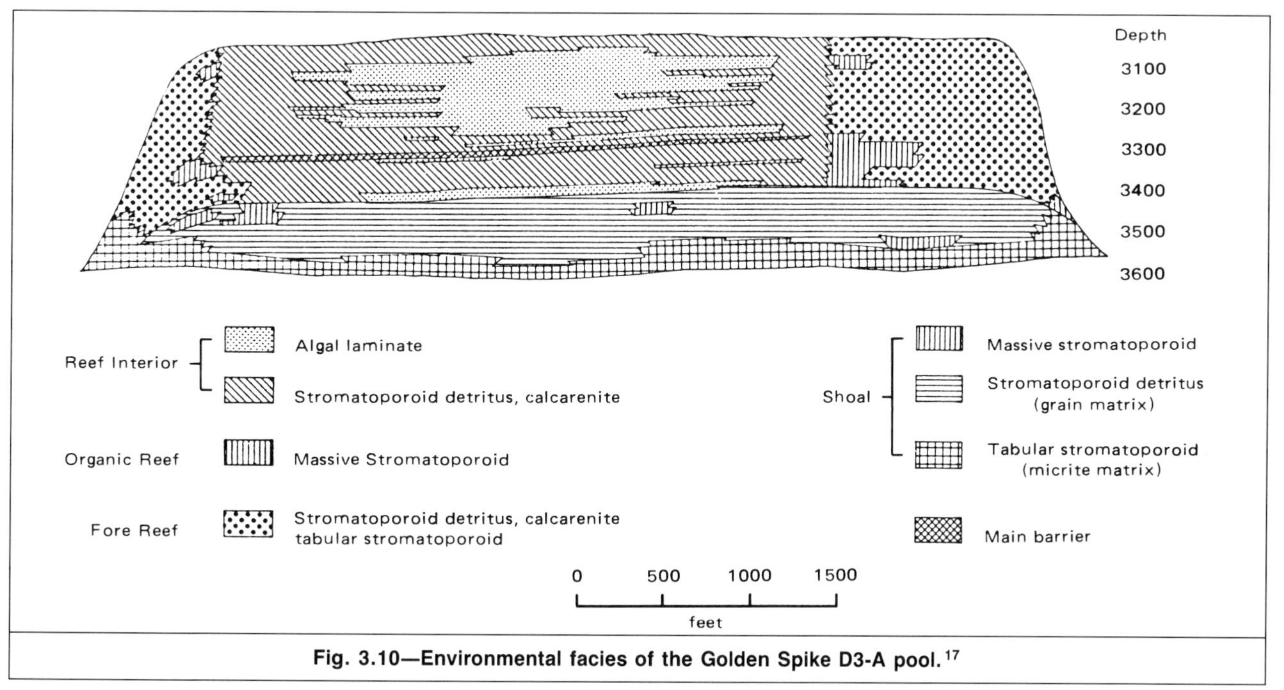

Fig. 3.10—Environmental facies of the Golden Spike D3-A pool.[17]

tial completion intervals and recognition of opportunities for recompletion are important factors in planning field development and optimizing field performance.

Miller and Rogers[20] used 2D radial models to study the performance of wells in a bottomwater-drive reservoir offshore Louisiana (Fig. 3.14). The models were used to answer two questions.

1. Could wells be tested safely at maximum production rates until water production was observed and then be cut back to eliminate water production without adversely affecting ultimate recovery?

2. What combination of withdrawal rates and resultant water production would yield the highest ultimate recovery commensurate with maximum profit?

After a wide range of reservoir parameters had been investigated, the authors concluded that a well could be tested until water production appears, and then could be shut in and returned to water-free production. They also found, for offshore Louisiana conditions, that higher production rates increased profits and did not significantly affect ultimate recovery of oil. They used calculated oil rate as a function of cumulative production for a range of total liquid rates (Fig. 3.15), together with economic factors, to reach these conclusions.

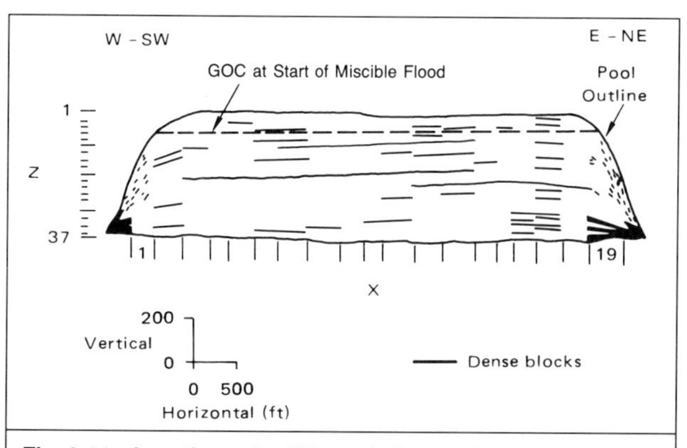

Fig. 3.11—Locations of grid boundaries and barriers to vertical flow in the Golden Spike model.[17]

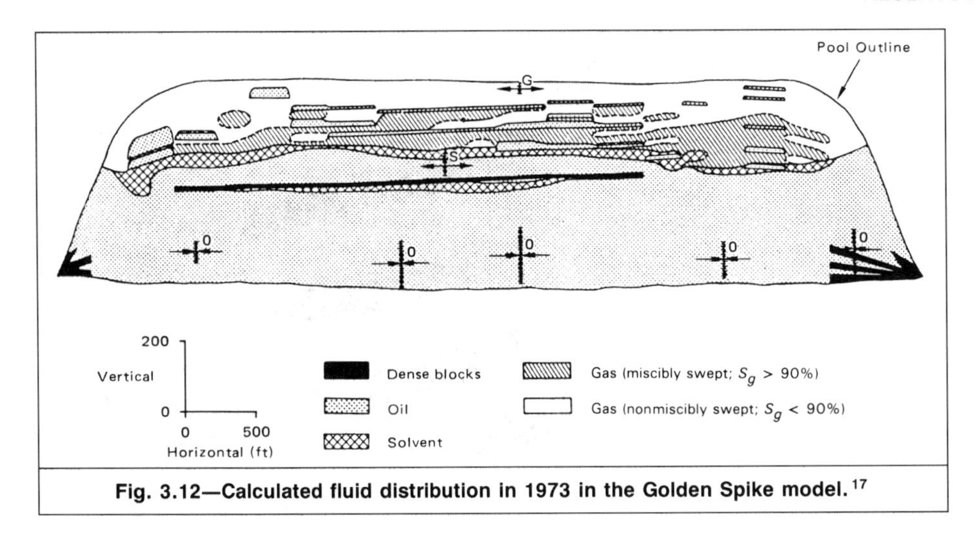

Fig. 3.12—Calculated fluid distribution in 1973 in the Golden Spike model.[17]

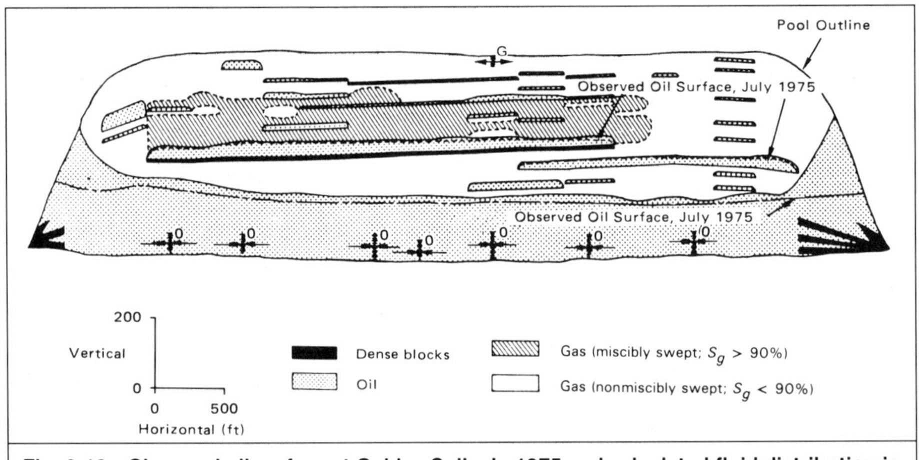

Fig. 3.13—Observed oil surface at Golden Spike In 1975 and calculated fluid distribution in the model.[17]

2D radial models have also been used to develop special relationships (well functions) for predicting well behavior in 2D areal model studies.[21] Chap. 7 discusses this subject in more detail.

An important application of both 2D cross-sectional and 2D radial models is the evaluation of the effect of production rate on reservoir performance and ultimate recovery. Beveridge *et al.*,[22] Lee *et al.*,[23] and Stright *et al.*[24] discuss how both kinds of models have been used to evaluate the effect of production rate on ultimate recovery for Canadian carbonate reservoirs.

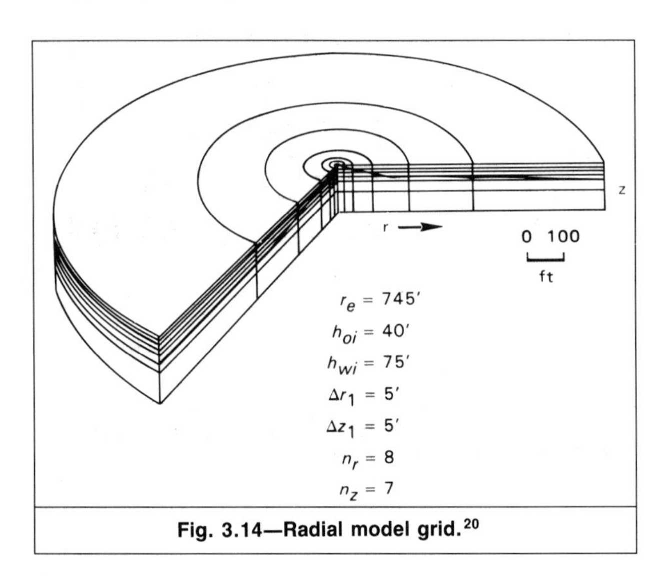

Fig. 3.14—Radial model grid.[20]

3.2.5 Multilayer Models. If a single field contains several *independent* reservoirs, each can be modeled in a separate study. If production from one reservoir influences that from another, however, both reservoirs may need to be represented in a single reservoir model. This "interdependence" can arise when (1) production or injection is commingled in wells, (2) reservoirs are in contact with a common aquifer, (3) common trunklines, separators, or other facilities make it necessary to treat several reservoirs with the same well-management routine, and (4) a fixed total rate for several reservoirs makes it necessary to use a single well-management routine.

A 3D model should be used if significant crossflow can occur either directly between the reservoirs, in the aquifer, or at wells. Otherwise, either a 3D or a 2D simulator may be used. If a 2D simulator is selected, each reservoir should be represented as a region of the model with no flow permitted between regions (Fig. 3.16). To define production and injection rates by wells and zones, the well-management routine in 2D or 3D models must be able to handle the interaction between reservoirs, wells, and surface facilities.

3.2.6 3D Models. It may be necessary or desirable to use 3D models for a number of reasons.

1. Reservoir geometry may be too complex to reduce to a combination of cross-sectional and areal models. Reservoirs having shales and other flow barriers that are continuous over large areas, but with permeable "windows" where crossflow occurs, are difficult to model in only two dimensions.

2. Reservoir fluid mechanics may be so complex that 2D representations are difficult to analyze. Reservoirs in a more advanced stage of depletion fall into this category; they require precise modeling to distinguish between the performances resulting from alternative depletion plans.

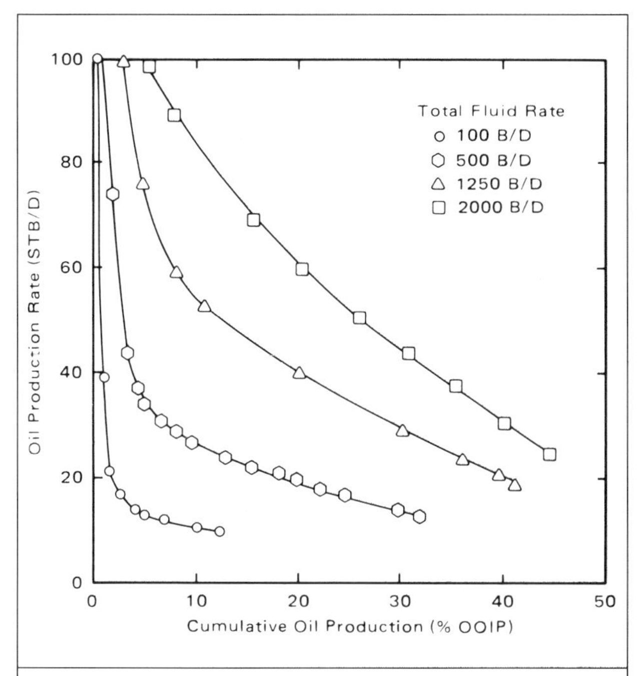

Fig. 3.15—Predicted effect of rate on the performance of a bottomwater-drive reservoir.[20]

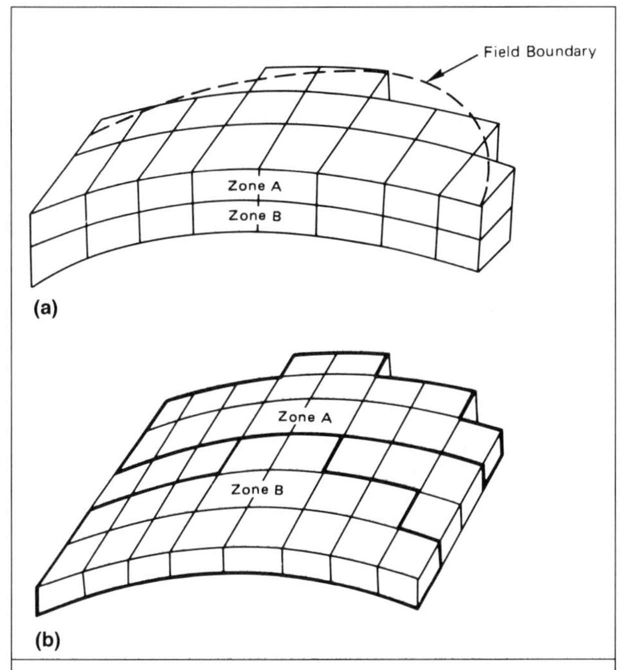

Fig. 3.16—Modeling of a multilayer reservoir: (a) with a 3D model, and (b) with a 2D model.

3. The displacement to be studied may be dominated by vertical flow as, for example, near wells where both cusping and coning may occur. Both areal and vertical detail may be needed that can be obtained only in 3D segment models.

4. Occasionally, 2D simulation is more troublesome and expensive than 3D modeling. Modeling some reservoirs that are areally complex and highly stratified can require dozens, or even hundreds, of sets of pseudofunctions.

5. Studies to be used in negotiations or to demonstrate responsible reservoir management may not be credible to an audience unfamiliar with the many valid applications of pseudofunctions.

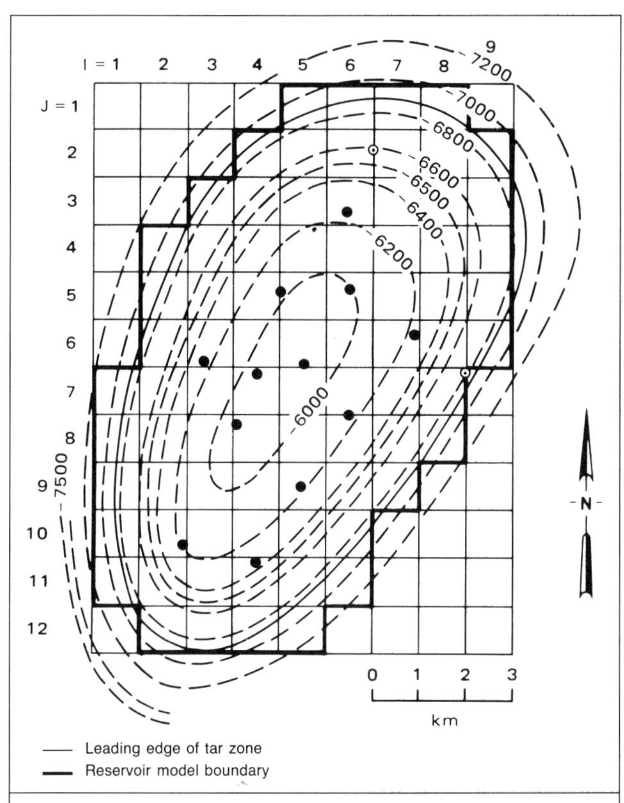

Fig. 3.17—Structure contour map showing model grid—top of Reservoir A, Khursaniyah.[25]

One problem sometimes associated with 3D models is unwieldy model size; an adequate model may have so many gridblocks that it is time-consuming to use and produces results too late to influence decisions. Plan carefully to avoid this situation.

Boberg *et al.*[25] applied a 3D water/oil model to the Khursaniyah reservoir in Saudi Arabia to study peripheral water injection. The 3D model was needed because the field contains five zones that are in communication at the crest but not in the flank regions (Figs. 3.17 and 3.18). Water influx occurs only into the lowermost zone because impermeable tar is located at the oil/water contact (OWC) in the others. The water can migrate upward into other zones from the lowermost zone as depletion proceeds.

Killough and Foster[26] used a 3D, three-phase model to study behavior of the Empire ABO field in New Mexico. A 3D model with 22 vertical layers was used in initial studies; later, a 3D model with three layers was used. The authors stated that a 2D areal model was not selected because the large variations in thickness and dip of the reservoir would introduce a considerable amount of nonorthogonality into a single-layer areal model. Also, there was concern that pseudo-relative permeabilities and capillary pressures could not properly represent gravity effects. Although the authors did not indicate the magnitude of error that would result from the use of

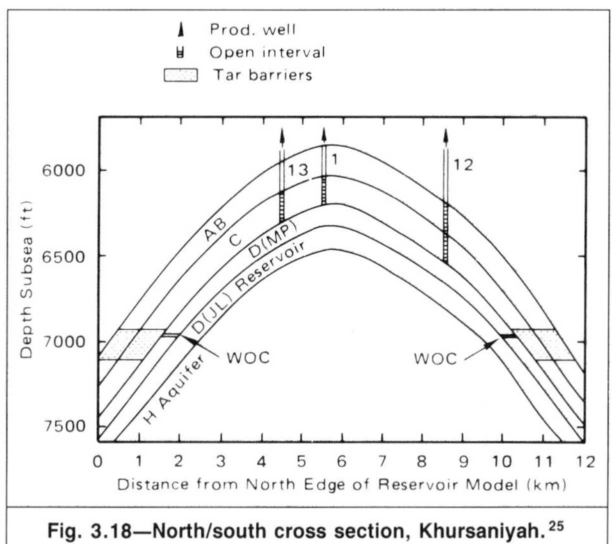

Fig. 3.18—North/south cross section, Khursaniyah.[25]

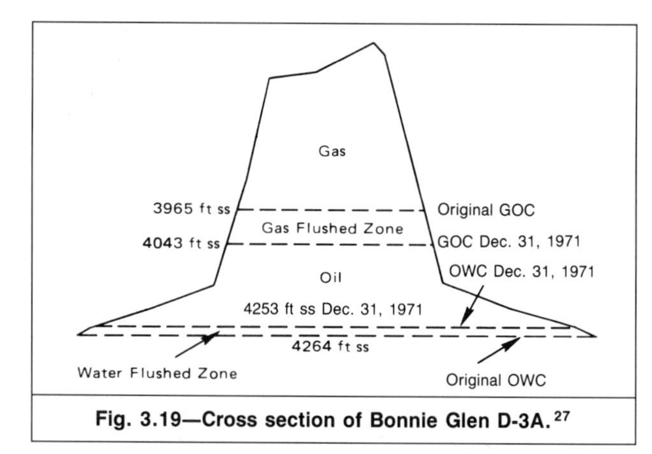

Fig. 3.19—Cross section of Bonnie Glen D-3A.[27]

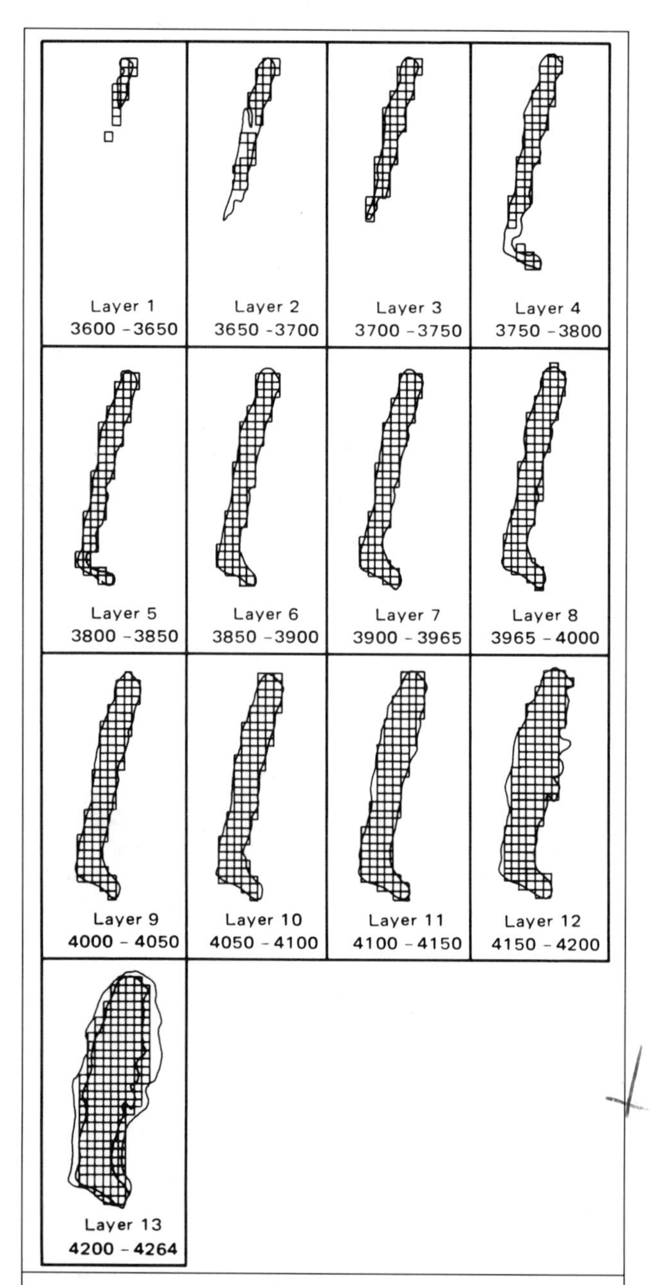

Fig. 3.20—Grid system in the Bonnie Glen model.[27]

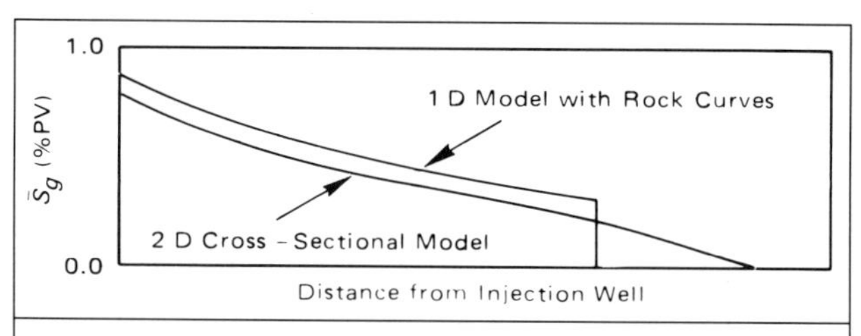

Fig. 3.21—Comparison of gas saturation profiles predicted with 2D and 1D models.

an areal model, they reported that the behavior of the 3-layer model agreed closely with that of the 22-layer model. The 3-layer model used vertical-equilibrium (VE) pseudo-relative permeabilities for horizontal-flow calculations. Normal rock relative permeability relationships were needed to model vertical flow realistically.

Thompson and Thachuk[27] discuss the use of a 3D model to simulate gas cycling of the Bonnie Glen D-3A pool in Alberta, Canada. The model was selected because the geometry of the dolomitized biotherm reef was highly complex (Figs. 3.19 and 3.20). Results from simpler models were used to design the final 3D model.

Weber *et al.*[28] describe a full-field, 3D model used in studies of an oil-rim reservoir in Nigeria. Although 2D areal models probably could have been used satisfactorily, a 3D model with three vertical layers was selected to improve definition of the geology and to provide more insight into physical flow processes. Each of the three layers represented a different rock facies.

3.3 Simplification of Complex Problems

As previously stated, a major challenge in reservoir simulation is to develop the simplest model of the reservoir that will allow proper decisions to be made regarding reservoir development and operation. Sec. 3.3 discusses several approaches that allow the engineer to use relatively simple models in complex reservoir situations.

3.3.1 Pseudo-Relative-Permeability and Capillary-Pressure Functions. Relative-permeability and capillary-pressure relationships must be defined to represent multiphase flow of fluids in reservoir rock properly. These "rock" relationships are normally measured in the laboratory with rock samples from the reservoir under study. Reservoir models that use rock curves can provide meaningful results if the number of vertical and areal gridblocks is large enough. If vertical gridding is coarse, however, use of rock curves will, in most cases, produce incorrect results. (See Chap. 2).

To illustrate, consider the calculation of frontal movement and gas-saturation distribution for gas injection into a low-dip oil reservoir. Gas will move faster along the top of the reservoir than along the base, resulting in overriding and low vertical sweep. Fig. 3.21 shows the average gas-saturation profile, correctly calculated with rock curves in a finely gridded, 2D cross-sectional model. To use an extreme case for the sake of comparison, gas-saturation distribution was also calculated in a model with no vertical gridding (1D in this case—the coarsest vertical gridding possible). Rock relative-permeability and capillary-pressure curves were used without modification in the model. This model gave a much different, unrealistically optimistic gas-saturation profile and much later gas breakthrough because it did not account for gas overriding.

Rock curves may also produce unduly pessimistic results. For instance, in the previous case, if the gas-injection rate had been relatively low, resulting in a long depletion time for the field, oil left behind in the gas-invaded region could drain downward to the base of the section and create a thin zone with relatively high oil saturation. Oil could then flow along the base of the reservoir to the gas/oil contact (GOC). As with gas overriding, the model with coarse vertical gridding and unmodified rock functions (the 1D model, in this case) cannot accurately account for this oil-drainage mechanism and will give pessimistic results. Pessimistic results may also be obtained in model studies of some water/oil displacement processes, particularly if the oil/water mobility ratio is unfavorable.

The need for vertical gridding in the model can be reduced or eliminated if "average" relative-permeability and capillary-pressure functions can be defined that will produce the same initial fluid distribution, fluid movement, and pressure distribution as a model with vertical gridding. These pseudo-relative-permeability and capillary-pressure relationships provide good engineering solutions in many situations. Contacts with users throughout the industry suggest that hundreds of successful reservoir studies have been conducted with pseudofunctions.

Two types of pseudofunctions have been widely used in reservoir studies. Coats *et al.*[29] described VE pseudofunctions. Jacks *et al.*[19] and Kyte and Berry[30] discussed dynamic pseudofunctions, which include VE pseudos as a subcategory.

3.3.2 VE Pseudofunctions. The VE concept assumes that, as depletion proceeds, gravity and capillary forces will be in equilibrium vertically in every gridblock in the reservoir model. In other words, differences between the pressures in the oil and water (or oil and gas) phases are exactly balanced by capillary pressure, which in turn fixes the vertical-saturation distribution. This is equivalent to having potentials of each phase constant vertically. If this condition is satisfied, a 3D problem can be reduced to a 2D areal problem, and cross-sectional problems can be adequately represented in one dimension. The VE assumption applies to single gridblocks and does not imply that fluid contacts are in equilibrium areally. Indeed, when applied properly, VE pseudofunctions can be used in areal models to simulate gas overriding oil or water underrunning oil.

Obviously, capillary pressure equilibrium within each gridblock is not totally consistent with nonequilibrium areally. It follows, then, that the VE pseudofunction concept cannot precisely model the vertical dimension, but it is adequate for many reservoir problems. The applicability of any set of pseudofunctions should be confirmed by test runs that compare results that use pseudofunctions with those obtained from models having detailed vertical segmentation and using rock curves. Procedures for making this comparison are discussed later.

VE pseudo-relative permeabilities can be derived very simply. First, rock capillary-pressure curves are used to define vertical-saturation distributions for a range of values of average saturation. The vertical-saturation distribution determines the vertical distribution of rock relative permeabilities because rock relative permeability is a function of saturation. An overall average value of relative permeability can then be computed for each value of average water saturation. The calculation should account for stratification by properly weighting relative permeability and saturation. For water, for example, the equations are

$$\bar{S}_w = \frac{\int_0^h \phi_z S_{wz} dz}{\int_0^h \phi_z dz} = \frac{V_w}{V_p} \quad \text{(3.1)}$$

and

$$k_{prw} = \frac{\int_0^h k_z k_{rwz} dz}{\int_0^h k_z dz} = \frac{kh_w}{kh}, \quad \text{(3.2)}$$

where

k_{prw} = pseudo-relative permeability to water,
h = sand thickness,
k_z = permeability parallel to the bedding plane at Point z,
k_{rwz} = rock relative permeability to water at Point z,
z = distance in vertical direction (or, usually, direction normal to the bedding plane),
kh_w = total effective permeability to water,
kh = total permeability thickness,
S_{wz} = water saturation at Point z,
$\bar{S}_w$ = average water saturation,
ϕ_z = porosity at Point z,
V_w = total volume of water, and
V_p = total PV.

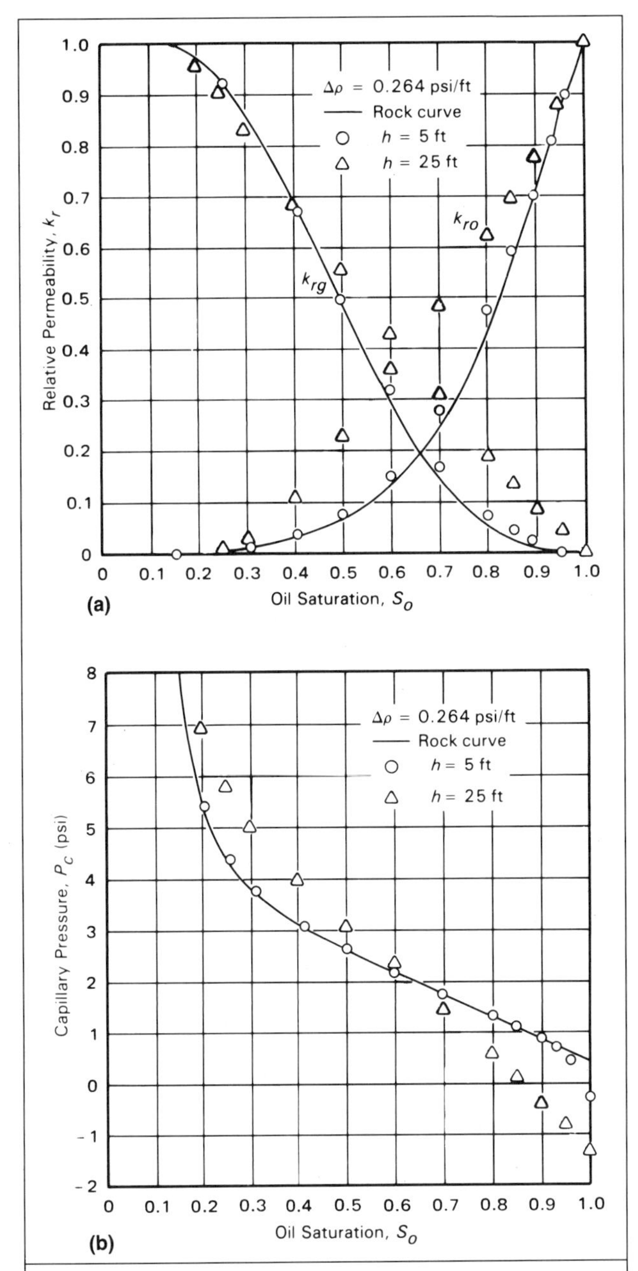

Fig. 3.22—Typical pseudo-relative-permeability and capillary-pressure curves illustrating effects of formation thickness (after Ref. 29).

Note that k_z should be the reference permeability for the rock relative permeability curves. For imbibition water/oil relative permeability curves, this is often the effective permeability to oil at irreducible water saturation and may not be the same as the air permeability of the dry rock.

A single application of Eqs. 3.1 and 3.2 will yield one point on an equilibrium pseudo-relative-permeability/saturation curve. Successive applications of the equations over a range of average saturation values will define the entire curve.

To derive VE pseudo-capillary-pressure functions, one must first select a reference depth at which the pseudo-capillary-pressure values apply. This is usually the top, bottom, or midpoint of the sand. The choice of the reference point is completely arbitrary, because the equilibrium vertical-saturation distribution can be established uniquely if one value of capillary pressure and the depth at which that value of capillary pressure applies is known. It is assumed, of course, that fluid densities are known and that laboratory capillary-pressure data—i.e., rock curves—are available. From the saturation distribution, the average saturation can be calculated by Eq. 3.1. Thus, for every value of rock capillary pressure defined at the reference depth, there is a unique value for

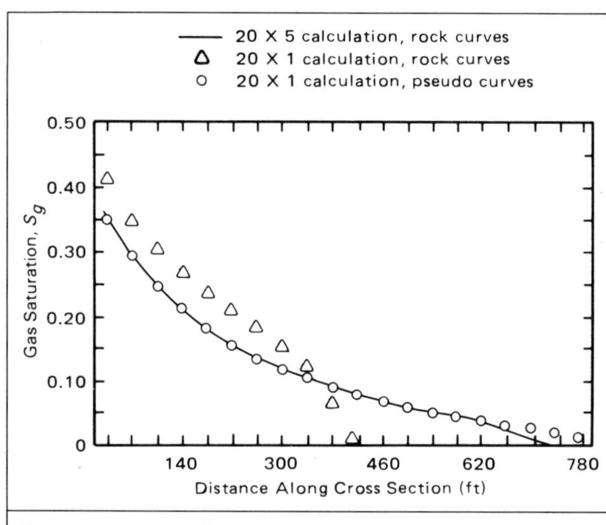

Fig. 3.23—Comparison of saturation profiles in 2D cross-sectional and 1D areal models (after Ref. 31).

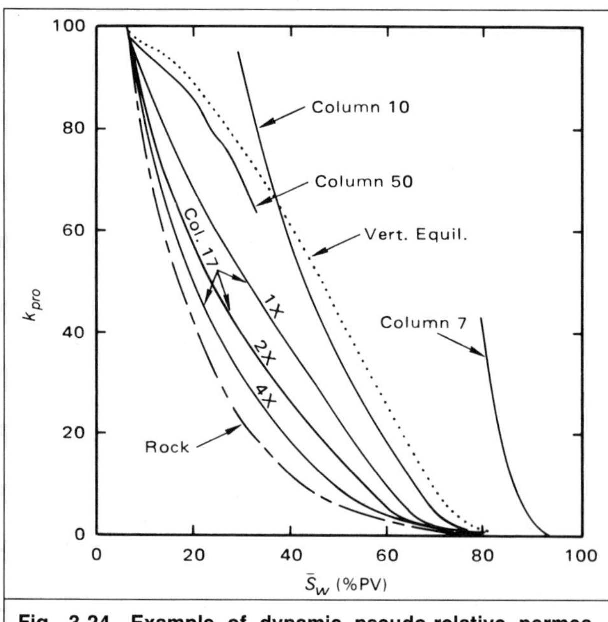

Fig. 3.24—Example of dynamic pseudo-relative permeabilities.[19]

the vertical average saturation. The capillary-pressure/saturation relation defined in this manner is the VE pseudo-capillary-pressure function.

Fig. 3.22 depicts typical rock capillary-pressure and relative-permeability curves and the pseudocurves that result for two particular sand thicknesses. The figure shows that the integration process causes the slope of the pseudorelationships to become more nearly linear than the corresponding rock relationships. The tendency toward linearity increases with increasing sand thickness as the transition zone spans a decreasing fraction of the total sand thickness.

Results summarized in Figure 3.23 demonstrate that simulations that use VE pseudocurves can agree closely with the correct behavior, whereas results obtained with rock curves will be in error.[31] The figure shows depth-averaged gas saturation vs. distance along a dipping (3° [0.05-rad]) cross section. Gas was injected at the crest into the initially oil-saturated formation. The vertical slice is 800 ft [244 m] long and 25 ft [7.6 m] thick. A 2D cross-sectional calculation was performed with rock relative-permeability and capillary-pressure curves. The calculated gas saturations were then depth-averaged and plotted as the solid line in Fig. 3.23. The circular points correspond to a 1D areal calculation that used VE pseudocurves, reflecting the assumption of VE throughout the thickness. The triangular points correspond to a 1D calculation that used rock relative-permeability and capillary-pressure curves and reflect the implied assumption that fluid saturation is uniform throughout the thickness. Results of the areal calculation with VE pseudocurves are essentially identical with those from the cross-sectional model.

Pseudo-relative-permeability and capillary-pressure functions can be developed with the assumption of a complete segregation of phases. Complete segregation could occur, for example, when capillary/gravity equilibrium creates a transition zone that is much thinner than the oil zone. Coats *et al.*[32] developed equations for both functions that apply to situations involving complete segregation. van Poollen *et al.*[33] present similar relationships for pseudo-relative-permeability functions in complete segregation situations. These methods lend themselves to calculation of VE pseudofunctions by the simulator, saving the engineer the trouble of entering tables of relative permeability and capillary pressure.

Coats *et al.*[29,32] developed a dimensionless group for estimating whether the assumption of VE is satisfactory. A more stringent test of the validity of the assumption is needed, however, if VE pseudofunctions are used in models of stratified reservoirs. In these cases, cross-sectional models should be used to confirm that the use of VE pseudofunctions is justified. Factors that promote VE include high vertical permeability, low flow rates, reservoir homogeneity, and low fluid viscosities.

3.3.3 Dynamic Pseudofunctions. It is often not appropriate to assume VE in actual field situations. In this case, either dynamic pseudo-relative permeabilities must be used or the third dimension must be represented in the simulator. Dynamic pseudofunctions rely on the use of cross-sectional models that represent the reservoir in question and are calculated from the cross-sectional model results. It has been observed empirically that 1D models that use dynamic pseudofunctions can simulate accurately the performance of the 2D cross-sectional models from which they were derived. Dozens of such comparisons have been made successfully, providing broad empirical support for the use of this approach.

Dynamic pseudo-relative permeabilities are determined by editing results from cross-sectional runs. At each output record, the average water saturation and the pseudo-relative permeabilities to oil and water are determined for each block in appropriate columns of the cross-sectional model. If desired, a pseudo-relative-permeability function can be developed for each column in the cross-sectional model. Fig. 3.24 is a plot of the relative-permeability functions calculated from a cross-sectional model illustrated in Fig. 3.25. The pseudofunctions vary with location. For example, compare the curve for Col. 17 in the full oil zone with those for Cols. 7 and 10 in the oil/water transition zone. Dynamic pseudofunctions also vary with the depletion rate simulated in the cross-sectional model. Higher rates move the dynamic pseudo-relative-permeability curve closer to the rock curve.

The shapes of the dynamic and VE curves also depend on sand thickness, the stratification of porosity and permeability, and location relative to the transition zone. Thus, each column of blocks may have its own set of pseudofunctions, although differences between columns are frequently minor or can be accounted for by correlation of the data. For example, Jacks *et al.*[19] describe correlation of pseudofunctions with initial fluid saturation and fluid velocities. Fig. 3.26 shows a correlation of k_{pro} with total fluid velocity developed from a set of cross-sectional models run over a range of flow rates.

Each system should be evaluated independently to identify important variables and to determine the best techniques for correlating and applying pseudofunctions. Even with correlation, several sets of pseudofunctions may be needed to represent flow in an areal model that has wide variations in stratification and/or initial saturations. It may also be necessary to use different sets of pseudofunctions for flow along dip and normal to dip.

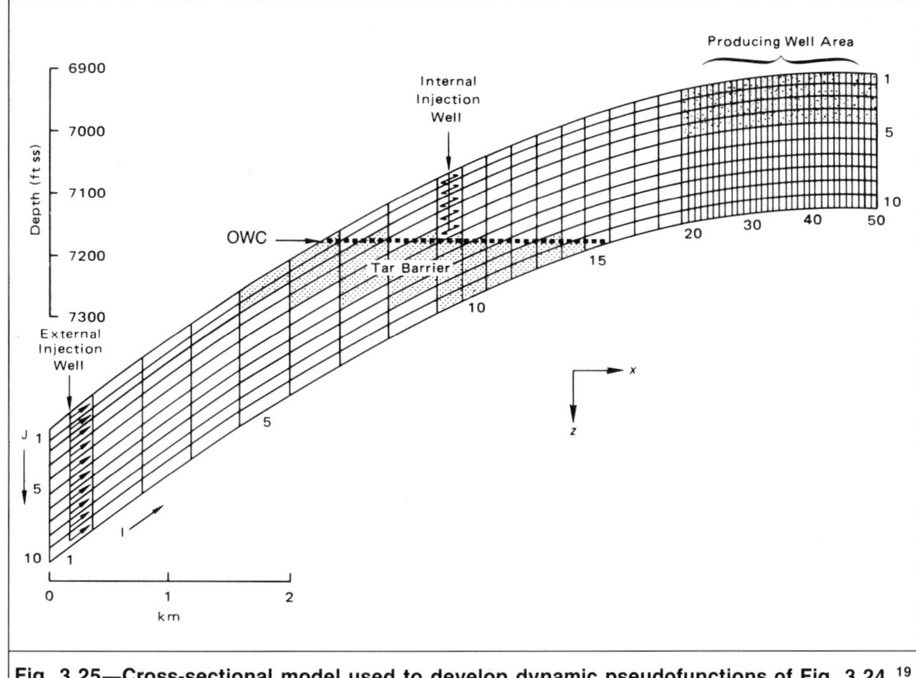

Fig. 3.25—Cross-sectional model used to develop dynamic pseudofunctions of Fig. 3.24.[19]

Before dynamic pseudo-relative permeabilities can be used with confidence, their validity must be demonstrated. Validation is normally achieved in a 1D simulation that models the cross-sectional model. In cases where directionally dependent pseudo-relative permeabilities are used, validation may be needed in a 2D areal simulation that models a 3D system.

Block depths for the 1D model are obtained from the midpoint depths of each column. The horizontal length, Δx, of each block is the same as that of the corresponding column in the cross section, and all blocks have the same width (in the implicit y direction). Thickness-weighted average porosities and permeabilities are determined from the cross-sectional model.

Fig. 3.27a[19] compares water-saturation distribution at different times along the length of equivalent 1D and cross-sectional models. In this particular example, the agreement between the two models is excellent at all times. An important point here is that a combination of dynamic pseudo-relative permeabilities and VE pseudo-capillary pressures were used in the 1D model. VE pseudo-capillary pressures were needed to obtain the correct initial fluid distribution in the areal model. From a practical standpoint, this is the most important function of pseudo-capillary pressure. In a situation where no initial WOC or GOC is present, use of VE pseudo-capillary pressure is still recommended, particularly for low rates of fluid displacement.

Fig. 3.27b illustrates the errors in saturation distribution that resulted when Jacks *et al.*[19] used VE pseudo-relative permeabilities rather than dynamic functions. Displacement behavior predicted with VE pseudofunctions in the 1D model was much more efficient than that predicted by the cross section.

Jacks *et al.* also compared results from a 3D model with those from a 2D areal model that used dynamic pseudo-relative permea-

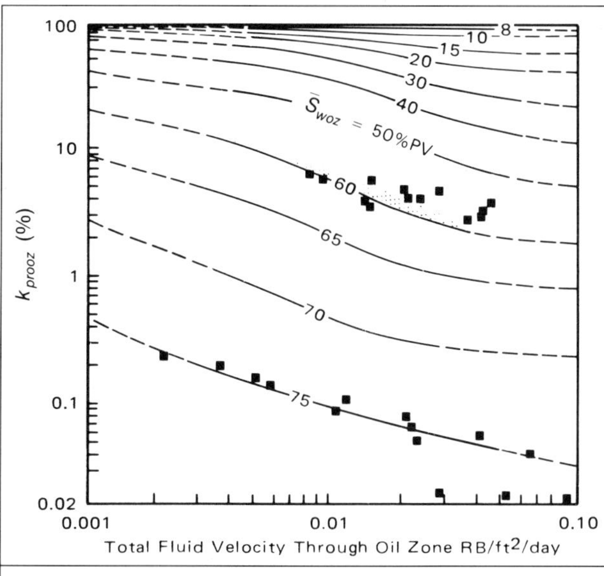

Fig. 3.26—Correlation of pseudo-relative permeability and fluid velocity.[19]

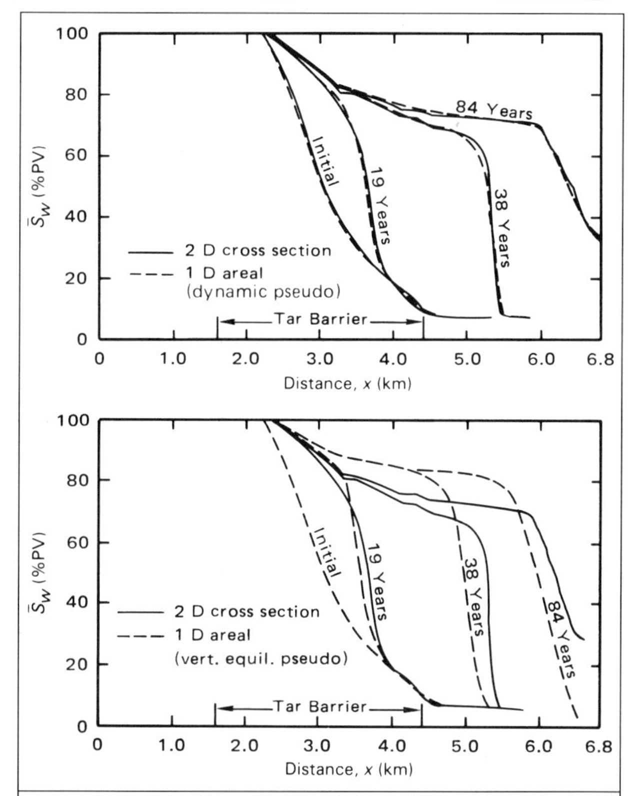

Fig. 3.27—Comparison of results from 2D and 1D models[19]: (a) with dynamic pseudofunctions in 1D model, and (b) with VE pseudofunctions in 1D model.

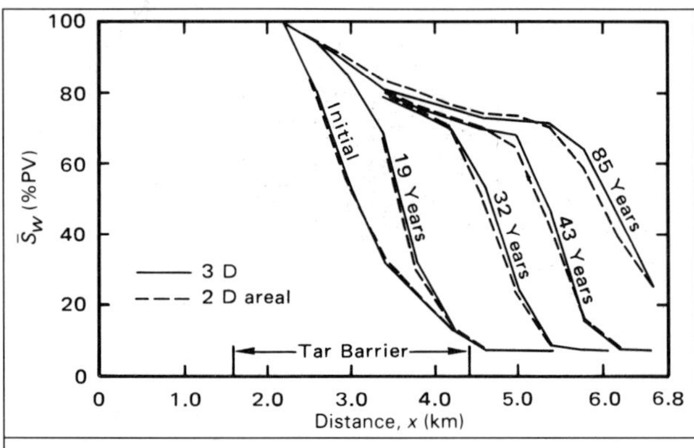

Fig. 3.28—Comparison of results from 3D and 2D models.[19]

bilities. Fig. 3.28 shows the excellent agreement between average water-saturation distributions calculated in the two models.

The method used by Jacks *et al.* to calculate dynamic pseudo-relative permeabilities for each column of blocks containing *n* layers in a cross-sectional model is as follows:

$$\bar{S}_w = \frac{\sum_{i=1}^{n} (\phi h S_w)_i}{\sum_{i=1}^{n} (\phi h)_i}, \quad \text{(3.3a)}$$

$$k_{pro} = \frac{\sum_{i=1}^{n} (khk_{ro})_i}{\sum_{i=1}^{n} (kh)_i}, \quad \text{(3.3b)}$$

and

$$k_{prw} = \frac{\sum_{i=1}^{n} (khk_{rw})_i}{\sum_{i=1}^{n} (kh)_i}. \quad \text{(3.3c)}$$

Kyte and Berry[30] describe a procedure that is more complex than the conventional pseudo approach of Jacks *et al.*[19] Their method gives better agreement with cross-sectional model results in some situations. In this method, dynamic pseudo-capillary-pressure functions, as well as dynamic pseudo-relative-permeability functions, are developed from cross-sectional models. Use of the dynamic pseudo-capillary pressures in an areal model transfers the effects of different flow potentials in different layers of the cross-sectional model to the areal model. Experience has shown that in most applications of pseudofunctions, dynamic pseudo-capillary-pressure functions are not needed.

Pseudofunctions can also be used in 3D models to reduce the number of blocks in the vertical or dip-normal direction. Killough and Foster[26] discussed the use of *block* pseudo-relative-permeability functions in a three-layer 3D model. Before they are used in a 3D model, block pseudofunctions should be validated in cross-sectional models to ensure that their use to reduce the number of vertical blocks is appropriate.

3.3.4 Windowed Models. The windowed-model approach combines an areally extensive coarse grid and a localized fine grid. A coarse-grid model containing both the aquifer and the oil reservoir is first used to simulate overall field behavior. A window is defined around the oil zone and a fine-grid model of the region within the window is constructed for more-detailed studies of oil-zone behavior. Flux or potential distribution at the window boundaries, determined as a function of time with the coarse-grid model, is used as a boundary condition for the fine-grid model. An example coarse-grid model and the corresponding fine-grid model of the field area within the window are illustrated in Fig. 3.29. The windowed-model technique can be used for both oil and gas reservoirs.

Graham and Smart[34] automatically linked coarse- and fine-grid models. The linked models were executed sequentially at each timestep, and flux information was passed automatically between them.

An aquifer/reservoir windowed-model set is often a good alternative to a single model that contains both the aquifer and the oil zone. The windowed models will use fewer gridblocks to model both the aquifer and the reservoir—particularly if the aquifer is modeled in two dimensions and the reservoir is modeled with a 3D simulator. When windowed models are used, ensure that pressures at the window boundaries of the two models are nearly identical throughout the study; otherwise, boundary fluxes will be incorrect. Chap. 5 describes the use of variable grid sizes to reduce the number of gridblocks in models.

3.3.5 Naturally Fractured Reservoirs. Naturally fractured reservoirs are probably the most complex of all reservoir systems. Developing a reliable, detailed description of the matrix/fracture system, modeling it realistically, and evaluating the reliability of simulation results are all extremely difficult. The orientation, width,

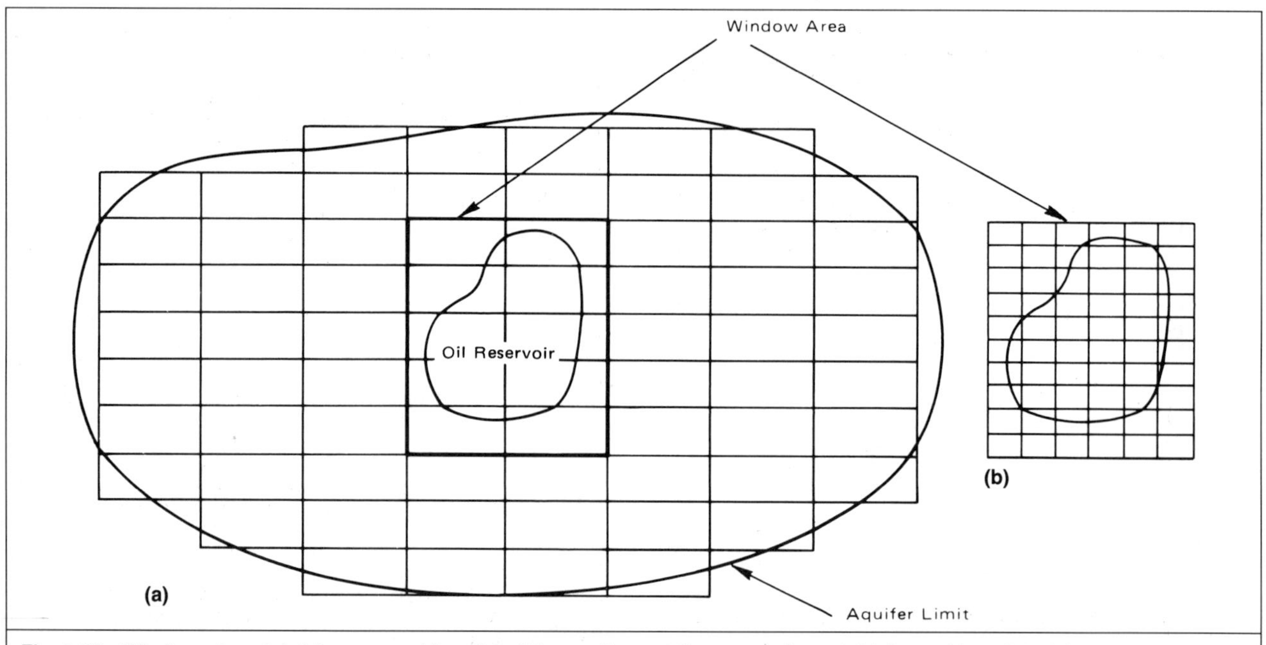

Fig. 3.29—Windowed model: (a) coarse-grid model of the aquifer and the reservoir, and (b) fine-grid model of the windowed area.

and spacing of the fractures are needed to describe the fracture system and to define the geometric configuration of the matrix blocks. In addition, such properties of individual matrix blocks as porosity, permeability, and saturation functions (wettability) must be defined just as they are for unfractured reservoirs.

Flow to wells is mainly through the fracture system; matrix-block permeability is almost always far below the effective permeability of the fracture system. The matrix usually contains most of the oil or gas, however, because fracture porosity (typically from 0.1 to 1.0% of bulk volume) is much less than that of the matrix. Thus, transfer of fluids from the matrix block to the fracture system is necessary for significant recovery of the hydrocarbons from the reservoir.

A conventional simulator can be used to model a fractured system if enough gridblocks are used.[35] This approach is feasible for studying the behavior of single matrix blocks but results in an impractically large number of gridblocks for a model of an entire field or even the drainage area around an individual well. Use of simplified methods is required for most field situations. For reservoirs where there is only single-phase flow (pressure depletion of gas or oil reservoirs above the bubblepoint), realistic simplification of the model is relatively straightforward. For reservoirs where multiphase flow and gravity and capillary-pressure forces influence reservoir recovery behavior, however, development of a useful model can be complex and challenging. Obtaining meaningful results from simulation requires thorough knowledge of the fluid mechanics involved and of the simplifying assumptions programmed into the simulator. Three types of simplified models that have been used successfully for specific reservoir studies are discussed in Secs. 3.3.5.1 through 3.3.5.3.

3.3.5.1 Conventional Simulator With Anisotropic Permeability. Here the matrix and fractures are considered as one system. Thus, a gridblock has porosity equal to the total matrix and fracture porosity. Anisotropic permeability is used in the model to represent the effective permeability of the fracture/matrix system normal and parallel to the main fracture trend. This method has been applied to predict gas-reservoir depletion or to calculate sweep patterns for waterfloods and gas-cycling projects. Its use is appropriate for single-phase flow of gas or oil if the pressure difference between the matrix block and the surrounding fracture system is always small. For two-phase flow, use should be restricted to calculation of sweep patterns where mobility ratio is one for all fluid saturations in the fractures.

3.3.5.2 Source/Sink Models. This approach models the fracture system and depends on the use of special source/sink terms in a conventional simulator to represent interchange of fluids between the matrix blocks and the fractures.[36] These terms allow relationships to be used that determine how much oil to add to the fractures and how much gas or water to remove from them at each timestep in the simulation. The source/sink terms must be developed from an independent source—e.g., scaled laboratory experiments, field history, or a detailed model of a matrix block and surrounding fractures—to determine the effects of viscous, gravity, and capillary forces on movement of oil, gas, and water between the matrix and the fracture as a function of time. Development of realistic source/sink terms can be a complex process because the entire range of conditions to which the matrix block is exposed during the prediction period must be included in their development. The source/sink terms can be designed to handle many factors, including pressure effects and contact reversals. If the simulator that uses the source/sink terms shows that complete range of conditions was not fully anticipated, however, new source/sink terms may have to be developed. Because this approach also assumes that matrix pressure equals fracture pressure, other approaches may be more appropriate when large pressure differences are expected.

3.3.5.3 Dual-Porosity Models. Dual-porosity simulators represent both the matrix and fracture systems, but fluid distribution within the matrix and transfer of fluids from the matrix to the fractures are represented by various simplified methods.[37-39] There are two types. The first type models porosity of the fracture and matrix in each gridblock and fluid flow from block to block through the fractures but does not allow fluid flow through the matrix.[37,38]

The second type is both a dual-porosity and dual-permeability simulator that can represent flow in both the fracture and the matrix—i.e., flow between gridblocks can simulate flow in either the matrix or the fracture system.[39] This type of simulator could be appropriate if gridblocks are smaller than matrix blocks in one or more directions. For both types, transfer functions in the simulator approximate the movement of fluids from the matrix blocks to the fracture. The functions depend on the shape and dimensions of the matrix block, transmissibility of the block, relative permeability, capillary pressure, and density difference between phases. Because fluid distribution in the matrix is not represented accurately, normal rock relative-permeability and capillary-pressure relationships will not always produce meaningful answers. (Also, unsteady-state pressure response may not be properly represented.) More-realistic relationships must be developed from laboratory experiments, field history, or a detailed conventional model simulating the matrix block and surrounding fractures.

Most simulators represent each matrix block or a group of matrix blocks by only a single gridblock.[37,38] Some simulators subdivide each matrix block into a set of gridblocks[40] (subdomains) to model viscous, gravity, and capillary forces in each matrix block more realistically without increased definition in the fracture system. If enough gridblocks are used to represent the matrix blocks, the latter approach would realistically model the fluid mechanics of the system, but would be much more costly than the first type of dual-porosity model previously described.

The first type of dual-porosity model is useful for modeling pressure depletion of gas reservoirs where pressure in matrix blocks is very different from that in the surrounding fractures. Use of either type for reservoir studies involving multiphase flow may be appropriate if the fluid-flow mechanisms are understood and parameters used in the transfer functions are realistic over the range of conditions experienced by matrix blocks during the field life being simulated.

There is limited experience in applying the source/sink, dual-porosity, and dual-porosity/permeability methods to field situations. Thus, discussing when they will work well or poorly is not yet appropriate. Simpler systems, such as two-phase problems where fluid-contact reversals do not occur (no hysteresis effects), are more likely to be handled realistically than more complex ones. The dual-porosity/permeability approach should be considered only when gridblock height or lateral extent is less than that of the matrix block. The source/sink-term approach should be considered when the other approaches do not provide realistic transfer of fluids between the matrix and the fractures, or are too costly.

3.4 Representation of Reservoir Fluids

3.4.1 Compressibility. When fluid expansion does not play an important role in recovery behavior, fluids may be assumed to be incompressible. Water/oil displacement above the bubblepoint, where pressure level will not vary with time, is one example. Cross-sectional areal models and 3D models are, at times, run in the incompressible mode for this type of process. Even in studies of gas/oil systems, incompressible models may be used to evaluate areal or vertical sweep efficiency if pressure gradients are small vs. pressure level. The compressible-fluid mode must be used in studies of aquifer behavior for waterdrive reservoirs, solution-gas-drive behavior, gas-cap-expansion behavior, or combinations of these. Also, studies of individual wells for which transient-pressure behavior is being modeled must be able to handle compressible fluids.

3.4.2 Single-Phase vs. Multiphase Simulation. Most reservoir flow problems require multiphase rather than single-phase simulation. Types of problems for which single-phase solutions are sufficient include (1) expansion of water in aquifers (water influx problems, recharge of aquifers, or dewatering areas around mines), (2) single-well transient pressure problems and interference between wells in single-phase systems, (3) depletion of gas reservoirs when there is no water influx, and (4) lease-line drainage problems in gas or oil reservoirs where other phases are not mobile.

Multiphase simulation must be used to evaluate water/oil and gas/oil displacements. If water/oil displacement involves solution-gas evolution, gas-cap expansion, or gas injection, three-phase simulation should be used. For two- or three-phase gas/oil systems, many problems can be solved by black-oil simulators, which treat the hydrocarbon phases as if they had only two components. Conventional water/oil displacement processes are almost always studied with black-oil simulators. In solution-gas-drive, gas-cap-expansion, or gas-injection studies, black-oil simulators are commonly used if the oil formation factor is less than 2.

When the oil formation factor is greater than 2, black-oil simulation may still be used if oil and gas formation factors, gas in solution, and oil and gas viscosities as functions of pressure can be determined accurately by calculation or experiment. However, if the oil formation factor is greater than 2, compositional models (more than two hydrocarbon components) should normally be used, because they can predict changes in produced fluid properties that can occur as depletion proceeds. If reservoir pressure declines significantly, recovery may not be predicted realistically unless compositional models are used.

Compositional methods are usually needed in studies of gas reservoirs that drop below their dewpoints during depletion. Dry gas injection to cycle such reservoirs after liquid dropout has occurred also falls into this category. Compositional simulation is also needed to account for intermediates picked up by gas during oil displacement by dry gas injection, particularly in volatile oil reservoirs.

More-complex processes may require the use of compositional, miscible, or thermal simulation. Some of these processes are enriched gas drive, high-pressure gas injection, surfactant/polymer processes, and steamdrive. (See Chap. 11.)

Pressure in a reservoir will sometimes fall below the bubblepoint and then later increase, creating an opportunity for free gas to redissolve. If all gas released from solution is still available to contact the oil from which it came, no special simulation treatment is necessary to model re-solution. The gas should dissolve to an extent consistent with the relationship between solution GOR and pressure. If gas segregation has occurred, however, special treatment is necessary to estimate what fraction of oil in a gridblock is in contact with free gas, to recognize when the single-phase condition is reached, and to define the oil-property curves applicable above the new bubblepoint.

Steffensen and Sheffield[41] and Stright *et al.*[42] discuss treatment of gas that is assumed to be able to dissolve in all the oil in a block. This assumption is valid for cross-sectional models or 3D models with sufficient vertical detail. It may be a poor assumption, however, for areal models or for coarsely gridded cross-sectional or 3D models that cannot model segregation of gas adequately. These types of models will yield optimistic results if, for example, they are used to study injection of gas into an under-saturated oil zone.

3.4.3 Variable Fluid Properties. Fluid properties (μ_o, B_o, R_s, etc.) vary vertically and areally in some reservoirs at discovery. Pronounced variation can be represented by assigning different fluid properties to different regions of the model. In black-oil simulation, it is important to recognize how a simulator treats fluid properties when fluids move from one region to another. Unless special methods are used, the simulator will change such fluid properties as viscosity and FVF as the fluids cross boundaries between regions.In reality, of course, fluids retain their properties as they move in the reservoir unless mixing occurs between different oils or pressure changes. Ridings[43] described a method to account for changes in properties as fluids move from one region to another. The method assumes instantaneous mixing of the fluid entering the gridblock with fluid already in the block. The disadvantage of this approach is that the amount of mixing will depend on the number of gridblocks used and may not be representative of the actual mixing in the reservoir.

Compositional models can be used to model variable fluid properties, but they too may lead to unrealistic fluid mixing if gridblock definition is too coarse.

Point tracking is sometimes used to follow fluids with different properties as they move through the reservoir.

3.5 Representation of Reservoir Rock

The complexity of fluid flow in a heterogeneous reservoir is one of the major reasons reservoir simulators are needed in reservoir engineering studies. Homogeneous models can be used to investigate other factors when there are only minor variations in permeability or porosity. When there are major variations in permeability and porosity, however, heterogeneous models are needed. Variations that usually justify heterogeneous models include (1) areal permeability variations that may restrict areal drainage or decrease sweep of injected material, (2) vertical stratification with resultant channeling of injected materials in high-permeability zones, (3) discontinuous shales or other very low-permeability material that may influence vertical or areal sweep efficiency, (4) discontinuous permeable zones that may affect vertical sweep efficiency, and (5) natural fractures or fissures that may reduce recovery from rock matrix.

3.5.1 Distribution of Absolute Permeability and Porosity. Definition of the level and distribution of permeability and porosity is a necessary prerequisite to model flow behavior under both steady-state and unsteady-state conditions. It is important to consider the scale of heterogeneity that should be represented to reflect reservoir behavior properly. All reservoirs vary vertically on a minute scale, but it is not practical and not necessary to represent this very small scale of heterogeneities. However, larger heterogeneities that are still too small to represent directly (i.e., smaller than a single gridblock) may need to be considered. It is sometimes desirable to test the sensitivity of predicted reservoir performance to such small-scale heterogeneities to determine whether they are significant enough to model. Certainly, heterogeneities that can be represented directly should be modeled. For example, distinct zones that are continuous between two or more wells usually need to be designed into the reservoir model. Even in this instance, if the permeability difference between zones is modest, it may not be necessary to represent each zone separately.

In cross-sectional or 3D models, the same attention should be given to vertical permeability as to horizontal permeability. The magnitude of vertical permeability and its variation areally as well as vertically can have an important influence on calculated behavior.

3.5.2 Relative Permeability. Both the endpoint values and the shapes of relative-permeability functions influence calculated results. Frequently, more than one set of relative permeabilities are needed because variations of the functions from one rock type to another may be important.

Relative-permeability relationships are influenced by the history of the rock/fluid system. At a given saturation, relative permeabilities in a displacement in which the wetting-phase saturation is increasing (imbibition) may differ markedly from those applicable when the wetting phase is decreasing (drainage). If, during depletion, the direction of saturation change reverses, hysteresis effects will influence reservoir performance and should be accounted for when reservoir behavior is simulated. Some simulators have the capability to sense saturation reversals and to introduce hysteresis effects into relative-permeability functions automatically. Other simulators require that the relative-permeability curves be changed manually when saturation reversals occur. The latter procedure can become tedious if frequent stops and restarts of the calculation are required. See Chap. 4 for a more detailed discussion of relative-permeability selection.

3.5.3 Capillary Pressure. Capillary pressure plays a major role in defining the initial distribution of fluids in a reservoir and can have a significant influence on fluid movement. For displacements dominated by gravity, capillary pressure will control the vertical saturation distribution. In highly fractured oil reservoirs, the dominant producing mechanism can be capillary imbibition of water. Capillarity may also be an important force if high- and low-permeability strata communicate sufficiently well to permit crossflow.

In most reservoirs, however, capillarity tends to be significant only in establishing initial saturations and in controlling fluid distributions at the pore level, thus influencing multiphase relative permeabilities. Consequently, precise definition of capillary-pressure functions is not a critical factor in developing models of higher-permeability, relatively homogeneous reservoirs. Endpoints of the capillary-pressure and relative-permeability curves must be defined, of course, because they establish endpoint saturations and, thus, the saturation range within which multiphase flow can occur. Omitting capillary pressure entirely may be justified in some cases if the simulator will accommodate this option and if run time is not increased significantly. In 2D areal model calculations that use pseudofunctions, capillary pressure may not be omitted.

Capillary-pressure/saturation relationships are also "history-dependent." If there is a reversal in the direction of saturation change during a simulation, it may be necessary to use capillary-pressure hysteresis functions in the calculations.

3.6 Well Models—Coupling Between Well and Reservoir

3.6.1 Methods for Representing Wells. Realistic modeling of wells is one of the most challenging aspects of reservoir simulation. Ideally, the grid system of a reservoir model would be sufficiently detailed to model near-wellbore behavior. Then pressures and saturations in the gridblock or column of blocks containing a well could be used directly to calculate production or injection rates. In most models, however, gridblocks containing wells are too coarse to model wells directly.

An obvious exception is the single-well (r,z) coning model. Here, definition can be fine near the well and coarse near the outer edge of the model. In these models, calculated pressures and saturations at the well gridblocks can closely represent actual well values.

If production or injection rates are known or can be estimated from other sources (in simulations of field history, for example), the rate data can be used without attempting to estimate wellbore pressures. When future performance is simulated, however, rates usually will not be known and it will be necessary to estimate formation face pressures. Calculated pressures, p_b, in gridblocks containing wells can be corrected to formation face pressure, p_{wf}, by Peaceman's[44] equations:

$$p_{wf}=p_b-\frac{q_t}{R}, \quad (3.4)$$

where q_t is production or injection rate, and

$$R=\frac{0.00708kh}{\ln 0.2\Delta x/r_w}, \quad (3.5)$$

where Δx is horizontal block length. For an injection well, rate is a negative quantity.

Eq. 3.5 applies to square blocks with a single well located in the center of an interior block. Other corrections have been developed by Peaceman[45] and by Kuniansky and Hillestad[46] for other geometries (e.g., when the well is off center, more than one well exists in the block, the well block is a corner or edge block, the gridblocks are nonsquare, or when permeability is anisotropic).

When field shut-in pressures are to be compared with model-calculated pressures, special adjustments may be needed if shut-in time is not simulated. The adjustment procedure is discussed further in Chaps. 7 and 8. The procedure involves estimation of the shut-in time at which the pressure in the well would reach a value theoretically equivalent to the pressure calculated at the gridblock containing the well. If a field pressure value was measured at this time, no adjustment is needed. Otherwise, the field pressure or the model pressure must be corrected before comparisons are made. The correction must be calculated for each well. Of course, if pressure gradients in the vicinity of the well are low, the correction may be insignificant relative to the overall precision of the simulation.

3.6.2 Modification to Account for Coning, Partial Completions, and Stimulated Wells. Coning behavior is best studied in detail with radial (r,z) models in which fine gridding can be used near the well. The results from coning calculations (or in some situations from analytical solutions) can be used to develop special well functions for 2D areal or even coarsely gridded 3D models. (See Chap. 7.) Well functions allow realistic WOR or GOR to be calculated from saturations in blocks containing wells. Coning-model results can be used to develop adjustments to productivity indices (PI's) of dry wells to account for mobility changes as water (or gas) production begins. Even if coning is not significant, well functions and PI adjustments will be needed for partially penetrating wells.

Well stimulation or damage can be simulated by modifying the PI or injectivity index of the well in question, as long as the depth of damage or improvement is small compared with the size of the gridblock. Normally, the areal dimensions of a block containing a well in all models other than coning models are large enough to encompass the region of damage or stimulation of a well. An exception can be the stimulated region around a hydraulically fractured well; special handling may be needed in this case. Sometimes such wells are represented in detail by fine gridding around the fracture (Fig. 3.6). If the fracture length is less than the gridblock size, however, the PI or injectivity index of the well after fracturing can be used in a 2D areal model. If the fracture length is greater than the gridblock size, injection or production may need to be distributed between the block containing the well and the adjacent blocks. Detailed models of the well are useful in deciding how this distribution should be made.

3.6.3 Comprehensive Well-Management Routines. A major factor in the design of a model for a reservoir study is the kind of well-management routine that will be needed. If available routines do not have the required features, programming time must be accommodated in the study schedule.

Well-management routines can range from simple rate routines that specify potentials or rates at certain gridblocks to those that contain complex logic for predicting full-field behavior. In the latter case, the well-management routine usually accounts for the influence of the casing/tubing configuration on productivity or injectivity and also may account for flowline resistance. Configurations of surface facilities and their effect on field area capacities to produce oil, water, or gas and to inject water or gas can also be incorporated in the well-management routine. Well drilling, workovers, artificial-lift installation, and allocation of production and injection are also commonly part of the function of a full-field well-management routine.

Nomenclature

B_o = oil FVF, RB/STB [res m^3/stock-tank m^3]
h = layer or sand thickness, ft [m]
h_{oi} = thickness of original oil zone, ft [m]
h_{wi} = thickness of original water zone, ft [m]
k = permeability, md
k_{pro} = pseudo-relative permeability to oil, dimensionless
k_{prw} = pseudo-relative permeability to water, dimensionless
k_r = relative permeability, dimensionless
k_{ro} = relative permeability to oil, dimensionless
k_{prooz} = pseudo-relative permeability to oil in the oil zone, dimensionless
k_{rw} = relative permeability to water, dimensionless
k_{rwz} = rock relative permeability to water at Point z, dimensionless
k_z = permeability parallel to bedding plane at Point z, md
n = number of layers
n_r = number of gridblocks in r direction
n_z = number of gridblocks in z direction
Δp = pressure drop, psi/ft [kPa/m]
p_b = gridblock calculated pressures, psi [kPa]
p_{wf} = formation face pressure, psi [kPa]
P_c = capillary pressure, psi [kPa]
q_t = production or injection rate, RB/D [res m^3/d]
r = distance in r (radial) direction, ft [m]
r_e = outer radius, ft [m]
r_w = well radius, ft [m]
Δr_1 = length in r (radial) direction of upper gridblock, ft [m]
R = GOR, scf/res bbl [std m^3/res m^3]
R_s = solution GOR, scf/res bbl [std m^3/res m^3]
S_g = gas saturation, fraction
$\bar{S}_g$ = average gas saturation, fraction
S_o = oil saturation, fraction
S_w = water saturation, fraction
$\bar{S}_w$ = average water saturation, fraction
$\bar{S}_{woz}$ = average water saturation in oil zone, fraction
S_{wz} = water saturation at Point z, fraction
V_p = total PV, res bbl [res m^3]

V_w = total volume of water, res bbl [res m^3]
x = distance in x direction, ft [m]
x_1,x_2 = distance in x_1 and x_2 directions for curvilinear models, ft [m]
Δx = block length in x direction, ft [m]
y = distance in y direction, ft [m]
z = distance in z direction (vertical or direction normal to bedding plane), ft [m]
Δz_1 = length in z direction of inner gridblock, ft [m]
Θ = distance in Θ direction for 2D areal (r,Θ) models, ft [m]
μ_o = oil viscosity, cp [Pa·s]
$\Delta \rho$ = oil/water density difference, psi/ft [kPa/m]
ϕ = porosity, fraction
ϕ_z = porosity at Point z, fraction

Subscript

i = layer number

References

1. Craft, B.C. and Hawkins, M.F.: *Applied Petroleum Reservoir Engineering*, Prentice-Hall Inc., Englewood Cliffs, NJ (1959).
2. Lutes, J.L. *et al.*: "Accelerated Blowdown of a Strong Water-Drive Gas Reservoir," *JPT* (Dec. 1977) 1533-39.
3. Hirasaki, G.J.: "Sensitivity Coefficient for History Matching Oil Displacement Processes," *SPEJ* (Feb. 1975) 39-49.
4. Huppler, J.D.: "Numerical Investigation of the Effects of Core Heterogeneities on Waterflood Relative Permeabilities," *SPEJ* (Dec. 1970) 381-92; *Trans.*, AIME, **249**.
5. McCulloch, R.C., Langton, J.R., and Spivak, A.: "Reservoir Simulation of High Relief Reservoirs, Rainbow Field, Alberta, Canada," paper SPE 2237 presented at the 1968 SPE Annual Meeting, Houston, Sep. 29-Oct. 2.
6. Fussell, D.D.: "Single-Well Performance Predictions for Gas Condensate Reservoirs," *JPT* (July 1973) 860-70; *Trans.*, AIME, **255**.
7. Wadsley, W.A.: "Modeling Reservoir Geometry with Non-Rectangular Coordinate Grids," paper SPE 9369 presented at the 1980 SPE Annual Technical Conference and Exhibition, Dallas, Sept. 21-24.
8. Cottrell, C.W.: "The Application of Curvilinear Coordinate Systems to Predict the Behavior of Pattern Waterfloods in the Lekhwair Oil Field, Oman," paper SPE 9647 presented at the 1981 SPE Middle East Oil Technical Conference and Exhibition, Bahrain, March 9-12.
9. Miller, R.T. and Clements, R.L.: "Reservoir Engineering Techniques Used to Predict Blowout Control During the Bay Marchand Fire," paper SPE 3630 presented at the 1971 SPE Annual Meeting, New Orleans, Oct. 3-6.
10. Shirer, J.A., Ainsworth, W.J., and White, R.W.: "Selection of a Waterflood Pattern for the Jay-Little Escambia Creek Fields," paper SPE 4978 presented at the 1974 SPE Annual Meeting, Houston, Oct. 6-9.
11. Morse, R.A. and Von Gonten, W.D.: "Productivity of Vertically Fractured Wells Prior to Stabilized Flow," *JPT* (July 1972) 807-11.
12. Henderson, J.H., Dempsey, J.R., and Tyler, J.C.: "Use of Numerical Models to Develop and Operate Gas Storage Reservoirs," *JPT* (Nov. 1968) 1239-46.
13. Weaver, R.H.: "Simulation of Waterflood Behavior in a Reservoir Previously Invaded by Water," paper SPE 2984 presented at the 1970 SPE Annual Meeting, Houston, Oct. 4-7.
14. Kingston, P. E. and Niko, H.: "Development Planning of the Brent Field," *JPT* (Oct. 1975) 1190-98.
15. Dicharry, R.M., Perryman, T.L., and Ronquille, J.D.: "Evaluation and Design of a CO_2 Miscible Flood Project—SACROC Unit, Kelly-Snyder Field," *JPT* (Nov. 1973) 1309-18; *Trans.*, AIME, **255**.
16. DesBrisay, C.L., Gray, J.W., and Spivak, A.: "Miscible Flood Performance of the Intisar 'D' Field, Libyan Arab Republic," *JPT* (Aug. 1975) 935-43.
17. Reitzel, G.A. and Callow, G.O.: "Pool Description and Performance Analysis Leads to Understanding Golden Spike's Miscible Flood," *JPT* (July 1977) 867-72.
18. Richardson, J.G. *et al.*: "The Effect of Small, Discontinuous Shales in Oil Recovery," *JPT* (Nov. 1978) 1531-37.
19. Jacks, H.H., Smith, O.J.E., and Mattax, C.C.: "The Modeling of a Three-Dimensional Reservoir with a Two-Dimensional Reservoir Simulator—The Use of Dynamic Pseudo Functions," *SPEJ* (June 1973) 175-85.
20. Miller, R.T. and Rogers, W.L.: "Performance of Oil Wells in Bottom Water Drive Reservoirs," paper SPE 4633 presented at the 1973 SPE Annual Meeting, Las Vegas, Sept. 30-Oct. 3.
21. Chappelear, J.E. and Hirasaki, G.J.: "A Model of Oil-Water Coning for Two-Dimensional, Areal Reservoir Simulation," *SPEJ* (April 1976) 65-74; *Trans.*, AIME, **261**.
22. Beveridge, S.B. *et al.*: "A Study of the Sensitivity of Oil Recovery to Production Rate," paper SPE 5129 presented at the 1974 SPE Annual Meeting, Houston, Oct. 6-9.
23. Lee, J.E. *et al.*: "The Effect of Rate on Recovery for Canadian Carbonate Reservoirs," paper SPE 5128 presented at the 1974 SPE Annual Meeting, Houston, Oct. 6-9.
24. Stright, D.H. Jr., Bennion, D.W., and Aziz, K.: "Influence of Production Rate on the Recovery of Oil From Horizontal Waterfloods," *JPT* (May 1975) 555-63.
25. Boberg, T.C. *et al.*: "Application of Inverse Simulation to a Complex Multireservoir System," *JPT* (July 1974) 801-08; *Trans.*, AIME, **257**.
26. Killough, J.E. and Foster, H.P. Jr.: "Reservoir Simulation of the Empire ABO Field: The Use of Pseudos in a Multi-Layered System," *JPT* (Oct. 1979) 279-88.
27. Thompson, F.R. and Thachuk, A.R.: "Compositional Simulation of a Gas-Cycling Project, Bonnie Glen D-3A Pool, Alberta, Canada," *JPT* (Nov. 1974) 1285-94.
28. Weber, K.J. *et al.*: "Simulation of Water Injection in a Barrier-Bar-Type, Oil-Rim Reservoir in Nigeria," *JPT* (Nov. 1978) 1555-65.
29. Coats, K.H. *et al.*: "Simulation of Three-Dimensional, Two-Phase Flow in Oil and Gas Reservoirs," *SPEJ* (Dec. 1967) 377-88; *Trans.*, AIME, **240**.
30. Kyte, J.R. and Berry, D.W.: "New Pseudo Functions to Control Numerical Disperson," *SPEJ* (Aug. 1975) 269-76.
31. Coats, K.H.: "Use and Misuse of Reservoir Simulation Models," *JPT* (Nov. 1969) 1391-98.
32. Coats, K.H., Dempsey, J.R., and Henderson, J.H.: "The Use of Vertical Equilibrium in Two-Dimensional Simulation of Three-Dimensional Reservoir Performance," *SPEJ* (March 1971) 63-71; *Trans.*, AIME, **251**.
33. van Poollen, H.K., Breitenbach, E.A., and Thurnau, D.H.: "Treatment of Individual Wells and Grids in Reservoir Modeling," *SPEJ* (Dec. 1968) 341-46.
34. Graham, M.F. and Smart, G.T.: "Reservoir Simulator Employing a Fine-Grid Model Nested in a Coarse-Grid Model," paper SPE 9372 presented at the 1980 SPE Annual Technical Conference and Exhibition, Dallas, Sept. 21-24.
35. Yamamoto, R.H. *et al.*: "Compositional Reservoir Simulator for Fissured Systems—The Single-Block Model," *SPEJ* (June 1971) 113-28.
36. Rossen, R.H.: "Simulation of Naturally Fractured Reservoirs With Semi-Implicit Source Terms," *SPEJ* (June 1977) 201-10.
37. Kazemi, H. *et al.*: "Numerical Simulation of Water-Oil Flow in Naturally Fractured Reservoirs," *SPEJ* (Dec. 1976) 317-26; *Trans.*, AIME, **261**.
38. Gilman, J.R and Kazemi, H.: "Improvements in Simulation of Naturally Fractured Reservoirs," *SPEJ* (Aug. 1983) 695-707; *Trans.*, AIME, **275**.
39. Blaskovich, F.T. *et al.*: "A Multi-Component Isothermal System for Efficient Reservoir Simulation," paper SPE 11480 presented at the 1983 SPE Middle East Oil Technical Conference and Exhibition, Bahrain, March 14-17.
40. Gilman, J.R.: "An Efficient Finite-Difference Method for Simulating Phase Segregation in the Matrix Blocks in Double-Porosity Reservoirs," *SPERE* (July 1986) 403-13.
41. Steffensen, R.J. and Sheffield, M.: "Reservoir Simulation of a Collapsing Gas Saturation Requiring Areal Variation in Bubble-Point Pressure," paper SPE 4275 presented at the 1973 SPE Numerical Simulation of Reservoir Performance Symposium, Houston, Jan. 10-12.
42. Stright, D.H. Jr. *et al.*: "Carbon Dioxide Injection Into Bottom-Water, Undersaturated Viscous Oil Reservoirs," *JPT* (Oct. 1977) 1248-58.
43. Ridings, R.L.: "Handling Fluid Properties in Reservoir Simulation Studies," paper SPE 3703 presented at the 1971 SPE California Regional Meeting, Los Angeles, Nov. 4-5.
44. Peaceman, D.W.: "Interpretation of Well Block Pressures in Numerical Reservoir Simulation," *SPEJ* (June 1978) 183-94; *Trans., AIME*, **265**.
45. Peaceman, D.W.: "Interpretation of Well-Block Pressures in Numerical Reservoir Simulation with Non-Square Grid Blocks and Anisotropic Permeability," *SPEJ* (June 1983) 531-43.
46. Kuniansky, J. and Hillestad, J.G.: "Reservoir Simulation Using Bottomhole Pressure Boundary Conditions," *SPEJ* (Dec. 1980) 473-86.

SI Metric Conversion Factors

bbl	× 1.589 873	E−01	=	m^3
ft	× 3.048*	E−01	=	m
ft^2	× 9.290 304*	E−02	=	m^2
miles	× 1.609 344*	E+00	=	km
psi/ft	× 2.262 059	E+01	=	kPa/m

*Conversion factor is exact.

Chapter 4
Selecting Reservoir-Rock and Fluid Properties Data

This chapter discusses the selection and assignment of rock and fluid properties to the individual gridblocks in a simulation model. Considerable judgment is involved in the selection of "representative" reservoir description data[1] for a model because there are seldom enough data and there are usually uncertainties in the available data. As an added complication, it is not yet possible to prescribe a definitive set of guidelines for collecting, interpreting, and assigning reservoir description data. The approach used in the following discussion is to outline some generally useful guidelines derived from experience and to cite and comment on pertinent literature.

The discussion focuses on the selection and assignment of reservoir-rock and fluid properties for a three-dimensional (3D), three-phase model of a reservoir system. The properties of simpler models usually can be defined considering the applicable part of the approach for the more complex 3D, multiphase case.

4.1 Data Required for Model Construction

The types of rock and fluid properties data normally required in model construction are listed in Table 4.1. Most of the discussions in this chapter concern the selection of the data—i.e., the collection, interpretation, and reduction of the data to a form that can be used in a simulator. Assignment of the data is considerably simpler than its selection, but pitfalls do exist. When rock and fluid properties are uniform or vary only gradually with distance, their assignment to the model is straightforward. If significant change in any influential rock or fluid property occurs over the distance modeled by a simulator block, however, special care must be taken to derive the best average value for assignment to each block.

The judicious assignment of gridblock properties will ensure that initial saturations are appropriately established in the model and that subsequent fluid movement through the heterogeneous reservoir rock will be reasonably simulated. Improper assignment of properties can yield misleading predictions from even the most sophisticated model.

4.2 Sensitivity of Results to Data Accuracy

Sensitivity studies are helpful in defining which rock and fluid parameters are important in solving a particular problem. Permeability and porosity are nearly always important parameters. In particular, the degree of continuity of permeable strata and the permeability contrast between strata frequently dominate reservoir behavior. (These topics are given considerable attention later in this chapter.) Even if representative permeability and porosity distributions are not available, however, a simple homogeneous model will sometimes provide valuable insight not obtainable from analytic methods or volumetric-balance calculations.

Sensitivity studies are especially useful for developing estimates for types of data that may be difficult to obtain. For example, it may not be practical to obtain measured values of vertical permeability to use in cross-sectional or 3D models. In these cases, sensitivity studies can define the potential error resulting from inaccuracy in the data. Usually, for example, for k_v/k_h ratios greater than about 0.1, calculated results are insensitive to the value of the ratio because of the relatively large area and short distance for vertical flow. Single-well coning problems are exceptions to this general rule. There is also a lower limit of k_v/k_h, perhaps 0.001, at which vertical flow becomes so small that the ratio need not be accurately defined. For k_v/k_h values between these limits, the accuracy required to ensure a reasonable simulation of reservoir performance must be determined with sensitivity studies.

Minor errors in describing oil properties are acceptable for models of reservoirs that contain "black oil" with more-or-less uniform properties. On the other hand, an accurate description of fluid properties is necessary when simulating reservoir performance if oil properties vary markedly with depth or with areal location.

The accuracy with which saturation functions should be described depends on the depletion mechanism and the stage of depletion. For example, gas/oil relative-permeability functions need definition only as pressure drops below the bubblepoint, or when gas injection is initiated.[1] Even then, errors in gas relative permeability may not be important. For example, when investigating the effect of gas injection rate on oil recovery, Coats[4] found that while oil relative permeability was of "overriding importance," gas relative permeability and gas/oil capillary pressure were of little significance.

4.3 Porosity and Permeability

4.3.1 Sources of Data. Porosity and permeability distributions are normally derived from core-analysis,[5] well-log,[6] and well-test data. Adequate resolution of inconsistencies between sets of data and interpolation to fill gaps in the data normally require some understanding of the geologic history of the reservoir. Because there are never enough data to remove all uncertainty from the definition of reservoir-rock properties, it is essential that consideration be given to all available information (laboratory analyses, field tests, geologic studies, etc.) and, of course, to actual field performance.

4.3.2 Developing a Reservoir Description. The approach to be taken in developing a description of a reservoir will depend largely on the condition of the reservoir data base. Frequently, planning for a major reservoir simulation study offers the first major incentive for cataloging all available data. Hence, for the first such study, it is usually most efficient to use a team effort so that geologists, geophysicists, log analysts, and engineers can pool their resources in a structured, coordinated program. The first effort of such a team should be to develop an understanding of the depositional environment (braided stream, delta bar, reef, etc.) as a basis for estimates of continuity of productive and nonproductive zones throughout the reservoir.[7-11] Figs. 4.1[12] and 4.2[13] illustrate the possible interactions of a reservoir description team. Results of this activity ideally will be to relate the properties of rock to its origin, as implied by Fig. 4.3.[14] The importance of a collaborative effort and typical results and benefits of such efforts are discussed in a number of excellent papers.[15-24]

Modern geophysical methods, particularly seismic methods, are valuable for providing several types of information to the reser-

TABLE 4.1—ROCK AND FLUID PROPERTIES

Symbol	Definition
Data To Describe Initial (Static) Condition	
	Rock
D	Formation top (structure)
h_t	Gross formation thickness
h_n	Net pay thickness
ϕ	Porosity at initial pressure
P_{cwo}* vs. S_w	Drainage (water/oil) capillary-pressure function
P_{cgo}* vs. S_g	Drainage (gas/oil) capillary-pressure function
	Fluid
B_o	Oil FVF
B_w	Water FVF
B_g	Gas FVF
ρ_o	Oil density at standard conditions
ρ_w	Water density at standard conditions
ρ_g	Gas density at standard conditions
Additional Data To Describe Gas/Oil Displacement (S_g Always Increasing)	
	Rock
k	Specific (absolute) permeability
k_{rg} and k_{ro} vs. S_o	Gas and oil relative-permeability functions (drainage)
c_f	Rock compressibility
	Fluid
R_s vs. p	Gas in solution vs. pressure
B_o vs. p	Oil FVF vs. pressure
B_g vs. p	Gas FVF vs. pressure
μ_o vs. p	Oil viscosity vs. pressure
μ_g vs. p	Gas viscosity vs. pressure
c_o	Oil compressibility
c_w	Water compressibility
Additional Data To Describe Water/Oil Displacement (S_w Always Increasing)	
	Rock
k_{rw} and k_{ro} vs. S_w	Oil and water relative-permeability functions (imbibition)
P_{cwo} vs. S_w	Imbibition (water/oil) capillary-pressure function
	Fluid
B_w vs. p	Water FVF vs. pressure
μ_w vs. p	Water viscosity vs. pressure
Additional Data To Describe Oil Invading a Gas Cap (S_w = Interstitial) or an Aquifer ($S_g = 0$)	
	Rock
k_{ro} and k_{rg} vs. S_o	Oil and gas relative-permeability functions (oil imbibition with hysteresis)
k_{ro} and k_{rw} vs. S_w	Water and oil relative-permeability functions (water drainage with hysteresis)
P_{cgo} vs. S_g	Imbibition (gas/oil) capillary-pressure function
Additional Data To Describe Three-Phase Flow	
	Rock
k_{ro}, k_{rg}, and k_{rw} vs. S_w	Three-phase relative-permeability functions**

*P_{cwo} and P_{cgo} need to be known at some definitive depth in the reservoir.

**These functions are seldom available by experimental measurement and are costly to obtain. Simultaneous flow of three phases usually occurs in only a small fraction of the reservoir, so Stone's[2,3] two-phase approximation is ordinarily acceptable. Three-phase capillary-pressure relationships are usually calculated from two-phase gas/oil and water/oil relationships.

voir description team. 3D seismic sections[25-27] are sometimes essential for preparing structure maps and determining the location and displacement of faults. These sections can also indicate the limits of reservoirs and, when integrated with well data, allow the construction of thickness maps.[26] Under certain conditions, lithology and porosity prediction can be undertaken, particularly when synthetic seismic models are constructed to aid the calibration of well and seismic data.[28,29] Furthermore, a special type of seismic data analysis (velocity estimation) can point out areas where fractures are common.[30] Ongoing research in many institutions is directed toward enlarging the utility of seismic data in reservoir description. A chief research area is to improve the capability to detect thin (<20-ft [<6-m]) beds with seismic data.

Vertical seismic profiling (VSP) is another useful seismic technique. This technique produces special wellbore data that are helpful, not only in preparing and calibrating other seismic data, but also in defining subsurface features, such as nearby faults and reservoir intervals, that are not penetrated by the wellbore. Sometimes it is possible to detect the limits of reservoir rock and to locate offset wells with a multioffset survey (a special type of VSP).[31]

A successful team will complete the first phase of reservoir description by using all available data and expertise to formulate 3D descriptions of porosity and permeability. This often results in a set of maps of porosity, permeability, thickness, and structural elevation. The entire reservoir or individual reservoir units may be mapped. Although the description must be "fixed" at some point so that the simulation study can proceed, the study schedule should accommodate periodic updates if more data become available from cores, logs, and field performance. This is especially important for fields that have just been placed on production; early pressure and production history can be valuable for fine-tuning porosity and permeability distributions.

4.3.3 Porosity. Reservoirs are broadly characterized lithologically as either siliclastic (sandstone) or carbonate (limestone or dolomite). The level of porosity in sands is often related to the primary or original textural properties—e.g., grain size, sorting, and the amount of fine-grained interstitial matrix. Additional postdepositional modifications, such as interparticle cement or pore-plugging diagenetic clays, tend to reduce porosity. Occasionally, grain leaching (as in the case of feldspar leaching) will increase porosity and modify the interparticle pore system.

Carbonates are generally characterized by complex pore systems. As in sandstones, the original interparticle porosity is influenced by textural properties. Significant amounts of isolated intraparticle porosity are often present in the biologically produced skeletal grains composing some carbonate reservoir rock. Fig. 4.4 illustrates Jardine *et al.*'s[13] differentiation between primary and secondary porosity in carbonates. Primary porosity develops during original deposition, while secondary porosity results from later alteration. Carbonates can be chemically active, and postdepositional or secondary changes may be extreme. Fig. 4.4 shows five alteration processes: fracturing, leaching, dolomitization, recrystallization, and cementation. Porosity can be reduced by cementation or increased by leaching of grains. Leaching can be grain-selective, depending on the original grain mineralogy. It is not uncommon to find carbonates with exceptionally high permeabilities.

Both sandstone and carbonate reservoirs may contain fractures that add only slightly to PV but greatly increase permeability.

Usually, the level and distribution of porosity in a reservoir can be defined adequately from logs that have been calibrated with cores.[32] If a reservoir is especially complex, it is advisable to core nearly all wells. (Examples include the Parentis field in France and the Jay-Little Escambia Creek field[33] in Alabama and Florida.)

It is important to consider the effect of overburden pressure on porosity[34,35] when using core data. Fig. 4.5 compares experimental and computed effects of pressure on porosity for different values of maximum formation compressibility, $c_{f\max}$, where $c_{f\max}$ is determined at 25,000 psi [172 MPa]. Particular attention should be paid to friable or poorly consolidated formations. The work of Mattax *et al.*[36] indicates that such formations may have compressibilities three to four times those of lithologically similar consolidated formations. In these cases, it is usually necessary to express compressibility as a pressure-dependent function, rather than as a constant.

Logs commonly used to obtain reservoir porosity include formation density, compensated neutron, and compensated sonic logs. Estimates of porosity frequently can be improved by combining results from all three logs.[37-39] Fig. 4.6 compares core porosities measured by the three logs. Note that the presence of gas leads to incorrect porosity values from the density and neutron logs, while the silty sand of Zone B causes both the sonic and the neutron logs to indicate porosities that are too high.

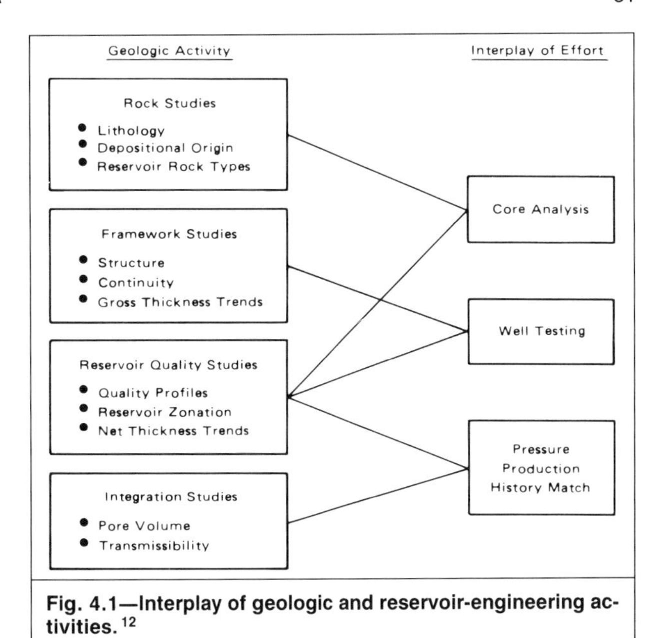

Fig. 4.1—Interplay of geologic and reservoir-engineering activities.[12]

The borehole gravity meter is sometimes recommended[40] as a deep-investigation porosity tool; however, interpretation of gravity-meter data frequently yields ambiguous results.

Porosity logs calibrated against valid core porosities frequently are more reliable than core data alone for well-to-well correlations of porosity, because core data sets are usually incomplete. Statistical methods to assist in the selection of correlatable zones are discussed in Refs. 41 through 43. Knowledge of the depositional environment and secondary processes that modified porosity are helpful in estimating the areal distribution of individual zones.

4.3.4 Permeability. The most difficult reservoir properties to define usually are the level and distribution of permeability. They are more variable than porosity[11,41] and more difficult to measure. Yet an adequate knowledge of permeability distribution is critical to the prediction of reservoir depletion by any recovery process.

The literature is rich in useful discussions of reservoir permeability and the origin and interpretation of its variability. Two excellent background publications are those of Hutchinson *et al.*,[8] who recorded permeability variations for a blanket shallow-marine deposit (Fig. 4.7), and Craig,[44] who discussed areal, vertical, and directional (anisotropic) permeability and reservoir-scale fractures.

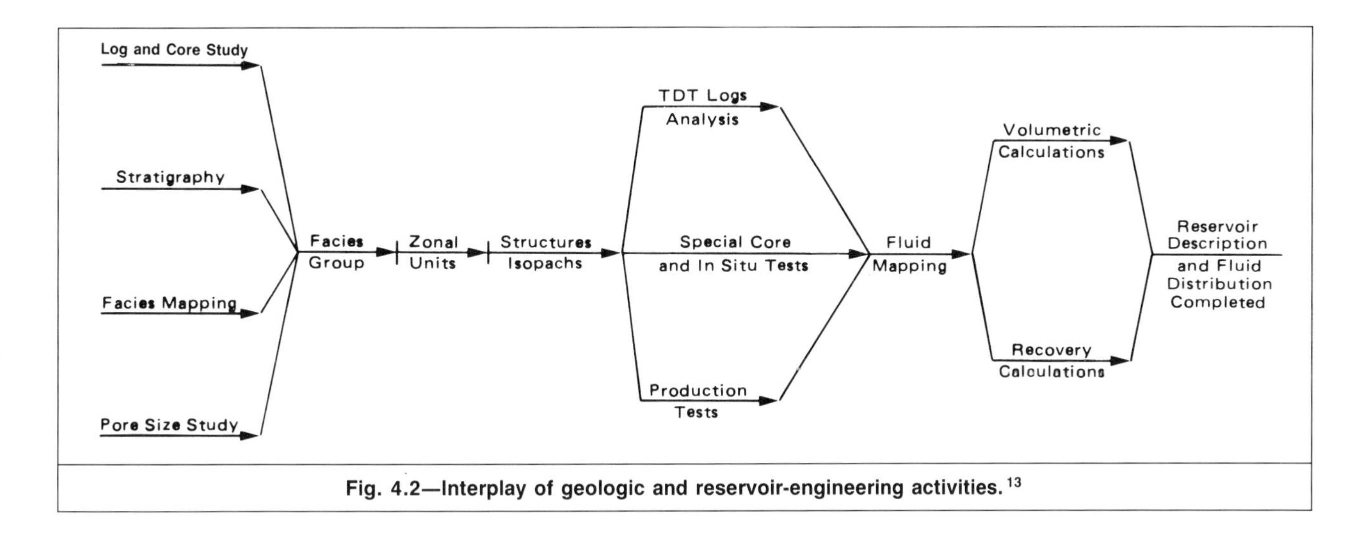

Fig. 4.2—Interplay of geologic and reservoir-engineering activities.[13]

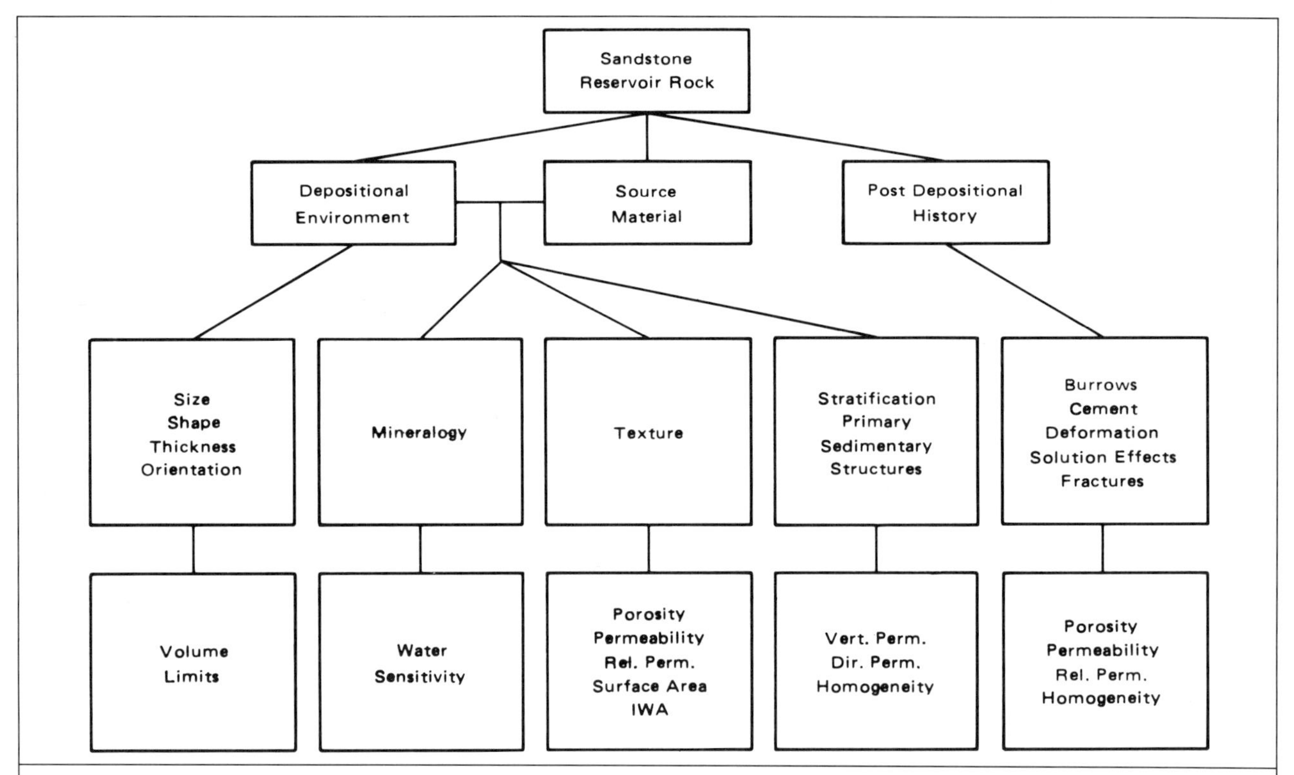

Fig. 4.3—General relationships between reservoir properties, rock properties, and origin of sandstones.[14] (Courtesy of PennWell Publishing Co.)

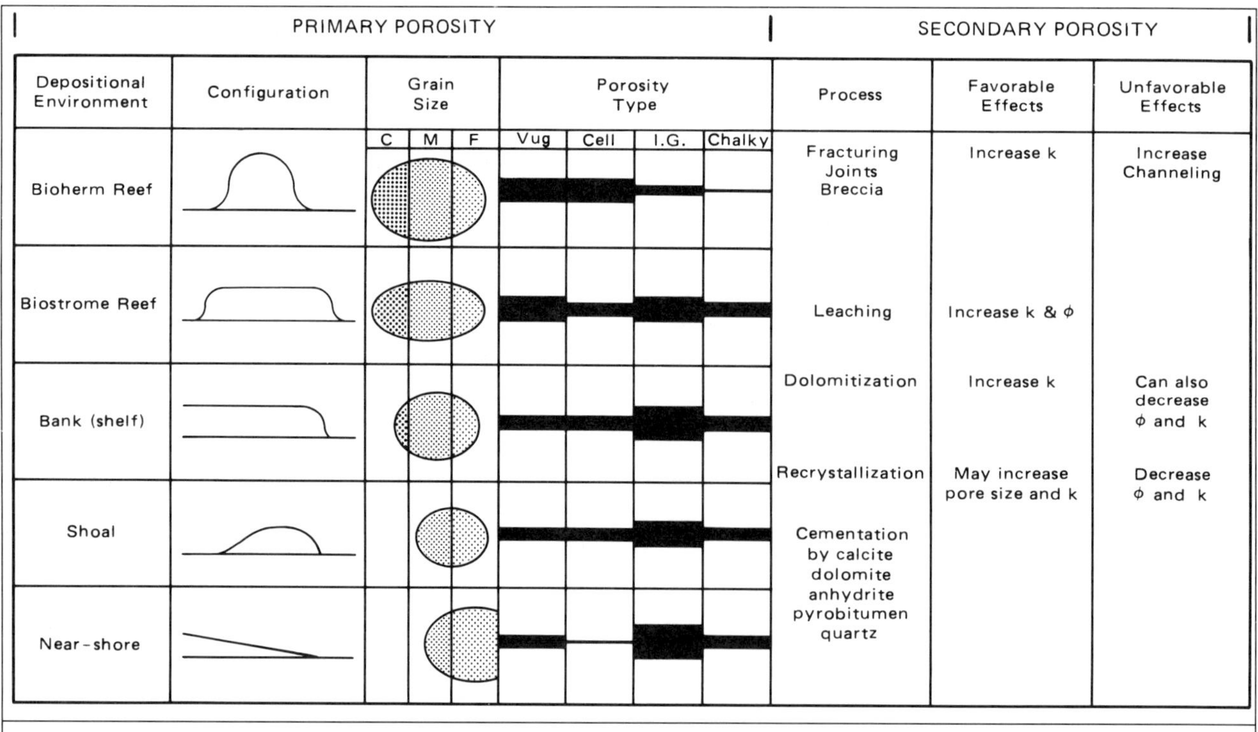

Fig. 4.4—Processes that alter the porosity of carbonates.[13]

There is no single, most-appropriate method for obtaining permeability data. If it is economically viable, an extensive coring and core analysis program probably will yield the best information for direct development of both the areal and the vertical distribution of permeability. The paper by Shirer[33] discusses an excellent example of this approach. Core analysis may be the only way to develop detailed permeability profiles of a reservoir section.

One should be aware of the potential inaccuracies in core analysis data. Sampling techniques and testing procedures may introduce error,[34,36,45,46] particularly in analyses of heterogeneous, vugular, friable, or clay-containing cores. Because most rock properties will vary areally and vertically in all reservoirs, care must be taken to ensure that core tests are run on appropriate samples. Because macroscopic heterogeneities are built into a reservoir model, core samples should be reasonably homogeneous so that heterogeneity will not be overexpressed in the model.[47,48]

If only sidewall cores or core cuttings are available, correlations between mercury-injection capillary pressure and brine permeability can be used.[49]

Because smaller-scale heterogeneities always exist, core permeabilities must be averaged to represent the flow characteristics of the entire reservoir or individual reservoir units. The proper method of averaging depends on how permeabilities were distributed as the rock was deposited and how they were altered by secondary processes. The choice of averaging technique is significant, as illustrated in Fig. 4.8.[50]

Arithmetic Average. If the permeable units extend laterally hundreds of feet around the well, flow within strata may be treated as if it is parallel and thickness-weighted arithmetic averaging should be used in calculations of horizontal flow. The arithmetic average is

$$\bar{k}_{arith} = \frac{\sum_{i=1}^{n} k_i h_i}{\sum_{i=1}^{n} h_i} \quad \text{. . . . .} \quad (4.1)$$

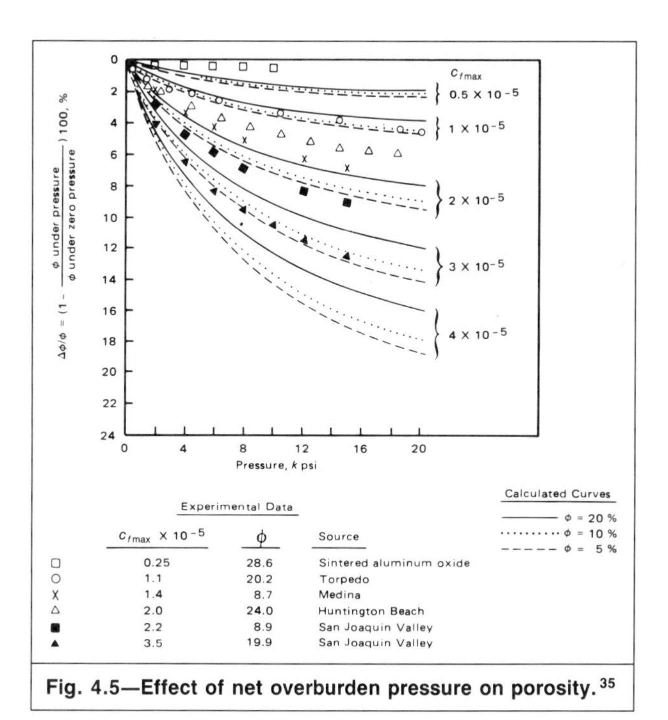

Fig. 4.5—Effect of net overburden pressure on porosity.[35]

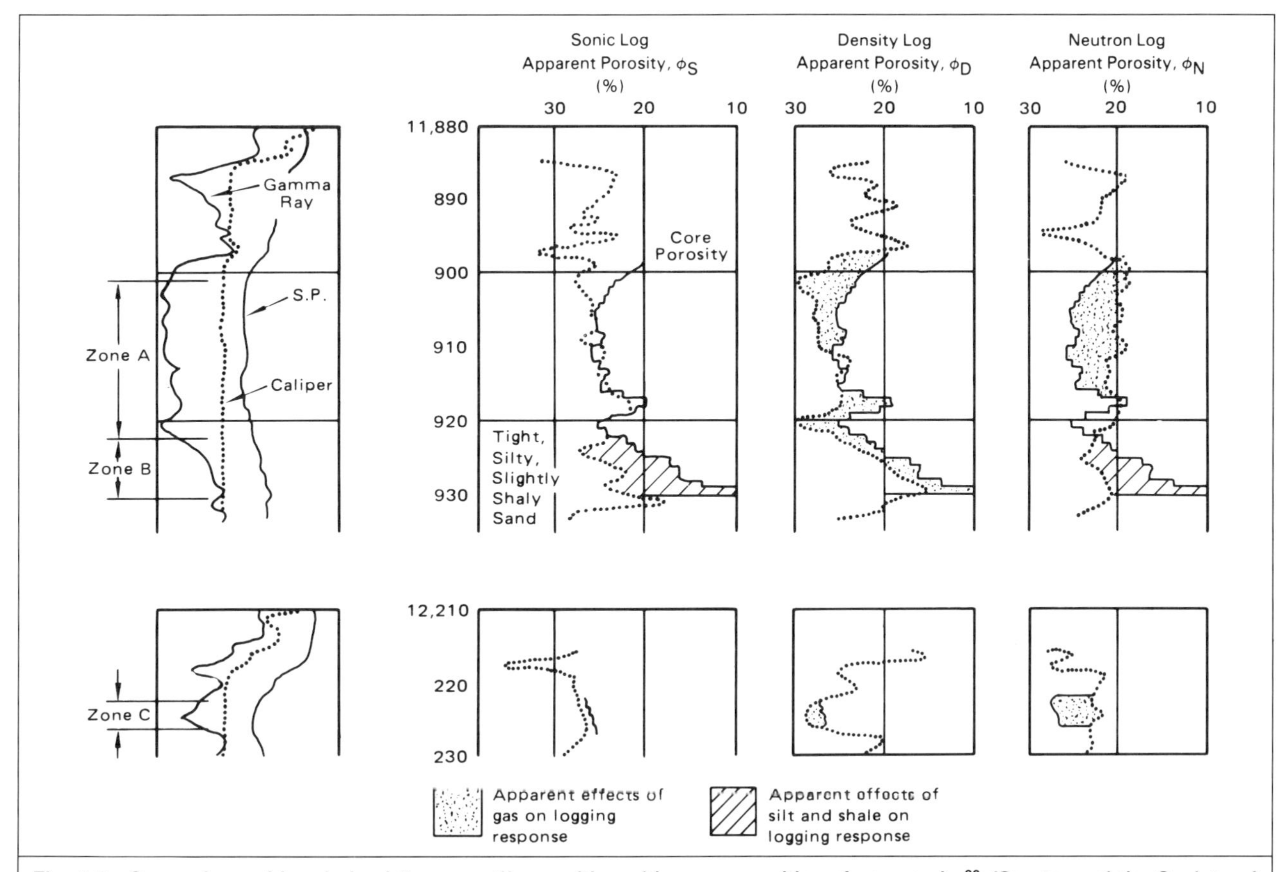

Fig. 4.6—Comparison of log-derived "apparent" porosities with core porosities of gas sands.[38] (Courtesy of the Society of Professional Well Log Analysts.)

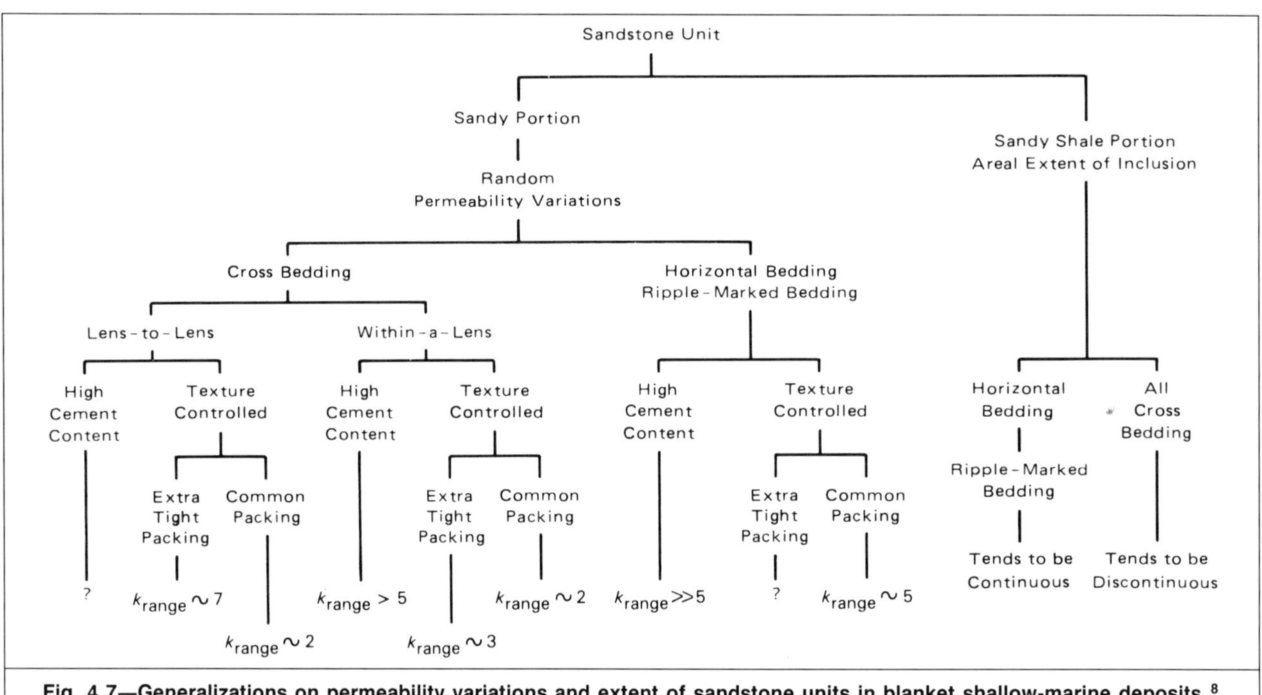

Fig. 4.7—Generalizations on permeability variations and extent of sandstone units in blanket shallow-marine deposits.[8]

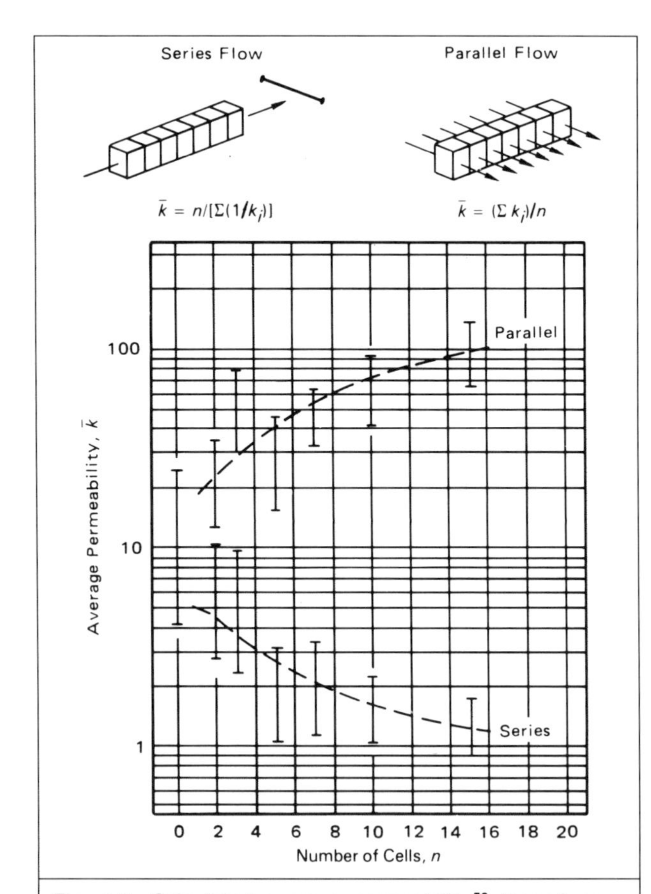

Fig. 4.8—Calculated average permeability[50] (based on n cells selected at random from a log-normal permeability distribution). (Courtesy of The Canadian Inst. of Mining and Metallurgy.)

Harmonic Average. If arithmetic averaging is correct for horizontal permeability, then harmonic averaging should be used in calculating permeability for vertical (series) flow. The harmonic average is

$$\bar{k}_{harm} = \frac{\sum_{i=1}^{n} h_i}{\sum_{i=1}^{n} h_i/k_i} \quad \text{(4.2)}$$

Geometric Average. If permeabilities are randomly distributed, the geometric average (or log mean) applies.[51] The geometric average is

$$\bar{k}_{geom} = \sqrt[n]{k_1 k_2 k_3 \ldots k_n} \quad \text{(4.3)}$$

In this case, both horizontal and vertical permeabilities normally should be obtained by geometric averaging.

4.3.5 Developing an Average Permeability. To develop an adequate description of reservoirs having zones formed in different depositional environments (and modified by varying secondary processes), it is necessary to determine an appropriate average permeability for each zone (or subzone if there are significant permeability variations within a zone). It is possible that arithmetic averaging might be correct for one zone while geometric averaging might be appropriate for another. For example, for marine-delta complexes and braided-stream deposits, arithmetic averaging often applies. For deposits formed by small meandering streams, geometric averaging may or may not apply. The proper method of averaging will depend on the nature of the heterogeneity in the primary direction of flow.

The most common method of measuring the average permeability-thickness of a reservoir section is well testing.[52,53] This method is particularly useful when only the areal distribution of permeability is required. Fig. 4.9 compares permeabilities calculated from pressure-buildup data with arithmetic averages of core data from the Jay-Little Escambia Creek field. The good agreement indicates that the arithmetic average is correct for this reservoir.

Permeabilities derived from well tests frequently differ from arithmetic averages of core permeabilities. For example, as indicated in Table 4.2, well-test data from the Judy Creek carbonate field in Canada yield much higher values for permeability thickness, kh, than do foot-by-foot, arithmetically averaged core permeabilities.

In contrast, Willcox and Riley[54] found that well-test permeabilities for the North Sea Leman field are typically much lower than core permeabilities. They attribute the low well-test values to cross-bedding and permeability "streakiness." It is sometimes desirable to conduct special geologic studies and to design new tests to resolve differences between well-test and core-analysis data. Detailed petrographic studies may reveal fractures, solution channels, cross-bedding, or permeability barriers that may not have been sampled when core plugs were analyzed. Spinner surveys, noise logs, temperature surveys, pulse tests, packer-isolated production tests, or even borehole televiewer scanning of selected wells may be required to resolve discrepancies between core- and well-test-derived permeabilities.

4.3.6 Correlating Permeability and Porosity. Because porosity—but not permeability—can be measured reliably by logging, it is often necessary to estimate permeabilities from logs with permeability/porosity correlations developed from core analysis data.[32] Correlations will be most reliable if they are developed for each major rock type present in the reservoir. Typical correlations are illustrated in Figs. 4.10 through 4.12 for the San Andres dolomite,[55] the Bradford sandstone,[56] and the Brent reservoir. The correlation for the San Andres dolomite cores is fair to good; even so, at a given porosity, the variability of permeability is about an order of magnitude. The correlation for the Brent reservoir in the North Sea was used to estimate permeabilities from log-derived porosities for intervals where no cores were recovered. Fig. 4.13 illustrates how log-derived and measured permeabilities were combined to develop a complete permeability profile for a Brent well.

Additional work of interest is discussed by Chilingar[57] and Wadman *et al.*,[58] who established foot-by-foot permeabilities for Prudhoe Bay wells from porosity transit times and permeability/porosity relationships. They also took well-test data into consideration in selecting the log k vs. ϕ relationship for each zone.

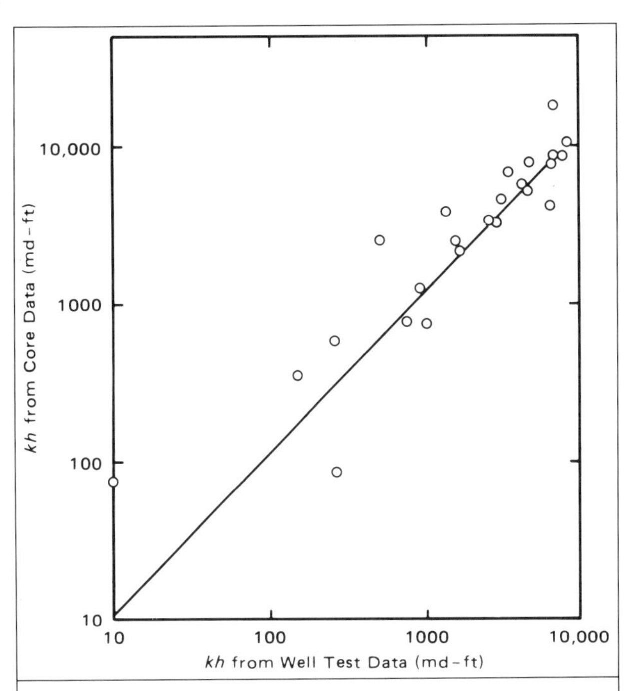

Fig. 4.9—Comparison of core data with well-test data, Jay-Little Escambia Creek field, Florida.

TABLE 4.2—COMPARISON OF CORE AND WELL-TEST DATA FROM PAY ZONES, JUDY CREEK FIELD

	kh (md-ft)		
	Well-Test Data		Core Data
Well Number	Buildup	Productivity Index	Arithmetic Average
S-3 Wells			
4 18 63 10 W5	3,069	7,848	2,686
4 29 63 10 W5	584	675	253
4 34 63 10 W5	13,900	5,145	823
2 8 64 10 W5	9,828	18,184	2,132
4 2 64 11 W5	16,187	7,234	1,355
4 22 64 11 W5	8,240	17,300	935
2 22 64 11 W5	2,685	7,071	2,049
Average	7,784	9,068	1,459
S-4 Wells			
2 19 63 10 W5	3,437	868	206
(second well test)	3,912	6,945	
10 21 63 10 W5	30,789	24,624	4,241
16 35 63 11 W5	2,010	3,342	58
4 9 64 10 W5	80,820	70,085	16,552
Average	29,382	26,249	5,264
S-3, S-4, S-5 Wells			
16 31 63 10 W5	1,920	2,885	4,082
4 32 63 10 W5	3,177	2,588	3,877
12 12 63 11 W5	6,465	5,284	1,220
10 22 63 11 W5	1,716	2,885	15,296
10 26 63 11 W5	805	1,812	3,398
10 33 63 11 W5	5,264	4,859	5,297
4 4 64 10 W5	46,132	113,652	6,446
12 4 64 10 W5	65,625	79,556	11,148
12 5 64 10 W5	29,160	47,039	10,713
4 6 64 10 W5	1,200	2,411	1,214
10 3 64 11 W5	2,403	2,301	4,552
2 10 64 11 W5	2,430	2,866	1,827
Average	13,858	22,344	5,756

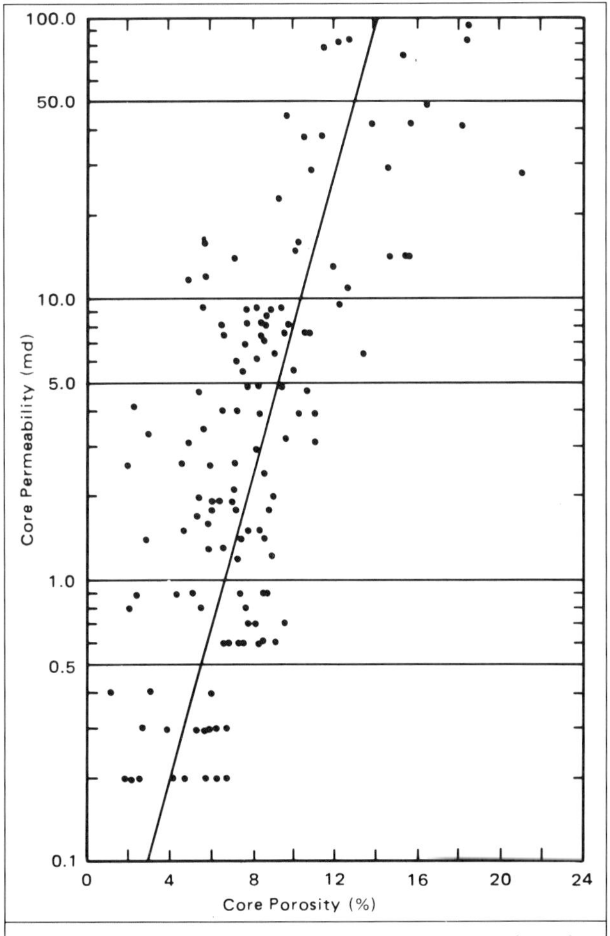

Fig. 4.10—Permeability/porosity correlation for cores from the Means field, San Andres dolomite.[55]

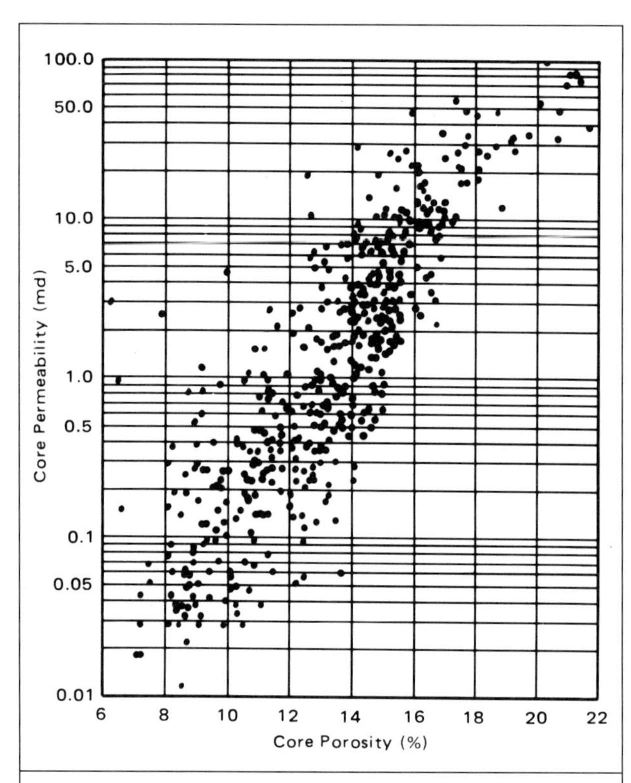

Fig. 4.11—Permeability/porosity correlation for cores from the Bradford sandstone.[56]

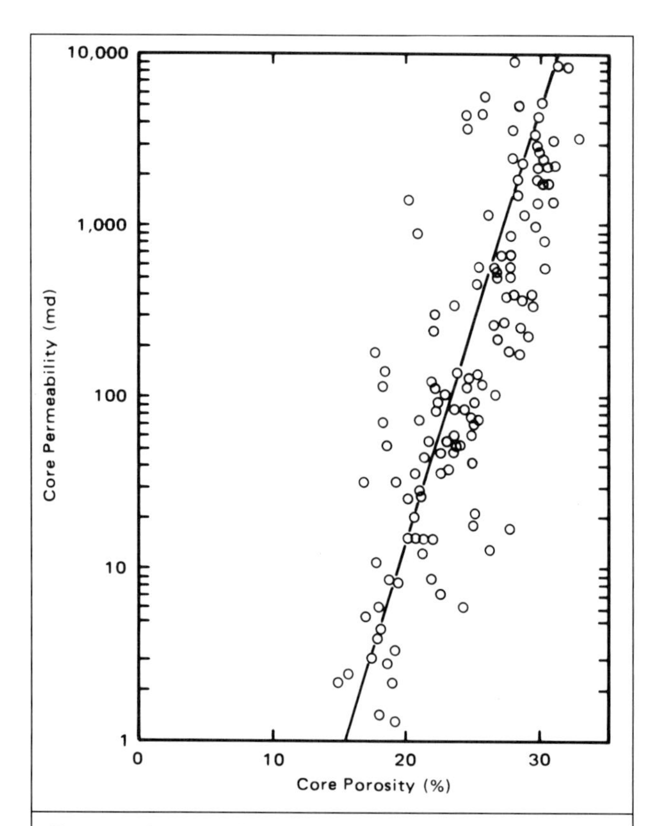

Fig. 4.12—Permeability/porosity correlation for cores from the Brent field.

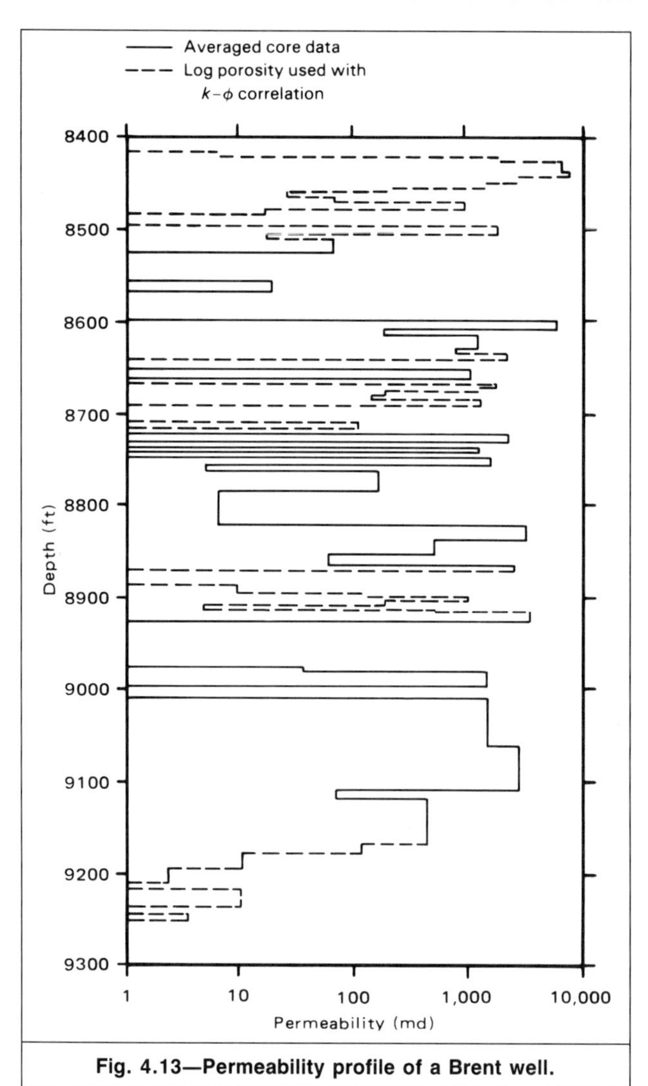

Fig. 4.13—Permeability profile of a Brent well.

Semiquantitative estimates of silt and clay content sometimes can be derived from multiple porosity logs.[37,38] These data, in conjunction with measured core porosities, can be correlated with core permeabilities to obtain qualitative estimates of permeability distribution. Figs. 4.14 and 4.15 illustrate the effects of silt and clay content and of calcite cement on sandstone permeability.

When a correlation of porosity vs. log permeability is used, permeability values should be derived from individual foot-by-foot porosities rather than from zone or interval averages. If all porosity values in a zone are first averaged, and the average value is used in a log permeability correlation, the derived permeability will be the geometric mean of the zone's permeabilities. It is obvious, of course, that the logarithm of an average taken from a set of data is not equal to the average of logarithms of the data, but frequently the two are inadvertently equated. Porosity values derived from well logs inherently are average values, with the type of average dependent on tool response and formation characteristics. As a consequence, permeabilities in highly stratified formations will tend to be underestimated by correlations with porosities from well logs.

4.3.7 Vertical Permeability. The discussion thus far has focused on horizontal (parallel-to-bedding-plane) permeability. It is also important to define vertical permeability. The lateral continuity of obstructions to vertical flow should be defined to the extent possible, particularly in bottomwater-drive reservoirs and in reservoirs where gas or water coning can cause operating problems. Continuity can best be defined by locating shale, silt, and lime mud zones, and by attempting well-to-well correlations of these zones. Vertical permeabilities of these zones should be measured when cores are sampled and analyzed.

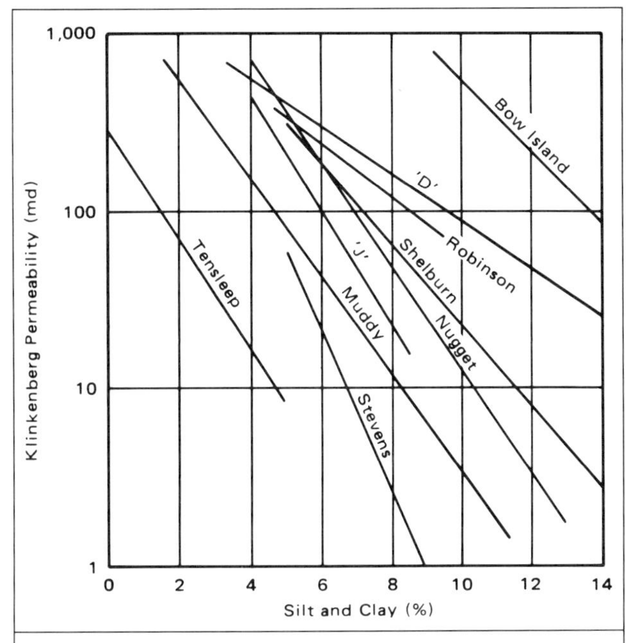

Fig. 4.14—Influence of silt and clay on sandstone permeability.[14] (Courtesy of PennWell Publishing Co.)

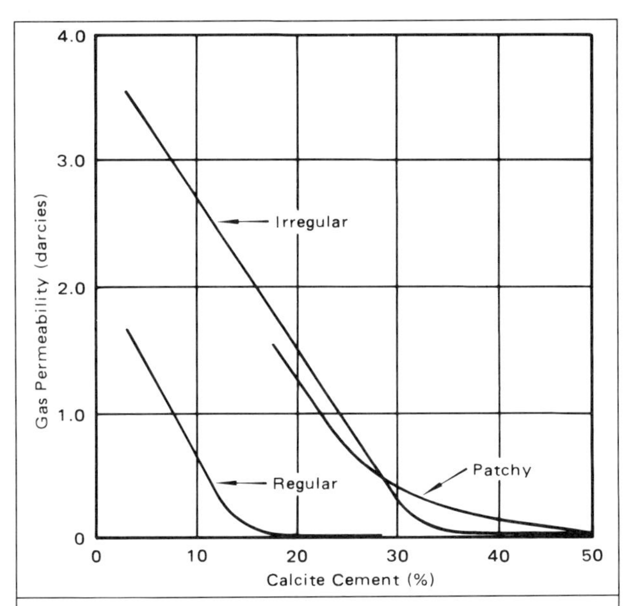

Fig. 4.15—Influence of amount and distribution of calcite cement on sandstone permeability.[14] (Courtesy of PennWell Publishing Co.)

Knowledge of depositional environment can be helpful when estimating the average areal extent of significant barriers to vertical flow[59,60] (Table 4.3). Vertical well tests can be used to measure effective vertical permeability in reservoirs ≧20 ft [≧6 m] thick.[61,62] Estimating the reduction in effective vertical permeability caused by numerous thin shales that extend only tens or hundreds of feet requires special study.[58,63] For example, Wadman *et al.*[58] modeled randomly distributed shales in the upper braided-stream zone at Prudhoe Bay. They developed graphs relating vertical permeability reduction to the amount of shale for 75- and 150-ft [23- and 46-m] -wide shales with lengths three times their widths (Fig. 4.16).

Some reservoirs, particularly carbonate reservoirs, may have thick sections that contain no extensive barriers to vertical flow. Vertical permeabilities within these intervals can be estimated by core analysis, preferably by measurements on whole cores[5] (rather than core plugs). Lishman[50] discussed caution that should be exercised in whole-core analysis to avoid false magnification of permeability anisotropy.

It is common practice to develop multiple cross sections and, where possible, to correlate permeability from well to well. Whenever possible, it is advisable to use well interference and pulse tests[52,64-66] or between-well acoustic tests to verify the continuity of major zones defined from the cross-sectional correlations.

As additional pressure and production data become available, areal permeability and porosity distributions should be updated regularly by history matching reservoir performance. Also be alert for data that can be used to update vertical-permeability estimates (Chap. 8).

4.4 Assignment of Rock Property Distributions to the Simulator

After agreement has been reached on the best geologic description of the reservoir, the engineer must decide how to represent the zones

TABLE 4.3—ASSOCIATION OF SHALE CONTINUITY AND ENVIRONMENT OF DEPOSITION

Principal Depositional Environment[59]	General Shale Continuity in Subenvironment: Continuous	Discontinuous	Some Considerations in Shale Barrier Description
Dunes (aeolian)		Interdune playas and wadi (stream) deposits	Shales rare
Alluvial fan	Lower fan "sheets"	Upper fan channels	Channel spacing and gradients; debris flow deposits
Braided stream		Channel braids and lateral secondary channels	Channel depth (based on fundamental bed thicknesses), valley width
Meandering stream	Flood basin (remnant in meandering-belt complexes)	Top part of point bars and abandoned channels	Channel depth (based on fundamental bed thicknesses), valley width
Upper deltaic plain	Flood basin (remnants, as above)	Upper point bar, abandoned channels, channel braids	Channel depth, coastal plain vs. valley confinement
Lower deltaic plain	Interdistributary areas	Distributary channels	Channel depth, spacing of distributaries .
Delta fringe	Areas marginal to river-mouth bars	River-mouth bars	Size of feeder river, wave, tidal, and strength of currents along the shore
Beaches/barrier Island	Lagoons, shoreface	Tidal inlet channel, shoreface	Shales uncommon in lower, rare in upper parts
Tidal flat	High flat	Low flat and channels	Tide range
Submarine fan	Lower fan "sheet"	Upper fan	Feeder canyon size, particle-size range

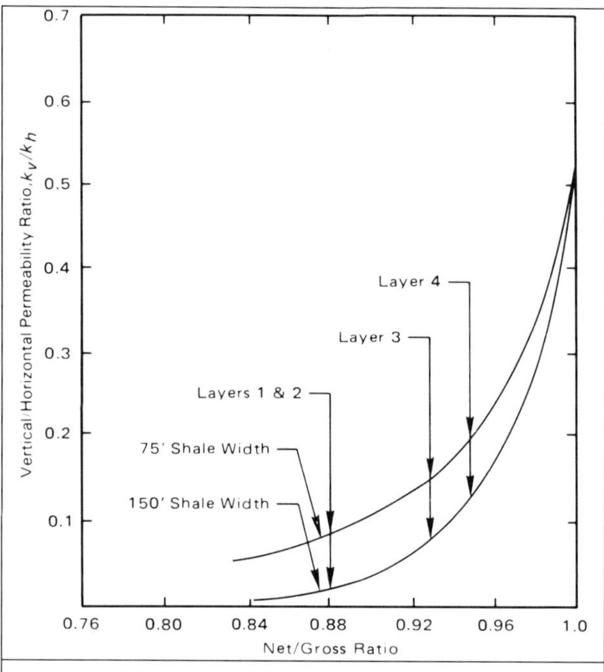

Fig. 4.16—Influence of shale barriers on vertical permeability.

realistically within the limitations of the grid system of the simulation model.

Selection of gridblock size and orientation is discussed from the model-builder's viewpoint in Chap. 5. Suffice it to say here that one must consider the magnitude and location of variations in permeability and saturation, the displacement process being studied, and the cost of making required simulation runs before deciding on final gridblock size and orientation. Areal grids should be aligned so that they are compatible with the major axis of permeability anisotropy. If no directional permeability is evident, align gridblocks with the predominant direction of advance of the water/oil contact (WOC) or gas/oil contact (GOC) or with the longest areal dimension of the reservoir to reduce the number of gridblocks. In cross-sectional studies, gridblock height is often governed by the location of impermeable barriers or major permeability contrasts, while block length is limited by rate of dip-angle change and computational restrictions on the length-to-width ratio.

Development of arrays of thickness, depth, porosity, and permeability in sufficient detail to build a simulator model can be laborious. The amount of work can be reduced significantly if appropriate computer programs are available to digitize and contour geologic maps and to generate rock property arrays.[67]

4.4.1 Thickness and Depth. Thickness and depth can be read from geologic maps at block centers or boundaries. Both net and gross pay thicknesses are needed, even though it is not always necessary to represent nonpay intervals with specific gridblocks. Depth continuity must be maintained, but relatively thin nonpay intervals (shale, lime mud, etc.) can be represented implicitly by reducing block porosity and permeability.

Steeply dipping reservoirs require special attention to ensure that input data for thickness, distance between block centers, and permeability are consistent. Hirasaki and O'Dell[68] discuss proper entry of data for this situation.

4.4.2 Porosity. Entry of porosity distributions into a reservoir simulator is comparatively easy. Porosity maps for each zone or the entire reservoir frequently show gradual changes in porosity, so an adequate porosity array can be obtained by overlaying the isoporosity map with a scaled grid and reading off block-centered values. If the map is generated by a contouring program, coding the program to pick porosity values at block centers will reduce time requirements for complex models. If lateral variation in porosity is significant, it may be necessary to enter area-weighted average values.

4.4.3 Permeability. Frequently, horizontal permeability (or permeability thickness) will not change markedly over the distance represented by a single gridblock. In this case, values can be read directly from an areal permeability map overlying a scaled map of the model grid. Alternatively, block boundary values can be derived by interpolation of block-center permeabilities.

If there are pronounced changes in horizontal permeability between gridblock centers, a more detailed analysis may be needed to select representative block boundary values. One approach is (1) to overlay the maps with a fine grid and (2) to use appropriate averages of map values at the boundaries of the fine grid to derive values for the coarser grid of the simulator model. Precise map interpretation procedures need not be developed at this time because gridblock permeabilities will almost always need adjustment during the history-matching phase.

Vertical permeability must also be specified for cross-sectional or 3D models. Values at block centers can be picked from maps for each zone of the reservoir or calculated from horizontal permeability and the ratio of vertical to horizontal permeability. Block-center values are often harmonically averaged to establish block boundary permeabilities. Modeling very high or very low permeability can be tricky and may require some experimentation with the model. Open fractures or meandering solution channels must be represented by very high vertical and horizontal permeabilities at appropriate locations. When the barriers to vertical flow are areally extensive, model gridding must be relatively fine to describe the tortuous vertical flow path. When barriers are smaller than a single gridblock, they are impossible to model directly. In this case, properties assigned to the individual gridblocks containing the barrier must be adjusted to model the barriers indirectly.

Thin shale or other dense zones are often represented by assigning zero vertical permeabilities at boundaries between strata. Impermeable barriers that are small relative to lateral block size are modeled by reducing the vertical permeability of the gridblock.

4.5 Capillary Pressure and Relative Permeability

Craig[44] gives an excellent discussion of water/oil capillary pressure and relative permeability, including the effects of wettability and hysteresis. For a given rock, these functions depend not only on saturation but also on the direction of saturation change. When the displacing fluid is the wetting phase (e.g., water or oil displacing gas), the saturation change is in the imbibition cycle. When the displacing fluid is the nonwetting phase (e.g., gas displacing oil), the saturation change is in the drainage cycle. In general, gas/oil and gas/water saturation functions are simpler to measure and to interpret than are water/oil functions because gas is always the nonwetting phase. (Gas/oil saturation functions are adequately described in reservoir engineering texts.)

Maps of the distribution of predominant rock types can be used to assign capillary-pressure and relative-permeability functions to different areas of the reservoir. This approach is particularly useful for heterogeneous limestone formations, but it is also useful for heterogeneous sandstone if rock classification takes into account grain size and sorting, as well as mineral content.

When the change in oil saturation is unidirectional, it is necessary to select only the drainage or imbibition curve that applies. If saturation reversals occur, however, it may be necessary to simulate hysteresis, in which case both drainage and imbibition curves are needed. Hysteresis saturation functions can be measured in the laboratory. The use of history-dependent saturation functions in simulation is addressed by Killough.[69]

4.5.1 Selection of Capillary-Pressure Data. Water/oil (or water/gas) capillary-pressure data are required to define the initial saturation distribution and to include capillarity in calculations of pressure gradients. Dynamic effects of capillarity are usually of minor importance. Capillary pressure can be a dominant force, however, in fractured, water-wet reservoirs that produce by water imbibition and in reservoirs in which high-permeability layers are in good communication with very-low-permeability layers. The importance of capillary pressure diminishes as flow rate increases (i.e., as the ratio of viscous to capillary forces increases).

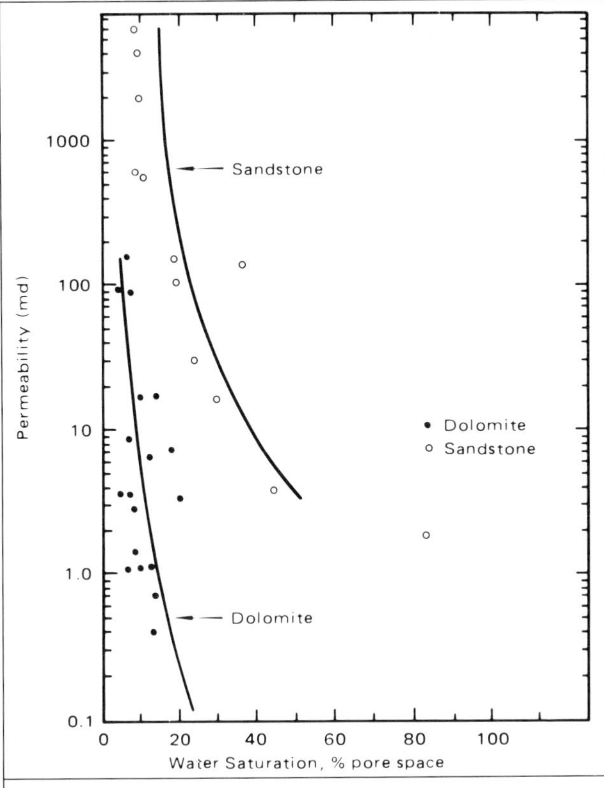

Fig. 4.17—Residual saturations in cores cut with oil-base mud.[57]

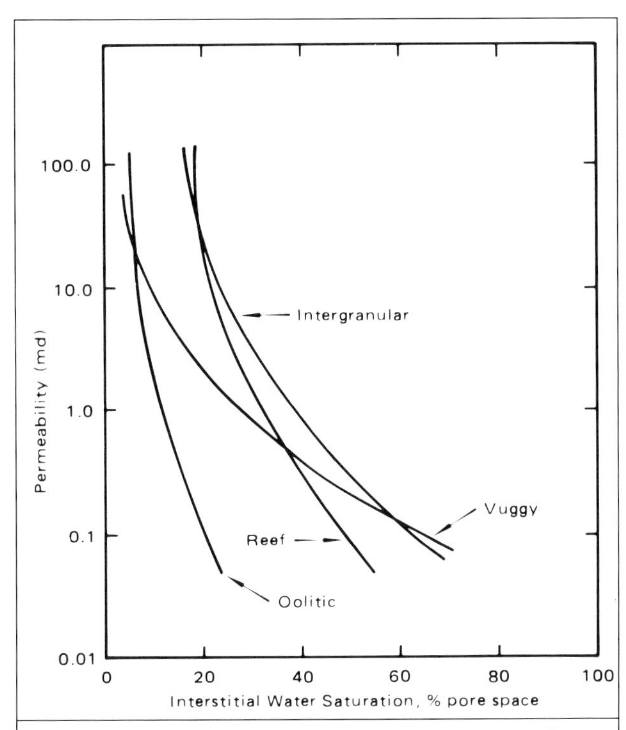

Fig. 4.18—Water distribution for typical carbonates[57] (approximately 60 ft above the free-water level).

Laboratory measurement of drainage capillary pressure is a routine part of core analysis. Converting laboratory measurements to field conditions, however, often introduces error because contact angle and interfacial tension are not known with precision. Thus, it is highly desirable to anchor laboratory data to interstitial water saturations measured in cores taken with oil-base mud[70,71] or with gas. When possible, the reference core sample should be taken from above the transition zone and it should be similar to cores used in the laboratory tests. Water saturations from oil-base cores taken through the oil/water transition zone are useful in selecting the appropriate water/oil capillary-pressure curves. Changes in rock type within the cored interval must be taken into consideration, of course.

Frequently, the only available data are a few laboratory capillary-pressure curves and a limited number of water-saturation estimates from well logs. In this case, the best estimate of saturation distribution is made by comparing saturation-depth plots from capillary-pressure data with similar plots derived from well-log data.

If one or more layers of clean sandstone or limestone have been logged, the log-derived saturation values should be given strong weight when selecting the most representative water saturation vs. depth function (i.e., drainage water/oil or water/gas P_c curve). Frequently, however, the accuracy of log-derived water saturations is doubtful and reliance must be placed on laboratory capillary-pressure curves.

Irreducible water saturation normally increases as permeability decreases. In low-permeability sandstones, the water saturation may be very high. However, Chilingar *et al.*[57] demonstrated that in some low-permeability oolites and dolomites, water saturation can be low (Figs. 4.17 and 4.18). Rockwood *et al.*[71] presented good correlations between porosity, interstitial water, and mercury-injection capillary-pressure curves for carbonate formations.

Surface tension between gas and oil increases as pressure declines from initial conditions. In some studies, it may be necessary to account for this effect by tying gas/oil capillary pressure to reservoir pressure.

4.5.2 Assignment of Capillary-Pressure Data. A single average capillary-pressure curve may be adequate for high-permeability sandstone reservoirs, but a set of curves will be required for more heterogeneous sandstone reservoirs. These curves frequently can be normalized and introduced into the model as a *J* function[72] that relates capillary pressure to porosity and permeability.

Many carbonate reservoirs are extremely heterogeneous and require capillary-pressure curves for each of several different rock types.[71] For some carbonate rock types, the *J* function can be used successfully.[73]

The initial equilibrium saturation distribution in a model normally should be established with drainage capillary-pressure curves. But if the producing mechanism involves imbibition, both drainage and imbibition curves must be used in the reservoir simulator. Processes that must be modeled with imbibition capillary pressures include (1) water displacing oil in a water-wet reservoir and (2) oil or water invading a gas cap. If the simulator does not have the capability of handling both drainage and imbibition capillary pressures, select the set causing the least error. If the transition-zone volume is a small fraction of the total reservoir volume and an imbibition displacement process is being simulated, the best selection would be the imbibition curve. On the other hand, if the transition zone is thick relative to total reservoir thickness, imbibition curves will lead to significant errors in the initial saturation distribution.

Gas/oil drainage capillary-pressure curves corrected to reservoir conditions should be used to establish the initial oil saturation distribution in a gas cap containing some oil.

Capillary-pressure data are normally introduced into the simulator as tables. Attention should be paid to constructing the tables, because some simulators are sensitive to slope changes between adjacent pairs of table entries. Large changes in slope can cause round-off or extrapolation errors during the simulation.

In simulations of three-phase systems, gas/oil and water/oil capillary pressures are commonly calculated from two-phase relationships.

4.5.3 Selection of Relative-Permeability Data. The basic shapes of relative-permeability curves for the principal rock types in a reservoir are usually defined by laboratory core tests on representative core samples. Shapes sometimes may be determined theoretically[74] for the less complex systems. Because relative permeability is influenced by pore geometry, wettability, fluid distribution, and saturation history, it is unlikely that averages of a few laboratory relative-permeability curves are adequate for most reservoirs. Therefore, any opportunity to verify laboratory-measured values with field-derived data should be pursued. Special well tests and coring or logging programs can be designed to check endpoint saturations.[75-79] Sometimes it is feasible to conduct well tests to check relative permeability.

Relative permeability to oil *at low oil saturations* can be critical in predicting reservoir behavior. This part of the k_{ro} curve can be difficult to obtain experimentally for gas/oil or water/oil systems that are not strongly water-wet. The best current laboratory method uses data from a centrifuge-driven displacement.[80] If measurements of this part of the curve are not available, it is usually desirable to evaluate the sensitivity of calculated reservoir performance to the shape of the k_{ro} curve at low oil saturations.

If pressure gradients in a water-invaded zone are critical to reservoir performance, it is important that water relative permeability at residual oil be known. In principle, and sometimes in practice, such data can be obtained by a well test in a watered-out well or by a water injection test in a production well. Note, however, that these tests are very difficult to conduct and interpret.

Critical gas saturation is difficult to obtain from core analysis. Any experimental value should be checked against field data, if possible. If reliable gas/oil ratio histories are available, critical gas saturation can be estimated from field performance.

Three-phase relative-permeability data are troublesome and time-consuming to measure. If three-phase data are unavailable, such indirect methods as the one proposed by Stone[2,3] can be used to derive three-phase values from two-phase data. An application of Stone's method is presented by Weaver.[81]

4.5.4 Assignment of Relative-Permeability Data. Separate relative-permeability curves should be used for each significant rock type; it is particularly important to use multiple relative-permeability curves in modeling reservoirs that possess extreme rock properties.

Relative permeabilities should not be introduced directly into two-dimensional areal models or into cross-sectional and 3D models in which vertical gridding is coarse. They should first be transformed into pseudo-relative permeabilities[82] to account for vertical flow and saturation distributions that cannot be adequately defined by coarse vertical gridding. (Pseudofunctions are discussed in Chaps. 2, 3, 5, and 7.)

4.6 Fluid Properties

This section is confined to the discussion of fluid properties required for black-oil reservoir simulation. These properties include oil, water, and gas reservoir volume factors, viscosity, density, compressibility, and gas-in-solution in oil and in water. Additional data needed to simulate volatile-oil and gas-condensate reservoirs are discussed in Chap. 11.

The most reliable way of obtaining reservoir oil properties and gas/oil relationships is by analysis of bottomhole or reconstituted fluid samples.[83,84] When measured data are not available, approximate oil-property and gas/oil relationships can be generated from generalized correlations.[84,85] Acceptable gas and water properties can always be obtained from existing correlations.[83,86-88]

4.6.1 Selection of Fluid Property Data. Fluid property data either describe the properties of reservoir fluids or relate reservoir volumes to surface volumes. Both kinds of data are discussed briefly in the following paragraphs; terms that are specific to the petroleum industry are defined.

4.6.1.1 Volumetric and Physical Properties of Reservoir Fluids. *Oil, gas, and water viscosities,* μ_o, μ_g, and μ_w. Oil viscosity is obtained from laboratory PVT measurements; gas and water viscosities are usually taken from existing correlations.[83,87,88]

Oil, gas, and water densities, ρ_o, ρ_g, and ρ_w. Densities can be calculated from PVT measurements or obtained from existing correlations.[83,87,88]

Oil, gas, and water compressibilities, c_o, c_g, and c_w. Oil compressibility is obtained from PVT measurements. Compressibility is identically the slope of the formation volume factor, B_o, curve at pressures above the bubblepoint. Gas and water compressibilities can be found in textbooks.[83,87]

Oil relative volume factor, V_o/V_{bp}, is the ratio of the oil-phase volume at a given pressure, V_o, to the volume the oil would occupy at initial saturation pressure, V_{bp}; it is calculated from PVT data.

4.6.1.2 Data That Relate Reservoir Volumes to Surface Volumes. *Oil Formation Volume Factor,* B_o, is the ratio of the specific volume of oil with its dissolved gas at reservoir conditions to the specific volume of oil at stock-tank conditions. The oil formation volume factor is a function of the composition of the system, pressure, temperature, and the manner in which gas and oil are separated; it is obtained from PVT measurements.

Gas Formation Volume Factor, B_g, is the ratio of the specific volume of free gas in the reservoir to its specific volume at standard surface conditions. This factor need not be measured experimentally because it can be calculated. Calhoun[89] presents charts of B_g vs. pressure.

Water Formation Volume Factor, B_w, whose definition parallels that of B_o, is normally an insignificant factor in reservoir studies. It can be calculated from information available in the literature.[83]

Dissolved GOR's and gas/water ratios (GWR's), R_s and R_{sw}, are the standard volumes of gas dissolved in oil and water, respectively, at reservoir temperature and at a given pressure. The dissolved GOR is a significant factor in reservoir performance and should be determined experimentally, if possible. The dissolved GWR can be found in Ref. 83 for pressures up to about 3,000 psi [20.7 MPa]. For higher pressures, refer to Blount *et al.*[86]

4.6.2 Variation of Fluid Properties With Depth and Area. In low-closure fields, fluid properties usually are uniform throughout the reservoir. In high-closure reservoirs, however, fluid properties can vary significantly with depth and sometimes with areal location. In these reservoirs, solution GOR and API gravity normally decrease with depth, while oil viscosity increases with depth. In the Tensleep sandstone reservoir of the Elk Basin field,[90] over a depth range of 1750 ft [533 m], gas in solution ranged from 134 to 490 scf/bbl [24 to 88 std m^3/m^3] and wellhead API gravity ranged from 27 to 31°API [0.89 to 0.87 g/cm^3]. In the LL-370 reservoir[91] of Venezuela, over a depth range of 1,500 ft [457 m], R_s ranged from 230 to 460 scf/bbl [41 to 83 std m^3/m^3], while the API gravity ranged from 18 to 28°API [0.95 to 0.89 g/cm^3].

The Ghawar Arab-D reservoir in Saudi Arabia is composed of several nearly flat structures. Ghawar is very large (the continuous oil zone is more than 150 miles [241 km] long) and, although within any single structure fluid properties do not vary appreciably, the total change in properties is significant. Maximum variations over the entire length of the reservoir are about 100 scf/STB, 0.3 cp, and 4°API [18 std m^3/stock-tank m^3, 0.3 mPa·s, and 1.04 g/cm^3]. Reservoir temperature also varies enough areally to require adjustment of PVT properties.

In general, if closure exceeds a few hundred feet or if a field is large, enough fluid samples should be taken to ensure that any significant trends in reservoir fluid properties are defined.

4.6.3 Assignment of Fluid Properties. Fluid properties are normally entered into the simulator as tables, with properties defined as functions of pressure. An alternative method is to express the fluid property relationships analytically with appropriate polynomials.[92]

Separate sets of tables may be needed to account for variations in fluid properties with depth or area.[92] Chap. 3 discusses the potential simulation errors that may result from modeling fluid movement from one PVT region to another.

An effect that is frequently overlooked is the reduction in reservoir temperatures caused by injection of large volumes of fluid. Injection water that is 100°F [56°C] cooler than the reservoir can increase fluid viscosities enough within a radius of several hundred feet from the injection well to cause a major reduction in water injectivity. If injection well capacity is expected to be a problem, it may be necessary to adjust PVT properties with time to account for the temperature changes.

4.7 Establishing Initial Pressure and Saturation Distributions

Initial gas, oil, and water pressure distribution and initial saturation distributions must be defined in the reservoir model. Pressure data are usually referenced to some datum depth. It is convenient to specify a pressure and saturation at the datum depth and then to calculate phase pressure arrays with fluid densities and depths. The following paragraphs outline commonly used methods for initializing pressure and saturation distributions and discuss complications caused by multiple WOC's or GOC's, tilted contacts, and fluid properties that vary with depth.

4.7.1 Common Equilibrium Initialization Method. The most frequently used initialization method "initializes on the oil phase." Oil pressure is calculated for each gridblock; then saturations and other phase pressures are derived from capillary pressures and phase pressure gradients. A better procedure is to "initialize on the water phase," but either approach is satisfactory if used properly.

When initializing on the oil phase, the following steps are involved.

1. Select an oil-phase reference pressure, p_1, a reference water/oil capillary pressure, P_{c2}, a reference gas/oil capillary pressure, P_{c3}, and the depths at which these reference pressures apply (D_1, D_2, and D_3, respectively).
2. Calculate oil pressures at the centers of all gridblocks.
3. Calculate water pressures at the centers of all blocks with the oil pressure at D_2, capillary pressure P_{c2}, and the water pressure gradient.
4. Calculate gas pressures with the oil pressure at D_3, capillary pressure P_{c3}, and the gas pressure gradient.
5. Having established block-centered pressures for oil, gas, and water, read the oil, gas, and water saturations at block centers from the appropriate capillary-pressure curves.

4.7.2 Complicating Conditions. Because density/pressure relationships are generally nonlinear, the phase-pressure-vs.-depth relationships required in Steps 2 through 4 usually should be obtained by iteration.

If more than one reservoir communicates with the same aquifer, it is advantageous to initialize on the water phase by selecting a water reference pressure, calculating water pressures for each gridblock depth, and then calculating oil and gas pressures.

If the reservoir contains multiple WOC's or GOC's, the procedure is the same as previously discussed, except that a reference oil pressure and capillary pressure must be known for one gridblock in each area of the field that contains a separate contact. The areas are then initialized individually.

When fluid properties vary with depth or area and multiple fluid property tables are being used, caution must be exercised in initializing pressure and saturation distributions. Values assigned at block centers can depend on the order in which the values are computed and assigned.

Tilted WOC's are common in reservoirs connected with dynamic aquifers. Two approaches can be considered for modeling the tilt: (1) simulate both aquifer and reservoir, and model the flow conditions that have caused the contact to tilt, or (2) impose a tilted contact on the reservoir model by shifting the capillary-pressure curve up or down, block by block or subarea by subarea, as saturations are initialized. The second approach should not be used if the shifted level of the capillary-pressure curves would cause major changes in displacement or sweep efficiency of water.

If a reservoir has a long, poorly documented production history, it is sometimes necessary or more efficient not to model discovery conditions but to start the reservoir simulation at some appropriate point in the life of the reservoir. For example, the model might be initialized by developing pressure and saturation distributions from recent field data, reading the distributions into the model, and starting the simulation from these nonequilibrium conditions. This approach may also be applied in a study in which model performance matches overall reservoir performance, but individual well pressures or saturations are not well matched. In this case, short-term predictions will be improved if detailed pressure and saturation distributions derived from recent field observations are introduced into the simulator at the end of the history match.

Nomenclature

B_g = gas FVF, RB/scf [res m^3/std m^3]
B_o = oil FVF, RB/STB [res m^3/stock-tank m^3]
B_w = water FVF, RB/STB [res m^3/stock-tank m^3]
c_f = rock compressibility, psi^{-1} [kPa^{-1}]
$c_{f\max}$ = maximum formation compressibility, psi^{-1} [kPa^{-1}]
c_g = gas compressibility, psi^{-1} [kPa^{-1}]
c_o = oil compressibility, psi^{-1} [kPa^{-1}]
c_w = water compressibility, psi^{-1} [kPa^{-1}]
D = depth to formation top (structure), ft [m]
D_1, D_2, D_3 = depths at which p_1, P_{c2}, and P_{c3} apply, respectively, ft [m]
h = layer, sand thickness, or thickness of each cell, ft [m]
h_n = net pay thickness, ft [m]
h_t = gross formation thickness, ft [m]
i = cell number
k = specific (absolute) permeability, md
$\bar{k}$ = average permeability, md
$\bar{k}_a$ = arithmetic average permeability, md
k_h = horizontal permeability, md
k_{rg} = relative permeability to gas, fraction
k_{ro} = relative permeability to oil, fraction
k_{rw} = relative permeability to water, fraction
k_v = vertical permeability, md
kh = permeability thickness, md-ft [md·m]
n = number of cells
p = pressure, psi [kPa]
p_1 = oil-phase reference pressure at depth D_1, psi [kPa]
P_c = capillary pressure, psi [kPa]
P_{cgo} = drainage gas/oil capillary pressure, psi [kPa]
P_{cwo} = drainage water/oil capillary pressure, psi [kPa]
P_{c2} = reference water/oil capillary pressure at depth D_2, psi [kPa]
P_{c3} = reference gas/oil capillary pressure at depth D_3, psi [kPa]
R_s = solution GOR, scf/RB [std m^3/res m^3]
R_{sw} = solution gas/water ratio, scf/RB [std m^3/res m^3]
S_g = gas saturation, fraction
S_o = oil saturation, fraction
S_w = water saturation, fraction
V_{bp} = volume oil would occupy at initial saturation pressure, res bbl [res m^3]
V_o = oil-phase volume at a given pressure, res bbl [res m^3]
μ_g = gas viscosity, cp [Pa·s]
μ_o = oil viscosity, cp [Pa·s]
μ_w = water viscosity, cp [Pa·s]
ρ_g = gas density at standard conditions, lbm/ft^3 [kg/m^3]
ρ_o = oil density at standard conditions, lbm/ft^3 [kg/m^3]
ρ_w = water density at standard conditions, lbm/ft^3 [kg/m^3]
ϕ = porosity at initial pressure, fraction
ϕ_D = density log apparent porosity, fraction
ϕ_N = neutron log apparent porosity, fraction
ϕ_S = sonic log apparent porosity, fraction

References

1. Staggs, H.M. and Herbeck, E.F.: "Reservoir Simulation Models—An Engineering Overview," *JPT* (Dec. 1971) 1428-36.
2. Stone, H.L.: "Probability Model for Estimating Three-Phase Relative Permeability," *JPT* (Feb. 1970) 214-18; *Trans.*, AIME, **249.**
3. Stone, H.L.: "Estimation of Three-Phase Relative Permeability and Residual Oil Data," *J. Cdn. Pet. Tech.* (Oct.-Dec. 1973) 53-61.

4. Coats, K.H.: "Use and Misuse of Reservoir Simulation Models," *JPT* (Nov. 1969) 1391–98.
5. Keelan, D.K.: "Core Analysis for Aid in Reservoir Description," *JPT* (Nov. 1982) 2483–91.
6. Timur, A.: "Advances in Well Logging," *JPT* (June 1982) 1181–85.
7. Zeito, G.A.: "Interbedding of Shale Breaks and Reservoir Heterogeneities," *JPT* (Oct. 1965) 1223–28; *Trans.*, AIME, **234.**
8. Hutchinson, C.A. Jr., Dodge, C.F., and Polasek, T.L.: "Identification, Classification and Prediction of Reservoir Nonuniformities Affecting Production Operations," *JPT* (March 1961) 223–30.
9. Alpay, O.A.: "A Practical Approach to Defining Reservoir Heterogeneity," *JPT* (July 1972) 841–48.
10. Groult, J., Reiss, L.H., and Montadert, L.: "Reservoir Inhomogeneities Deduced from Outcrop Observations and Production Logging," *JPT* (July 1966) 883–91; *Trans.*, AIME, **237.**
11. Pryor, W.A.: "Reservoir Inhomogeneities of Some Recent Sand Bodies," *SPEJ* (June 1972) 229–45; *Trans.*, AIME, **253.**
12. Harris, D.G.: "The Role of Geology in Reservoir Simulation Studies," *JPT* (May 1975) 625–32.
13. Jardine, D. *et al.*: "Distribution and Continuity of Carbonate Reservoirs," *JPT* (July 1977) 873–85.
14. Hewitt, C.H.: "How Geology Can Help Engineer Your Reservoirs," *Oil & Gas J.* (Nov. 14, 1966) **64,** 171–78.
15. Craig, F.F. Jr. *et al.*: "Optimized Recovery Through Continuing Interdisciplinary Cooperation," *JPT* (July 1977) 755–60.
16. Harris, D.G. and Hewitt, C.H.: "Synergism in Reservoir Management—The Geologic Perspective," *JPT* (July 1977) 761–70.
17. LeBlanc, R.J. Sr.: "Distribution and Continuity of Sandstone Reservoirs—Parts 1 and 2," *JPT* (July 1977) 776–804.
18. Sneider, R.M. *et al.*: "Predicting Reservoir Rock Geometry and Continuity in Pennsylvanian Reservoirs, Elk City Field, Oklahoma," *JPT* (July 1977) 851–66.
19. Reitzel, G.A. and Callow, G.O.: "Pool Description and Performance Analysis Leads to Understanding Golden Spike's Miscible Flood," *JPT* (July 1977) 867–72.
20. Jardine, D. *et al.*: "Distribution and Continuity of Carbonate Reservoirs," *JPT* (July 1977) 873–85.
21. Morgan, J.T., Cordiner, F.S., and Livingston, A.R.: "Tensleep Reservoir Study, Oregon Basin Field, Wyoming—Reservoir Characteristics," *JPT* (July 1977) 886–96.
22. Cordiner, F.S. and Livingston, A.R.: "Tensleep Reservoir Study, Oregon Basin Field, Wyoming—Engineering Plans for Development and Operation, South Dome," *JPT* (July 1977) 897–902.
23. McGee, P.R.: "Use of a Well Model To Determine Permeability Layering From Selective Well Tests," *JPT* (Nov. 1980) 2023–28.
24. Hearn, C.L. *et al.*: "Geological Factors Influencing Reservoir Performance of the Hartzog Draw Field, Wyoming," *JPT* (Aug. 1984) 1335–44.
25. Gaarenstroom, L.: "The Value of 3D Seismic in Field Development," paper SPE 13049 presented at the 1984 SPE Annual Technical Conference and Exhibition, Houston, Sept. 16–19.
26. Ritchie, W.: "The Role of 3D Seismic Technique in Improving Oilfield Economics," paper SPE 13053 presented at the 1984 SPE Annual Technical Conference and Exhibition, Houston, Sept. 16–19.
27. Stiles, J.H. and McKee, J.W.: "Cormorant: Development of a Complex Field," paper SPE 15504 presented at the 1986 SPE Annual Technical Conference and Exhibition, New Orleans, Oct. 5–8.
28. Ausburn, B.E., Ashoke, K., and Wittick, T.R.: "Modern Seismic Methods—An Aid to the Petroleum Engineer," paper SPE 6862 presented at the 1977 SPE Annual Technical Conference and Exhibition, Denver, Oct. 9–12.
29. De Buyl, M., Guidish, T., and Black, P.: "Reservoir Description From Seismic Lithologic Parameter Estimation," paper SPE 15505 presented at the 1986 SPE Annual Technical Conference and Exhibition, New Orleans, Oct. 5–8.
30. Neidell, N.S. and Beard, J.H.: "Progress in Stratigraphic Seismic Exploration and the Definition of Reservoirs," *JPT* (May 1984) 709–26.
31. Cramer, P.W.: "Reservoir Development Using Offset VSP Techniques in the Denver-Julesberg Basin," *JPT* (Feb. 1988) 197–205.
32. Boyer, R.C.: "Geologic Description of East Velma West Block, Sims Sand Unit, for an Enhanced Oil Recovery Project," *JPT* (Aug. 1985) 1420–28.
33. Shirer, J.A., Langston, E.P., and Strong, R.B.: "Application of Field-Wide Conventional Coring in the Jay-Little Escambia Creek Unit," *JPT* (Dec. 1978) 1774–80.
34. Keelan, D.K.: "A Critical Review of Core Analysis Techniques," *J. Cdn. Pet. Tech.* (April–June 1972) **11,** 42–55.
35. Dobrynin, V.M.: "Effect of Overburden Pressure on Some Properties of Sandstone," *SPEJ* (Dec. 1962) 360–66; *Trans.*, AIME, **225.**
36. Mattax, C.C., McKinley, R.M., and Clothier, A.T.: "Core Analysis of Unconsolidated and Friable Sands," *JPT* (Dec. 1975) 1423–32.
37. Savre, W.C.: "Determination of a More Accurate Porosity and Mineral Composition in Complex Lithologies with the Use of the Sonic, Neutron and Density Surveys," *JPT* (Sept. 1963) 945–59.
38. Glanville, C.R.: "Log Interpretations of Gas Sands from Multiple-Porosity and Resistivity Logging Programs," *The Log Analyst* (July–Aug. 1970) 3–11.
39. Hall, J.E.: "The Importance of a Complete Suite of Logs in an Old Reservoir," *JPT* (June 1983) 1178–86.
40. Jageler, A.H.: "Improved Hydrocarbon Reservoir Evaluation Through Use of Borehole-Gravimeter Data," *JPT* (June 1976) 709–18.
41. Law, J.: "Statistical Approach to the Interstitial Heterogeneity of Sand Reservoirs," *Trans.*, AIME (1944) **155,** 202–22.
42. Testerman, J.D.: "A Statistical Reservoir-Zonation Technique," *JPT* (Aug. 1962) 889–93; *Trans.*, AIME, **225.**
43. Bennion, D.W. and Griffiths, J.C.: "A Stochastic Model for Predicting Variations in Reservoir Rock Properties," *SPEJ* (March 1966) 9–16; *Trans.*, AIME, **237.**
44. Craig, F.F. Jr.: *The Reservoir Engineering Aspects of Waterflooding,* Monograph Series, SPE, Richardson, TX (1971) **3.**
45. Waylam, D.A. and McCaleb, J.A.: "Elk Basin Madison Heterogeneity—Its Influence on Performance," *Waterflooding,* Reprint Series 2a, SPE, Richardson, TX (1973) 17–23.
46. McLatchie, A.S., Hemstock, R.A., and Young, J.W.: "Effective Compressibility of Reservoir Rock and its Effects on Permeability," *JPT* (June 1958) 49–51; *Trans.*, AIME, **213.**
47. Rosman, A. and Simon, R.: "Flow Heterogeneity in Reservoir Rocks," *JPT* (Dec. 1976) 1427–28.
48. Huppler, J.D.: "Numerical Investigation of the Effects of Core Heterogeneities on Waterflood Relative Permeabilities," *SPEJ* (Dec. 1970) 381–92; *Trans.*, AIME, **249.**
49. Swanson, B.F.: "A Simple Correlation Between Permeabilities and Mercury Capillary Pressures," *JPT* (Dec. 1981) 2498–2504.
50. Lishman, J.R.: "Core Permeability Anisotropy," *J. Cdn. Pet. Tech.* (April–June 1970) 79–84.
51. Warren, J.E. and Price, H.S.: "Flow in Heterogeneous Porous Media," *SPEJ* (Sept. 1961) 153–69; *Trans.*, AIME, **222.**
52. Matthews, C.S. and Russell, D.G.: *Pressure Buildup and Flow Tests in Wells,* Monograph Series, SPE, Richardson, TX (1967) **1.**
53. Earlougher, R.C. Jr.: *Advances in Well Test Analysis,* Monograph Series, SPE, Richardson, TX (1977) **5.**
54. Willcox, P.J. and Riley, H.G.: "Performance Matching for a North Sea Gas Field," paper SPE 5535 presented at the 1975 SPE Annual Technical Conference and Exhibition, Dallas, Sept. 28–Oct. 1.
55. George, C.J. and Stiles, L.H.: "Improved Techniques for Evaluating Carbonate Waterfloods in West Texas," *JPT* (Nov. 1978) 1547–54.
56. Levorsen, A.I.: *Geology of Petroleum,* second edition, W.H. Freeman Publishing Co., San Francisco (1967) 128–29.
57. Chilingar, G.V. *et al.*: *Oil and Gas Production from Carbonate Rocks,* American Elsevier Publishing Co., New York City (1972) 99.
58. Wadman, D.H., Lamprecht, D.E., and Mrosovsky, I.: "Joint Geologic/Engineering Analysis of the Sadlerochit Reservoir, Prudhoe Bay Field," *JPT* (July 1979) 933–40.
59. Richardson, J.G. *et al.*: "The Effect of Small, Discontinuous Shales on Oil Recovery," *JPT* (Nov. 1978) 1531–37.
60. Weber, K.J.: "Influence of Common Sedimentary Structures on Fluid Flow in Reservoir Models," *JPT* (March 1982) 665–72.
61. Burns, W.A. Jr.: "New Single-Well Test for Determining Vertical Permeability," *JPT* (June 1969) 743–52; *Trans.*, AIME, **246.**
62. Prats, M.: "A Method for Determining the Net Vertical Permeability Near a Well From In-Situ Measurements," *JPT* (May 1970) 637–43; *Trans.*, AIME, **249.**
63. Prats, M.: "The Influence of Oriented Arrays of Thin Impermeable Shale Lenses or of Highly Conductive Natural Fractures on Apparent Permeability Anisotropy," *JPT* (Oct. 1972) 1219–21.
64. Johnson, C.R., Greenborn, R.A., and Woods, E.G.: "Pulse Testing: A New Method for Describing Reservoir Flow Properties Between Wells," *JPT* (Dec. 1966) 1599–1604; *Trans.*, AIME, **237.**
65. Hirasaki, G.J.: "Pulse Tests and Other Early Transient Pressure Analysis for In-Situ Estimation of Vertical Permeability," *SPEJ* (Feb. 1974) 75–90; *Trans.*, AIME, **257.**
66. Kamal, M.M.: "Interference and Pulse Testing—A Review," *JPT* (Dec. 1983) 2257–70.
67. Thu, G.S. *et al.*: "Exploration, Development, and Reservoir Engineering Studies for the Tapis Field, Offshore Peninsular Malaysia," *JPT* (June 1983).
68. Hirasaki, G.J. and O'Dell, P.M.: "Representation of Reservoir Geometry for Numerical Simulation," *SPEJ* (Dec. 1970) 393–404; *Trans.*, AIME, **249.**
69. Killough, J.E.: "Reservoir Simulation with History-Dependent Saturation Functions," *SPEJ* (Feb. 1976) 37–48; *Trans.*, AIME, **261.**
70. Edinger, W.M.: "Interpretation of Core-Analysis Results on Cores Taken with Oil or Oil-Base Muds," *Drill. and Prod. Prac.*, API, New York City (1949) 229–40.

71. Rockwood, S.H., Lair, G.H., and Langford, B.J.: "Reservoir Volumetric Parameters Defined by Capillary Pressure Studies," *JPT* (Sept. 1957) 252-59; *Trans.*, AIME, **210.**
72. Havlena, D.: "Interpretation, Averaging and Use of the Basic Geological-Engineering Data," *Waterflooding*, Reprint Series 2a, SPE, Richardson, TX (1973) 236-47.
73. Brown, H.W.: "Capillary Pressure Investigations," *Trans.*, AIME (1951) **192,** 67-74.
74. Honarpour, M., Koederitz, L.F., and Harvey, A.H.: "Empirical Equations for Estimating Two-Phase Relative Permeability in Consolidated Rock," *JPT* (Dec. 1982) 2905-08.
75. Deans, H.A. and Shallenberger, L.K.: "Single-Well Chemical Tracer Method to Measure Connate Water Saturation," paper SPE 4755 presented at the 1974 Improved Oil Recovery Symposium, Tulsa, April 21-24.
76. Kidwell, C.M. and Guillory, A.J.: "A Recipe for Residual Oil Saturation Determination," *JPT* (Nov. 1980) 1999-2008.
77. Murphy, R.P. and Owens, W.W.: "The Use of Special Coring and Logging Procedures for Defining Reservoir Residual Oil Saturations," *JPT* (July 1973) 841-50; *Trans.*, AIME, **255.**
78. Tomich, J.F. *et al.*: "Single-Well Tracer Method To Measure Residual Oil Saturation," *JPT* (Feb. 1973) 211-18; *Trans.*, AIME, **255.**
79. Murphy, R.P., Foster, G.T., and Owens, W.W.: "Evaluation of Waterflood Residual Oil Saturations Using Log-Inject-Log Procedures," *JPT* (Feb. 1977) 178-86.
80. Hagoort, J.: "Oil Recovery by Gravity Drainage," *SPEJ* (June 1980) 139-50.
81. Weaver, R.H.: "Simulation of Waterflood Behavior in a Reservoir Previously Invaded by Water," *JPT* (Aug. 1972) 909-15.
82. Jacks, H.H., Smith, O.J., and Mattax, C.C.: "The Modeling of a Three-Dimensional Reservoir with a Two-Dimensional Reservoir Simulator—The Use of Dynamic Pseudo Functions," *SPEJ* (June 1973) 175-85.
83. Amyx, J.W., Bass, D.M. Jr., and Whiting, R.L.: *Petroleum Reservoir Engineering*, McGraw-Hill Book Co., New York City (1960).
84. Standing, M.B.: *Volumetric and Phase Behavior of Oil Field Hydrocarbon Systems*, Reinhold Publishing Corp., New York City (1952) 20-73.
85. Vasquez, M. and Beggs, H.D.: "Correlations for Fluid Physical Property Prediction," *JPT* (June 1980) 968-70.
86. Blount, C.W. and Price, L.C.: "Solubility of Methane in Water Under Natural Conditions—A Laboratory Study," report Dept. of Geology, Idaho State U., Pocatello, ID (1982).
87. McCain, W.D. Jr.: *The Properties of Petroleum Fluids*, Petroleum Publishing Co., Tulsa (1973) 82-196.
88. Katz, D.L. *et al.*: *Handbook of Natural Gas Engineering*, McGraw-Hill Book Co., New York City (1959) 69-222.
89. Calhoun, J.C. Jr.: *Fundamentals of Reservoir Engineering*, U. of Oklahoma Press, Norman (1953) 19.
90. Espach, R.H. and Fry, J.: "Variable Characteristics of the Oil in the Tensleep Sandstone Reservoir, Elk Basin Field, Wyoming and Montana," *Trans.*, AIME (1951) **192,** 75-82.
91. McCord, D.R.: "Performance Predictions Incorporating Gravity Drainage and Gas Cap Pressure Maintenance—LL-370 Area, Bolivar Coastal Field," *Trans.*, AIME (1953) **198,** 231-48.
92. Crichlow, H.B.: *Modern Reservoir Engineering—A Simulation Approach*, Prentice-Hall Inc., Englewood Cliffs, NJ (1977) 160-66.

SI Metric Conversion Factors

ft	× 3.048*	E−01	= m
psi	× 6.894 757	E+00	= kPa

*Conversion factor is exact.

Chapter 5
Selecting Grid and Timestep Sizes

Chaps. 3 and 4 discussed factors that are important in the design of a reservoir model and described the procedures used in selecting and processing reservoir data. This chapter and those following discuss considerations and decisions that affect the accuracy, reliability, and cost of the results that can be generated with a model. This chapter examines the process of grid-size and timestep selection. Chap. 6 discusses formulation of the equations and the methods used to solve them. It will be clear that the selection of time and space increments is closely linked to the type of model, the variability of reservoir properties, and the kind of solution technique used.

At the heart of a finite-difference formulation of the reservoir simulation problem is the spatial segmentation of the reservoir model into a pattern of mesh points or gridblocks and the division of the total time interval into some sequence of smaller timesteps. The mathematical representation of fluid flow involves the selection of spatial increments—Δx, Δy, and Δz—and a sequence of time increments, Δt. (See Chap. 2 and Appendix B.)

5.1 Criteria for Selecting Gridblock Size

Gridblock and timestep sizes must be small enough to satisfy five requirements. They must (1) identify saturations and pressures at the specific locations and times required by the study; (2) describe the geometry, geology, and initial physical properties of the reservoir adequately; (3) describe dynamic saturations and pressure profiles in sufficient detail to meet the objectives of the reservoir study; (4) model reservoir fluid mechanics properly; and (5) be compatible with the mathematics in the solution segments of the simulator so that the solutions to the fluid-flow equations are accurate and stable.

The fifth requirement is frequently the most demanding, but the simulator user must first attempt to satisfy Requirements 1 through 4 so that successful simulation will give answers to the right questions.

5.2 Selection of Gridblock Size

To be an effective engineering tool, a reservoir model must simulate future reservoir behavior under one or more production or injection strategies. The aspects of behavior that are most important include well productivity or injectivity, pressure levels and fluid saturations in the vicinity of individual wells, producing GOR's, WOR's, and gas/water ratios, displacement efficiency, and overall recovery efficiency.

5.2.1 Locations Where Pressure and Saturation Levels Must Be Known. The first step in developing a preliminary design of a reservoir model is to identify the locations at which pressure and saturation levels must be known. The spatial locations could include all existing and planned well locations or could be limited to some smaller subset of them. The grid must be sufficiently fine that reservoir behavior at each desired location can be identified. This exercise will define minimum segmentation in space.

Although minimum segmentation identifies locations at which reservoir behavior must be defined, greater segmentation is usually required. To illustrate, Fig. 5.1 compares a minimum grid that might correspond to a reservoir to be developed on a repeated five-spot pattern with an actual areal grid that might be used in a simulation of that reservoir.

5.2.2 Representation of Geometry, Geology, and Physical Properties. The external boundary of the reservoir is the most obvious geometric factor that must be represented. In some cases, the grid system can be oriented so that reservoir boundaries correspond to the edges of the grid. In cases when external boundaries have a more complex shape, areas that fall outside the reservoir can be represented by removing the corresponding blocks from the computations or by assigning them zero permeability and PV.

Another descriptive factor that can exert a major influence on the selection of gridblock sizes is the presence of internal barriers to fluid flow, including shale breaks, reservoir discontinuities, and nonconducting faults. Such barriers are generally included in the model by assigning a zero permeability at the boundary of appropriate interior gridblocks. Gridblock boundaries must be chosen to approximate the location of the barriers to flow. Representation of internal barriers need be made only if the barriers are substantial enough to affect flow behavior seriously. Fig. 5.2 shows a grid system selected to represent reservoir limits and shale barriers. Fig. 5.3[1] illustrates a grid system constructed so that gridblock boundaries with zero permeability represent sealing faults in the reservoir.

Significant changes in permeability and porosity should be represented by a boundary between layers in the model. Highly stratified reservoirs may require extensive grid segmentation in the vertical direction. On the other hand, if there is little vertical variation in properties, vertical segmentation may not be needed solely for descriptive purposes. (It will be shown later that vertical segmentation may still be needed to represent the dynamic behavior of reservoir fluids even within a homogeneous layer.) Usually, 10 to 20 gridblocks in the vertical direction are sufficient to describe the reservoir and to define dynamic fluid behavior. The number of gridblocks needed to represent a zone and the number of zones modeled frequently can be reduced without affecting calculated reservoir performance; it is important to keep this possibility in mind when constructing large models.

Grid definition in a transition zone must be fine enough to describe the saturation distribution, pressure gradients, and displacement efficiency in the zone with the accuracy required by the study. If adequate grid definition is not practical, pseudo-relative-permeability and capillary-pressure relationships should be used.

Variations in initial fluid properties—e.g., oil viscosity, saturation pressure, and solution GOR—sometimes dictate finer grid definition in some regions of the model than is required by other design factors. For example, a viscous or "heavy-oil" zone near a water/oil contact (WOC) or saturation pressures that are functions of depth or areal position must be considered when selecting grid sizes. A grid that inadequately represents such variations vertically or laterally could result in poor prediction of average pressures, pressure gradients, or gas saturations. If there is a significant variation in the composition of gas in a gas cap or a gas field, the appropriate grid definition to represent such a trend is a necessary prerequisite for meaningful gas cycling and blowdown studies.

5.2.3 Representation of Dynamic Saturation and Pressure Behavior. In addition to the reservoir-description factors just discussed, there are several dynamic factors that need to be considered in selecting grid size. For example, a coarsely defined saturation distribution can lead to errors in calculated producing rates and displacement efficiencies. Some of these factors involve

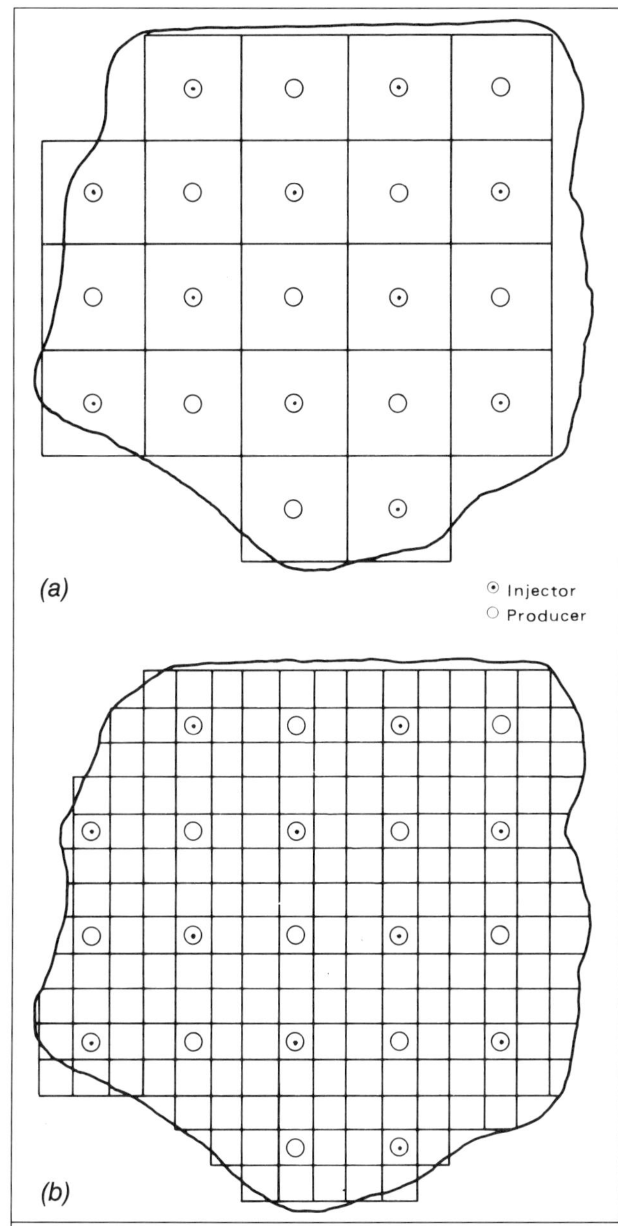

Fig. 5.1—Example of grid systems (a) to identify locations at which performance data are needed and (b) to provide adequate segmentation for simulation.

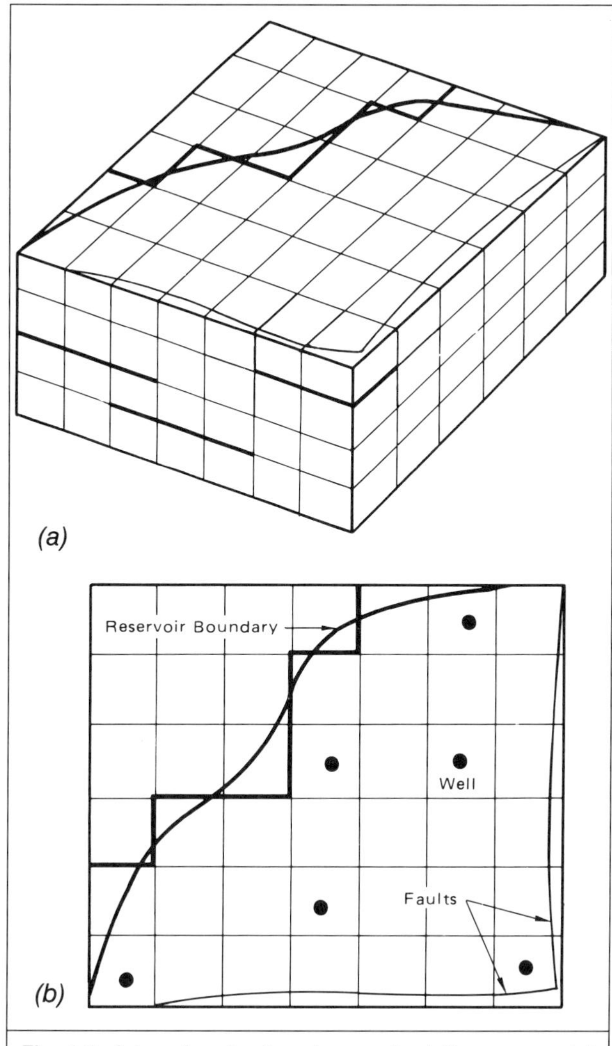

Fig. 5.2—Internal and external geometry influences model design.

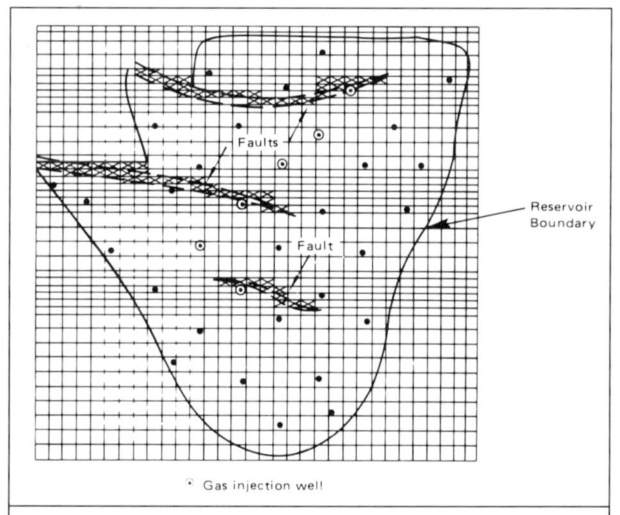

Fig. 5.3—Example of use of zero permeability to model barriers to flow.[1]

areal and vertical resolution, while others, such as numerical dispersion, influence the accuracy of the calculations involved in solving the flow equations. (Mathematical aspects will be discussed later.)

To represent the dynamics of reservoir behavior adequately, a reservoir model must have three capabilities. First, it must be able to describe pressures in the reservoir as a function of time. Accurate calculation of pressures is needed for the prediction of well productivities and, ultimately, for the estimation of total recovery.

Second, if there is more than one mobile phase in the reservoir, the model must be able to describe the locations and movement of the individual fluids. Appropriate vertical segmentation can be important if there is significant vertical movement or segregation of fluids. For example, vertical segmentation is important when modeling a reservoir in which gas override is expected.[2]

Third, the model should be able to represent correctly the injection and production behavior of the wells and their dependence on pressure and saturation in the vicinity of those wells. Frequently, representation of individual wells in areal and three-dimensional (3D) models is not practical. On the other hand, wells can be modeled satisfactorily in a radial model with small grid dimensions near the well. Thus one solution to the problem of representing wells in areal and 3D models is to incorporate in these models results from simulations with more-accurate well models.[3-5]

Each of these capabilities will be discussed in more detail in the following sections.

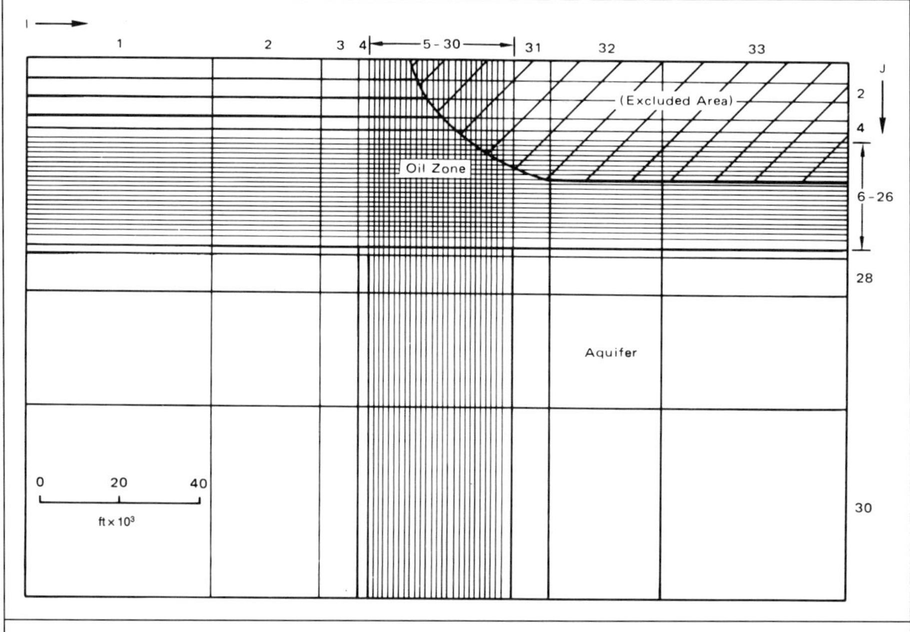

Fig. 5.4—Typical areal grid in which a single-phase region is modeled with large blocks.

5.2.4 Effect of Block Size on Calculated Pressure and Productivity. If a region of a reservoir contains only one mobile phase and if there are no wells in that region, relatively few blocks will be required for adequate representation of pressure in that region. Gridblocks representing an aquifer or a gas cap, for example, often can be many times larger than those used to represent multiphase regions. Fig. 5.4 shows a typical areal grid that uses large blocks in an aquifer. Pressure gradients in the aquifer are adequately modeled. Even if the aquifer represented in Fig. 5.4 contained water-injection wells, it could still be modeled adequately with the grid shown, provided that detailed description of the behavior of individual injectors is not needed. Oil zones containing producing wells are usually modeled with smaller gridblocks, even if oil is the only phase flowing in these zones, because predictions of the behavior of individual producers are almost always desired.

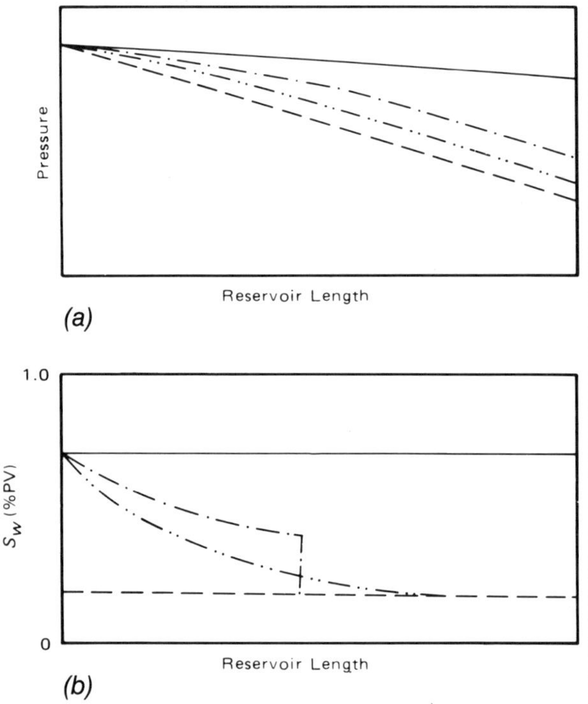

In multiphase regions, pressure representation is more complex. Gridblocks must adequately define saturations because errors in the calculated saturation distribution can result in errors in fluid mobilities that translate directly into errors in calculated pressures. Fig. 5.5 illustrates possible saturation and pressure profiles at various times during a waterflood at a favorable mobility ratio. Clearly, accurate pressure profiles are possible only if saturation profiles are accurate.

Staggs and Herbeck[1] studied the effect of block size on predicted flow rate. They used several two-phase black-oil models of a 5-acre [2-ha] one-quarter five-spot to model a 1 : 1 mobility-ratio waterflood in which a constant bottomhole pressure was maintained at both wells. The only difference between the models was the number of areal gridblocks—3×3, 4×4, 5×5, and 6×6 grids—as shown in Fig. 5.6. Before waterflooding, the reservoir had been produced by solution gas drive and a gas saturation had been established. In each case, the reservoir model took about 1 year to repressure before oil production responded to the waterflood. Results summarized in Fig. 5.6 demonstrate the significant relationship between grid size and calculated performance.

Staggs and Herbeck[1] conclude that at least two blocks should be used between offsetting production and injection wells. Our experience suggests that more than two blocks between offsetting wells are needed for most problems.

Reservoir Length

(a)

Reservoir Length

(b)

Fig. 5.5—Hypothetical pressure and saturation profiles illustrating the need for adequate segmentation. Profiles are shown for initial, final, and two intermediate conditions in the life of a hypothetical reservoir.

5.2.5 Effect of Block Size on Calculated Displacement Efficiency. At this point we will reintroduce the concept of numerical dispersion. The origin of dispersion must be understood if one is to use simulators effectively, because dispersion can have a pronounced impact on the number of blocks required to represent saturation profiles. We will discuss the effects of this phenomenon and the influence that gridblock-size selection can have in controlling the distortion of the saturation profile caused by dispersion. Later in this chapter we will introduce some approaches that sometimes can be used to reduce numerical dispersion without having to resort to very small gridblocks.

Recall from Chap. 2 that a model grid system can be viewed as a number of interconnected, stirred tanks. Also, with the mobility weighting scheme most often used, the proportion of fluids flowing from one tank to another is a function largely of average saturations in the upstream tank. In the second timestep of the waterflood discussed in Chap. 2, some water will flow with the oil into the second "tank" *regardless of the length of the timestep and the size of the gridblock*. Hence, in the example model, some water will move into the producing well block in a number of timesteps equal to the number of gridblocks defining the shortest path between the water-injection and oil-production wells. The model, therefore, cannot simulate reservoir behavior accurately because the saturation distribution early in the waterflood will always be at least slightly in error.

A major consequence of errors in saturation distribution can be a misrepresentation of displacement and sweep efficiencies. Calculated efficiencies can be influenced by grid segmentation both areally and vertically. Areal and vertical effects will be considered separately in the following discussion.

5.2.5.1 Areal Saturation Distribution. In the example linear waterflood described in Chap. 2, breakthrough of water at the producing well occurred too early and, as a result, the calculated displacement efficiency at breakthrough was too low. If this simple model had been used as part of a study of waterflood potential of an actual field, the conclusions from the study would have been unduly pessimistic and might have resulted in a recommendation to install water handling facilities long before they were needed.

Of course, the example model is much simpler than those generally used in actual studies, but it does illustrate the problem. Fig. 5.7 demonstrates the grid-size effect in a more realistic model containing up to 40 gridblocks between wells. These models were used in a study of the Jay-Little Escambia Creek reservoir in Florida and Alabama. In this instance, the Buckley-Leverett analytic solution of the waterflood behavior indicated that, at the time of this comparison, the front should have moved 38% of the distance to the producing well and that the front should be sharp. Fig. 5.7 compares the analytic results with the numerical results obtained by models containing 10, 20, and 40 gridblocks. Note the improvement in the accuracy of the solution as the number of gridblocks increases.

The effect of numerical dispersion is generally to decrease the calculated displacement efficiency at breakthrough. The amount of dispersion varies from model to model but the error tends to be most serious in simulations in which favorable mobility ratios result in sharp saturation fronts and, consequently, in very efficient displacement of oil or gas. Numerical dispersion tends to smear out the sharp front and mask the benefits of favorable mobility.

Fig. 5.8 shows results of another example calculation demonstrating the effect of grid size on recovery efficiency of a displacement in which the mobility ratio is favorable. A waterflood in a 3 : 1 linedrive pattern was modeled with 10, 20, 30, 50, and 200 gridblocks. A 160-acre [65-ha] pattern element is shown in the figure. Calculated recoveries at different water-cut levels for two types of producers are plotted vs. the number of gridblocks. As the number of gridblocks increased, the calculated recovery efficiency increased and the predicted recovery at a given producing water cut increased.

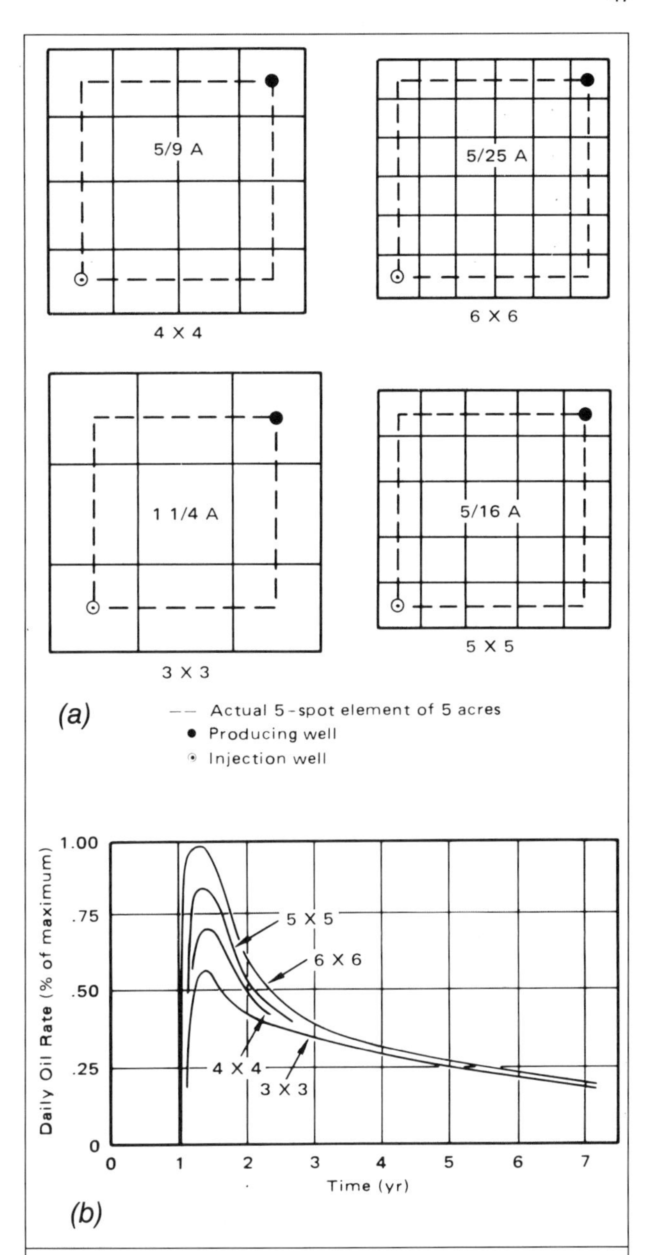

Fig. 5.6—Influence of grid spacing on performance predictions[1]: (a) models used to study the effect of spacing and (b) oil rates predicted by the models.

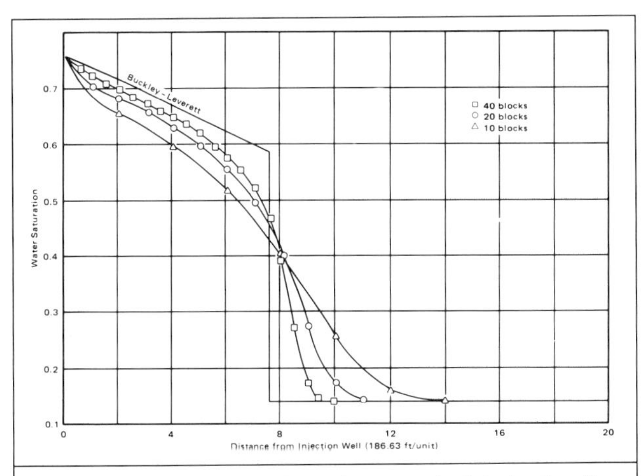

Fig. 5.7—Influence of grid spacing on calculated saturation distribution in a linear model.

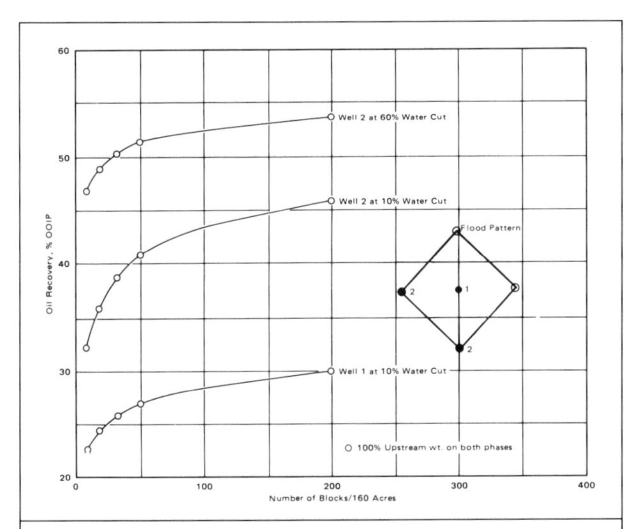

Fig. 5.8—Influence of grid spacing on calculated oil recovery from a linedrive waterflood at a favorable mobility ratio.

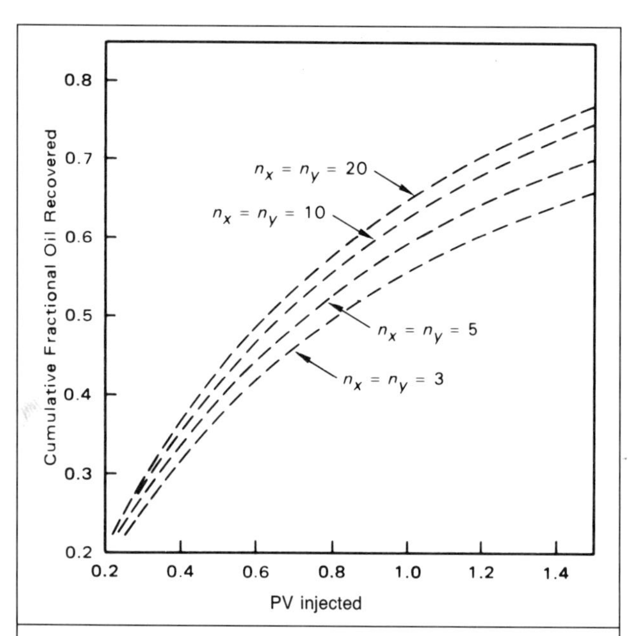

Fig. 5.9—Influence of grid spacing on calculated oil recovery from a five-spot waterflood at an unfavorable mobility ratio.[6]

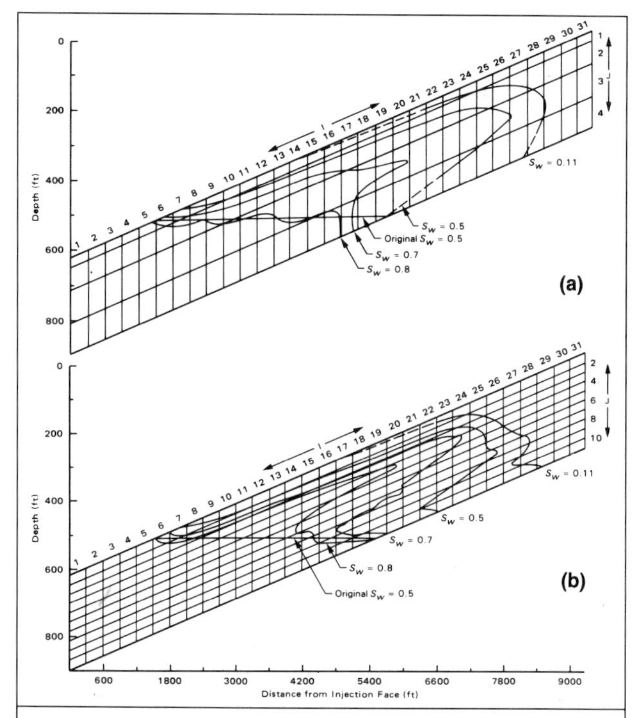

Fig. 5.10—Influence of a vertical grid spacing on cross-sectional model performance. Calculated saturation distributions are for flank waterdrive models having (a) 4 vertical gridblocks and (b) 10 vertical blocks.

In contrast to its underprediction of recovery efficiency, a model with too few gridblocks tends to overpredict areal sweep efficiency because it does not fully account for the impact of fingering or cusping, especially when mobility ratios are unfavorable. The combined effect of errors in recovery efficiency and sweep efficiency was studied by Todd *et al.*,[6] who investigated the effect of grid spacing on recovery in a five-spot waterflood at an unfavorable mobility ratio of 3.0. Results of their work are summarized in Fig. 5.9. The increased areal sweep in models with fewer blocks did not completely offset the reduced displacement efficiency. As a result, predicted recovery was lower in models with fewer blocks.

5.2.5.2 Vertical Saturation Distribution. Insufficient grid segmentation in the vertical direction may also cause errors in calculated displacement efficiency. The errors result primarily from failure of a model with coarse vertical segmentation to model thin fingers or regions of high oil or gas saturation that can form by gravity drainage. Consider, for example, the water/oil displacement represented in Fig. 5.10. The reservoir system is a flank waterdrive with updip oil production. The first 31 gridblocks in the flow direction are shown. Fig. 5.10a shows the saturation profiles some time after the start of production in a grid system with four vertical gridblocks. Fig. 5.10b shows the profiles at the same time in a model with 10 gridblocks in the vertical direction. The displacement efficiencies calculated with these two grid systems and with a third system having 30 vertical layers are compared in Table 5.1.

In models of high-permeability reservoirs, it is especially difficult to represent the correct saturation profile adequately, because at almost any practical depletion rate, gravity drainage will be effective enough to cause a small layer of oil to collect just above the base of a reservoir in a gas-invaded region or just under the top of a reservoir in a water-invaded region. If the gridblocks are not small enough to represent this thin region of high oil saturation, oil mobilities will be incorrectly computed and the calculated rate of oil drainage will be erroneously low. Detailed segmentation is needed to solve this problem correctly. In case the reservoir has a large number of continuous shales, segmentation of each vertical zone must be considered. This would be the case, for example, if gas overrunning is expected in a field and if the gas may overrun both at the top of the reservoir and immediately under a number of major shales.

Fig. 5.11 shows a 3D reservoir grid used by Staggs and Herbeck[1] to represent an oil field that initially contained saturated oil. A continuous impermeable shale separates the field into two thick sand units. The field was first modeled with four vertical layers. The model was expected to show release of solution gas followed by migration of free gas upstructure to form a secondary

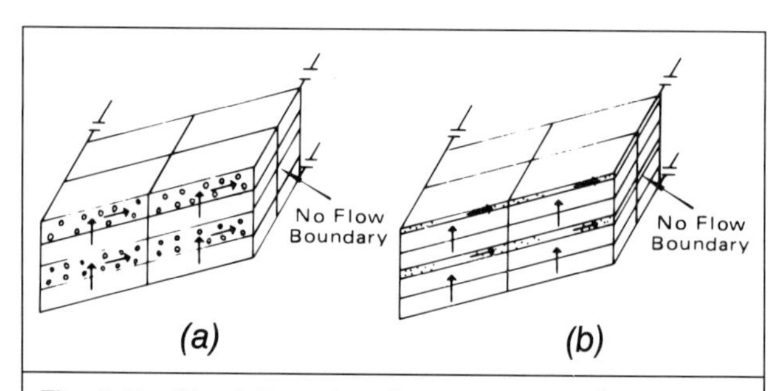

Fig. 5.11—Simulation of updip gas migration[1]: (a) model with inadequate vertical segmentation and (b) model with adequate segmentation provided by addition of a thin layer at the top of each of the two sand units.

TABLE 5.1—EFFECT OF VERTICAL DETAIL ON PREDICTED WATERFLOOD EFFICIENCY

Number of Layers in Model	Displacement Efficiency (% OIP)	Recovery Efficiency (% OIP)
4	52.1	47.2
10	55.1	49.6
30	58.9	52.0

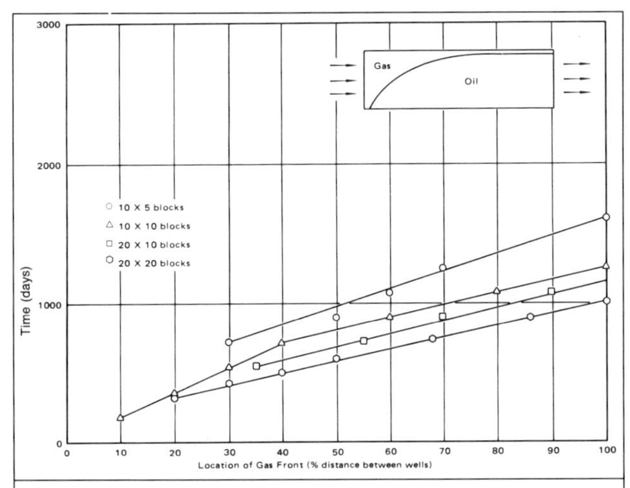

Fig. 5.12—Influence of grid spacing on predicted gas movement in horizontal gas/oil displacement.

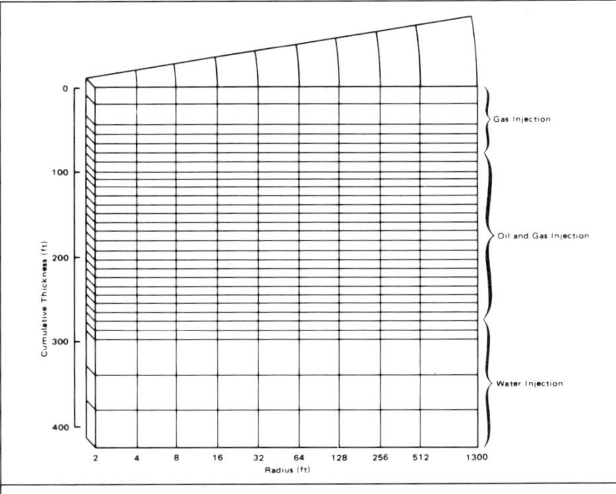

Fig. 5.13—Typical grid system for well models (note geometric scale of horizontal distance).

gas cap. In the simulation, however, gas was released from solution but failed to migrate to the top of the structure. When the model was modified to include a small gridblock representing a thin zone at the top of each unit, gas built up in the thin layer and migrated effectively.

Each sand unit of this example had to be segmented separately because there was no vertical communication between sands. The important point is that when thin fingers of high fluid saturations are likely, increased segmentation may be needed to represent an appropriate fluid distribution.

An alternative to the use of fine vertical gridding in a large model is to use pseudo-relative-permeability curves. The pseudofunctions can be developed from smaller models in which fine gridding is practical. Pseudofunctions are discussed in Chaps. 2 through 4.

We have seen that increased definition can be important in modeling fluid behavior near the top and bottom of reservoirs and under continuous shales when formation of thin fluid layers is likely. This same increase in definition sometimes is needed above and below small discontinuous shale layers. A typical problem was described by Richardson *et al.*,[7] who modeled gravity drainage of oil from the gas-invaded region of a braided-stream deposit containing two discontinuous shale barriers. The gas/oil contact (GOC), initially at the base of the top row of blocks, moved downward with time as gas was introduced into the top of the model. Oil was trapped as a bubble above the shales by the advancing gas. In less than 1 year, the oil bubble had decreased in size until it approached the thickness of the smallest gridblocks. The study clearly demonstrates that in displacements of this type, small blocks are required immediately above the shales and at shale tips to define oil movement accurately.

Fig. 5.12 further illustrates that an insufficient number of gridblocks in either the vertical or horizontal direction can lead to errors in predicted displacement efficiency and vertical sweep efficiency. The figure summarizes results of a cross-sectional model study of the movement of a gas front between a gas-injection well and a production well. It was anticipated that gas would tend to override the oil in a thin layer, as shown in the inset of the figure. The process was modeled with grid systems that were 10 (vertical) $\times$ 5 (horizontal), 10×10, 20×10, and 20×20. Fig. 5.12 is a plot of the location of the leading edge of the gas front as a function of time in models with these grid systems. The predicted rate of gas movement and the calculated vertical sweep efficiency were functions of the number of blocks in the models.

The problem can be especially severe if the gas is miscible with the oil. In that case, the smearing of the gas layer in blocks that are too thick vertically can result in highly optimistic estimates of recovery because essentially all the oil contacted by the gas will be recovered. Likewise, coarse segmentation vertically or horizontally near an injection well can result in overestimation of the portion of the reservoir that will be contacted by the miscible gas.

Experience indicates that 10 to 20 vertical layers are usually sufficient to model either a gasflood or a waterflood. If this degree of segmentation is not possible for the model of an entire field, the use of pseudo-relative-permeability curves should be considered.

5.2.6 Gridblock Sizes in Radial Geometry. The preceding discussion dealt with the grid definition necessary to represent the shape of fluid fronts between wells and its effect on vertical sweep efficiency. Special treatment is needed for the region immediately adjacent to a well. In this region, fluid fronts and contacts can undergo rapid changes in shape. As a consequence, pressure and saturation behavior and vertical sweep efficiency near a well cannot be represented in an areal or 3D model having large gridblocks. This limitation can be overcome by using a separate radial model to represent a single well and its immediate vicinity and then using *well functions* to incorporate results of the single-well model into the larger reservoir model. Well functions are special source-and-sink terms that relate producing oil rates, GOR's, or WOR's to saturations and pressures in the large blocks.[3,4] Well functions are discussed in detail in Chap. 7.

Some simulators couple single-well models with a full-field model by running the two types of models concurrently and transferring results between the two at each timestep.[8] This coupling of models can effectively model individual well behavior but the approach is not practical for models that involve a large number of wells.

Radial models are especially useful for studying coning and other near-wellbore effects. In general, the gridblock sizes in such a model follow a common pattern (see Fig. 5.13). Blocks adjacent to the wellbore are small enough to permit the shape of a cone or other encroachment processes to be mapped accurately. Typically, in the first column, blocks are 1 to 3 ft [0.3 to 1 m] in radial extent; the gridblocks then increase progressively in size outward from the well, by factors of 2 or 3. Ten to 20 columns of blocks normally are used.

Acceptable sizes for the interior blocks of a model designed specifically to study coning can be derived using hand calculations to estimate cone shape and size.[9] If these calculations indicate that coning will not be severe, relatively large gridblocks can be used; in some water/oil models, blocks in the first columns may be as large as 100 ft [30 m] in radius. The vertical gridding in a coning model should be designed so that behavior near perforations can be adequately modeled. The smallest layers should be at and just above the top of the perforations if gas coning is to be studied, or at and just below the bottom of the perforations for water coning. Grid design should also be capable of representing discontinuous shale breaks if any are present in the well, because shale breaks can have a great effect on coning behavior. Between 12 and 20 vertical layers are generally sufficient for a coning model, although some models have included up to 30 or more layers to be sure of adequate segmentation.

5.2.7 Variable Grid Size. Using a model in which grid size is not uniform can be an effective way to ensure adequate grid definition at minimum cost. For example, a saving in computing cost can be realized by using very large blocks in single-phase regions, as dis-

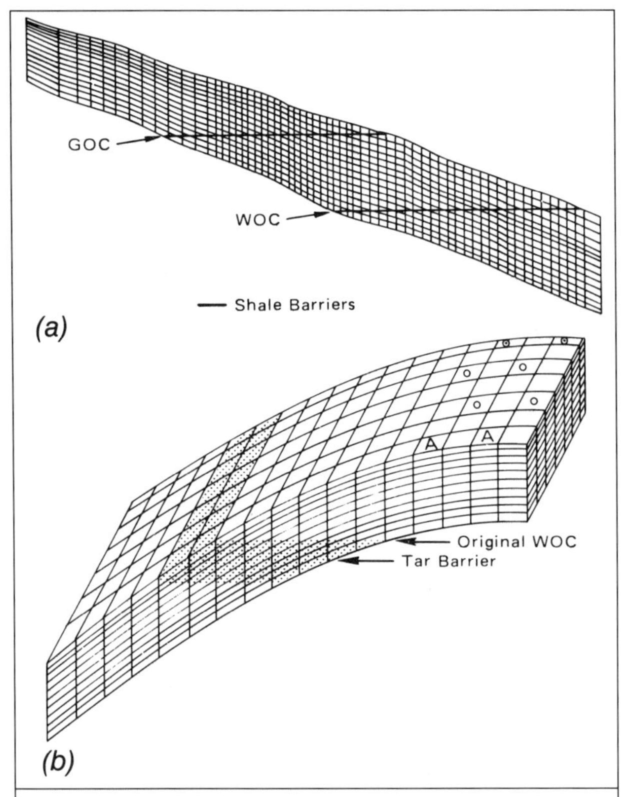

Fig. 5.14—Example grid systems used in reservoir simulation studies: (a) cross-sectional model and (b) 3D model.

cussed earlier. Two notes of caution should be added here. First, the blocks must not be so large that flow response is "instantaneous"—i.e., there must be a sufficient number of blocks to model the transient behavior of the reservoir/aquifer system. Second, extreme contrasts in gridblock dimensions can cause difficulty in solving the flow equations in some simulators.

In addition to the obvious advantage of having large gridblocks when possible, there is also a significant advantage to be gained by varying grid size to obtain increased grid definition in regions of special interest, as for example in near-well regions to model coning and cusping. With a nonuniform grid system, small blocks need not be used in other areas of the field where definition is not so critical.[10]

Most often, refinement of specific areas of the grid still adheres to the "regular" segmentation, in which each block has only one neighboring block on each side. Recently, however, options have been developed that permit blocks to have multiple neighbors on a side.[11] Such "locally refined grids" can be very useful in obtaining refinement in areas of interest without incurring the cost of extra blocks in other areas of the model. This approach changes the form of the matrix equations, however, and the simulator must be specifically designed to handle the added complexity.

5.2.8 Checking Sensitivity to Gridblock Sizes. We have discussed guidelines and considerations that are important in the selection of gridblock sizes. Once a grid system is selected, what can be done to verify that the grid is appropriate for the study? It is essential at this stage of model design to redefine the questions to be answered by the study. Specifically, determine what aspects of fluid movement must be known to develop and to support conclusions of the study and what specific predictions of reservoir behavior are needed.

Having redefined the questions to be answered, the most direct way to verify the adequacy of grid selection is to refine the grid (by a factor of 2, for example) and to determine whether the answers to the questions change significantly. If the model is large, it may be more practical to use this approach in subsets of the large model by constructing smaller models that contain only the regions of most interest. The comparisons to be made normally include saturation and pressure distributions, displacement and recovery efficiencies, and the production and injection performances of wells or regions. Insensitivity to grid definition is almost always a definitive check of the sufficiency of the grid.

As a second check, once the simulation is started, early performance in a small part of the field should be compared with performance calculated by classic (analytic) methods. This approach obviously has limitations, but it often can be useful in evaluating whether performance of the model is realistic.

5.3 Example Grids

Although the problem of gridblock-size selection is complex and is influenced by specific reservoir properties and by the specific questions to be answered in a study, it is possible to identify some guidelines that can usually be applied.

1. In general, 10 to 20 vertical gridblocks are sufficient for a cross-sectional model. The number of gridblocks in the flow direction depends on the number of wells to be modeled and on horizontal variations in properties, but usually 20 to 80 blocks are sufficient.

2. Typically, areal models should have 30 to 100 gridblocks in each direction. Grid dimensions in the two directions tend to be similar. There usually are few computational problems when an areal model is run, and the number of gridblocks can be large relative to other types of models.

3. Radial models usually have 10 to 30 vertical gridblocks and 10 to 20 horizontal gridblocks. The total number of gridblocks usually is much smaller than in other models, and the sensitivity runs that are almost always necessary with these models can be made relatively cheaply.

4. 3D models must have a larger number of gridblocks than one- and two-dimensional (2D) models and usually are the most expensive models to use. The areal dimensions of a 3D grid necessarily are similar to those of an areal grid. It may be necessary to compromise vertical segmentation to control the total number of blocks in the model. Typically, the number of vertical blocks in a model of an entire field is restricted to from three to seven. Substantially more vertical definition is practical in a 3D model of only a portion of a field. Note also that the size of a model can be highly dependent on the type of computer used in the simulation. Simulators written to use vector computers can often handle very large 3D models cost-effectively. In some cases, the number of blocks in the vertical direction has been 10 to 15 in a model containing a total of 50,000 gridblocks.

Figs. 5.4, 5.13, and 5.14 are drawings of grids used in typical studies.

5.4 Selection of Timesteps

We have seen that compromise is usually necessary when gridblock sizes are selected for a reservoir model. Compromise is also necessary when a sequence of time increments to use in the simulation is selected. Too large a timestep will reduce the quality of answers, while too small a timestep will increase computer time, calendar time, and cost.

5.4.1 Timing of Simulator Input and Output. During the major portion of a reservoir simulation, flow profiles and flow directions will have been established, relatively large timesteps of equal length can be used, and the simulation will proceed smoothly. During this period, timestep size may be limited only by the frequency of output desired, timing of changes to the input data, or action required by reservoir-management considerations. For example, a typical length for timesteps in history matching might be 1 to 3 months to coincide with monthly recording of well rate changes. At other times in the simulation, the timesteps must be restricted in size so that changes in some preselected parameter can be limited to fall within a preset range or tolerance.

5.4.2 Consequences of Unrestricted Timestep Sizes. The three most common consequences of using a timestep that is too large are that (1) calculated mobilities are incorrect because mobilities change so much during a timestep that use of a single value for a phase mobility is inappropriate; (2) numerical dispersion is unacceptably large; and (3) some reservoir property—usually pressure—changes so much during a single timestep that the physics of the system cannot be described adequately.

If the mobilities are not calculated correctly, then, of course, individual fluid flow rates between gridblocks will be in error and fluid saturation profiles will be distorted. In other words, the solutions to the flow equations will be incorrect. If a fully implicit formulation is being used, there may be no indication of error because the solutions can be erroneous and yet be stable.

Reservoir fluid mechanics will not be modeled properly if some property changes so much during a timestep that changes in the physics of the system are not recognized. For example, saturated oil in a gridblock in which pressure is falling rapidly should liberate a large volume of gas that should then become mobile and either percolate toward the top of the system or flow toward a production well. If the timestep is too large, however, the onset of gas evolution will not be recognized, gas will not be mobile during the timestep, and an unrealistic gas saturation will be calculated by the simulator.

5.4.3 Automatic Timestep Selection. Most simulators have the capability to set timesteps automatically by calculating the values of preselected parameters and adjusting timesteps until changes in the parameters meet specified tolerance criteria. The parameters and their tolerances vary from simulator to simulator and may be either set automatically or selected by the user. In either case, after the simulator takes a timestep, it usually tests against tolerances. If these are not met, the calculations made with the timestep are discarded and a smaller timestep is selected. Some of the most commonly used parameters and tolerances are the following.

1. *Pressure change.* The magnitude of an acceptable pressure change will depend on the problem being solved, of course. If, at a particular time, free gas is present or expected, the tolerance will be a few pounds per square inch. On the other hand, in simulations of some processes, such as a waterflood at pressures above the bubblepoint, tolerances of up to 100 psi [700 kPa] are acceptable.

2. *Saturation change.* This is a frequently applied criterion. The size of an acceptable saturation change will depend on the formulation of the equations solved, the simulator being used, and the technique used to estimate saturation functions. Common values for acceptable saturation change range from 5 to 10% PV. With fully implicit formulations, larger changes can sometimes be tolerated.

3. *Transmissibility coefficient.* This is essentially a modification of the saturation-change criterion except that tolerances are put directly on the coefficients used in the flow equations.

4. *Material-balance error.* This criterion is not always applicable (see Chap. 6) and may be difficult to use effectively. In general, a "large" error in material balance indicates that the solution to the equations is in error ("large" may be difficult to define here).

5. *Time truncation error.* Controlling timestep size to keep time truncation errors within desired tolerances[12,13] is useful in problems in which nonlinearities in pressure or saturation functions are especially strong.

5.4.4 Selection of Timesteps To Start the Simulation. At very early times in a simulation, or any time there is a significant change in the operation being modeled, there usually are large and rapid changes in flow magnitude. At these times, timesteps must be shortened to allow the model to adjust to the change.

The first such event is startup of simulation. At startup, the model usually either will be at equilibrium with no established flow potentials or will have specified pressures and saturations at certain locations in the reservoir. In the first instance, corresponding to discovery conditions, small timesteps must be taken until potential gradients and flow directions are established. Initial timesteps of 5 to 10 days are usually small enough to begin the simulation. If fluid production per timestep is small vs. the volume of gridblocks that contain wells, initial timesteps of 15 days or more might be acceptable.

In the second instance, corresponding to a time after the reservoir has been placed on production, not all potential gradients will be specified correctly and small timesteps must be taken until flow potentials can properly readjust.

In either instance, once an initial timestep is successfully taken, subsequent steps can be sequentially larger, leading eventually to the basic timesteps discussed earlier. A typical sequence of steps involves doubling the timestep size for each step until the maximum size is achieved.

Another event that may require a reduction in timestep size is a change in production or injection rates. When a well is producing or injecting at a relatively constant rate, a pressure profile is established in the vicinity of that well. If a large rate change occurs, the profile will change drastically and there will be large changes in the magnitude, and possibly in the direction, of fluid movement. Small timesteps may be required here for the reasons previously discussed. In the most drastic instances—e.g., when producers are converted to injectors—timesteps may have to be reduced to less than 0.01 day immediately after the rate change.

5.4.5 Comparison of Timesteps Used in Explicit and Implicit Formulations. Recall from Chap. 2 that flow parameters that are functions of pressure and saturation may be treated explicitly, implicitly, or semi-implicitly. (For a detailed discussion, see Chap. 6, Appendix B, and Refs. 14 through 18.) Explicit treatment, in which the parameters are assumed to maintain the same value during a timestep that they had at the beginning of the timestep, is often the least satisfactory, especially if a timestep is large. If the saturations and pressures are not changing rapidly, however, as in some areal models with large gridblocks, an explicit treatment can be acceptable and timesteps of reasonable length can be used without introducing large errors in calculated flow rates. When they are applicable, explicit techniques are more economical than other methods. In many simulations, and particularly in simulation of coning, release of gas from solution, and percolation of gas, the use of implicit or semi-implicit techniques is a practical necessity. Otherwise, unacceptably small timesteps will be required to prevent pressure or saturation oscillations and to achieve convergence of the solution.[19-21]

5.4.6 Verifying Acceptability of Timestep Sizes. Regardless of the formulation used and the criteria applied to select timesteps, it is desirable to test whether the resultant sequence of timesteps will produce a sufficiently accurate simulation. As in the case of gridblock size, the best way to answer this question is to perform sensitivity runs. A portion of the reservoir should be simulated first with the selected sequence of timesteps and then with smaller timesteps (smaller by a factor of 2 to 3). If no significant difference in behavior is observed, the selected sequence of timesteps may be used with confidence.

5.5 Limiting Numerical Dispersion

At the beginning of this chapter, we introduced the requirements to be satisfied when gridblock and timestep sizes are selected. The fifth requirement is compatibility with the mathematics of the simulator so that the solution is sufficiently accurate. We have discussed how numerical dispersion can introduce distortions in the computed saturation profiles. We have also seen that one effective way to limit the effect of numerical dispersion is to increase the number of gridblocks in the principal direction(s) of fluid flow. In large studies, however, the total number of blocks in a model usually will be limited by cost and other practical considerations.

The conflict between the desire for large numbers of blocks to limit numerical dispersion and the need for small numbers of blocks to limit computer costs is difficult to resolve. We mentioned earlier that a certain minimum number of blocks is needed to define a saturation and pressure profile. Yet some reservoirs are drilled with such small spacing that inserting even one block between adjacent producing wells is not practical. Indeed, some reservoirs, particularly older, shallow fields, may have such close well spacing that they must be modeled with several producing wells occupying the same gridblock. Of course, accurate mapping of saturation and pressure between injectors and producers is not possible under this circumstance because resolution is too low, numerical dispersion is too high, or both. Two intermediate blocks between an injector and a producer may be regarded as a lower limit of resolution for rational mapping of the areal distribution of saturation, and at this limit, numerical dispersion may be unacceptably large.

Several modifications to standard reservoir modeling procedures and formulations have been proposed to reduce the effect of nu-

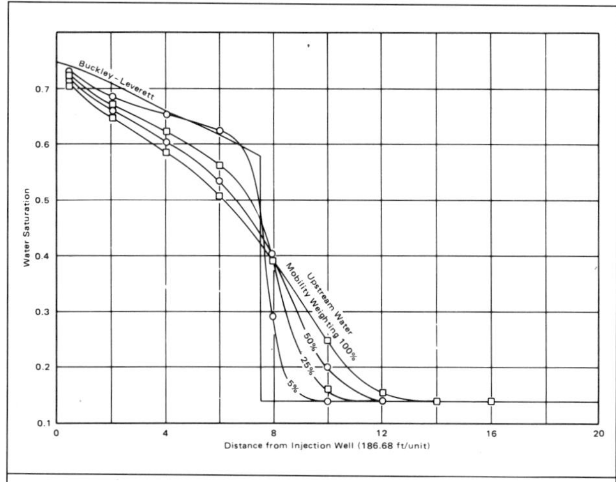

Fig. 5.15—Influence of mobility weighting on simulation accuracy.

merical dispersion without vastly increasing the size of the model. None of these modifications is entirely satisfactory but a few are useful. The modifications involve either (1) use of mobility weighting techniques, (2) extension of the pseudofunction approach, (3) calculation of frontal velocities, or (4) use of alternative solution methods.

5.5.1 Mobility Weighting. The technique that appears to be most useful is the *two-point, upstream mobility weighting scheme* described by Todd *et al.*[6] In this approach, the relative permeability for flow across the boundary between two gridblocks is calculated by extrapolating the relative permeabilities of the two upstream blocks to a point on the boundary.

This technique reduces numerical dispersion and is widely used. Be cautioned, however, that for some combinations of saturations in the two upstream blocks, unrealistic (negative or very large) values of relative permeability can result from the extrapolation. Realistic bounds must be placed on the acceptable range of values.[6] Another limitation of this approach is the implicit assumption that the two "upstream" grid locations lie on a flow streamline and, hence, that saturations can be extrapolated with the values in those two blocks. If the flow streamlines are complex, this assumption will not be valid and the approach may lead to unrealistic relative permeabilities.

Advance of the displacing phase can be reduced by using a *partial downstream weighting method* in which the mobility is calculated from a combination of the mobilities of the upstream and downstream blocks. The calculation involves interpolation to boundaries between gridblocks, or the fraction of downstream weighting can be selected arbitrarily. For example, 75% downstream weighting would reflect an arbitrary choice of an average of 75% of the mobility of fluid in the downstream block and 25% of the mobility in the upstream block.

The effect of various weighting ratios on the saturation profile for a 10-gridblock linear waterflood model is illustrated in Fig. 5.15. As the fraction of downstream weighting increases, the sharpness of the displacement front increases and the saturation profile gets closer to the theoretically correct Buckley-Leverett profile. At some ratio of downstream to upstream weighting, the calculated frontal saturation will overshoot the Buckley-Leverett profile.

Clearly, partial downstream weighting can reduce numerical dispersion. However, it has serious drawbacks. First, the optimal percentage of downstream weighting to apply will depend on the characteristics of the particular reservoir/fluid system. Second, reducing the mobility of the displacing phase introduces errors in the pressure profile even when the saturation profile is a close match of the Buckley-Leverett profile. Rather than use arbitrary weighting of upstream and downstream mobilities, it is probably better to use the Todd extrapolation method.

Combined weighting techniques are modifications of the partial downstream weighting approach that attempt to eliminate distortion of the pressure profile. One approach is to calculate total mobility between gridblocks with upstream weighting and to calculate the ratio of mobilities with some downstream component. This procedure combines the benefits of upstream and partial downstream weighting. This technique should be used with care because it can result in oscillations in the solution.

5.5.2 Pseudofunctions. Relative-permeability curves used in areal models can be modified to restrict the movement of the displacing phase until the saturation of that phase reaches a level determined from simulations in finely gridded cross-sectional models. The effect is to sharpen the saturation front and to make linear flow through a single block behave like flow through several blocks arranged in series. This technique is an extension of the "pseudofunction" approach discussed in Chaps. 2 through 4. Kyte and Berry[22] discuss the modified relative-permeability curves in detail. They present an example simulation in which, with the modified pseudofunction shown in Fig. 5.16a, a 20,000-gridblock areal model was reduced to a 2,000-gridblock model without a significant increase in dis-

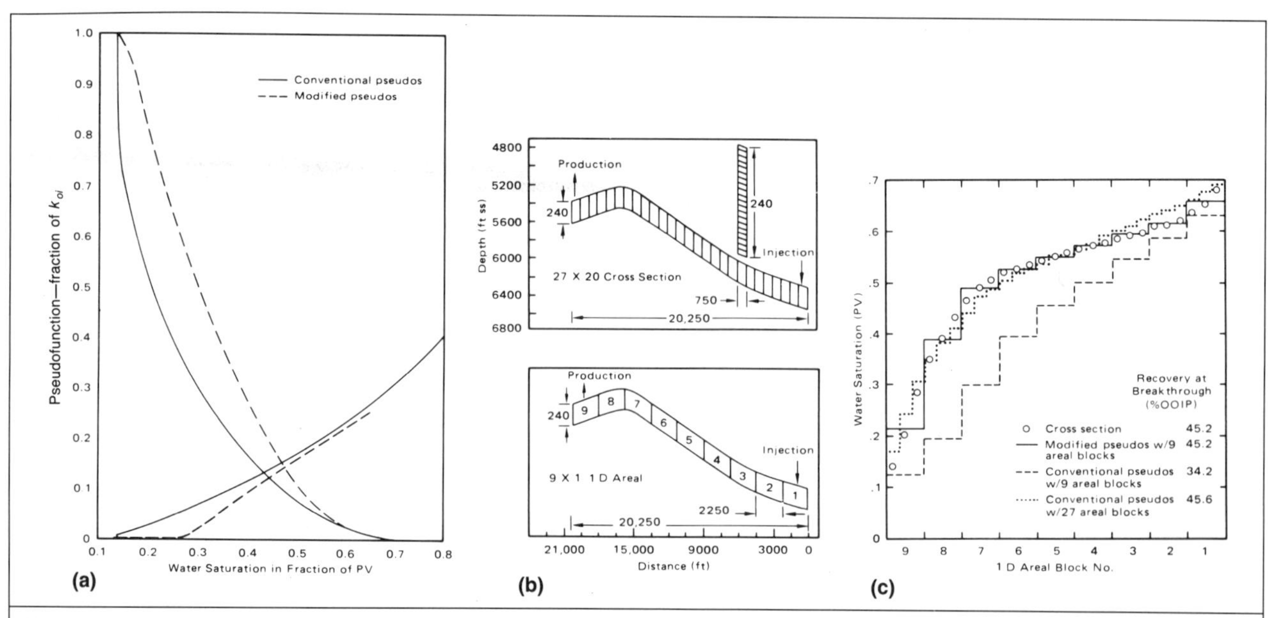

Fig. 5.16—Example of use of modified pseudo-relative-permeability functions to reduce numerical dispersion (after Ref. 22): (a) modified and conventional pseudofunctions, (b) cross-sectional and 1D models used to evaluate the procedure, and (c) comparison of results using conventional and modified pseudofunctions.

TABLE 5.2—GRID SIZES USED IN MODELS TO STUDY GRID-ORIENTATION EFFECT

Parallel		Diagonal	
Grid Size*	Number of Gridblocks	Grid Size*	Number of Gridblocks
0.202	8×8	0.2	6×6
0.101	15×15	0.1	11×11
0.050	29×29	0.05	21×21

*Grid size is expressed as a fraction of the distance along the edge of the five-spot pattern between the injection and production wells.

persion. The example was a 2D areal reservoir model of a reservoir under waterflood. Both conventional and modified pseudocurves were constructed in an attempt to make the water/oil flow behavior of a nine-gridblock linear model match the behavior of a 27×20-gridblock cross-sectional model. The models are shown in Fig. 5.16b. Fig. 5.16c compares the water saturation profiles developed in the 20×27 cross-sectional model, a 27-gridblock linear model with conventional pseudocurves, and the nine-gridblock model with and without the modified pseudocurves. In this instance, the nine-gridblock model with modified pseudos performed as well as the 27-gridblock model with conventional pseudos.

5.5.3 Calculation of Frontal Velocities. A proposed alternative approach to limit numerical dispersion is a method called "variably timed flux updating."[23,24] In this method, the fluxes are not updated every timestep. Instead, the number of timesteps required for a fixed concentration to travel across a gridblock is estimated and the flux is updated at a corresponding frequency. The approach works best in one dimension, but has been extended to multiple dimensions.

5.5.4 Alternative Solution Methods. Galerkin techniques discussed in Ref. 25 seem to have some potential as a way to minimize numerical dispersion. These techniques involve finite-element rather than finite-difference formulations of the flow equations. To date, Galerkin techniques have met with only limited success.

Results obtained with any of the above techniques should be compared in at least one run with results using a finely gridded model and upstream weighting.

5.6 Grid Orientation

The geometry of the reservoir system frequently is the major factor determining the orientation of the model grid. Three other factors need to be considered, however, when orienting the grid.

1. Permeability anisotropy should be preserved.
2. Deviation of the grid system from orthogonality should be minimized.
3. The influence of solution errors resulting from "the grid orientation" effect should be minimized.

5.6.1 Permeability Anisotropy. If reservoir permeability is substantially higher or lower than average in any one direction, the grid axes must be aligned with the axes of the directional permeability. Otherwise, it will not be possible to construct a grid system that will model the anisotropy in permeability correctly.

5.6.2 Orthogonality of the Grid System. The equations used in reservoir simulators are derived for orthogonal grid systems. That is, each column of blocks is at right angles to each row of blocks. If the gridblocks are not orthogonal, as in Fig. 5.14a and b, the equations are not strictly applicable and the answers generated by a simulator may not be accurate. Sometimes, however, as in the 3D model shown in Fig. 5.14b, the physical boundaries of the reservoir and the shape of the bedding planes do not lend themselves to an orthogonal grid. In such cases, if the curvature is slight, a nonorthogonal grid can be used and the results will be acceptable. Grid systems, however, should not be designed with angles between adjacent gridblock boundaries of more than a few degrees.

For reservoirs for which the orthogonal, cartesian grid is not appropriate, a curvilinear grid should be considered.[26-29] Flow equations for a curvilinear grid are similar to those for an orthogonal grid except that PV and transmissibility terms are multiplied by a factor related to the shape of the grid.

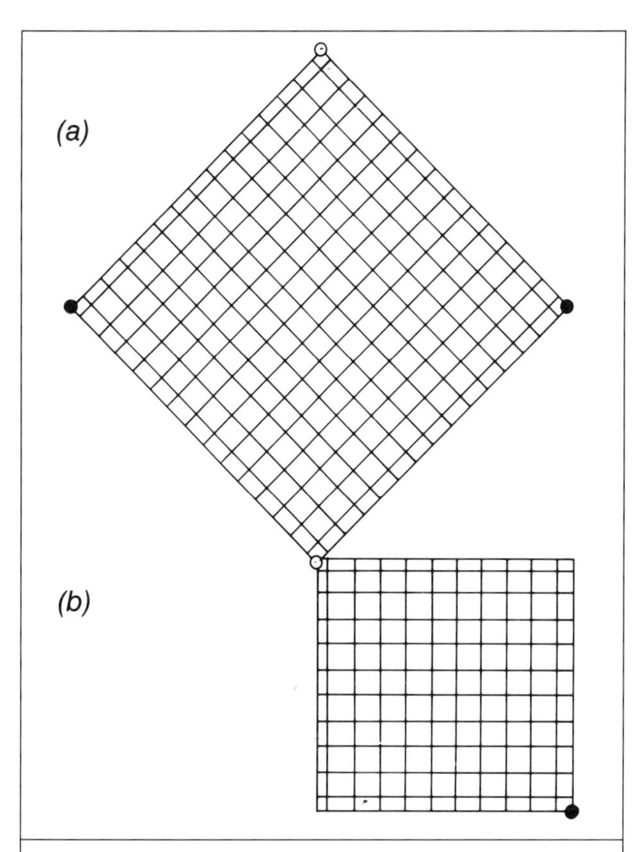

Fig. 5.17—Example of (a) parallel and (b) diagonal grid orientations.

5.6.3 The Grid Orientation Effect. Even for an orthogonal reservoir grid that models an isotropic reservoir, there can still be an effect of grid orientation on calculated results. This effect was discussed qualitatively in Chap. 2. To discuss the effect more quantitatively, we will examine the results of simulations of one-quarter of a five-spot waterflood pattern using the models illustrated in Fig. 5.17. Waterfloods at water/oil mobility ratios of 1.0 and 10.0 were simulated in both the parallel and the diagonal grid systems for the grid sizes in Table 5.2.

Results of simulation of the unit mobility ratio flood are summarized in Fig. 5.18a and b for the diagonal and parallel grids, respectively. Performance of the diagonal-grid model is not sensitive to the number of gridblocks in the model. Oil recovery predicted by the parallel-grid model, on the other hand, increased significantly as the number of gridblocks increased, but was below that predicted by the diagonal model at all grid spacings.

For simulations of displacements at mobility ratios that are favorable, neutral, or slightly unfavorable, the grid-orientation effect can be reduced by refining the grid. Diagonal orientation is less likely to introduce distortion caused by grid orientation than is parallel orientation.

The grid-orientation effect is more pronounced for unfavorable mobility ratios, as indicated by results of the 10 : 1 unfavorable mobility ratio waterflood (see Fig. 5.19). In this case, as the grids are refined, performance of parallel and diagonal models actually diverges. Also summarized in this figure by a dotted line is a recovery curve predicted for this flood by Yanosik and McCracken,[30] who used a nine-point finite-difference formulation of the flow equations. The nine-point formulation allows flow between a gridblock and all eight surrounding blocks, including those diagonally adjacent, as symbolically illustrated in Fig. 5.20. In simulations with the nine-point formulation, the performances of diagonal and parallel models tend to converge as the spacing is refined.

5.6.4 Approaches to Reduce Grid-Orientation Effect. In general, neither parallel nor diagonal orientation can be used reliably

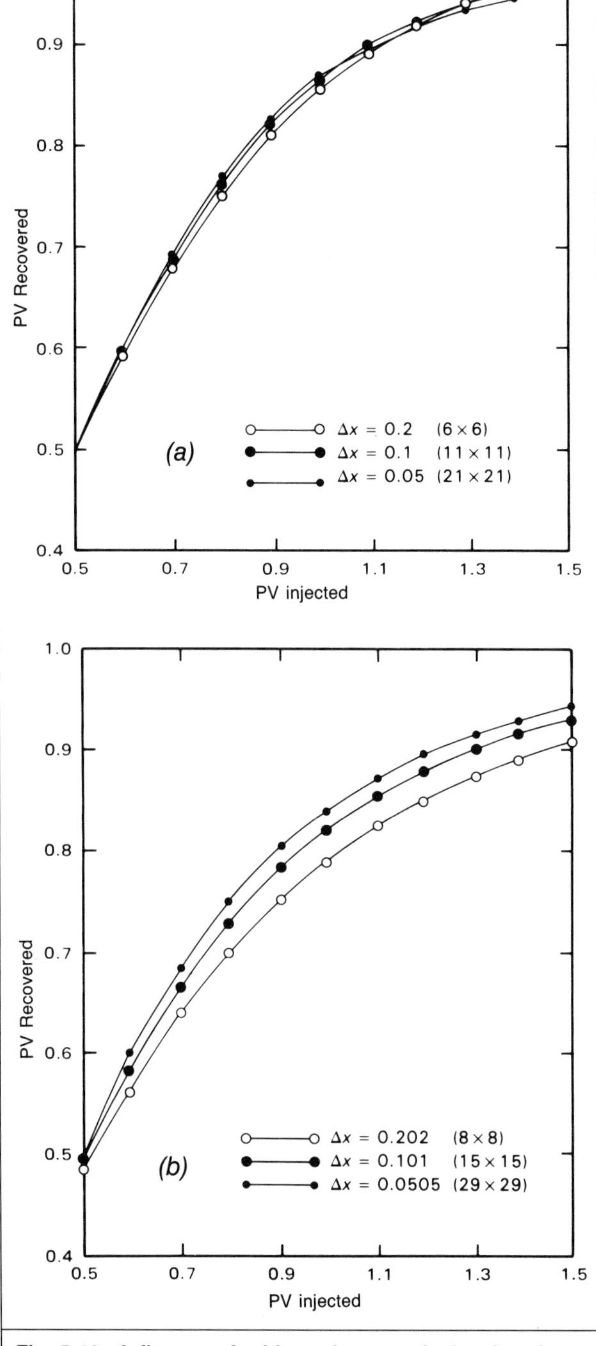

Fig. 5.18—Influence of grid spacing on calculated performance of unit mobility ratio displacements: (a) diagonal grid and (b) parallel grid.

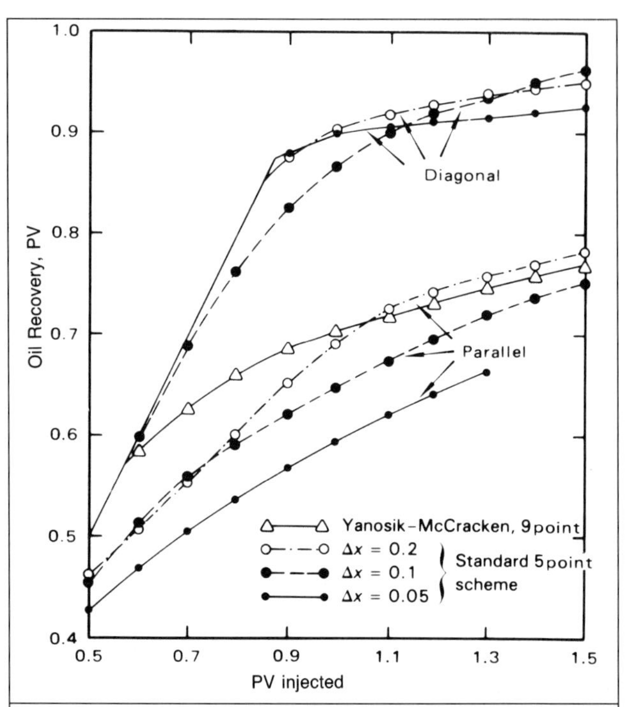

Fig. 5.19—Influence of grid spacing and equation formulation on calculated performance of unfavorable mobility ratio displacements (after Ref. 30).

for displacements at highly adverse mobility ratios. Possible alternative methods include nine-point formulations[30-32] and the application of two-point upstream mobilities.[6] The use of a curvilinear grid system designed so that gridblock boundaries follow the flow path[26-29] can be useful in special circumstances. More promising general solutions may result from research on the use of triangular grid systems[33] and various finite-element methods.[25,34]

The nine-point formulation is possibly the most reliable current solution to the grid-orientation problem. The increased reliability is obtained for a cost, however. The nine-point formulation couples diagonal as well as parallel blocks and, therefore, increases the work required to solve the flow equations. Most simulators do not have the option of selecting this approach.

The standard five-point formulation can be used to generate acceptable results by initializing the model with injection fluid in a circle surrounding the injection well, as shown in Fig. 5.21a. In this example, an initial radius of 20% of the distance from injector to producer and a saturation corresponding to residual oil behind the front were used. For more precision, a theoretical radial distribution of saturations could be used as input. Results of this approach for a 10 : 1 unfavorable mobility ratio flood in the one-quarter five-spot model discussed above are shown in Fig. 5.21b. As the grid is refined, recovery tends to approach that predicted with the nine-point formulation. The parallel model appears to be somewhat more reliable than the diagonal model.

Todd *et al.*[6] have shown that application of the two-point upstream method for calculating mobilities can reduce (but not eliminate) the discrepancy in performance of parallel and diagonal grid models. This approach has been found useful by several organizations and is incorporated into some reservoir simulators as a user-selected option.

The use of curvilinear grids requires definition of boundaries that are parallel to the expected flow paths in the model. If boundaries can be defined correctly, all flow would then be parallel to block boundaries and there would be no orientation effect. Flow paths are difficult to determine, however, and usually will vary with time in simulations of complex problems.

The use of triangular grids is a promising approach but is essentially untested. The advantage of this type of grid, illustrated in Fig. 5.22, is that grid boundaries are not aligned primarily in one direction and flow can progress equally easily in several different directions. The result is that the differences between diagonal and parallel orientation are reduced. Watts and Silliman[33] showed that most simulations could be adapted to this approach with minor modification. Finite-element approaches also seem to be somewhat effective in reducing the grid-orientation effect, but these methods tend to be inefficient.

5.7 Cost Considerations

One of the objectives of the activities discussed in this chapter, Chaps. 3 and 4, and to some extent, Chap. 6 is the development of a reservoir model that is optimal in size and complexity—large enough and complex enough to be adequate for its intended use, but otherwise as simple as possible. If that objective has been kept in mind when constructing the model, most of the major factors influencing the cost of testing and using the model will have been

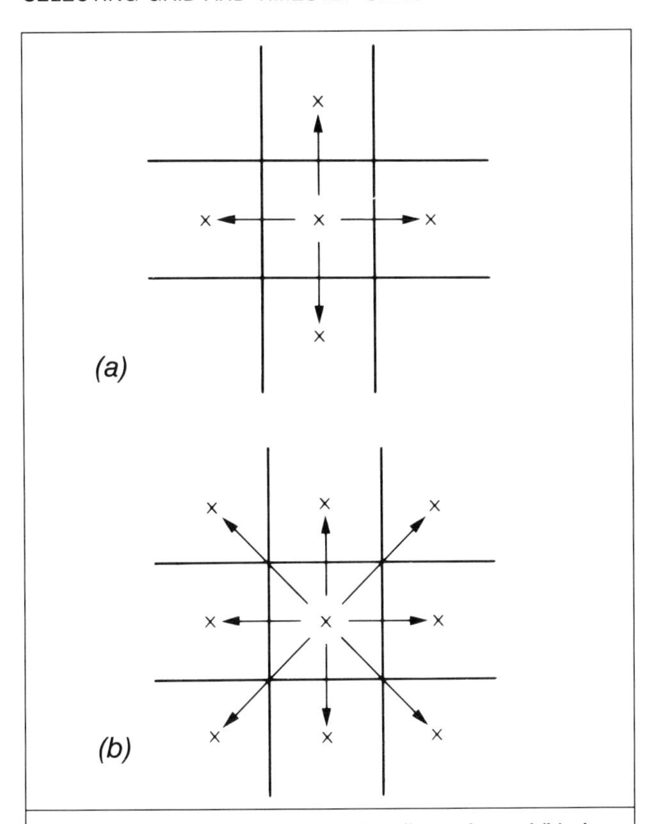

Fig. 5.20—Symbolic illustration of (a) five-point and (b) nine-point formulations of flow equations.

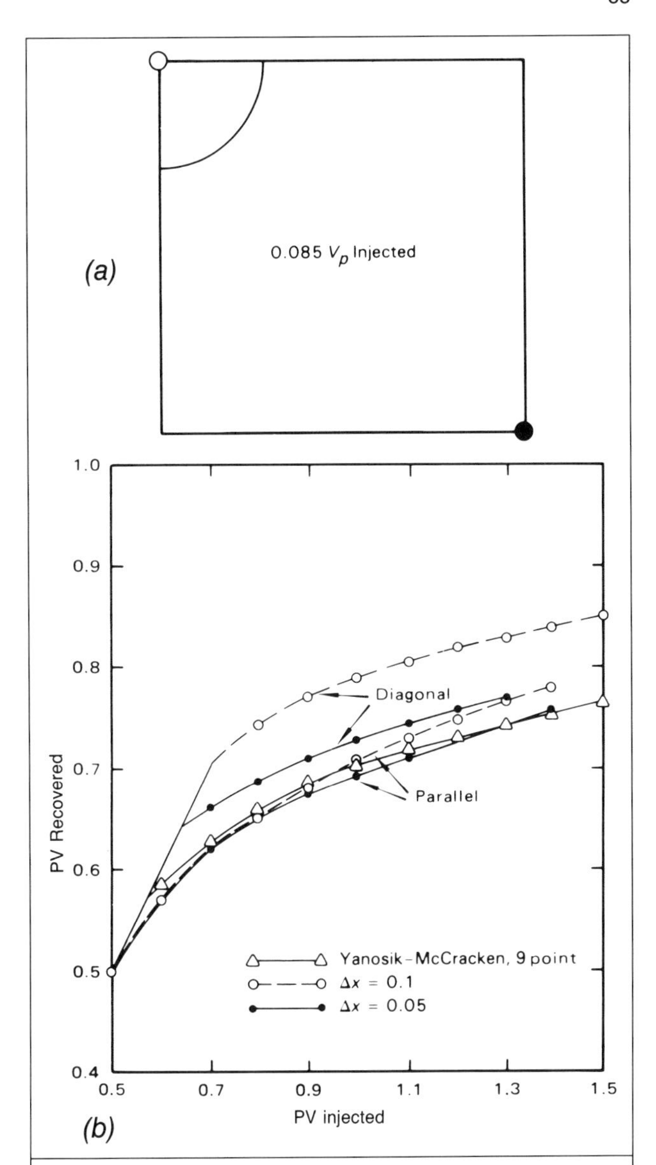

Fig. 5.21—Use of initial high displacing-phase saturation near the wellbore to reduce grid orientation (after Ref. 30): (a) typical initial conditions and (b) calculated performance of unfavorable mobility ratio displacement (compare with Fig. 5.19).

dealt with, although perhaps indeliberately, while it was being designed and built. In regard to model design and cost, a few general remarks that do not appear elsewhere in this monograph may be useful.

1. Experience indicates that computing costs currently account for 20 to 50% of the total cost of most reservoir simulation studies; manpower accounts for most of the rest of the cost. We appear to be in a major transition period, however, with respect to computing hardware. As a consequence, the balance between manpower and computing costs undoubtedly will change dramatically in the next decade. Even now, the balance is influenced strongly by the type of computing hardware used.

2. Increasing the number of gridblocks in a model will increase computing expense for two reasons. The cost of a single timestep will increase because the amount of computation will be a function of the number of gridblocks, regardless of the solution method used. In addition, because a larger number of gridblocks implies a decrease in block size, timesteps must be shorter to satisfy tolerance criteria discussed earlier. For example, if some maximum is imposed on saturation change, smaller blocks cannot tolerate as much throughput during a single timestep as larger blocks; hence, the number of timesteps must be increased.

3. More "expensive" solution methods may, in the long run, be less expensive than alternative methods if they are much easier to use than the alternative methods. For example, although more costly in computer time, a detailed 3D model may be less manpower-intensive and overall cheaper to use than a combination of a cross-sectional model (to develop pseudofunctions) followed by a 2D areal model.

Nomenclature

I,J = gridblock numbers
k_{oi} = oil permeability at initial water saturation, md
n_x, n_y = number of blocks in x and y directions
S_w = water saturation, %PV
Δt = length of timestep, days
Δx, Δy,
Δz = block length in x, y, and z directions, respectively, ft [m]

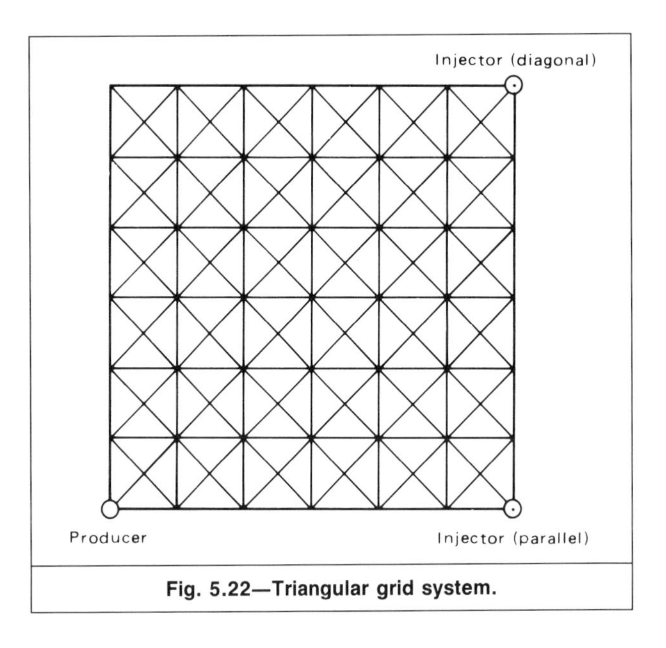

Fig. 5.22—Triangular grid system.

References

1. Staggs, H.M. and Herbeck, E.F.: "Reservoir Simulation Models—An Engineering Overview," *JPT* (Dec. 1971) 1428–36.
2. van Poollen, H.K.: "The Wise Use of Reservoir Models," *APEA J.* (1971) **11,** 131–34.
3. Woods, E.G. and Khurana, A.K.: "Pseudofunctions for Water Coning in a Three-Dimensional Reservoir Simulator," *SPEJ* (Aug. 1977) 251–62.
4. Chappelear, J.E. and Hirasaki, G.J.: "A Model of Oil-Water Coning for Two-Dimensional, Areal Reservoir Simulation," *SPEJ* (April 1976) 65–72; *Trans.,* AIME, **261.**
5. van Poollen, H.K., Breitenbach, E.A., and Thurnau, D.H.: "Treatment of Individual Wells and Grids in Reservoir Modeling," *SPEJ* (Dec. 1968) 341–46.
6. Todd, M.R., O'Dell, P.M., and Hiraski, G.J.: "Methods for Increased Accuracy in Numerical Reservoir Simulators," *SPEJ* (Dec. 1972) 515–30; *Trans.,* AIME, **253.**
7. Richardson, J.G. *et al.*: "The Effect of Small, Discontinuous Shales on Oil Recovery," *JPT* (Nov. 1978) 1531–37.
8. Mrosovsky, I. and Ridings, R.L.: "Two-Dimensional Radial Treatment of Wells Within a Three-Dimensional Reservoir Model," paper SPE 4286 presented at the 1973 SPE Symposium on Numerical Simulation of Reservoir Performance, Houston, Jan. 10–12.
9. Muskat, M.: *Physical Principles of Oil Production,* McGraw-Hill Book Co., New York City (1949) 226–36.
10. van Poollen, H.K., Bixel, H.C., and Jargon, J.R.: "Reservoir Modeling—10, Applications of Multiphase Immiscible Fluid-Flow Simulator," *Oil & Gas J.* (June 29, 1970) 58–63.
11. Heinemann, Z.E., Gerken, G., and von Hantelmann, G.: "Using Local Grid Refinement in a Multiple-Application Reservoir Simulator," paper SPE 12255 presented at the 1983 SPE Reservoir Simulation Symposium, San Francisco, Nov. 15–18.
12. Sammon, P.H. and Rubin, B.: "Practical Control of Timestep Selection in Thermal Simulation," *SPERE* (March 1986) 163–70.
13. Jensen, O.K.: "An Automatic Timestep Selection Scheme for Reservoir Simulation," paper SPE 9373 presented at the 1980 SPE Annual Technical Conference and Exhibition, Dallas, Sept. 21–24.
14. van Poollen, H.K., Bixel, H.C., and Jargon, J.R.: "Reservoir Modeling—9, Here are Fundamental Equations for Multiphase Fluid Flow," *Oil & Gas J.* (May 11, 1970) 72–78.
15. Blair, P.M. and Weinaug, C.F.: "Solution of Two-Phase Flow Problems Using Implicit Difference Equations," *SPEJ* (Dec. 1969) 417–24; *Trans.,* AIME, **246.**
16. Nolen, J.S. and Berry, D.W.: "Tests of the Stability and Time-Step Sensitivity of Semi-Implicit Reservoir Simulation Techniques," *SPEJ* (June 1972) 253–66; *Trans.,* AIME, **253.**
17. Letkeman, J.P. and Ridings, R.L.: "A Numerical Coning Model," *SPEJ* (Dec. 1970) 418–24; *Trans.,* AIME, **249.**
18. MacDonald, R.C. and Coats, K.H.: "Methods for Numerical Simulation of Water and Gas Coning," *SPEJ* (Dec. 1970) 425–36; *Trans.,* AIME, **249.**
19. Chappelear, J.E. and Rogers, W.L.: "Some Practical Considerations in the Construction of a Semi-Implicit Simulator," paper SPE 4276 presented at the 1973 SPE Symposium on Numerical Simulation of Reservoir Performance, Houston, Jan. 10–12.
20. Spillette, A.G., Hillestad, J.G., and Stone, H.L.: "A High-Stability Sequential Solution Approach to Reservoir Simulation," paper SPE 4542 presented at the 1973 SPE Annual Meeting, Las Vegas, Sept. 30–Oct. 3.
21. van Poollen, H.K., Bixel, H.C., and Jargon, J.R.: "Reservoir Modeling—11, Comparison of Multiphase Models," *Oil and Gas J.* (July 27, 1970) 124–29.
22. Kyte, J.R. and Berry, D.W.: "New Pseudo Functions to Control Numerical Dispersion," *SPEJ* (Aug. 1975) 269–76.
23. Larson, R.G.: "Controlling Numerical Dispersion by Variably Timed Flux Updating in One Dimension," *SPEJ* (June 1982) 399–408.
24. Larson, R.G.: "Controlling Numerical Dispersion by Variably Timed Flux Updating in Two Dimensions," *SPEJ* (June 1982) 409–19.
25. Rachford, H.H. Jr.: "A Sampling of Variational Methods," paper SPE 5720 presented at the 1976 SPE Symposium on Numerical Simulation of Reservoir Performance, Los Angeles, Feb. 19–20.
26. Hirasaki, G.J. and O'Dell, P.M.: "Representation of Reservoir Geometry for Numerical Simulation," *SPEJ* (Dec. 1970) 393–404; *Trans.,* AIME, **249.**
27. Robertson, G.E. and Woo, P.T.: "Grid Orientation Effects and the Use of Orthogonal Curvilinear Coordinates in Reservoir Simulation," *SPEJ* (Feb. 1978) 13–19.
28. Sonier, F. and Chaumet, P.: "A Fully Implicit Three-Dimensional Model in Curvilinear Coordinates," *SPEJ* (Aug. 1974) 361–70; *Trans.,* AIME, **257.**
29. Leventhal, S.H., Klein, M.H., and Culham, W.E.: "Curvilinear Coordinate Systems for Reservoir Simulation," *SPEJ* (Dec. 1985) 893–901.
30. Yanosik, J.L. and McCracken, T.A.: "A Nine-Point Finite-Difference Reservoir Simulator for Realistic Prediction of Adverse Mobility Ratio Displacements," *SPEJ* (Aug. 1979) 253–62; *Trans.,* AIME, **267.**
31. Bertiger, W.I. and Padmanabhan, L.: "Finite Difference Solutions to Grid Orientation Problems Using IMES," paper SPE 12250 presented at the 1983 SPE Reservoir Simulation Symposium, San Francisco, Nov. 15–18.
32. Shah, P.C.: "A Nine-Point Finite Difference Operator for Reduction of the Grid Orientation Effect," paper SPE 12251 presented at the 1983 SPE Reservoir Simulation Symposium, San Francisco, Nov. 15–18.
33. Watts, J.W. and Silliman, W.J.: "Numerical Dispersion and the Origins of the Grid-Orientation Effect," paper 96C presented at the 1980 AIChE Annual Meeting, Chicago, Nov. 17.
34. Ewing, R.E., Russell, T.F., and Wheeler, M.F.: "Simulation of Miscible Displacement Using Mixed Methods and a Modified Method of Characteristics," paper SPE 12241 presented at the 1983 SPE Reservoir Simulation Symposium, San Francisco, Nov. 15–18.

SI Metric Conversion Factors

acres ×	4.046 873	E−01	= ha
ft ×	3.048*	E−01	= m

*Conversion factor is exact.

Chapter 6
Selecting the Numerical Solution Method

Chap. 5 discussed the decisions that must be made to balance the selection of gridblock and timestep size with cost and time constraints. Most simulators also require the user to choose between several methods for solving the flow equations and may permit some control over the methods used to formulate the equations. These choices will control the ease of use, accuracy, and to some degree, the cost of the simulations.

This chapter discusses the formulations and solution methods that are most commonly offered in a simulator. Equation-solving methods will be described and a few general guidelines on the choice of options to be used for a given reservoir-modeling circumstance will be presented.

To simplify the presentation, saturation equations are used in discussions of equation formulation, mobility weighting, and numerical dispersion; pressure equations are used in descriptions of solution methods. Solution methods involving both pressure and saturation are discussed specifically in Appendix C.

6.1 Terminology

The term *solution methods* is often used in a general way to cover all the formulation decisions and solution options that are made by either the simulator developers or the user. As background for reading the literature, as well as for practical simulation activities, it is useful to recognize the distinction between *formulation options* and *equation-solving methods.* The two differ in their effect on the reliability, cost, and accuracy of simulator results. *Formulation* refers to the type and structure of the equations—i.e., how the reservoir flow problems are reduced to and expressed in equations. The formulation may be designed to aid in the solution of the problem, but it is not per se a part of the equation-solving method. Table 6.1 lists terms that are often used in conjunction with either equation formulation or solution. The purpose of listing these terms is to provide a sample of the jargon that is found in the simulation literature. Some terms appear on both lists; their meanings depend on how they are used.

Theoretically, if the timesteps and gridblock dimensions chosen for a simulation model are small enough, and if the timesteps are small enough relative to gridblock dimensions, the formulation decisions (factors in Col. 1 of Table 6.1) should become unimportant. In practical reservoir simulation, however, the space and time increments are almost never "small," and the formulation decisions may determine the accuracy of simulation results.

Once the formulation decisions have been made, equally important decisions remain concerning the methods of solving the equations. Several different methods are usually available in a simulator, and a proper choice will minimize the computer resources necessary to obtain a solution.

6.2 Formulating the Equations

The objectives of the following discussion are (1) to develop typical material-balance equations that can be used in a simulator, (2) to illustrate formulation options, and (3) to explain further the concepts of "explicit" and "implicit" functions.

6.2.1 Material-Balance Equations. Chaps. 2 and 5 discussed block size, timestep size, and mobility weighting. With that background in mind, consider the small waterflood model, Fig. 6.1, first discussed in Chap. 2. For simplicity, assume that the system is incompressible and that injection/production rates are specified. Thus the total flow rate, q_t, into and out of a gridblock is the same for all blocks. (*Rate-specified boundary conditions* are imposed on the gridblocks containing wells.) The components of a simple oil material balance on one of the interior blocks (Block 2) can be developed as follows.

Flow rate of oil into the block is represented by

$$q_{in}=q_t f_{o_{1-2}}. \quad (6.1)$$

Flow rate of oil out of the block is shown by

$$q_{out}=q_t f_{o_{2-3}}. \quad (6.2)$$

The rate with which oil accumulates in the block is

$$q_{in}-q_{out}=q_t f_{o_{1-2}}-q_t f_{o_{2-3}}$$
$$=q_t(f_{o_{1-2}}-f_{o_{2-3}}). \quad (6.3)$$

The rate with which oil saturation in the gridblock changes is

$$\frac{q_{in}-q_{out}}{V_{p_2}}=\frac{q_t}{V_{p_2}}(f_{o_{1-2}}-f_{o_{2-3}}), \quad (6.4)$$

where

q_t = total flow rate of all fluids,
$f_{o_{1-2}}, f_{o_{2-3}}$ = fractional flow of oil at Block 1,2 and 2,3 interfaces, respectively, and
V_{p_2} = PV of Gridblock 2.

The fractional-flow terms are functions of saturation and need to be defined before the equation can be solved. Definition of the function involves several formulation decisions. The first decision concerns the saturations to use in evaluating the fractional-flow terms at the Block 1,2 and Block 2,3 interfaces. An appropriate decision is to use *upstream mobility weighting* (Chap. 2). This decision defines the terms $f_{o_{1-2}}$ and $f_{o_{2-3}}$ to be the oil fractional flows, f_{o_1} and f_{o_2}, evaluated at the saturations that exist in Blocks 1 and 2, respectively. The overall material balance now becomes

$$S_{o_2}^{n+1}-S_{o_2}^{n}=\Delta t\left[\frac{q_t}{V_{p_2}}(f_{o_1}-f_{o_2})\right]. \quad (6.5)$$

Or, for reasons that will become apparent later, we may rearrange the equation to

$$\frac{S_{o_2}^{n+1}-S_{o_2}^{n}}{\Delta t}=\frac{q_t}{V_{p_2}}(f_{o_1}-f_{o_2}), \quad (6.6)$$

TABLE 6.1—TERMINOLOGY

Equation Formulation	Equation Solving
Implicit formulation	Direct methods
Implicit mobilities	Iterative methods
Fully implicit	Explicit methods
Semi-implicit	Gaussian elimination
Explicit formulation	Band solvers
Mobility weighting	Natural orderings
Implicit pressure, explicit saturation (IMPES)	D4 orderings
Sequential solution	Nested dissection
Simultaneous solution	Convergence
Iterative methods	Relaxation methods
Convergence	Successive overrelaxation (SOR)
	Line successive overrelaxation (LSOR)
	Corrected line successive overrelaxation (LSORC)
	ADI
	Strongly implicit procedure (SIP)
	Conjugate gradient
	Nested factorization

where

Δt = length of timestep,

$S_{o_2}^{n+1}$ = oil saturation in Gridblock 2 at end of timestep $n+1$, and

$S_{o_2}^{n}$ = oil saturation in Gridblock 2 at beginning of timestep.

The superscripts on the saturations designate the time level at which the function is evaluated. In this terminology, n is the last timestep already taken and $n+1$ is the timestep under consideration. Obviously, the end of n is the beginning of $n+1$. Another formulation decision that must be made before values for the fractional flows can be calculated is when to evaluate f_{o1} and f_{o2}. The simplest decision is to evaluate the fractional-flow terms at the beginning of the timestep. This would be an *explicit formulation.* In this case, $S_{o_2}^{n+1}$ would be the only unknown in the equation and the saturation change during the timestep could be easily calculated as

$$S_{o_2}^{n+1}-S_{o_2}^{n}=\Delta t\left[\frac{q_t}{V_{p_2}}(f_{o_1}^{n}-f_{o_2}^{n})\right]. \quad (6.7)$$

An *explicit function* can be expressed directly in terms of other known quantities. The formulation decision leading to the explicit representation in Eq. 6.7 was the decision to evaluate fractional flows at saturations that existed at the beginning of the timestep.

The decision could be to evaluate the fractional-flow terms at saturations S_o^{n+1} that will exist at the end of the timestep. The material-balance equation would be

$$S_{o_2}^{n+1}-S_{o_2}^{n}=\Delta t\left[\frac{q_t}{V_{p_2}}(f_{o_1}^{n+1}-f_{o_2}^{n+1})\right]. \quad (6.8)$$

Eq. 6.8 is an *implicit* formulation of the equation. In this case, because f_o^{n+1} is a function of S_o^{n+1}, which is not known at the start of the timestep, another decision must be made—the procedure used to estimate f_o^{n+1}. One approach is to estimate the functions by extrapolation, using knowledge of the shape of the fractional-flow function. Even though the fractional-flow curve is generally not very linear, a common method is to use a linear extrapolation:

$$f_o^{n+1}=f_o^n+\frac{\mathrm{d}f_o^n}{\mathrm{d}S_o}(S_o^{n+1}-S_o^n).$$

Now it is possible to write the material-balance equation as

$$S_{o_2}^{n+1}-S_{o_2}^{n}=\Delta t\left\{\frac{q_t}{V_{p_2}}\left[(f_{o_1}^{n}-f_{o_2}^{n})+\frac{\mathrm{d}f_{o1}^n}{\mathrm{d}S_{o_1}}(S_{o_1}^{n+1}-S_{o_1}^{n})-\frac{\mathrm{d}f_{o2}^n}{\mathrm{d}S_{o_2}}(S_{o_2}^{n+1}-S_{o_2}^{n})\right]\right\}. \quad (6.9)$$

Because this equation has two unknowns, S_{o1}^{n+1} and S_{o2}^{n+1}, neither can be calculated directly from known quantities. If a similar material-balance equation is written for each of the four gridblocks in the model, however, the resultant system of four equations will contain only the four unknown saturations, which can be evaluated by solving the equations simultaneously. Eq. 6.9 is a type of implicit formulation, but because an approximation is involved in evaluation of f_o, the formulation is not "fully" implicit and is called "semi-implicit." (Eq. 6.8 is fully implicit.) Leading to the *semi-implicit* formulation in Eq. 6.9 was the decision to approximate the fractional-flow terms by extrapolation to saturations S_o^{n+1} that would exist at the end of the timestep.

Eq. 6.9 is more convenient to use if it is rearranged:

$$\left(\frac{\Delta t q_t}{V_{p_2}}\frac{\mathrm{d}f_{o1}^n}{\mathrm{d}S_{o_1}}\right)(S_{o_1}^{n+1}-S_{o_1}^{n})-\left(\frac{\Delta t q_t}{V_{p_2}}\frac{\mathrm{d}f_{o2}^n}{\mathrm{d}S_{o_2}}+1\right)(S_{o_2}^{n+1}-S_{o_2}^{n})$$

$$=-\frac{\Delta t q_t}{V_{p_2}}(f_{o_1}^{n}-f_{o_2}^{n}). \quad (6.10)$$

An equation like Eq. 6.10 is needed for every gridblock in the model. The structure of the resultant set of equations will be more apparent if shorthand notation is used in Eq. 6.10. As shorthand symbols, let

$$a_i=\frac{\Delta t q_t}{V_{p_i}}\frac{\mathrm{d}f_{o_{i-1}}^n}{\mathrm{d}S_{o_{i-1}}},$$

$$b_i=-\left(\frac{\Delta t q_t}{V_{p_i}}\frac{\mathrm{d}f_{o_i}^n}{\mathrm{d}S_{o_i}}+1\right),$$

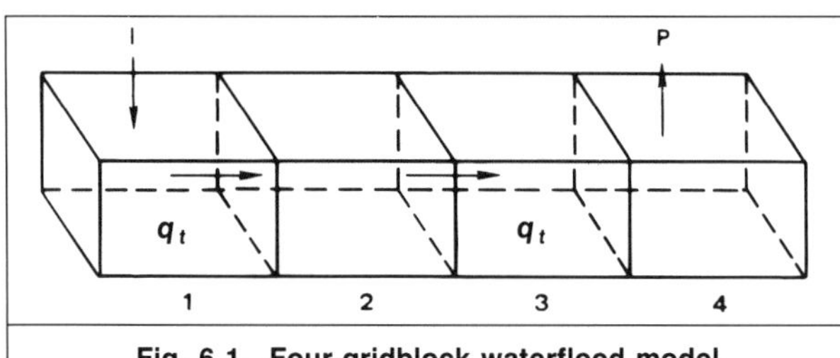

Fig. 6.1—Four-gridblock waterflood model.

$$d_i = -\frac{\Delta t q_t}{V_{p_i}}(f^n_{o_{i-1}} - f^n_{o_i}), \text{ and}$$

$$\Delta S_{o_i} = S^{n+1}_{o_i} - S^n_{o_i},$$

where the subscript i refers to gridblock numbers, as in Eqs. 6.1 through 6.10.

Eq. 6.10 now becomes

$$a_2 \Delta S_{o_1} + b_2 \Delta S_{o_2} = d_2. \quad \text{(6.11)}$$

Note that a_2, b_2, and d_2 are combinations of known quantities; ΔS_{o1} and ΔS_{o2} are unknown.

Eq. 6.11 is the material-balance equation for Gridblock 2. Similar equations for the three other blocks in the system complete the set of material-balance equations for the four-block waterflood model.

$$\begin{aligned} a_1 \Delta S_{o_0} + b_1 \Delta S_{o_1} &= d_1 \\ a_2 \Delta S_{o_1} + b_2 \Delta S_{o_2} &= d_2 \\ a_3 \Delta S_{o_2} + b_3 \Delta S_{o_3} &= d_3 \\ a_4 \Delta S_{o_3} + b_4 \Delta S_{o_4} &= d_4. \end{aligned} \quad \text{(6.12)}$$

The term $a_1 \Delta S_{o0}$ could be interpreted conceptually as oil flux into Gridblock 1 through the outer boundary of the model. In this problem, however, Block 1 contains a water-injection well, injecting water only at specified rate q_t, and there is no oil flux into Block 1. Hence, $a_1 \Delta S_{o0} = 0$. Likewise, at Block 4, there is a production well whose oil rate is equivalent to the oil flux out of the block.

6.2.2 Pressure Equations. Eq. 6.12 is a saturation equation that adequately describes the four-gridblock waterflood model. No equations involving pressure are needed for this model because the system was defined as incompressible with arbitrarily specified total flow rate (the water-injection rate). In modeling real systems, however, either a separate set of pressure equations must be solved sequentially with saturation equations or equations containing both pressure and saturation must be solved.[1] In this chapter, the pressure and saturation equations are treated separately. For a two-dimensional (2D) model, the pressure equations take the following form:

$$B_{i,j}(p_{i,j} - p_{i,j-1}) + D_{i,j}(p_{i,j} - p_{i-1,j}) - F_{i,j}(p_{i+1,j} - p_{i,j})$$
$$- H_{i,j}(p_{i,j+1} - p_{i,j}) = q_{i,j},$$

where p is the pressure in the gridblock identified by the two subscripts i and j, and B, D, F, and H contain all terms (mobility, cross-sectional area, distance, pressure functions, etc.) that, when multiplied by pressure gradient, determine flow rate. $q_{i,j}$ is a source term representing injection or production wells* if they are present in Block i,j. Collecting coefficients of $p_{i,j}$ gives

$$-B_{i,j}p_{i,j-1} - D_{i,j}p_{i-1,j} - F_{i,j}p_{i+1,j} - H_{i,j}p_{i,j+1}$$
$$+ (B+D+F+H)_{i,j}p_{i,j} = q_{i,j}.$$

Let $E_{i,j} = (B+D+F+H)_{i,j}$. Then,

$$-B_{i,j}p_{i,j-1} - D_{i,j}p_{i-1,j} + E_{i,j}p_{i,j} - F_{i,j}p_{i+1,j}$$
$$- H_{i,j}p_{i,j+1} = q_{i,j}. \quad \text{(6.13)}$$

Because these letter coefficients will be used a number of times in this chapter, it will be convenient to establish a standard nomenclature. The nomenclature is defined pictorially in Fig. 6.2.

*$q_{i,j}$ may also represent flux into a window area. See Chap. 3.

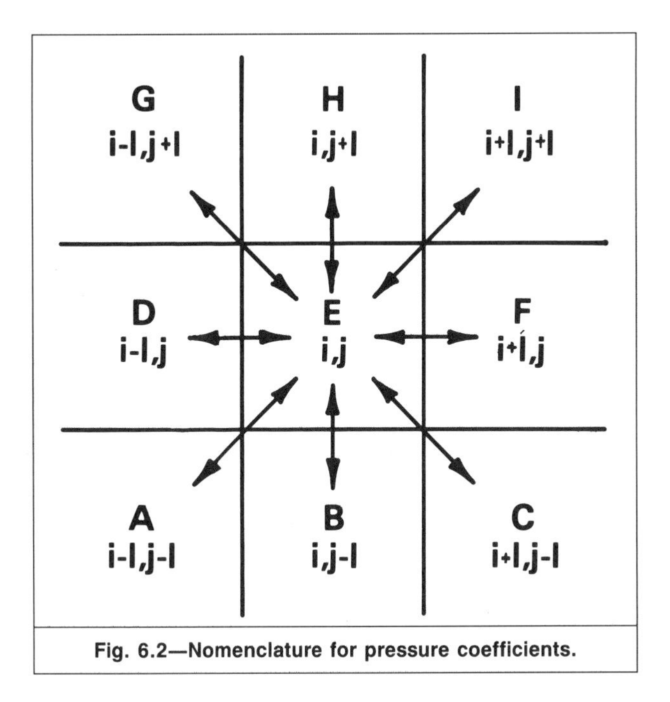

Fig. 6.2—Nomenclature for pressure coefficients.

The coefficients A, C, G, and I are usually zero because there can be no diagonal flow between blocks.* Note that these coefficients do not appear in Eq. 6.13. [We shall see later, in a discussion of the strongly implicit procedure (SIP), that "phantom" diagonal flow terms sometimes appear and must be dealt with.] Eq. 6.13 will be discussed further in Sec. 6.7.

6.3 Formulation Options

Many of the decisions that must be made in the numerical formulation of the flow equations are made by the simulator developers. Among these decisions are the choice of solution variables (pressures, saturations, or capillary pressures) and the selection of the equation-manipulation techniques (simultaneous or sequential). Options usually left to the user are the method of mobility weighting and the degree of implicitness used in the formulation.

6.3.1 Choices of Solution Variables. In a three-phase problem, there are several possible choices of solution variables from a group, including phase pressures (three), phase saturations (three), and capillary pressures (two). Ultimately, there will be three unknowns for every block. The remaining variables are related to the three unknowns through capillary pressure and from the axiom that the three phase saturations must sum to one.

In simulations involving fewer than three phases, the number of unknowns per gridblock is reduced (two for a two-phase system and one for a single-phase system), and the number of possible choices is reduced correspondingly.

6.3.2 Implicit Functions. In current usage, the term *fully implicit* has some ambiguity. Generally, the term is correctly used to indicate that all pressure and saturation functions are evaluated at the advanced time level. Sometimes, however, it is used to identify an iterative scheme that can be used to approximate a solution to within a prescribed tolerance. Although inexact in this usage, the term is not entirely inappropriate, because most pressure and saturation functions are nonlinear and can be evaluated to various degrees of accuracy. Correspondingly, if only one first-order approximation is attempted, the procedure may be called "semi-implicit."

In general, the *more implicit* a formulation is, the more stable** the solutions will be. It does not necessarily follow that simulators

*A so-called nine-point formulation of the flow equation can be interpreted as having diagonal flow terms.

**A solution is stable if errors made in the computation do not propagate and grow in later stages of the computation. A computation scheme is unstable if errors propagate and grow uncontrollably.

should be formulated with implicit evaluations of all dependent variables and all functions of these variables. For some problems, implicit formulations may lead to so much numerical dispersion that solutions are too inaccurate to accept. It is also generally true that the equations generated from implicit formulations are more costly to solve than those generated from other formulations. Considering all these factors, many simulators are written with options on the formulation. The user can then at least partially select the formulation most suited to the particular application.

General guidelines are that (1) pressures are always evaluated implicitly, and (2) functions of pressure and saturation may or may not be evaluated implicitly, depending on the type of problem.

6.3.3 Equation-Manipulating Techniques. Another formulation choice usually made by the developers of reservoir simulators concerns the "manipulation" of the equations when they are solved. The two most useful techniques are referred to as *simultaneous* and *sequential.* In the simultaneous approach to solving a three-phase problem, all three dependent variables for each gridblock are included in the same set of equations. In the sequential approach, the equations are manipulated to separate the solution of the pressure equation from that of the saturation equation. These manipulations eliminate saturations so that the first step consists of a solution for one unknown (a phase pressure) per gridblock. The second step then solves for two unknowns (two phase saturations) per gridblock.

The most commonly used sequential approach is called implicit pressure, explicit saturation (IMPES).[2,3] In this procedure, the saturations are eliminated by adding the individual phase material-balance equations and by assuming that capillary pressure does not change during a timestep. The resultant equation has only one unknown, a phase pressure, which is obtained by simultaneous solution of a set of equations. Then saturations are determined explicitly by solving material-balance equations. Although dependable when used in applications for which it is well suited, IMPES does have stability limitations resulting from explicit treatment of mobility and capillary pressure.

One advantage of a sequential approach over a simultaneous approach is lower cost. Another advantage is flexibility—the same equation-solving technique need not be imposed in all steps of the solution. Instead, the most suitable technique can be chosen for each step.

Several methods[4-6] have successfully taken advantage of the cost savings associated with sequential approaches. In the method of Spillette *et al.*,[6] for example, a pressure solution is obtained as in the IMPES method. Subsequently, a total velocity is calculated, which [for a one-dimensional (1D) problem] is independent of the time level at which the capillary pressure is evaluated. The total velocity is then used in a second step in which capillary pressures and mobilities can be evaluated implicitly. The method is more stable than IMPES but it is also more costly because it solves a system of simultaneous equations to calculate saturations, whereas IMPES calculates saturations explicitly. The overall cost of this sequential implicit procedure is about twice that of the IMPES method.

6.3.4 Mobility Weighting. In multiphase systems, one or more relative permeabilities must be assigned that will control the flow of the individual phases from one gridblock to the next. Generally, the term *mobility weighting* designates the saturation or combination of saturations that is used to determine the phase mobilities. Concepts involved were discussed in Chaps. 2 and 5; they are summarized briefly here.

There are many possible selections for mobility weighting within the extremes of fully "upstream" and fully "downstream" weighting. In upstream weighting, the most common choice, mobilities are evaluated at saturations that exist in the block from which the fluid phases are flowing. Although it is possible to use any weighting between upstream and downstream, maintaining acceptable accuracy and stability narrows the practical range of choices.

Upstream weighting is the most reliable in terms of stability and ease of solution. However, upstream weighting can cause an exaggerated smearing of the saturation fronts (see Sec. 6.4). Full downstream weighting is probably never used in simulators because it almost always leads to incorrect and unrealistic answers.

Another upstream weighting method, proposed by Todd *et al.*,[7] uses information from the two blocks immediately upstream from the flow boundary in question. Specifically, the method estimates relative permeabilities at the flow boundary by extrapolation of relative permeabilities evaluated at the two upstream blocks. Some care must be exercised in the implementation of the technique to ensure that the extrapolated values are physically realistic. This two-point upstream method leads to better solutions at displacement fronts than does conventional single-point upstream weighting.

6.4. Numerical Dispersion

The discussions in Chaps. 2 and 5 and earlier in this chapter demonstrate that approximations inherent in practical formulations of the equations for reservoir simulation introduce errors. One such error is numerical dispersion. Refer to the earlier discussions for a qualitative explanation of the origin of numerical-dispersion errors. A less pictorial and more quantitative description of numerical dispersion can be developed by comparing the actual form of the equations used in simulation with the underlying differential equations. The following discussion compares the differential and difference forms of the simplified material-balance equation (Eq. 6.7).

Eq. 6.7, generalized for any Gridblock i, is

$$S_{o_i}^{n+1}-S_{o_i}^{n}=\Delta t\left[\frac{q_t}{V_{p_i}}(f_{o_{i-1}}^{n}-f_{o_i}^{n})\right].$$

The volume term in this equation, V_{p_i}, can also be expressed as a product of porosity, ϕ, block length in the flow direction, Δx, and cross-sectional area available for flow. Likewise, the flow rate, q_t, can be written as a velocity, v_t, times the cross-sectional area open to flow. Making these substitutions and rearranging terms leads to the following equation:

$$\frac{S_{o_i}^{n+1}-S_{o_i}^{n}}{\Delta t}=v_t\frac{f_{o_{i-1}}^{n}-f_{o_i}^{n}}{\Delta x}. \qquad (6.14)$$

In Eq. 6.14, porosity is included in the velocity term, v_t, as a simplification. Further simplified, this equation can be expressed as

$$\frac{\Delta S}{\Delta t}=-v_t\frac{\Delta f}{\Delta x}. \qquad (6.15)$$

Note that the subscripts on S and f have been omitted because the equation applies to any phase. Because f is dependent on only saturation, it is more appropriate to express the equation as

$$\frac{\Delta S}{\Delta t}=-v_t\frac{\mathrm{d}f}{\mathrm{d}S}\frac{\Delta S}{\Delta x}. \qquad (6.16)$$

For small values of Δt and Δx, this becomes the differential equation

$$\frac{\partial S}{\partial t}=-v_t\frac{\mathrm{d}f}{\mathrm{d}S}\frac{\partial S}{\partial x}. \qquad (6.17)$$

Eq. 6.17 is an accurate description of the physics of the displacement process, but Eq. 6.16 is the equation actually solved in a simulator that uses this formulation. And Eq. 6.16 is not exactly equal to Eq. 6.17 except in the limit of infinitely small values of Δt and Δx. Use of practical values for Δx and Δt will lead to some error.

If S is a smooth function of t, the difference term, $\Delta S/\Delta t$, can be expressed as a Taylor series:

$$\frac{\Delta S}{\Delta t}=\frac{S^{n+1}-S^{n}}{\Delta t}=\frac{\partial S}{\partial t}+\tfrac{1}{2}\frac{\partial^2 S}{\partial t^2}\Delta t+\tfrac{1}{6}\frac{\partial^3 S}{\partial t^3}\Delta t^2+\ldots.$$

Similarly, if S is a smooth function of x, and weighting is upstream, i.e., saturation in the upstream block is used in the difference equation,

$$\frac{\Delta S}{\Delta x}=\frac{S_i-S_{i-1}}{\Delta x}=\frac{\partial S}{\partial x}-\tfrac{1}{2}\frac{\partial^2 S}{\partial x^2}\Delta x+\tfrac{1}{6}\frac{\partial^3 S}{\partial x^3}\Delta x^2 \ldots .$$

Clearly, by solving for $\Delta S/\Delta t$ and $\Delta S/\Delta x$ rather than $\partial S/\partial t$ and $\partial S/\partial x$, we introduce additional terms (errors) of the form

$$\tfrac{1}{2}\frac{\partial^2 S}{\partial t^2}\Delta t+\tfrac{1}{6}\frac{\partial^3 S}{\partial t^3}\Delta t^2 \ldots$$

and

$$-\tfrac{1}{2}\frac{\partial^2 S}{\partial x^2}\Delta x+\tfrac{1}{6}\frac{\partial^3 S}{\partial x^3}\Delta x^2 \ldots .$$

The first term in the series usually is the only one of consequence, so essentially

$$\frac{\Delta S}{\Delta t}=\frac{\partial S}{\partial t}+\tfrac{1}{2}\frac{\partial^2 S}{\partial t^2}\Delta t \text{ and } \frac{\Delta S}{\Delta x}=\frac{\partial S}{\partial x}-\tfrac{1}{2}\frac{\partial^2 S}{\partial x^2}\Delta x.$$

Substituting these expressions into Eq. 6.16 gives

$$\frac{\partial S}{\partial t}+\tfrac{1}{2}\frac{\partial^2 S}{\partial t^2}\Delta t=-v_t\frac{df}{dS}\left(\frac{\partial S}{\partial x}-\tfrac{1}{2}\frac{\partial^2 S}{\partial x^2}\Delta x\right).$$

Rearranging the equation so that it can be compared directly with Eq. 6.17 gives

$$\frac{\partial S}{\partial t}=-v_t\frac{df}{dS}\frac{\partial S}{\partial x}+\tfrac{1}{2}v_t\frac{df}{dS}\frac{\partial^2 S}{\partial x^2}\Delta x-\tfrac{1}{2}\frac{\partial^2 S}{\partial t^2}\Delta t. \quad \ldots\ldots\ldots (6.18)$$

Note that Eq. 6.18 contains two terms that are not in Eq. 6.17. The significance of the two terms will be more apparent if an equivalent alternative expression, derived from Eq. 6.17, can be substituted for $\partial^2 S/\partial t^2$. Differentiating Eq. 6.17 with respect to t, assuming df/dS is constant, gives

$$\frac{\partial^2 S}{\partial t^2}=-v_t\frac{df}{dS}\frac{\partial}{\partial t}\left(\frac{\partial S}{\partial x}\right)=-v_t\frac{df}{dS}\frac{\partial}{\partial x}\left(\frac{\partial S}{\partial t}\right)$$

$$=v_t^2\left(\frac{df}{dS}\right)^2\frac{\partial^2 S}{\partial x^2}.$$

Substituting the above expression for $\partial^2 S/\partial t^2$ transforms the last term in Eq. 6.18 to

$$\tfrac{1}{2}v_t^2\left(\frac{df}{dS}\right)^2\frac{\partial^2 S}{\partial x^2}\Delta t.$$

The two extra terms in Eq. 6.18 can now be expressed as

$$\left[\tfrac{1}{2}v_t\frac{df}{dS}\Delta x-\tfrac{1}{2}v_t^2\left(\frac{df}{dS}\right)^2\Delta t\right]\frac{\partial^2 S}{\partial x^2}$$

or

$$\frac{v_t}{2}\frac{df}{dS}\left(\Delta x-v_t\frac{df}{dS}\Delta t\right)\frac{\partial^2 S}{\partial x^2},$$

and Eq. 6.18 becomes

$$\frac{\partial S}{\partial t}=-v_t\frac{df}{dS}\frac{\partial S}{\partial x}+\frac{v_t}{2}\frac{df}{dS}\left(\Delta x-v_t\frac{df}{dS}\Delta t\right)\frac{\partial^2 S}{\partial x^2}. \quad \ldots\ldots\ldots (6.19)$$

Thus the difference form of the material-balance equation is not equivalent to the rigorous differential equation but, instead, approximates the more complicated expression shown in Eqs. 6.18 and 6.19.

Eq. 6.19 is analogous to a diffusion-convection differential equation

$$\frac{\partial c}{\partial t}=-v_t\frac{\partial c}{\partial x}+d\frac{\partial^2 c}{\partial x^2}. \quad \ldots\ldots\ldots (6.20)$$

The coefficient of $\partial^2 S/\partial x^2$ in Eq. 6.19 is analogous to d, the diffusion or dispersion coefficient in Eq. 6.20. For the assumptions inherent in this example, upstream weighting and an explicit formulation, an expression for d is

$$d=\frac{v_t}{2}\frac{df}{dS}\left(\Delta x-v_t\frac{df}{dS}\Delta t\right).$$

A similar development for an implicit formulation gives

$$d=\frac{v_t}{2}\frac{df}{dS}\left(\Delta x+v_t\frac{df}{dS}\Delta t\right).$$

The term *numerical dispersion* comes from this comparison with the diffusion-convection equation. A more complete discussion of numerical dispersion appears in Refs. 1 (Pages 65 through 81) and 7.

Note that with upstream weighting, the Δx and Δt contributions are additive in an implicit formulation, but tend to be offsetting in an explicit formulation. Hence an implicit formulation will always produce more dispersion than an explicit formulation. It might seem that numerical dispersion could be eliminated from an explicit formulation with upstream weighting through proper choice of Δx and Δt. Because the terms in the expression are not constant, however, selection of precisely offsetting values of Δt and Δx is difficult even for this simple 1D problem. Inappropriate choices of Δx and Δt could lead to negative dispersion coefficients, with the result that solutions to the flow equations would be physically unreal or oscillatory (a stable solution is possible only if numerical-dispersion coefficients are positive).

Unfortunately, it is not possible to take full advantage of the knowledge gained from this simple 1D error analysis. Similar analysis of reservoir-sized problems (multiphase and multidimensional) is impractical. Too many of the terms that determine the numerical-dispersion coefficient are variable: Δx, Δy, and Δz are rarely uniform, Δt usually changes throughout the simulation, the velocities in the coordinate directions will not be constant, and the derivatives of the fractional-flow curves are not constant. Consequently, there has been little effort to analyze these types of errors beyond the simplified 1D problems. There has been some effort, however, toward controlling or at least accounting for numerical dispersion.[8,9] Refer to Chap. 5 for comments on this subject.

6.5 Choosing the Formulation Option

As mentioned earlier, many simulators do not offer a choice of formulations. If options are available, optimal decisions regarding their use can save computer time. Formulation options that may be available include IMPES and semi-implicit and implicit formulations.

Many 2D areal problems can be handled with IMPES-type formulations. This is especially true of water/oil systems with relatively weak capillary-pressure effects. In systems where capillary-pressure forces are strong relative to viscous or gravity forces, however, it may be necessary to treat capillary pressure semi-implicitly or implicitly in the saturation solution.

Systems containing dissolved gas may require the use of implicit or semi-implicit mobilities to handle the rapid gas movement that may occur when the pressure drops below the bubblepoint pressure. The need is most evident in dipping areal models, cross sections, or three-dimensional (3D) models. If the software has the option, selective implicitness on gas-phase mobility may be sufficient. If the option is available, it may also be sufficient in low-dip reservoirs to limit use of the implicit treatment to the vertical component of flow.

In single-well, radial cross sections, implicit or semi-implicit mobilities are almost always necessary. The combination of small gridblocks and high throughput results in rapid changes in saturations, and when an IMPES formulation is used, timesteps may be prohibitively small. The inability of early simulators to cope with such well problems as coning was the primary incentive for the development of implicit formulations.

Simulations of some processes require more stability than can be obtained with semi-implicit terms, even in simultaneous formulations. Examples include thermal processes, flow in naturally fractured reservoirs, and sometimes gas coning. In these cases, a fully implicit, simultaneous formulation is needed.

Many simulators that have implicit options allow selective application of the options. Selective application can be useful if the models have relatively large gridblocks. In this case, it is usually desirable to evaluate source terms (well rates) explicitly, even if interblock flow is evaluated implicitly. The use of explicit source terms allows more precise management of wells.

Because cost typically increases as the degree of implicitness in a formulation increases, a desirable alternative is to optimize use of the implicit formulation by allowing the degree of implicitness to vary both with location and time. Such an approach has been suggested by Thomas and Thurnau,[10,11] who developed algorithms that automatically fix the level of implicitness depending on the rate of change of a variable—e.g., pressure or saturation. This option should be considered if it is available.

Simulators using implicit, simultaneous formulations generally provide the most trouble-free operation. It is important to remember, however, that implicit formulations also produce the most numerical dispersion. It will usually be the user's responsibility to be aware of the relationship between timestep size and dispersion and to balance timestep size and cost accordingly.

6.6 Matrix Equations

Matrix algebra is the *de facto* language used in discussions of solution methods, and some familiarity with the subject is a prerequisite for reading the remainder of this chapter. Because those who use simulators seldom need or have the opportunity to use matrix algebra in their normal activities, a brief review of the matrix operations used in this chapter and mentioned most often in reservoir simulation literature is included here.

6.6.1 Matrix Notation. When sets of such equations as Eq. 6.12 are large, as in a reservoir simulator, they are difficult to discuss and virtually impossible to manipulate unless they are expressed as matrices. Matrix notation is illustrated with a typical small set of linear equations:

$$a_{11}p_1+a_{12}p_2+a_{13}p_3=q_1$$

$$a_{21}p_1+a_{22}p_2+a_{23}p_3=q_2$$

$$a_{31}p_1+a_{32}p_2+a_{33}p_3=q_3 \quad \ldots\ldots (6.21)$$

There are three unknowns: p_1, p_2, and p_3; all other quantities are known. In matrix format, the equations become

$$\begin{bmatrix} a_{11} & a_{12} & a_{13} \\ a_{21} & a_{22} & a_{23} \\ a_{31} & a_{32} & a_{33} \end{bmatrix} \begin{bmatrix} p_1 \\ p_2 \\ p_3 \end{bmatrix} = \begin{bmatrix} q_1 \\ q_2 \\ q_3 \end{bmatrix}, \quad \ldots\ldots (6.22)$$

or symbolically, $Ap=q$.

The subscripts of the matrix elements generally refer to the row and column locations of the elements. In some of the literature on simulation, subscripts attached to elements in a matrix will identify simulator gridblock location rather than matrix element location. The distinction is usually clear and the notation is not confusing.

A is the matrix of known coefficients and is a 3×3 *matrix*. Because it has the same number of rows as columns, it is a square matrix. The 3×1 matrices p and q are column* matrices; p is unknown, q is known. Individual equations can be regenerated by multiplying elements of a given row, in turn from left to right, by the elements of the column vector of unknowns, in turn from top to bottom, and equating the sum of the products to the element of the column of knowns in that row. For example,

$$\begin{bmatrix} a_{11} & a_{12} & a_{13} \end{bmatrix} \begin{bmatrix} p_1 \\ p_2 \\ p_3 \end{bmatrix} = a_{11}p_1+a_{12}p_2+a_{13}p_3=q_1. \quad \ldots (6.23)$$

In matrix form, but with gridblock locations retained as subscripts, Eq. 6.12 becomes

$$\begin{bmatrix} b_1 & 0 & 0 & 0 \\ a_2 & b_2 & 0 & 0 \\ 0 & a_3 & b_3 & 0 \\ 0 & 0 & a_4 & b_4 \end{bmatrix} \begin{bmatrix} \Delta S_{o_1} \\ \Delta S_{o_2} \\ \Delta S_{o_3} \\ \Delta S_{o_4} \end{bmatrix} = \begin{bmatrix} d_1 \\ d_2 \\ d_3 \\ d_4 \end{bmatrix}. \quad \ldots\ldots (6.24)$$

The number of diagonals in the coefficient matrix is a measure of the extent to which the equations couple, or link, changes in one gridblock to changes in other blocks. In the example 1D waterflood model, each block is coupled through the saturation equation (Eq. 6.5) to only one (upstream) block. Thus the coefficient matrix contains only two diagonals, the *principal diagonal* (b_1 through b_4) and the one immediately to the left of the principal diagonal (a_2 through a_4). In this particular example, the coefficient matrix is a *lower triangular matrix,* so called because all elements above the principal diagonal are zeros. In a more general implicit formulation of a 1D problem, blocks will be coupled to both upstream and downstream neighbors and there will be diagonals both right and left of the main diagonal. All other elements not on one of the three diagonals are zero. A matrix of this type is a *tridiagonal matrix.* It is also a *band matrix of bandwidth 3.* A matrix, such as a tridiagonal matrix, having many of its elements equal to zero is a *sparse* matrix.

Coefficient matrices for 2D and 3D problems will, in general, contain a main diagonal plus a number of additional diagonals equal to the number of gridblocks adjacent to a given gridblock. Thus, the coefficient matrix for a 2D problem has five diagonals and that for a 3D problem has seven. The additional diagonals are equally spaced on both sides of the main diagonal at distances that are related to the number of blocks in a row of a 2D or 3D problem and the number of blocks in a plane in a 3D problem. All these matrices are band matrices and all are sparse.

6.6.2 Matrix Algebra. The simplest operation on matrices is addition. To sum two or more matrices, simply add corresponding elements:

$$\begin{bmatrix} a_{11} & a_{12} \\ a_{21} & a_{22} \end{bmatrix} + \begin{bmatrix} b_{11} & b_{12} \\ b_{21} & b_{22} \end{bmatrix} = \begin{bmatrix} a_{11}+b_{11} & a_{12}+b_{12} \\ a_{21}+b_{21} & a_{22}+b_{22} \end{bmatrix}.$$

Eq. 6.23 illustrated the rule for multiplication of matrices: elements of rows are multiplied by elements of columns and summed. The formula for a single element $(ap)_{rc}$ in Row r and Column c of a product matrix AP is

$$(ap)_{rc} = \sum_{k=1}^{n} a_{rk}p_{kc}, \quad \ldots\ldots (6.25)$$

*Conventional nomenclature calls for lower-cased letters to represent column and row matrices.

where n is the number of columns in A (or rows in P). Obviously, for this operation to be meaningful, the number of elements in a row of A must equal the number of elements in a column of P. Expressed differently, to multiply A times P, in that order, the number of columns in A must equal the number of rows in P; i.e., the matrices must be *conformable*. The product matrix will have the same number of rows as A and the same number of columns as P.

In the product AP, A is said to be *post*multiplied by P or P is *pre*multiplied by A. Note that the order of multiplication matters—i.e., in general, $AP \neq PA$. However, it is always true that $A(BC) = (AB)C$.

A few examples of matrix multiplication follow.

$$\begin{bmatrix} a_{11} & a_{12} \end{bmatrix} \begin{bmatrix} p_1 \\ p_2 \end{bmatrix} = a_{11}p_1 + a_{12}p_2,$$

$$\begin{bmatrix} a_{11} & a_{12} \\ a_{21} & a_{22} \end{bmatrix} \begin{bmatrix} p_1 \\ p_2 \end{bmatrix} = \begin{bmatrix} a_{11}p_1 + a_{12}p_2 \\ a_{21}p_1 + a_{22}p_2 \end{bmatrix},$$

and

$$\begin{bmatrix} a_{11} & a_{12} \\ a_{21} & a_{22} \end{bmatrix} \begin{bmatrix} p_{11} & p_{12} \\ p_{21} & p_{22} \end{bmatrix} = \begin{bmatrix} a_{11}p_{11} + a_{12}p_{21} & a_{11}p_{12} + a_{12}p_{22} \\ a_{21}p_{11} + a_{22}p_{21} & a_{21}p_{12} + a_{22}p_{22} \end{bmatrix}.$$

Note that

$$\begin{bmatrix} a_{11}p_1 + a_{12}p_2 \\ a_{21}p_1 + a_{22}p_2 \end{bmatrix}$$

is a new column matrix with two elements, and that

$$\begin{bmatrix} a_{11}p_{11} + a_{12}p_{21} & a_{11}p_{12} + a_{12}p_{22} \\ a_{21}p_{11} + a_{22}p_{21} & a_{21}p_{12} + a_{22}p_{22} \end{bmatrix}$$

is a new square matrix with four elements.

A few additional definitions and operations follow in more-or-less random order. As implied earlier, the *principal diagonal* of a matrix is the sequence of terms on the diagonal from upper left to lower right. A *lower triangular matrix* has all zeros above the principal diagonal; an *upper triangular matrix* has all zeros below the principal diagonal. A matrix having ones on the principal diagonal and zeros for all other elements is the *identity* matrix. It is usually designated by I; it is always a square matrix and serves the same purpose in matrix algebra that unity does in ordinary arithmetic. For example, a matrix multiplied by I is unchanged. Also, A^{-1}, the *inverse* of a square matrix A, is a matrix such that $A(A^{-1}) = (A^{-1})A = I$.

Any reordering of the rows of the identity matrix such that the ones are not all on the principal diagonal is a *permutation* matrix. A permutation matrix is useful for changing the order of rows and/or columns in other matrices. For example,

$$\begin{bmatrix} a_{11} & a_{12} & a_{13} \\ a_{21} & a_{22} & a_{23} \\ a_{31} & a_{32} & a_{33} \end{bmatrix} \begin{bmatrix} 0 & 1 & 0 \\ 0 & 0 & 1 \\ 1 & 0 & 0 \end{bmatrix} = \begin{bmatrix} a_{13} & a_{11} & a_{12} \\ a_{23} & a_{21} & a_{22} \\ a_{33} & a_{31} & a_{32} \end{bmatrix}.$$

The *transpose* of a matrix, A^T, is a new matrix whose rows are identical to the columns of the original matrix, A.

$$\begin{bmatrix} a & b \\ c & d \end{bmatrix}^T = \begin{bmatrix} a & c \\ b & d \end{bmatrix}.$$

A matrix is *symmetric* if $A^T = A$.

The transpose of a column matrix is a row matrix, and vice versa. For example, if

$$p = \begin{bmatrix} p_1 \\ p_2 \\ \cdot \\ \cdot \\ \cdot \\ p_n \end{bmatrix},$$

then

$$p^T = \begin{bmatrix} p_1, p_2 \ldots p_n \end{bmatrix}.$$

By definition, the *inner product* of Column Matrices p and q is

$$p^Tq = q^Tp = \sum_{i=1}^{n} q_i p_i.$$

Note that the inner product is a one-by-one matrix—i.e., a scalar. The inner product is sometimes written (p,q).

Note also that the product of a column or row matrix and its transpose is the sum of the squares of the terms in the matrix. For example, if

$$p = \begin{bmatrix} p_1 \\ p_2 \\ \cdot \\ \cdot \\ \cdot \\ p_n \end{bmatrix},$$

then

$$p^Tp = \begin{bmatrix} p_1, p_2 \ldots p_n \end{bmatrix} \begin{bmatrix} p_1 \\ p_2 \\ \cdot \\ \cdot \\ \cdot \\ p_n \end{bmatrix} = \sum_{i=1}^{n} p_i^2.$$

This relationship will be mentioned later in a discussion of techniques that minimize the sum of the squares of the "residuals" or errors (in pressure, for example) remaining after an iteration has been completed.

The solution of the matrix equation $Ap = q$ is

$$p = Ip = A^{-1}Ap = A^{-1}q.$$

A solution will exist if the inverse A^{-1} of the coefficient matrix exists.* The computational task is to find A^{-1} and to multiply it by q, or to use some other method to form $A^{-1}q$. In practice, it usually is prohibitively expensive to calculate A^{-1}, and it is preferable to use a method that does not require calculation of the inverse of the complete coefficient matrix.

One such method is to find two matrices, L and U, that are *factors* of A such that $LU = A$ and such that matrix equations with L and U are relatively inexpensive to solve. The matrix equation then becomes $LUp = q$, which can be solved in two steps—first solving $Lg = q$ for a dummy variable g, and then solving $Up = g$ for p.

L and U are often taken to be lower triangular and upper triangular, respectively. For example, suppose we wish to factor

$$\underset{A}{\begin{bmatrix} a_{11} & a_{12} \\ a_{21} & a_{22} \end{bmatrix}}$$

into two factors of the forms

$$\underset{L}{\begin{bmatrix} \ell_{11} & 0 \\ \ell_{21} & \ell_{22} \end{bmatrix}} \underset{U}{\begin{bmatrix} 1 & u_{12} \\ 0 & 1 \end{bmatrix}}.$$

Their product is

$$\begin{bmatrix} \ell_{11} + 0 & \ell_{11}u_{12} + 0 \\ \ell_{21} + 0 & \ell_{21}u_{12} + \ell_{22} \end{bmatrix} = \underset{LU}{\begin{bmatrix} \ell_{11} & \ell_{11}u_{12} \\ \ell_{21} & \ell_{21}u_{12} + \ell_{22} \end{bmatrix}}.$$

*Except for incompressible problems with only rate-specified wells, the coefficient matrices in reservoir simulation always have inverses.

TABLE 6.2—SOLUTION METHODS

Direct	Iterative
Gaussian elimination	Relaxation
Band	Point
A3	SOR
D4	Jacobi
Nested dissection	Line and Block
Matrix decomposition	LSOR
	Block SOR
	Additive correction
	Alternating direction
	Factorization and minimization
	SIP
	Conjugate gradient
	Orthomin
	Nested factorization

If L and U are factors of A, then $LU=A$, and every element in the product LU will be identical to the corresponding element in A. That is,

$$\ell_{11}=a_{11}$$

and

$$\ell_{11}u_{12}=a_{12};$$

thus

$$u_{12}=\frac{a_{12}}{a_{11}},$$

$$\ell_{21}=a_{21},$$

and

$$\ell_{21}u_{12}+\ell_{22}=a_{22};$$

thus

$$\ell_{22}=a_{22}-\frac{a_{21}a_{12}}{a_{11}}.$$

Hence, the two factors are

$$\underbrace{\begin{bmatrix} a_{11} & 0 \\ a_{21} & a_{22}-\dfrac{a_{21}a_{12}}{a_{11}} \end{bmatrix}}_{L}\underbrace{\begin{bmatrix} 1 & a_{12}/a_{11} \\ 0 & 1 \end{bmatrix}}_{U}.$$

L and U are triangular matrices; L is a lower triangular matrix and U is an upper triangular matrix. If a_{11} happened to be zero, we could not form L and U, because we could not divide by a_{11}. In general, we might be forced to reorder columns or rows of A to avoid dividing by zero. The coefficient matrices arising in reservoir simulation, however, almost never require such reordering.

There are numerous variants of matrix factorization. These will not be discussed except to mention LDU factorization that, in addition to upper and lower triangular factors, includes a third, diagonal matrix as a factor.

6.7 Solution Methods

Most simulators provide more than one method for solving the reservoir flow equations. To select the best method for a particular problem, it is not necessary to know in detail how the available *solvers* work. It is useful, however, to understand the underlying principles of the various solution methods so that their strengths and weaknesses can be properly appreciated when one of several options must be exercised. It is also useful to develop and to maintain sufficient understanding of solution methods to be able to follow the literature.

In this section, we will describe, somewhat superficially, the solution methods that are most widely used currently. We will also describe a few techniques that are of historical significance only, but that remain useful for expository purposes. Table 6.2 lists the solution methods of interest; not all of these will be discussed. Additional discussion of the most useful current methods is included in Appendix C.

Solution methods are either iterative or direct. The basis of an iterative method is the development of an "approximate" solution to the system of equations. The approximation is replaced systematically until the answers "converge" to the "correct" answers. In a direct method, as the name implies, the algorithm that is used solves the equations "exactly" and will give a correct answer in a fixed number of steps.

6.7.1 Direct Methods.

6.7.1.1 Gaussian Elimination. A method of solving for p that leads to the same number of computations as LU factorization is Gaussian elimination. The idea in Gaussian elimination is to eliminate the first unknown, p_1, from all equations but the first, leaving a new system with one less equation and one less unknown. This process is repeated with the new system to eliminate p_2. A continuation of the process results in a sequence of smaller and smaller matrix equations until eventually the system is reduced to a scalar equation that can be solved by a division.

For instance, consider the small set of equations (Eq. 6.22) used earlier to illustrate matrix notation:

$$\begin{bmatrix} a_{11} & a_{12} & a_{13} \\ a_{21} & a_{22} & a_{23} \\ a_{31} & a_{32} & a_{33} \end{bmatrix}\begin{bmatrix} p_1 \\ p_2 \\ p_3 \end{bmatrix}=\begin{bmatrix} q_1 \\ q_2 \\ q_3 \end{bmatrix}.$$

Working forward, eliminate a_{21} by multiplying Row 1 (the first equation) by a_{21}/a_{11} and subtracting the result from Row 2 (the second equation). Eliminate a_{31} in a similar manner. The result is

$$\begin{bmatrix} a_{11} & a_{12} & a_{13} \\ 0 & a_{22}-\dfrac{a_{12}a_{21}}{a_{11}} & a_{23}-\dfrac{a_{13}a_{21}}{a_{11}} \\ 0 & a_{32}-\dfrac{a_{12}a_{31}}{a_{11}} & a_{33}-\dfrac{a_{13}a_{31}}{a_{11}} \end{bmatrix}\begin{bmatrix} p_1 \\ p_2 \\ p_3 \end{bmatrix}$$

$$=\begin{bmatrix} q_1 \\ q_2-q_1\dfrac{a_{21}}{a_{11}} \\ q_3-q_1\dfrac{a_{31}}{a_{11}} \end{bmatrix} \quad \text{(6.26)}$$

or

$$\begin{bmatrix} a_{11} & a_{12} & a_{13} \\ 0 & a'_{22} & a'_{23} \\ 0 & a'_{32} & a'_{33} \end{bmatrix}\begin{bmatrix} p_1 \\ p_2 \\ p_3 \end{bmatrix}=\begin{bmatrix} q_1 \\ q'_2 \\ q'_3 \end{bmatrix}, \quad \text{(6.27)}$$

where the primed letters are shorthand symbols for the corresponding elements in Eq. 6.26.

Eliminate a'_{32} by multiplying Row 2 by a'_{32}/a'_{22} and subtracting the result from Row 3:

$$\begin{bmatrix} a_{11} & a_{12} & a_{13} \\ 0 & a'_{22} & a'_{23} \\ 0 & 0 & a''_{33} \end{bmatrix}\begin{bmatrix} p_1 \\ p_2 \\ p_3 \end{bmatrix}=\begin{bmatrix} q_1 \\ q'_2 \\ q''_3 \end{bmatrix}. \quad \text{(6.28)}$$

Eq. 6.28 can be solved explicitly for $p_3=q''_3/a''_3$ and, subsequently, for p_2 and p_1.

Note that the result of working forward converts the coefficient matrix to a triangular matrix with only one element in the last row. All terms to the left of the diagonal are zero, so this is an *upper triangular matrix*. Note also that even with this small set of equations, large amounts of arithmetic and storage are required for direct solution. There are many variants of Gaussian elimination; all require essentially the same amount of work and retain some other characteristics in common.

1. The coefficient matrix is converted into one or more triangular matrices that are then "easy" to solve.
2. A large fraction of the arithmetic is involved in the conversion to triangular form.

6.7.1.2 Band Matrix Equations. As mentioned earlier, the coefficient matrices in reservoir simulation problems are band matrices. For small band matrices, direct solution by factorization is an efficient method. For example, for 2D areal models less than 15 gridblocks in width, direct solution by factorization usually will be the preferred method. The concept of factorization was illustrated above for a 2×2 matrix, but that discussion did not show how factorization can exploit the sparseness of the matrix—i.e., the zeros outside the band. The effect of sparseness on the amount of work required to solve the equations will be illustrated here for a 3×3 band matrix:

$$\underset{A}{\begin{bmatrix} a_{11} & a_{12} & 0 \\ a_{21} & a_{22} & a_{23} \\ 0 & a_{32} & a_{33} \end{bmatrix}} \underset{p}{\begin{bmatrix} p_1 \\ p_2 \\ p_3 \end{bmatrix}} = \underset{q}{\begin{bmatrix} q_1 \\ q_2 \\ q_3 \end{bmatrix}} . \qquad (6.29)$$

A will be factored into upper and lower triangular matrices, chosen such that the upper triangular matrix contains only ones on its main diagonal.

$$\underset{L}{\begin{bmatrix} \ell_{11} & 0 & 0 \\ \ell_{21} & \ell_{22} & 0 \\ \ell_{31} & \ell_{32} & \ell_{33} \end{bmatrix}} \underset{U}{\begin{bmatrix} 1 & u_{12} & u_{13} \\ 0 & 1 & u_{23} \\ 0 & 0 & 1 \end{bmatrix}} = \underset{A}{\begin{bmatrix} a_{11} & a_{12} & 0 \\ a_{21} & a_{22} & a_{23} \\ 0 & a_{32} & a_{33} \end{bmatrix}} . \qquad (6.30)$$

The product LU equals

$$\begin{bmatrix} \ell_{11}+0+0 & \ell_{11}u_{12}+0\ +0 & \ell_{11}u_{13}+0\ \ +0 \\ \ell_{21}+0+0 & \ell_{21}u_{12}+\ell_{22}+0 & \ell_{21}u_{13}+\ell_{22}u_{23}+0 \\ \ell_{31}+0+0 & \ell_{31}u_{12}+\ell_{32}+0 & \ell_{31}u_{13}+\ell_{32}u_{23}+\ell_{33} \end{bmatrix} .$$

Setting corresponding elements in LU and A equal (and omitting unnecessary zeros) gives

$$\begin{aligned} &\ell_{11}=a_{11} \quad \ell_{11}u_{12}=a_{12} \quad \ell_{11}u_{13}=0 \\ &\ell_{21}=a_{21} \quad \ell_{21}u_{12}+\ell_{22}=a_{22} \quad \ell_{22}u_{23}=a_{23} . \\ &\ell_{31}=0 \quad \ell_{32}=a_{32} \quad \ell_{32}u_{23}+\ell_{33}=a_{33} \end{aligned} \qquad (6.31)$$

All elements in L and U can now be solved in terms of elements of A:

$$\underset{L}{\begin{bmatrix} a_{11} & 0 & 0 \\ a_{21} & a_{22}-\dfrac{a_{12}a_{21}}{a_{11}} & 0 \\ 0 & a_{32} & a_{33}-a_{32}\dfrac{a_{11}a_{23}}{a_{11}a_{22}-a_{12}a_{21}} \end{bmatrix}}$$

$$\times \underset{U}{\begin{bmatrix} 1 & \dfrac{a_{12}}{a_{11}} & 0 \\ 0 & 1 & \dfrac{a_{11}a_{23}}{a_{11}a_{22}-a_{12}a_{21}} \\ 0 & 0 & 1 \end{bmatrix}} . \qquad (6.32)$$

The elements ℓ_{31} and u_{13} are zero because a_{31} and a_{13} are zero. More generally, if $a_{rc}=0$ for all r and c for which $|r-c|>[(w-1)/2]$, then $\ell_{rc}=0$ and $u_{rc}=0$ for the same set of r's and c's. (w is the bandwidth of the matrix—i.e., the total number of diagonals needed to define the matrix.)

The triangular form of the two matrices makes it easy to solve for p. Recall that $LUp=q$ because $Ap=q$ and $LU=A$. As stated earlier, the solution is a two-step process.

1. Define a dummy variable g and let $Up=g$. Then, solve the equation $Lg=q$ for g.
2. Knowing g, solve $Up=g$ for p.

Step 1. $Lg=q$.

$$\underset{L}{\begin{bmatrix} \ell_{11} & 0 & 0 \\ \ell_{21} & \ell_{22} & 0 \\ 0 & \ell_{32} & \ell_{33} \end{bmatrix}} \underset{g}{\begin{bmatrix} g_1 \\ g_2 \\ g_3 \end{bmatrix}} = \underset{q}{\begin{bmatrix} q_1 \\ q_2 \\ q_3 \end{bmatrix}} .$$

Thus, $g_1=q_1/\ell_{11}$, $g_2=(q_2-\ell_{21}g_1)/\ell_{22}$, and $g_3=(q_3-\ell_{32}g_2)/\ell_{33}$, where the values of ℓ_{11}, ℓ_{21}, etc., are given in Eq. 6.32.

Step 2. $Up=g$.

$$\begin{bmatrix} 1 & u_{12} & 0 \\ 0 & 1 & u_{23} \\ 0 & 0 & 1 \end{bmatrix} \begin{bmatrix} p_1 \\ p_2 \\ p_3 \end{bmatrix} = \begin{bmatrix} g_1 \\ g_2 \\ g_3 \end{bmatrix} .$$

Thus, $p_3=g_3$, $p_2=g_2-u_{23}p_3$, and $p_1=g_1-u_{12}p_2$, where, again, the values u_{12} and u_{23} are given in Eq. 6.32.

Some readers may find it useful to solve a numerical problem with this method. For example, solve for p_1, p_2, and p_3 in the matrix equation

$$\begin{bmatrix} 1 & 1 & 1 \\ 1 & 2 & 3 \\ 1 & 3 & 5 \end{bmatrix} \begin{bmatrix} p_1 \\ p_2 \\ p_3 \end{bmatrix} = \begin{bmatrix} 15 \\ 34 \\ 53 \end{bmatrix} .$$

6.7.1.3 Ordering the Equations. In solving the three subequations in Eq. 6.22, the first terms of the second and third equations were eliminated by appropriate operations on the first equation and then on the modified second equation. Alternatively, terms in the first and second or first and third equations could have been eliminated. The order of the equations is arbitrary and, for a set of equations with no zero terms, the order of elimination does not influence the amount of work that must be done to solve the equations. If many terms in a set of equations are zero, however, the amount of work to solve the set can be very dependent on how the zero terms are handled. This point is readily illustrated with a small set of equations in which some terms are zero.

$$\underset{A_1}{\begin{bmatrix} a_{11} & a_{12} & a_{13} \\ a_{21} & 0 & a_{23} \\ 0 & a_{32} & a_{33} \end{bmatrix}} \underset{p}{\begin{bmatrix} p_1 \\ p_2 \\ p_3 \end{bmatrix}} = \underset{q}{\begin{bmatrix} q_1 \\ q_2 \\ q_3 \end{bmatrix}} . \qquad (6.33)$$

Elimination of a_{21} from the coefficient matrix requires one division and two multiplications: a_{21}/a_{11}, and a_{21}/a_{11} times a_{12} and a_{13}. The result is

$$\underset{A_2}{\begin{bmatrix} a_{11} & a_{12} & a_{13} \\ 0 & a'_{22} & a'_{23} \\ 0 & a_{32} & a_{33} \end{bmatrix}} .$$

By contrast, elimination of a_{11} requires one division and only one multiplication: a_{11}/a_{21} and a_{11}/a_{21} times a_{23}.

$$\underset{A_3}{\begin{bmatrix} 0 & a_{12} & a'_{13} \\ a_{21} & 0 & a_{23} \\ 0 & a_{32} & a_{33} \end{bmatrix}} .$$

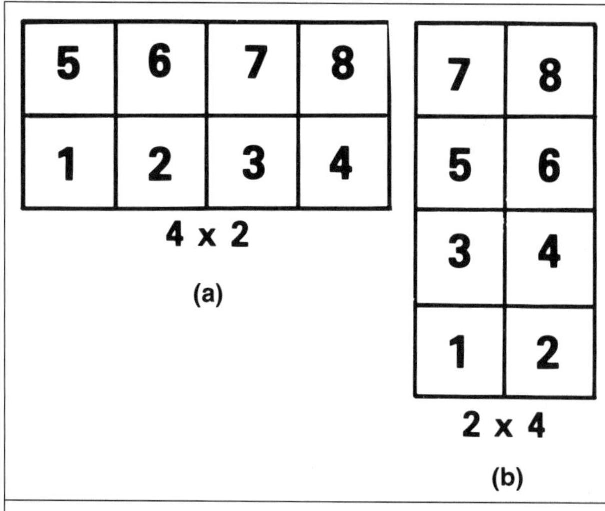

Fig. 6.3—Standard ordering of model gridblocks: (a) 4 × 2 and (b) 2 × 4.

(a) 4 x 2

	1	2	3	4	5	6	7	8
1	X	X			X			
2	X	X	X			X		
3		X	X	X			X	
4			X	X				X
5	X				X	X		
6		X			X	X	X	
7			X			X	X	X
8				X			X	X

(b) 2 x 4

	1	2	3	4	5	6	7	8
1	X	X	X					
2	X	X		X				
3	X		X	X	X			
4		X	X	X		X		
5			X		X	X	X	
6				X	X	X		X
7					X		X	X
8						X	X	X

Fig. 6.4—Shorthand notation for coefficient matrices: (a) 4 × 2 and (b) 2 × 4.

In either case, a_{32} can be eliminated with one division and one multiplication:

$$A_2 \rightarrow \begin{bmatrix} a_{11} & a_{12} & a_{13} \\ 0 & a'_{22} & a'_{23} \\ 0 & 0 & a'_{33} \end{bmatrix}$$
$$A_4$$

and

$$A_3 \rightarrow \begin{bmatrix} 0 & a_{12} & a'_{13} \\ a_{21} & 0 & a_{23} \\ 0 & 0 & a'_{33} \end{bmatrix}.$$
$$A_5$$

Thus, to solve the equations through the route $A_1 \rightarrow A_2 \rightarrow A_4$ requires five coefficient multiplication/divisions compared with four multiplication/divisions for the route $A_1 \rightarrow A_3 \rightarrow A_5$. Observe that A_4 has one less zero than A_5. In effect, one of the multiplications in $A_1 \rightarrow A_2$ was wasted in filling in the zero at Location 2,2. The objective of all sparse matrix techniques for direct solution is to order the equations in a way that minimizes the number of zeros that are filled in during the process of elimination.

6.7.1.4 Standard Ordering. To continue the discussion, it will be convenient to use another bit of shorthand notation. In a coefficient matrix, the presence of a nonzero element will be identified by "x"; if an element is zero, the appropriate space will be left blank. With this notation,

$$\begin{bmatrix} a_{11} & a_{12} & 0 \\ a_{21} & a_{22} & a_{23} \\ 0 & a_{32} & a_{33} \end{bmatrix}$$

is represented as

$$\begin{bmatrix} x & x & \\ x & x & x \\ & x & x \end{bmatrix}.$$

Simplified notations will also be used to identify gridblocks for the purpose of indicating the order in which terms in the pressure equations for gridblocks appear in the coefficient matrix. A gridblock will be identified by a single number, and terms in the equations will be keyed to gridblock numbers.

For example, in standard ordering, blocks in an $(N_x) \times (N_y)$ model (N_x blocks in each row and N_y blocks in each column) are numbered row by row in sequence within a row from Rows 1 through N_y. For example, 4×2 and 2×4 models are numbered as shown in Fig. 6.3. With the simplified notation, the pressure equation (refer to Eq. 6.13) for Block 2 of the 4×2 model is

$$D_2 p_1 + E_2 p_2 + F_2 p_3 + H_2 p_6 = q_2,$$

where the subscripts refer to block numbers. The equation involves only four pressures because Block 2 communicates only with Blocks 1, 3, and 6. The coefficient matrices for these two models are shown in Fig. 6.4.

The total number of equations, $N_x \cdot N_y = 8$, is the same for both models, of course, but the distribution of terms within the matrices for the two models differs. The coefficient matrix for the 4×2 model is a band matrix of Bandwidth 9; i.e., the matrix spans nine diagonals even though Upper and Lower Diagonals 3 and 4 are empty. The matrix for the 2×4 model has a bandwidth of 5.

The work required to solve a set of band matrix equations with the factorization method discussed earlier is a function of the bandwidth as well as the number of equations. Solving the 4×2 model in Fig. 6.4 would take more than twice as much work as solving the 2×4 model. Thus, if a standard ordering of the equations is used, numbering should be in sequence in the "short" direction.

6.7.1.5 Other Orderings. Of the many conceivable ordering schemes, those used most in current simulations are the standard ordering, A3, D4, and nested dissection. Ordering of a 6×5 block model with A3 and D4 ordering is illustrated in Fig. 6.5. Scheme A3 is also known as red/black or checkerboard ordering for reasons that are apparent in the figure. In D4 ordering, numbering is in order along alternate diagonals. Locations of the elements in the resultant matrices are illustrated in Figs. 6.6 and 6.7, adapted from Price and Coats.[12]

The sparseness of the upper left quadrant of these two orderings of the equation facilitates use of Gaussian elimination to remove all terms in the lower left quadrant. This operation is conveniently expressed in matrix notation if the matrices are *partitioned* at the boundaries of the quadrants into four blocks, each of which includes all the elements of the quadrant it represents; i.e.,

$$\begin{bmatrix} B_{11} & B_{12} \\ B_{21} & B_{22} \end{bmatrix}.$$

Note that partitioning is not an arithmetic operation; it is only convenient shorthand notation. The set of equations can then be expressed as

$$\begin{bmatrix} B_{11} & B_{12} \\ B_{21} & B_{22} \end{bmatrix} \begin{bmatrix} p_1 \\ p_2 \end{bmatrix} = \begin{bmatrix} q_1 \\ q_2 \end{bmatrix}. \quad \text{(6.34)}$$

In this instance, Gaussian elimination on the partitioned matrix is expressed in the same manner as if the matrix represented two simple

(a)

13	28	14	29	15	30
25	10	26	11	27	12
7	22	8	23	9	24
19	4	20	5	21	6
1	16	2	17	3	18

(b)

5	22	10	27	14	30
18	6	23	11	28	15
2	19	7	24	12	29
16	3	20	8	25	13
1	17	4	21	9	26

Fig. 6.5—Ordering of gridblocks: (a) A3 and (b) D4.

equations: eliminate B_{21} by multiplying the first equation by $B_{21}B_{11}^{-1}$ and subtracting the result from the second equation. The result is

$$B'_{22}p_2 = q'_2,$$

where

$$B'_{22} = B_{22} - B_{21}B_{11}^{-1}B_{12}$$

and

$$q'_2 = q_2 - B_{21}B_{11}^{-1}q_1.$$

Only a small amount of work is required to form B'_{22}, because B_{11} is a diagonal matrix and its inverse, B_{11}^{-1}, is simply the term-by-term reciprocal of each of the diagonal terms. To complete the solution, solve $B'_{22}p_2 = q'_2$ by band Gaussian elimination (most of the work is in this step), then solve for p_1.

Additional nonzero entries created by forming B'_{22} for the D4 ordering are indicated by zeros in Fig. 6.7. Although matrices for A3 and D4 orderings appear almost identical, the D4 scheme is more efficient than A3. D4 is more difficult to program, however, and has more computational overhead, so A3 is sometimes preferred.

For models with a large number of blocks, the most efficient ordering of equations for direct solution is obtained by *nested dissection.*[13] This scheme orders the equations in small groups that are within larger groups. These larger groups are, in turn, within still larger groups, and the order continues in this fashion. The result is an increase in the density of terms near the main diagonal of the matrix and a consequent reduction in the number of empty terms that must be filled during the elimination process. A general impression of the ordering is apparent in Fig. 6.8, which shows that

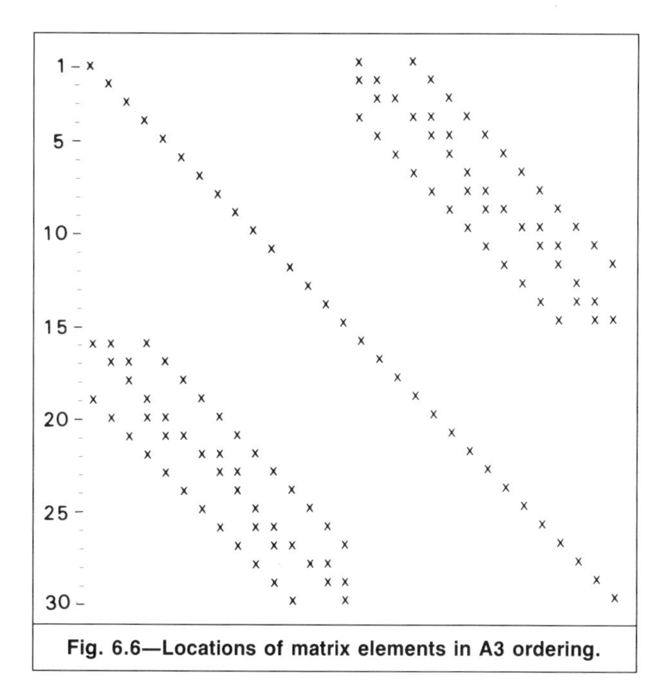

Fig. 6.6—Locations of matrix elements in A3 ordering.

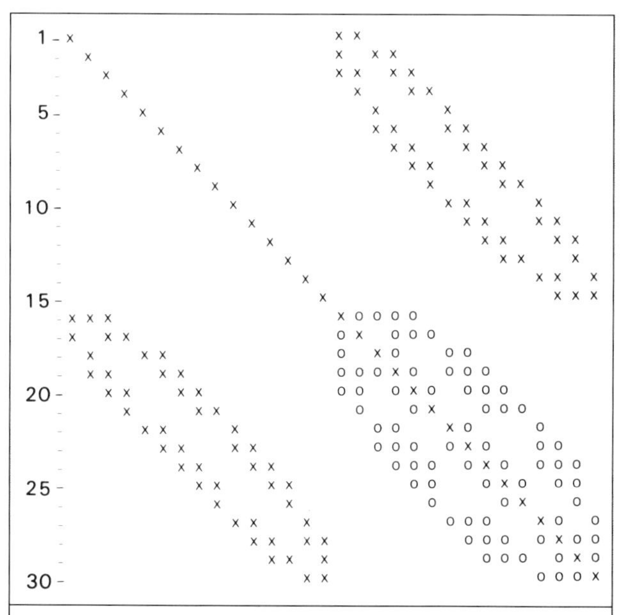

Fig. 6.7—Locations of matrix elements in D4 ordering. (Zeros represent elements added in the elimination process. See text.)

nested-dissection ordering separates a 5×5 grid into four corner "nests" and a "cross." Visually, the ordering seems less structured than standard, A3, or D4 ordering. The ordering is systematic, however, in that at any stage of the process, the terms to be eliminated next are associated with groups of gridblocks having the fewest remaining unknowns.

Graham and Jennings[14] demonstrated that for problems of practical size, nested dissection outperforms standard, A3, or D4 orderings. They cautioned that use of nested dissection requires careful design of the computer program to minimize the amount of computing overhead needed to manage the ordering scheme. Also, the scheme is not well-suited for implementation on vector computers.

6.7.2 Iterative Methods. In large areal models and in 3D models, it is usually more economical to solve a problem with iterative rather than direct methods. In an iterative method, a systematic repeated approximation procedure is used until the "answers" generated by the procedure approach the "true answers" to within specified tolerances (convergence criteria).

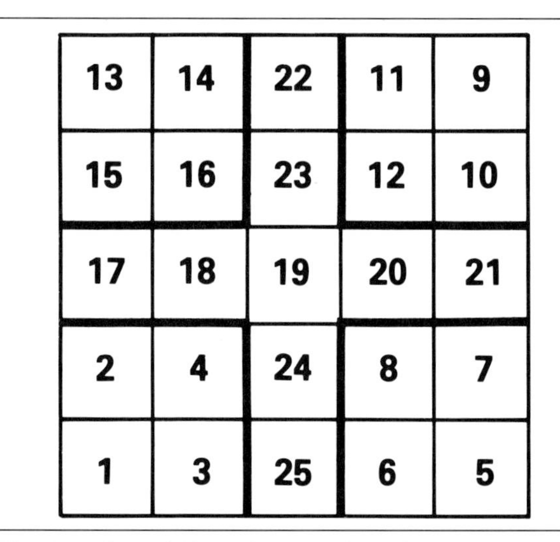

Fig. 6.8—Nested-dissection ordering of a 5×5 gridblock model.

The incentives to develop iterative methods stem from the work and storage dependence of direct methods on the numbers of gridblocks in each coordinate direction. The work required for a direct method can be (and usually is) many times that required for a single iteration of an iterative method. But the work required for an iterative method also depends on the number of iterations needed for the solution to meet convergence criteria. Hence, the rapidity with which an iterative method converges will be a primary factor in the comparison of one method with another.

Many iterative methods use *iteration parameters* to speed up solution convergence. The selection of these parameters sometimes is left to the user of the simulator because the parameters are dependent on both the solution method used and the particular problem being solved. Although a proper selection of method and parameters will usually lead to a solution, the selection process can be time-consuming and expensive. In some cases, it is not possible to find parameters that will lead to convergence and an alternative method must be used. Fortunately, most recently developed iterative methods require little or no user intervention.

6.7.2.1 Point Relaxation. Only the pressure equations will be considered in the following discussions. For an interior gridblock in a 2D model, recall that the general form of the equation is

$$-B_{i,j}p_{i,j-1}-D_{i,j}p_{i-1,j}+E_{i,j}p_{i,j}$$
$$-F_{i,j}p_{i+1,j}-H_{i,j}p_{i,j+1}=q_{i,j}.$$

There are five unknowns in this equation: the values of p at each gridblock. The known coefficients B, D, E, F, and H are functions of reservoir characteristics and gridblock dimensions. q is also known and may contain information concerning well rates and information from previous timesteps.

One way to solve for $p^n_{i,j}$ is to guess the values of all the other pressures:

$$p_{i,j}=\frac{1}{E_{i,j}}(q_{i,j}+B_{i,j}p_{i,j-1}+D_{i,j}p_{i-1,j}$$
$$+F_{i,j}p_{i+1,j}+H_{i,j}p_{i,j+1}).$$

When this calculation is repeated for all equations in the system, a new pressure array is created. This array is then checked to see if the values satisfy the gridblock equations. To do this, it is convenient to define a *residual* $r_{i,j}$ for each equation by rearranging the terms in the original equation:

$$r_{i,j}=q_{i,j}+(B_{i,j}p_{i,j-1}+D_{i,j}p_{i-1,j}-E_{i,j}p_{i,j}$$
$$+F_{i,j}p_{i+1,j}+H_{i,j}p_{i,j+1}).$$

If the new values satisfy the equations, then all residuals will be zero or very small. If not, the process is repeated with updated p values that are based on the previous iteration. This process is repeated until all the residuals are acceptably close to zero.

This type of iterative method is called a "point" iterative method because the method does not involve the simultaneous solution of coupled equations. Variations of this point method also have been considered. The Gauss-Seidel method uses the most recent estimates of pressures in neighboring blocks (i.e., in the evaluation of the right side of the original equation). Methods of this type are called "relaxation" methods (see Appendix C).

Other procedural variations have also been suggested in an effort to improve the convergence rate of the iterative scheme. For example, some relaxation methods use $p_{i,j}$ values calculated in the most recent iteration (e.g., $p^k_{i,j}$ from the kth iteration) to adjust values calculated in the next $(k+1)$ iteration. It seems intuitively reasonable that a procedure that includes a dependence on $p^k_{i,j}$ could lead to a better procedure. One possibility is as follows:

$$(p^{k+1}_{i,j})^{\text{new}}=p^k_{i,j}+\omega(p^{k+1}_{i,j}-p^k_{i,j}).$$

$(p^{k+1}_{i,j})^{\text{new}}$ is then used instead of $p^{k+1}_{i,j}$ in subsequent calculations for other gridblocks. This particular procedure has been called "overrelaxation" if the value of ω is greater than one. Although proper choice of ω will accelerate the convergence of the procedure, methods for determining the best choice of ω do not always work. The best value of ω will lie between 1 and 2; however, convergence speed can be sensitive to the exact choice.

6.7.2.2 Line and Block Relaxation. Successful application of point-relaxation methods in reservoir simulation is restricted to relatively simple reservoir descriptions. Because point methods are "explicit" methods in which only one unknown value is calculated at a time, some of the shortcomings of explicit methods noted in the formulations section also affect the solution of the equations. These restrictions have led to efforts to include more implicitness in the solution method. In line-relaxation methods, implicitness is preserved in one direction. The equations for a column or a row are solved simultaneously while the contributions of adjacent columns or rows are kept at their most recent estimates. In essence, a 2D problem is solved as a series of 1D problems. This "1D" approach is repeated for each column or row in the system, and the procedure is repeated until convergence is reached.

Although the work requirement for a single iteration of line relaxation is somewhat greater than for point relaxation, the convergence rate is faster and the overall work requirement is less for line relaxation.

In a line-relaxation procedure, the orientation of the lines is important. If there is a predominant direction of high transmissibility, the lines should be oriented in this direction.

"Block relaxation" is a natural extension of line relaxation, in which more than one line is included in the implicit portion of the overall procedure. As the number of lines included in the block is increased, the work required to solve the basic equations increases because the subsolutions are now 2D. In the limit, as the size of the block is increased to include the entire system, block relaxation is the same as a direct elimination method. For large problems, some optimal blocking exists that will minimize the total work requirement.

All the relaxation procedures described above can be extended to 3D problems. The subregions can be lines, groups of lines, planes, or groups of planes.

Attempts have been made to accelerate the convergence of a relaxation procedure by *correcting* the values of $p_{i,j}$ at some point in the iteration. A method suggested by Watts[15,16] provides an additive correction to each $p_{i,j}$ value in a given column (or row), which forces the $p_{i,j}$ values to be "better" in some sense and leads to a more rapid convergence. Each column will have a different additive correction value. The column corrections are found by requiring that the sum of the residuals for all blocks in a given column be zero when the residuals are evaluated with the corrected $p_{i,j}$ values. For 2D problems, the summation of residuals for each column leads to a tridiagonal set of equations involving the correction terms, because each column is directly influenced only by the immediately adjacent column. The column corrections are applied at selected iterations until convergence is reached.

6.7.3 Alternating Direction Methods. Peaceman and Rachford[17] proposed one of the first methods for solving the equations describing multidimensional reservoir flow problems. Computationally, their method is similar to line relaxation, with the implicit direction alternating successively between rows and columns. The method works well in systems having fairly uniform permeabilities and in problems in which the direction of fluid movement does not change drastically. In heterogeneous systems or when flow direction changes sharply (as in coning), however, there are superior methods. Because of these limitations, the method is seldom used.

6.7.4 Factorization and Minimization Methods. Among the most useful current methods for solving large simulation problems are those using *approximate-factorization* techniques. Recall that in direct elimination, the coefficient matrix is factored into triangular matrices with a series of arithmetic operations on the coefficient matrix. The procedures are rigorous and the factors are exact; i.e., the product of the factors is identical term-by-term with the original unfactored coefficient matrix. For larger problems, creating the factors can become prohibitively expensive. In an approximate-factorization scheme, the work of rigorous factorization is avoided by using factors whose product is similar but not identical to the original matrix. The advantage of developing approximate factors is that, to a degree, they can be designed for ease of solution. The disadvantage is that iteration is required to obtain a satisfactory solution.

6.7.4.1 SIP. The first approximate-factorization technique that was successfully applied to many types of simulation problems was Stone's[18] SIP. SIP will be discussed in some detail to illustrate the use of approximate factorization. It is probably easiest to explain SIP by considering the smallest model that will clearly demonstrate the features of the method (see Fig. 6.9). The pressure equations, written with subscripts referring to the gridblock numbers assigned to the model, are

Block

$$\begin{array}{c} 1\\2\\3\\4\\5\\6\\7\\8\\9 \end{array} \begin{bmatrix} E_1 & F_1 & & H_1 & & & & & \\ D_2 & E_2 & F_2 & & H_2 & & & & \\ & D_3 & E_3 & & & H_3 & & & \\ B_4 & & & E_4 & F_4 & & H_4 & & \\ & B_5 & & D_5 & E_5 & F_5 & & H_5 & \\ & & B_6 & & D_6 & E_6 & & & H_6 \\ & & & B_7 & & & E_7 & F_7 & \\ & & & & B_8 & & D_8 & E_8 & F_8 \\ & & & & & B_9 & & D_9 & E_9 \end{bmatrix}$$

$$A$$

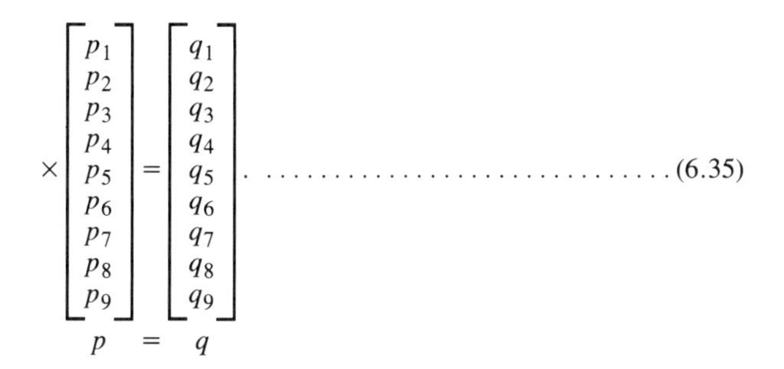

$$\times \begin{bmatrix} p_1\\p_2\\p_3\\p_4\\p_5\\p_6\\p_7\\p_8\\p_9 \end{bmatrix} = \begin{bmatrix} q_1\\q_2\\q_3\\q_4\\q_5\\q_6\\q_7\\q_8\\q_9 \end{bmatrix} \qquad (6.35)$$

$$p \;=\; q$$

For simplicity, the appropriate positive or negative signs are embedded in the coefficients (nomenclature for the pressure coefficients in the above equations was defined earlier).

Previous discussions demonstrated that A can be factored into upper and lower triangular matrices, L and U. Suppose, for the moment, that all upper and lower terms that are zero in A are also zero in L and U, respectively, and that the diagonal terms of U

7	8	9
4	5	6
1	2	3

Fig. 6.9—Ordering of gridblocks in the model used to discuss SIP.

are all ones. If L and U can be found, they will contain terms at the positions indicated:

$$\begin{bmatrix} e_1 & & & & & & & & \\ d_2 & e_2 & & & & & & & \\ & d_3 & e_3 & & & & & & \\ b_4 & & & e_4 & & & & & \\ & b_5 & & d_5 & e_5 & & & & \\ & & b_6 & & d_6 & e_6 & & & \\ & & & b_7 & & & e_7 & & \\ & & & & b_8 & & d_8 & e_8 & \\ & & & & & b_9 & & d_9 & e_9 \end{bmatrix}$$

$$L$$

$$\times \begin{bmatrix} 1 & f_1 & & h_1 & & & & & \\ & 1 & f_2 & & h_2 & & & & \\ & & 1 & & & h_3 & & & \\ & & & 1 & f_4 & & h_4 & & \\ & & & & 1 & f_5 & & h_5 & \\ & & & & & 1 & & & h_6 \\ & & & & & & 1 & f_7 & \\ & & & & & & & 1 & f_8 \\ & & & & & & & & 1 \end{bmatrix} \qquad (6.36)$$

$$U$$

Define A' to be the product of L and U. A' contains the following terms:

$$\begin{bmatrix} E'_1 & F'_1 & & H'_1 & & & & & \\ D'_2 & E'_2 & F'_2 & G'_2 & H'_2 & & & & \\ & D'_3 & E'_3 & & G'_3 & H'_3 & & & \\ B'_4 & C'_4 & & E'_4 & F'_4 & & H'_4 & & \\ & B'_5 & C'_5 & D'_5 & E'_5 & F'_5 & G'_5 & H'_5 & \\ & & B'_6 & & D'_6 & E'_6 & & G'_6 & H'_6 \\ & & & B'_7 & C'_7 & & E'_7 & F'_7 & \\ & & & & B'_8 & C'_8 & D'_8 & E'_8 & F'_8 \\ & & & & & B'_9 & & D'_9 & E'_9 \end{bmatrix} \qquad (6.37)$$

$$A'$$

If L and U were exact factors of A, A' would be identical to A. A' and A are structurally similar. However, A' is not identical to A; A' contains terms on C' and G' diagonals whose elements are all zero in A. Hence, L and U are not exact factors of A.

To examine the significance of the extra terms, consider the equations generated from $A'p=q$ for Block 5:

$$B'_5p_2+C'_5p_3+D'_5p_4+E'_5p_5+F'_5p_6+G'_5p_7+H'_5p_8=q_5. \qquad (6.38)$$

The equation contains terms with coefficients in Blocks 3 and 7 that are diagonal to Block 5 and should not be coupled with it. (There can be no flow directly between Blocks 3 and 5 or Blocks 7 and 5.) If the diagonal terms could be somehow eliminated or reduced to relative insignificance, then A' would be sufficiently similar to A to be used in an iterative scheme to solve the pressure equations.

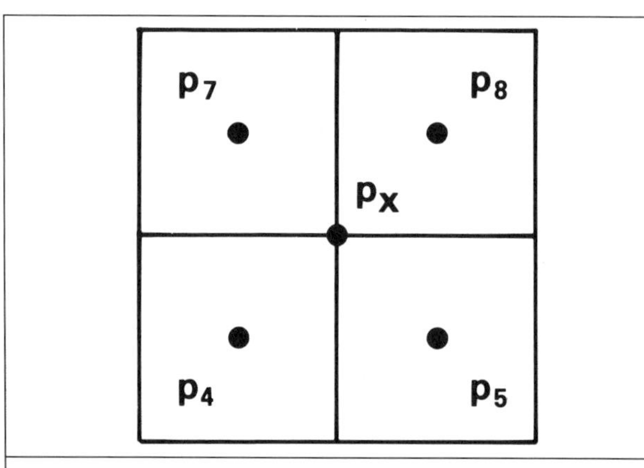

Fig. 6.10—Conceptual model illustrating the method used in SIP to estimate pressures in diagonal gridblocks.

In SIP, the effect of the extra terms is reduced by subtracting from A' an estimate of the values of these terms. Stone[18] deduced that estimates of pressures in the diagonal blocks could be derived from pressures in adjacent blocks. For example, the pressure in Block 7 that appears in the equation for Block 5 can be estimated from pressures in Blocks 4, 5, and 8 (Fig. 6.10).

As Fig. 6.10 suggests, if pressure gradients throughout the model vary relatively smoothly, then

$$p_x \simeq \frac{p_4+p_8}{2} \simeq \frac{p_7+p_5}{2},$$

from which

$$p_7 \simeq p_4+p_8-p_5.$$

In a similar manner,

$$p_3 \simeq p_2+p_6-p_5.$$

To add needed flexibility, because these values are inexact, the estimates are multiplied by an arbitrary parameter, α_k, whose value can be changed, if desired, at each iteration, k. The equation for Block 5, modified as previously described to "cancel" the spurious pressure terms, becomes

$$B'_5p_2+C'_5[p_3-\alpha_k(p_2+p_6-p_5)]+D'_5p_4+E'_5p_5+F'_5p_6$$
$$+G'_5[p_7-\alpha_k(p_4+p_8-p_5)]+H'_5p_8=q_5. \quad (6.39)$$

If p_3 and p_7 were exactly cancelled by the above subtraction, the C' and G' terms would vanish and Eq. 6.39 would be identical to Eq. 6.38; the primed coefficients, other than C' and G', would then be identical to coefficients in A, the original coefficient matrix.

Subtraction of the estimated pressures modifies L and U accordingly. The modified terms can be derived by collecting terms, removing the primes from the coefficients, and factoring as usual. For example,

$$b_5=B_5/(1+\alpha_k f_2),$$

$$d_5=D_5/(1+\alpha_k h_4),$$

$$e_5=E_5+\alpha_k b_5 f_2+\alpha_k d_5 h_4-b_5 h_2-d_5 f_4,$$

$$f_5=(F_5-\alpha_k b_5 f_2)/e_5,$$

and

$$h_5=(H_5-\alpha_k d_5 h_4)/e_5.$$

L and U, now with terms derived as above, can be used iteratively to solve the pressure equations. A series of values must be selected for the iteration parameter α_k. Simulators using SIP normally calculate these values because they should be tailored to a particular problem. See Appendix C for a discussion of iteration parameters and for a more rigorous description of SIP.

6.7.4.2 Minimization Methods. The most dependable current procedures for solving the pressure equations are minimization methods, such as *conjugate gradients.*[19] These methods almost always guarantee convergence to a solution,[20] usually are fast,[21-23] and do not require user intervention for the selection of iteration parameters.

Minimization methods are iterative and are almost always used in conjunction with *preconditioning* methods, such as the approximate-factorization methods just discussed. That is, a new matrix A' is created that "resembles" the true coefficient matrix A, but is designed such that A' is much more easily factored or inverted than A. Thus A' could be used to compute the *preconditioned matrix* $(A'^{-1}A)$. Explicit computation of this matrix, however, is unnecessary and is not done because of its expense.

Following is a qualitative description of minimization methods. Suppose the kth iteration has been completed and that p_k, the calculated values of p, are not acceptably close to their correct values. Recall that the equation being solved is $Ap=q$. Thus, the error in p leads to an error, r_k, in q equal to

$$A(p-p_k)=(q-Ap_k)=r_k.$$

The error in p, then, is

$$(p-p_k)=A^{-1}r_k.$$

The "true" values of the errors in p could be calculated by solving this equation but, of course, the intent is to avoid computing A^{-1}. The errors can be estimated by solving the equation with the approximate matrix A' rather than A. Thus, $(p-p_k)_E=A'^{-1}r_k$, where the subscript "E" denotes "estimate." For convenience in notation, let $t_k=(p-p_k)_E$. That is,

$$(p-p_k)\simeq t_k,$$

where

$$t_k=A'^{-1}r_k.$$

Because t_k is an estimate of the error in p, t_k can be used to adjust p_k to obtain updated estimates of pressure, p_{k+1}, which, presumably, contain less error than p_k.

$$p_{k+1}=p_k+t_k.$$

The process can be repeated for $k=0, 1, 2...$ until the estimated values of pressure converge to values acceptably close to the true values of p.

Convergence can be accelerated with an iteration parameter, α_k, such that $\alpha_k t_k$ rather than t_k is used to adjust p_k.

$$p_{k+1}=p_k+\alpha_k t_k. \quad (6.40)$$

Convergence will be even faster if the adjustment to p_k is influenced not only by t_k, the current value of t, but also the values of t from previous iterations. If a second iteration parameter, β_k, is used as a coefficient of t_{k-1}, the adjusted value of p then becomes

$$p_{k+1}=p_k+\alpha_k(t_k+\beta_k t_{k-1}+\beta_k\beta_{k-1}t_{k-2}$$
$$+\beta_k\beta_{k-1}\beta_{k-2}t_{k-3}+\ldots). \quad (6.41)$$

For convenience in notation, let $s_k=t_k+\beta_k s_{k-1}$. With this notation, Eq. 6.41 reduces to

$$p_{k+1}=p_k+\alpha_k s_k. \quad (6.42)$$

The iteration parameters α_k and β_k can be chosen so that errors in p and/or q are *minimized* as the iteration proceeds. An essential element of the iteration procedure is the automatic calculation of iteration parameters.

One of the first methods of this type was the conjugate-gradient[19] method, which minimizes the quantity

$$F_{k+1}=(p-p_{k+1})^T A(p-p_{k+1})=(p-p_{k+1})^T(q-Ap_{k+1}). \quad (6.43)$$

Note that the quantity that is minimized is the sum of the products of the estimated errors in p and q (refer to the discussion of a matrix transpose in Sec. 6.6). Unfortunately, this works only for symmetric matrices. Because reservoir simulation coefficient matrices are usually nonsymmetric, it is more appropriate to use methods that minimize

$$F_{k+1}=(p-p_{k+1})^T A^T A(p-p_{k+1})=(q-Ap_{k+1})^T(q-Ap_{k+1}). \quad (6.44)$$

This procedure minimizes the *sum of the squares* of the estimated errors in q (see Section 6.6.2). In essence, the result is a "least-squares" fit. This works for any matrix A that has an inverse. The most commonly used minimization method of this type is Vinsome's[24] orthomin method (see Appendix C).

A brief derivation* of α for the conjugate-gradient method will demonstrate the principles of this type of minimization technique. As indicated previously, the intent of the method is to use results from the most recent iteration, k, to minimize, in some fashion, the errors in p in the current iteration, $k+1$. In the conjugate-gradient method, the intent is to minimize the sum of the products of errors in p and q. That is, minimize F_{k+1} in Eq. 6.43. The iteration procedure is as follows.

1. Using the true coefficient matrix, compute the residual r_k:

$$r_k=q-Ap_k. \quad (6.45)$$

2. Using the approximate coefficient matrix, A', calculate initial estimates of the errors in p:

$$t_k=(p-p_k)_E=A'^{-1}(q-Ap_k)=A'^{-1}r_k. \quad (6.46)$$

3. Construct s_k as a linear combination of t_k and s_{k-1}:

$$s_k=t_k+\beta_k s_{k-1}. \quad (6.47)$$

4. Update the values of pressure:

$$p_{k+1}=p_k+\alpha_k s_k. \quad (6.48)$$

Clearly, the values of p_{k+1} will depend on the values of α_k and β_k used in the iteration. Hence F_{k+1} in Eq. 6.43 will be, in part, a function of α_k and β_k. Thus, F_{k+1} can be minimized by finding the values of α_k and β_k for which the derivatives of F_{k+1} with respect to α and β are zero—i.e., when

$$\frac{\partial F_{k+1}}{\partial \alpha}=0 \text{ and } \frac{\partial F_{k+1}}{\partial \beta}=0.$$

To find $\partial F_{k+1}/\partial \alpha$, substitute Eq. 6.48 into Eq. 6.43 and take the derivative.

$$F_{k+1}=[(p-p_k)-\alpha_k s_k]^T A[(p-p_k)-\alpha_k s_k] \quad (6.49)$$

and

$$\frac{\partial F_{k+1}}{\partial \alpha}=-s_k^T A[(p-p_k)-\alpha_k s_k]-[(p-p_k)-\alpha_k s_k]^T A s_k. \quad (6.50)$$

*The derivation was provided by a private communication from J.W. Watts III, Exxon Production Research Co., on June 1, 1986.

(The reader may wish to write out one term of Eq. 6.43 to verify Eq. 6.50.) If A is symmetric (see Sec. 6.6.2), the two terms of the derivative are equivalent and

$$\frac{\partial F_{k+1}}{\partial \alpha_k}=-2s_k^T A[(p-p_k)-\alpha_k s_k]. \quad (6.51)$$

Because

$$A(p-p_k)=Ap-Ap_k=q-Ap_k=r_k, \quad (6.52)$$

Eq. 6.51 can be written

$$\frac{\partial F_{k+1}}{\partial \alpha_k}=2[s_k^T(r_k-A\alpha_k s_k)].$$

If the derivative is equal to zero, then

$$s_k^T A(r_k-\alpha_k s_k)=s_k^T Ar_k-s_k^T\alpha_k s_k=0. \quad (6.53)$$

Solving for α_k yields

$$\alpha_k=\frac{s_k^T r_k}{s_k^T A s_k}. \quad (6.54)$$

To develop an expression for β, replace s_k in Eq. 6.49 with its equivalent from Eq. 6.47, take the derivative with respect to β, set the derivative equal to zero, and solve for β. The procedure will yield the following expression for β:

$$\beta_k=\frac{t_k^T r_k}{t_{k-1}^T r_{k-1}}. \quad (6.55)$$

6.7.4.3 Nested Factorization. One of the most reliable procedures for preconditioning a matrix for use in conjugate-gradient/orthomin methods is the *nested-factorization* procedure of Appleyard and Cheshire.[25] Nested factorization differs from previous approximate-factorization procedures in two interesting respects.

1. It does not factor A' into strictly upper and lower triangular matrices. Instead, it uses an LDU factorization that takes advantage of the inherently "nested" structure of the coefficient matrix by building the preconditioning matrix one dimension at a time. (See Eq. 6.35 for a visual impression of the "nesting" of coefficients. The D and F diagonals in that equation contain terms determining interactions *within* rows of blocks; the outlying B and H diagonals determine interactions *between* rows. Nested factorization exploits the potential of this structure.)

2. Nested factorization, in effect, rectifies errors of approximation by ensuring that the sum of all coefficients of a given pressure in A' and in the original coefficient matrix are equal. The result is that within every row of gridblocks (every plane of a 3D model), the material-balance errors sum identically to zero.

6.8 Selecting the Equation-Solving Technique

There are few definitive guidelines that can be offered as aids in the selection of an equation-solving technique. The selection may be influenced by many factors, including the availability of a particular method, the relative difficulty of finding optimal iteration parameters, and perhaps of most importance, the characteristics of the specific problem being solved. Model size and reservoir heterogeneity normally are the most important factors to consider. Clearly, the best approach is to select the technique on the basis of experimentation with the actual problem.

There are, however, a number of general guidelines that can be used with reasonable success in the absence of more definitive guidelines for a particular problem. These guidelines should be considered to be tentative and should be modified as data applicable to the problem become available. The guidelines were developed from experience and take into consideration cost, ease of use, and overall reliability.

Abbreviations used are number of gridblocks on the side of the model having the fewest number of blocks (N1), band-matrix direct solution method (BAND), nested factorization or other iterative method using conjugate-gradient/orthomin procedures (NF), line successive overrelaxation (with additive correction) and variants thereof (LSOR), and SIP.

6.8.1 Guidelines for Selecting a Solution Method.

Areal Models.

If N1 is small,* use BAND.

If N1 is intermediate, use either a direct solution method (e.g., BAND) with efficient ordering (such as A3, D4, or nested dissection) or NF.

If N1 is large, use an iterative method.

For large models, use NF.

Cross-Sectional Models.

For cross sections, use NF or LSOR unless N1 is very small.

If vertical communication is uniformly good, use LSOR.

3D Models.

A direct method will almost never be preferred in a 3D model.

If vertical communication is uniformly good, use LSOR. Otherwise, use NF or SIP.

In General.

If an iterative method is called for and there are too few data to make a conclusive decision, use NF. When using a vector computer, one normally should tend to favor the use of iterative methods over direct methods, the use of LSOR over SIP, and the use of LSOR and SIP over NF.

6.8.2 Comparison of Solution Methods in Practice.

There are a number of comparisons in the literature that can help in the initial selection of a technique. Price and Coats[12] compared work requirements of standard and alternate-diagonal direct methods and also included comparisons with selected iterative methods. Their work shows that for both 2D and 3D problems, the alternate-diagonal ordering will outperform standard ordering.

Settari and Aziz[26] compared the results of various iterative schemes for seven different problems. The problems they considered had various amounts of heterogeneity distributed over a square grid system. They concluded that no single method was superior for all the problems considered. Appleyard and Cheshire[25] showed that nested factorization outperforms other iterative procedures for the types of problems tested.

Our own experience with solution techniques has shown that direct methods can be used efficiently on models having fewer than about 40 blocks in the smallest plane. On models having more than about 15 blocks in the smallest plane, nested dissection is clearly a better ordering scheme than either standard or alternate-diagonal ordering if the equations are solved by direct solution procedures.

For larger problems, experience with SIP, LSOR, and nested factorization has shown that in situations with a uniformly oriented high contrast in transmissibility, LSOR is a very effective solution technique. This type of problem can arise if the vertical to horizontal permeability ratio of the rock is low or in nonradial cross sections and in 3D models where block dimensions will generally cause the transmissibility to be highest in the vertical direction. In problems where anisotropy is not well oriented, SIP or nested factorization have generally proved to be efficient techniques.

As stated earlier, there are many factors that control the effectiveness of an equation-solving technique. The complicated interactions of these factors make it very difficult to predict which method will be the most cost-effective for a given problem.

Hardware technology is a major factor in the selection of an equation-solving technique. The current transition from scalar to vector machines will change the cost-effectiveness of many methods because some methods vectorize better than others. Thus, the relative effectiveness of a solution method depends on the type of hardware on which the simulation is run, as well as on the numerical accuracy and efficiency inherent in the mathematics of the method.

*At the time of this writing, "small" is less than about 15 and "large" is greater than about 40.

Nomenclature

a_{rc} = term in Row r, Column c of Matrix A
A' = preconditioning matrix
c = concentration, fraction
d = diffusion or dispersion coefficient, ft^2/D [m^2/d]
D = diagonal matrix
f_o = fraction of oil flowing
Δf = change in fractional flow
L = lower triangular matrix
N_x = number of gridblocks in x direction
N_y = number of gridblocks in y direction
p = pressure, psi [kPa]
p_k = calculated values of pressures at iteration k
q = flow rate, RB/D [res m^3/d]
q_{in} = flow rate of oil into block, RB/D [res m^3/d]
q_{out} = flow rate of oil out of block, RB/D [res m^3/d]
q_t = total flow rate, RB/D [res m^3/d]
S_o = oil saturation, fraction
ΔS_{o_i} = oil saturation change in Gridblock i, fraction
t = time, days
Δt = length of timestep, days
U = upper triangular matrix
v_t = total velocity, ft/D [m/d]
V_{p_2} = PV of Gridblock 2, RB [res m^3]
w = bandwidth of matrix
x = distance in x direction, ft [m]
Δx = block length in x direction, ft [m]
Δy = block length in y direction, ft [m]
Δz = block length in z direction, ft [m]
α_k, β_k = iteration parameters
ϕ = porosity, fraction
ω = relaxation parameter

Subscripts

c = column number
E = estimated
i = gridblock number in x direction
j = gridblock number in y direction
k = iteration number
r = row number
$1 \rightarrow 2$ = Block 1,2 interface
$2 \rightarrow 3$ = Block 2,3 interface

Superscripts

n = last timestep taken
$n+1$ = timestep under consideration
new = new estimate
T = matrix transpose

References

1. Peaceman, D.W.: *Fundamentals of Numerical Simulation,* Elsevier Scientific Publishing Co., Amsterdam (1977) 139–53.
2. Sheldon, J.W., Harris, C.D., and Bavly, D.: "A Method for General Reservoir Behavior Simulation on Digital Computers," paper SPE 1521-G presented at the 1960 SPE Annual Meeting, Denver, Oct. 2–5.
3. Stone, H.L. and Garder, A.O. Jr.: "Analysis of Gas-Cap or Dissolved Gas Drive Reservoirs," *SPEJ* (June 1961) 92–104; *Trans.,* AIME, **222.**
4. Douglas, J., Peaceman, D.W., and Rachford, H.H.: "A Method for Calculating Multi-Dimensional Immiscible Displacement," *Trans.,* AIME (1959) **216,** 297–308.
5. MacDonald, R.C. and Coats, K.H.: "Methods for Numerical Simulation of Water and Gas Coning," *SPEJ* (Dec. 1970) 425–36; *Trans.,* AIME, **249.**
6. Spillette, A.G., Hillestad, J.G., and Stone, H.L.: "A High-Stability Sequential Solution Approach to Reservoir Simulation," paper 4542 presented at the 1973 SPE Annual Meeting, Las Vegas, Sept. 30–Oct. 3.
7. Lantz, R.B.: "Quantitative Evaluation for Numerical Diffusion (Truncation Error)," *SPEJ* (Sept. 1971) 315–20; *Trans.,* AIME, **251.**

8. Todd, M.R., O'Dell, P.M., and Hirasaki, G.J.: "Methods for Increased Accuracy in Numerical Reservoir Simulators," *SPEJ* (Dec. 1972) 515–30; *Trans.*, AIME, **253.**
9. Kyte, J.R. and Berry, D.W.: "New Pseudo Functions to Control Numerical Dispersion," *SPEJ* (Aug. 1975) 269–76.
10. Thomas, G.W. and Thurnau, D.H.: "Reservoir Simulation Using an Adaptive Implicit Method," *SPEJ* (Oct. 1983) 759–68.
11. Thurnau, D.H. and Thomas, G.W.: "The Mathematical Basis of the Adaptive Implicit Method," paper SPE 10495 presented at the 1982 SPE Symposium on Reservoir Simulation, Dallas, Jan. 31–Feb. 3.
12. Price, H.S. and Coats, K.H.: "Direct Methods in Reservoir Simulation," *SPEJ* (June 1974) 295–308; *Trans.*, AIME, **257.**
13. George, J.A.: "Nested Dissection of a Regular Finite Element Mesh," *SIAM J. Numerical Analysis* (April 1973) **10,** 345–63.
14. Graham, M.F. and Jennings, G.: "Efficient Sparse Matrix Implementation for Direct Methods in Reservoir Simulation," paper SPE 7682 presented at the 1979 SPE Symposium on Reservoir Simulation, Denver, Jan. 31–Feb. 2.
15. Watts, J.W.: "An Iterative Matrix Solution Method Suitable for Anisotropic Problems," *SPEJ* (March 1971) 47–51; *Trans.*, AIME, **251.**
16. Watts, J.W.: "A Method for Improving Line Successive Overrelaxation in Anisotropic Problems—A Theoretical Analysis," *SPEJ* (April 1973) 105–18; *Trans.*, AIME, **255.**
17. Peaceman, D.W. and Rachford, H.H.: "The Numerical Solution of Parabolic and Elliptic Differential Equations," *SIAM J. Numerical Analysis* (1955) **3,** 28–41.
18. Stone, H.L.: "Iterative Solution of Implicit Approximations of Multidimensional Partial Differential Equations," *SIAM J. Numerical Analysis* (1968) **5,** 530–58.
19. Meijerink, J.A. and van der Vorst, H.A.: "An Iterative Solution Method for Linear Systems of which the Coefficient Matrix is a Symmetric M-Matrix," *Mathematics of Computation* (Jan. 1977) **31,** 148.
20. Watts, J.W.: "A Conjugate Gradient-Truncated Direct Method for the Iterative Solution of the Reservoir Simulation Pressure Equation," *SPEJ* (June 1981) 345–53.
21. Towler, B.F. and Killough, J.E.: "Comparison of Preconditioners for the Conjugate Gradient Method in Reservoir Simulation," paper SPE 10490 presented at the 1982 SPE Symposium on Reservoir Simulation, New Orleans, Jan. 31–Feb. 3.
22. Wallis, J.R.: "Incomplete Gaussian Elimination as a Preconditioning for Generalized Conjugate Gradient Acceleration," paper SPE 12265 presented at the 1983 SPE Symposium on Reservoir Simulation, San Francisco, Nov. 15–18.
23. Tan, T.B.S. and Letkeman, J.P.: "Application of D4 Ordering and Minimization in an Effective Partial Matrix Inverse Iteration Method," paper SPE 10493 presented at the 1982 SPE Symposium on Reservoir Simulation, New Orleans, Jan. 31–Feb. 3.
24. Vinsome, P.K.: "Orthomin, an Iterative Method for Solving Sparse Sets of Simultaneous Linear Equations," paper SPE 5729 presented at the 1976 SPE Symposium on Numerical Simulation of Reservoir Performance, Los Angeles, Feb. 19–20.
25. Appleyard, J.R. and Cheshire, L.M.: "Nested Factorization," paper SPE 12264 presented at the 1983 SPE Symposium on Reservoir Simulation, San Francisco, Nov. 15–18.
26. Settari, A. and Aziz, K.: "A Generalization of the Additive Correction Methods for Iterative Solution of Matrix Equations," *SIAM J. Numerical Analysis* (1973) **10,** 506.

Chapter 7
Well Management: Designing and Controlling Production Parameters

This chapter discusses the philosophy, design, hierarchy of control, and theoretical basis of a well-management routine for translating field operating conditions and constraints into mathematical boundary conditions and logic acceptable to a reservoir simulator.

7.1 Overall Design of a Well-Management Routine

A well-management routine sets well rates or pressures, implements operating policies, and satisfies operating constraints at the levels of producing interval, well, well group, reservoir, and field (Fig. 7.1). A reservoir simulator needs a well-management routine to translate historical production/injection data and actual or desired field operating conditions and constraints into acceptable controls for the reservoir model. This usually requires that such operating constraints as production and injection facility limits, statutory allowables, market demand, well capacities, gas/oil ratio (GOR) and water/oil ratio (WOR) limits, minimum and maximum desired reservoir pressures, and minimum and maximum injection rates be imposed correctly as boundary conditions of the individual gridblock representing part or all of a well in the reservoir model. In applying boundary conditions, the well-management routine should have the flexibility to switch from historical production and injection rates when simulating past performance to more general physical relationships that must control the producing rate when predicting future performance.

7.1.1 Tasks Performed by the Well-Management Routine. Well-management routines can vary greatly in complexity. In its simplest form, a well-management routine assigns user-specified well rates or pressures to individual producing blocks in the simulator at specified times. This simplified form is often referred to as a *rate routine*. More sophisticated routines may also perform the following tasks.

1. Shut in, work over, recomplete, or redrill wells according to user-specified criteria (such as WOR and GOR limits and minimum allowable oil rates).
2. Calculate wellbore and flowline hydraulics.
3. Initiate artificial lift (gas lift or pumps).
4. Switch flowing wells between production systems having different backpressures.
5. Optimize the level and distribution of well rates to match field production-facility capacities and the availability of gas for gas lift.
6. Alter any of the preceding to maintain targeted reservoir or field oil or gas rates.
7. Control water or gas injection rates to maintain a specified average reservoir pressure.
8. Return produced water to specified locations in the reservoir.
9. Perform coning calculations.
10. Relate the producing GOR and WOR of a well to gridblock average saturations by means of well pseudofunctions.
11. Allow manual override by the user.
12. Check well-management-routine data for completeness and consistency.
13. Translate literal well names into well-sequence numbers that the simulator can interpret.

In addition, a good well-management routine realistically and effectively integrates wellbore constraints into simulations of future reservoir performance by automatically implementing a logical sequence of workovers, recompletions, replacements, and additions (as by infill drilling) of reservoir model wells according to user-specified guidelines, with the objective of maximizing economical oil recovery.

7.1.2 Production Constraints. Constraints on producing rates of wells may have their origin in the physical laws governing fluid flow in the reservoir and surface system and in external controls imposed by statute, political expediency, economics, or operating guidelines.

Common *physical* constraints include well productivity, wellbore and flowline hydraulics, and facility capacity.

1. *Well productivity* is a function of reservoir rock and fluid properties, fluid saturations, and type and effectiveness of well completions. Well productivity is affected by reservoir permeability, fluid viscosity, oil bubblepoint pressure, relative permeability, perforation quantity and quality, fraction of formation open to flow, well stimulation, well drainage volume, and in gas wells, turbulent flow near the wellbore.[1-6]
2. *Wellbore hydraulics* is influenced by bottomhole pressure (BHP), wellhead pressure, measured and vertical depth, gas/liquid ratio (GLR), WOR, tubing size, and lift mechanism (such as natural flow, gas lift, or subsurface pump).[7-9]
3. *Surface system hydraulics* is influenced by choke size, flowline size and configuration, separator backpressure, and the number of flowing phases.[4,7,8]
4. *Surface facility capacity* may be controlled by one or more component capacities (such as liquid- and gas-handling capacity of separators, injection and gas lift compressor capacity, pump capacity, and water-disposal capacity).

External production constraints may be imposed by regulatory agencies, the operator, or market forces.

1. *Statutory controls* are legal constraints imposed by regulatory bodies for conservation, market demand, or political purposes. These constraints include oil-production allowables and GOR limits on a well, lease, or reservoir basis, gas- and water-injection credits, production allowable transfer rules, and reservoir pressure level.
2. *Operating guidelines* set acceptable limits on rates, pressures, and fluid ratios. These guidelines are normally self-imposed (1) to minimize such problems as sand production, coning, water underrun, or gas overrun, (2) to maximize recovery by controlling net voidage and reservoir pressure, or (3) to maximize economic factors.
3. *Wellbore utility and availability* depend on drilling and workover economics, the number of reservoir zones, the positions of fluid fronts, and mechanical and corrosion problems.
4. *Economic production* limits.
5. *Market constraints.*
6. *Disposition of produced gas.*

7.1.3 Mathematical Boundary Conditions. The constraints discussed in the last section must be translated into mathematical

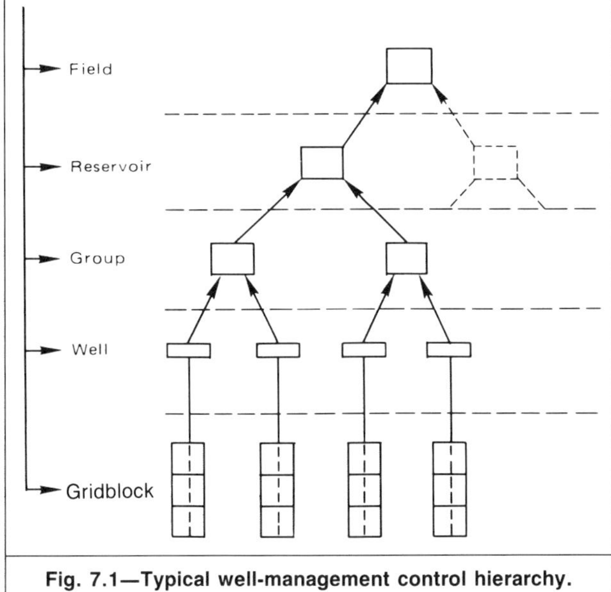

Fig. 7.1—Typical well-management control hierarchy.

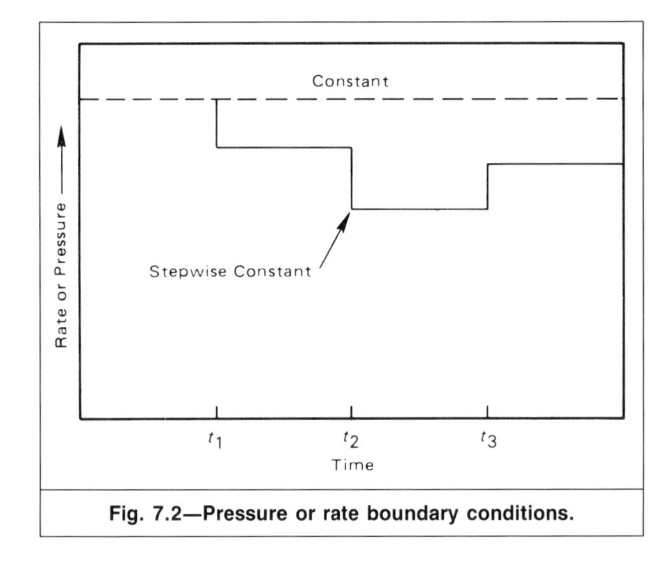

Fig. 7.2—Pressure or rate boundary conditions.

boundary conditions in the reservoir model. These conditions are created through physical and empirical relationships and programming logic that are applied in the desired time sequence at the desired model location under desired performance conditions. As discussed in Appendix B, two basic boundary conditions can be applied in a simulator at individual producing blocks: constant rate or constant pressure.

Through application of the constant-rate boundary condition, production or injection rates in the model can be held constant over time, or they can be held stepwise constant over increments of time, but allowed to vary between time intervals (Fig. 7.2). Likewise, application of the constant-pressure boundary condition will hold production or injection pressures in the model constant or stepwise constant.

7.2 Logic Structure

In a workable well-management routine, all decisions are based on objective and quantifiable decision rules. For example, the WOR is less than or greater than a control value. Key to the operation of these rules is a hierarchy of control (Fig. 7.1) and a status classification system for wells and facilities.

7.2.1 Typical Decision Rules. A well-management routine should perform ordinary surveillance of wells, groups of wells, and reservoir units in the reservoir model. It should also be able to take some elementary actions that might be prescribed by a surveillance engineer for an actual field. These actions include the following.

1. Shut in wells at prescribed WOR and GOR limits.
2. Convert wells to artificial lift as dictated by low wellhead pressures or low flowing well rates that result from declining reservoir pressure and/or increasing water production.
3. Implement response to statutory limits by compliance with production penalties for high GOR's, limits on lease gas production, lease, platform, and field production allowables, and concession or production-sharing contract rules.
4. Add new completions in response to WOR and GOR performance of wells by implementing workovers or recompletions, or by drilling new wells.
5. Allocate production among wells and producing intervals for control of coning and fluid-contact movement.
6. Control pressure by (1) scheduling the injection/production ratio and the timing of injection-capacity increments to maintain reservoir pressure for optimal natural flow or gas lift efficiency, or maximum recovery efficiency and (2) keeping injection pressures below the reservoir fracture pressure.

7.2.2 Well and Facility Classification. A well and facility status classification system allows rapid checking of the status of a well to determine whether a well or group of wells is an appropriate candidate for some specific action. In computer language, these status codes are represented by a key word array or bit string assigned to each well and group. One such classification system for wells and facilities is discussed in this section.

7.2.2.1 Well Level Classification. In reservoir simulation terminology, the term "well" is somewhat akin to the term "completion" in common oilfield parlance. That is, a simulator well represents a completion or minimum group of completion intervals, the flow of which can be isolated and tested in a surface facility. For example, a "dual or triple completion well" in oilfield terms would be "two or three wells" in simulator terminology. Table 7.1 classifies simulator wells according to well type, mode of operation, status, boundary condition, shut-in condition, workover potential, and recompletion potential.

In this classification system, a well that is a three-phase producer with gas lift and that has been shut in for low rate with no workover/recompletion potential is a "three-phase.producer.shut-in.gas lift.low rate.none.none," or 1.1.2.2.1.0.0. Of course, some combinations are not allowable. For example, there is no single-phase water injector with oil rate specified (4.2.1.3.0.0.0).

Linked lists of wells of a given status are convenient for rapid retrieval when action is required because of a change in status at a higher control level. For example, assume that at a given timestep a status change occurs in the group production mode (discussed later) from "natural flow only" to "artificial lift available." When this happens, a linked list of wells categorized as "producer.shut-in.low rate" accesses these wells as candidates for artificial lift. If linked lists have not been maintained, the wells must be identified by an exhaustive search of the complete well list.

7.2.2.2 Group- or Reservoir-Level Classification. Levels above wells in the control hierarchy, such as well groups or reservoirs, are classified by production mode and by facility and rig availability, as shown in Table 7.2.

For example, a well group without artificial lift, with water-handling facilities only, and with a workover rig or rigs available is "natural flow.water handling.workover," or 1.1.1.

7.2.3 Hierarchy of Control.[10-12] The order in which multilevel constraints are implemented can be important because it can have a pronounced effect on the computational efficiency of the well-management routine. Select an order of testing and implementation that is logical and that minimizes the number of iteration cycles. In general, the routine should examine the lowest units (wells) first to see whether a status change is needed (shut-in, workover, recompletion, artificial lift). Then the capacity of each of these units, subject to their individual constraints, should be determined. Next, the sum of these capacities should be tested against the constraints of the next higher aggregation of units (group, reservoir, field). Any deviations from these constraints are allocated back to successively lower units in the hierarchy until all constraints have been satisfied. At these higher levels, wells are worked over or recom-

TABLE 7.1—CLASSIFICATION OF SIMULATOR WELLS

Number	Terminology
Well Type	
0.	Unspecified (allocates a well whose type will be assigned by the user at a later model time)
1.	Two- or three-phase
2.	Oil (single-phase)
3.	Gas (single-phase)
4.	Water (single-phase)
Mode of Operation	
0.	Unspecified
1.	Producer
2.	Injector
Status	
0.	Undrilled but available as a future drilling location
1.	Active
2.	Shut-in
3.	Abandoned
Boundary Condition	
0.	Unspecified
1.	Natural flow
2.	Artificial lift
3.	Oil rate specified
4.	Gas rate specified
5.	Water rate specified
6.	Total liquid rate specified
7.	Pressure (i.e., potential) specified
Shut-In Condition	
0.	None (active well)
1.	Low rate
2.	High WOR
3.	High GOR
4.	Mechanical problem
Workover Potential	
0.	None
1.	Workover, up
2.	Workover, down
3.	Workover, either up or down
Recompletion Potential	
0.	None
1.	One or more zones

TABLE 7.2—CLASSIFICATION OF LEVELS ABOVE WELLS

Number	Terminology
Production Mode	
0.	Shut-in
1.	Only natural flow is currently available
2.	Artificial lift is available
Facility Availability	
0.	Unspecified
1.	Water handling (separation/disposal/injection) only
2.	Gas compression only
3.	Both water handling and gas compression
Rig Availability	
0.	None
1.	Workover
2.	Drilling
3.	Both workover and drilling

pleted and additional wells are drilled to offset deficiencies in meeting production-rate targets.

At times, it is impossible to develop an unambiguous control hierarchy because of interaction between two control levels. In this case, iteration between the two levels is necessary to satisfy constraints at both levels. In this situation, the user must be certain that the iteration procedure is stable and convergent; otherwise, ac-

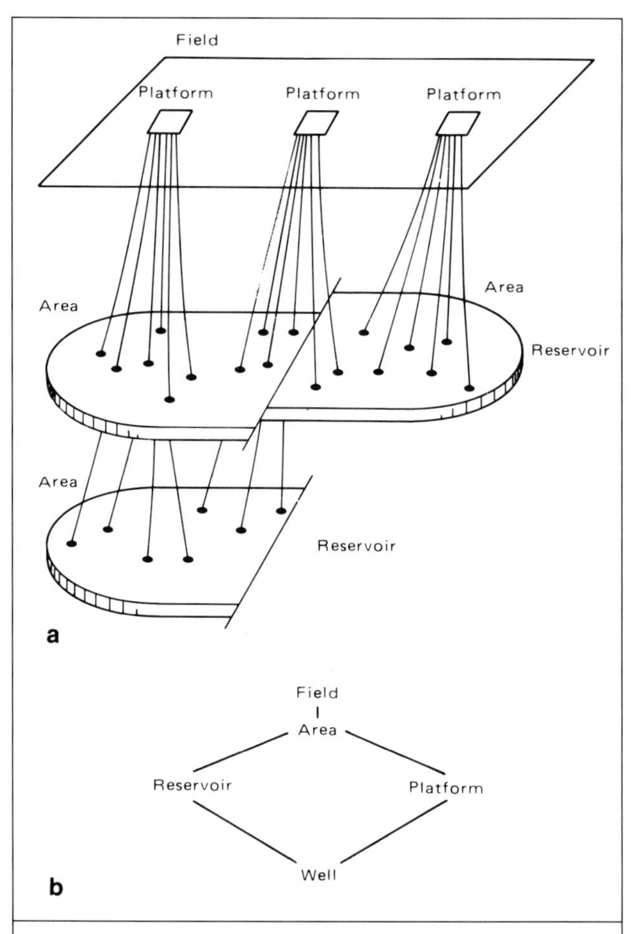

Fig. 7.3—Interdependent control hierarchy: (a) physical description and (b) logic linkage.

TABLE 7.3—TYPICAL CONTROLS

Well Level

Oil-production wells
- Maximum oil production rate
- Minimum oil production rate
- Maximum GOR
- Maximum WOR
- Minimum BHP

Water-injection wells
- Maximum water-injection rate—rate boundary condition
- Specified wellbore potential—potential boundary condition or maintain current reservoir pressure

Gas wells
- Maximum gas-production rate
- Maximum gas-injection rate

Group Level
- Maximum oil-production capacity
- Maximum gas-production capacity
- Maximum water-production capacity
- Maximum gas-injection capacity
- Maximum water-injection capacity
- Injection of all produced water
- Injection of all free gas (gas produced in excess of solution gas)
- Maximum WOR or GOR

Field Level
- Oil-production target
- Gas-sales target
- Oil and gas system capacity from field to point of sale

tivities of the well-management routine can lead to oscillations or divergence. For example, a hierarchical conflict arises when a field contains several reservoir units developed by several offshore platforms and is subject to both platform and reservoir maximum rates (Fig. 7.3). Because a single well group (platform) produces from several reservoirs and each reservoir is produced through several groups (platforms), constraints must be applied iteratively unless one set of constraints is known always to dominate.

Typical controls that are implemented within the control hierarchy are listed in Table 7.3.

7.3 Logic Sequence

The surveillance, actions, and the timing of actions performed by a well-management routine are tailored to a particular reservoir and to a specific mode of operation for that reservoir. A few general examples illustrate how the well-management routine processes data while a simulation is in progress, and how it modifies boundary conditions that influence the simulation. The first example is typical of the simple *rate routines* frequently used in simulation of the past performance of a reservoir (Chaps. 2 and 8). The other examples demonstrate a few of the features that equip the well-management routine to make thorough, realistic management decisions in simulations of future reservoir performance.

7.3.1 History Mode. When simulating historical performance, a common procedure for well management is to specify historical oil-production rates and water- and gas-injection rates and allow WOR's and GOR's to be calculated from phase mobilities. It is useful to limit the maximum WOR's and GOR's to prevent excess reservoir voidage that may result from a poor initial selection of well functions and relative-permeability functions.

For oil-production wells, a well-management routine uses the following general logic to establish boundary conditions for a timestep in the history mode.

1. Use historical values of oil-production rates, q_o, for the well.
2. Calculate well GOR from phase mobilities and well functions. If this value exceeds the maximum permitted well GOR, R_{max}, then use the maximum permitted value for the well GOR.
3. Calculate well WOR from phase mobilities and well functions. If this value exceeds the maximum permitted well WOR, F_{womax}, then use the maximum permitted value for the well WOR.
4. Calculate gas rate, q_g, for the well as $q_g=Rq_o$. Calculate water rate, q_w, for the well as $q_w=F_{wo}q_o$.

An alternative to the previously described procedure is to specify historical production rates for all phases—gas, oil, and water. This is generally less desirable, because the model solution can become overconstrained if the specified relative-permeability curves are inconsistent with historical performance.

For gas production and injection wells, a well-management routine uses historical rates to establish boundary conditions for a timestep in the history mode.

7.3.2 Prediction Mode.

7.3.2.1 Setting Production and Injection Rates at Individual Wells, Groups of Wells, and for the Reservoir. For checking at the *well level* during predictions, typical logic flow at the beginning of each timestep is as follows.

1. If artificial lift is available, reactivate oil wells that were on natural flow but have been shut in for low flow rate. This requires that the group level production mode be "artificial lift available."
2. Calculate the capacity of each active producer and injector within constraints imposed by wellbore hydraulics, wellhead pressure, or bottomhole potential (Sec. 7.4).
3. Compare well GOR, WOR, and minimum BHP constraints against calculated values. Shut in wells that violate these constraints or reduce their rates by a specified factor. Shut in wells that violate the minimum oil-rate constraint.
4. Test production- and injection-well capacities against maximum well-rate constraints. Reduce rates on wells violating these constraints.
5. For oil wells on gas lift, compute the GLR and WOR to be used in the wellbore hydraulics calculation at the beginning of the next timestep. Then calculate gas-lift gas requirements.

Typical logic for checking *group level* constraints at the beginning of each timestep during predictions is as follows.

1. Calculate group oil, gas, and water production, and calculate water- and gas-injection rates.
2. Test group gas production against the group maximum gas production capacity. Reduce the production rate or shut in the highest-GOR oil wells to meet the constraint.
3. Test group water production against the group maximum water production capacity. Reduce the production rate or shut in the highest-WOR oil wells to meet the constraint.
4. Test group oil production against the group maximum oil-production capacity. Reduce the production rate or shut in the highest-rate oil wells to meet the constraint, or reduce the production rate of all wells proportionally.
5. Test group water injection against the group maximum water-injection capacity. Cut back the rate of all water-injection wells proportionally to meet the constraint.
6. If produced gas is being injected into gas-injection wells, test the group gas-injection rate against the group maximum gas-injection capacity. Cut back the production rate or shut in the highest-GOR wells to meet the constraint.
7. If gas is being produced from gas wells, check group gas production against the group maximum gas-production capacity. Cut back gas wells proportionally to meet this restriction.
8. Calculate amount of gas-lift gas required by oil producers on gas lift and amount of gas-lift gas available.
9. Compare the requirement for gas-lift gas with its availability. If requirement exceeds availability, then shut in high-WOR or low-BHP wells to reduce gas needs appropriately.

Typical logic for checking at the *field level* at the beginning of each timestep in prediction is as follows.

1. Calculate field oil-production rate.
2. If the field oil-production capacity is less than the field oil-production target, transfer to the workover algorithm (below) for all groups producing at less than maximum facility capacity. Calculate rates for workover wells and retest group constraints. If, after workovers, the field oil-production capacity is less than the oil-production target, transfer to the well drilling algorithm below. Calculate rates for drilled wells and retest group constraints.
3. If the field oil-production rate is greater than the field oil-production target, either reduce the production rate of the highest-rate oil wells or reduce all well rates proportionally to meet the constraint.
4. Calculate total field rate of dry gas available for sale as follows: Gas available for sale equals total gas produced minus shrinkage resulting from liquids removal minus fuel-gas requirement minus gas-lift gas requirement minus injection gas required for pressure maintenance minus average emergency flare resulting from compressor operational downtime.
5. If the field production rate of dry gas is greater than the field sales-gas target, and if gas-compression capacity and gas-injection wells are available, inject the excess gas. Drill injectors and/or add compression, if required.
6. If the field dry-gas rate is less than the field gas-sales target, try to produce enough additional gas to meet the target from gas wells and drill additional gas wells if allowed.
7. Store rates calculated by the well-management routine for each level (well, group, field) and update cumulative production and injection volumes.

7.3.2.2 Workover Algorithm. The objectives of the workover algorithm are (1) to minimize gas and water production and (2) to use wellbores effectively by sequentially developing depletable zones intersected by the wellbore. The desired result is good reservoir management, conservation of reservoir energy, maximum recovery of hydrocarbons by providing effective and timely drainage points, and optimal use of each wellbore.

The routine works over a given well by finding the gridblock in the well that is the worst offender in violating the GOR or WOR constraint (block with highest GOR or WOR). The routine changes the well classification of the offending block (to be discussed later), recalculates the block's phase mobilities, and applies a productivity-index (PI) reduction factor to the block mobilities to account for reduction in length and upward or downward movement of the com-

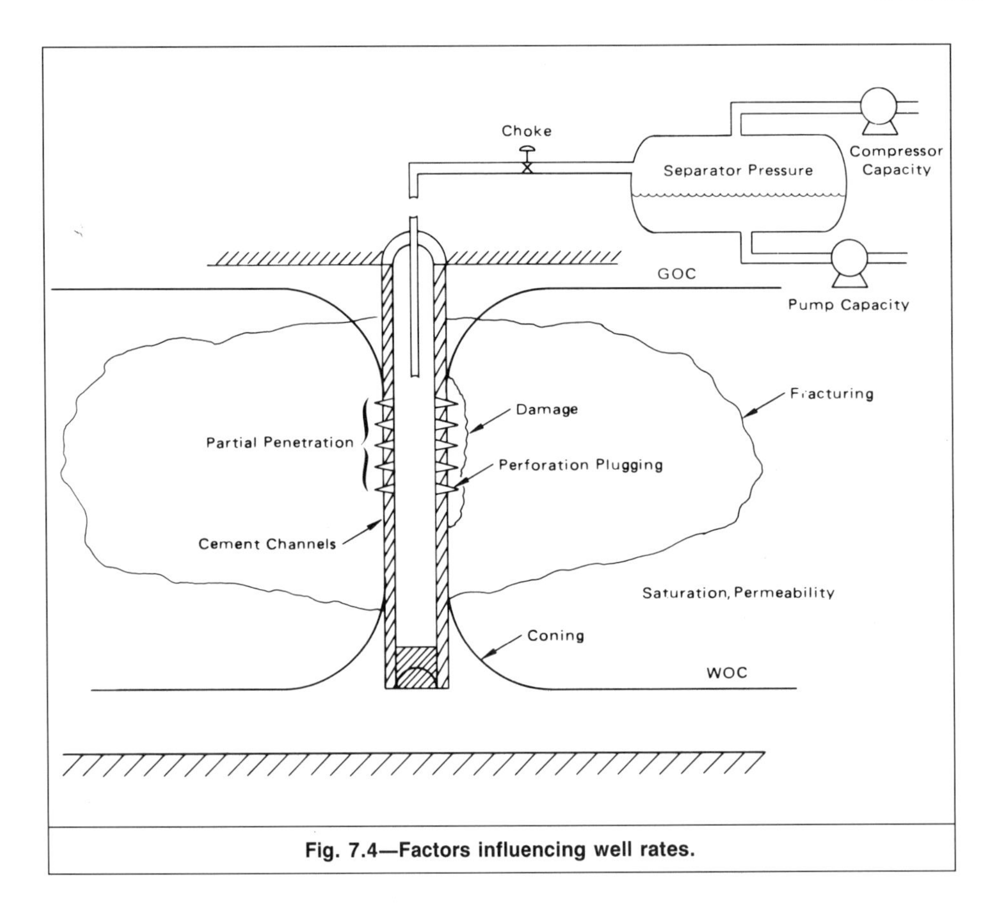

Fig. 7.4—Factors influencing well rates.

pletion interval in the block. If the block has no more workover possibilities, it is shut in, and the well-management routine tries to find an unopened block in the well that can be put on production. If all the blocks in a well become shut in, then the well's classification is changed to "shut in."

If a change in the classification of a well or of a single block in a multiblock well is made, the routine updates gridblock workover-status keys for each gridblock according to the following system:

0 = no change,
1 = gridblock shut in (high well GOR),
2 = gridblock shut in (high well WOR),
3 = gridblock opened for production (high well GOR),
4 = gridblock opened for production (high well WOR),
5 = gridblock worked over (high well GOR), and
6 = gridblock worked over (high well WOR).

7.3.2.3 ***Drilling Algorithm.*** The objective of the drilling algorithm is to drill wells at optimal locations and times to maintain production capacity while minimizing excess capacity. To model good reservoir management, logic in the algorithm is dominated by reservoir saturation and pressure parameters. Major data requirements for the routine are a drilling priority list, rig availability schedule, drilling time per well, and guideline pressures and saturations that trigger the drilling of new producers and injectors. Two modes for selecting drilling sites for producers are (1) follow a drilling priority list and (2) select the site having the highest datum pressure (ie., potential) in a region of high oil saturation.

The drilling routine tries to drill a new producer or injector if an acceptable site can be found and if the number of drilling wells required justifies the cost of drilling-rig mobilization and demobilization. If the routine successfully adds a well, a rate is determined for the well and the group, and field rates are adjusted.

7.4 Individual Well Behavior

A thorough understanding of the assumptions implicit in the way a simulator treats wells as "sources and sinks" is essential if one is to avoid serious mistakes in forecasting WOR, GOR, well pressures, well requirements and recovery efficiency. In essence, a gridblock containing a well is similar in all respects to all other gridblocks in the model. There is nothing internal to the grid system that recognizes the existence of a well, and the performance of a simulated well usually cannot be derived directly from pressure and fluid saturations in the well block. To calculate well performance, it is necessary to know or to assume how the pressures and saturations are distributed within the blocks representing the well. It is then possible to derive relationships called *well functions* that relate well performance parameters to simulator-block saturations and pressures. These relationships often must be derived by simulating the well drainage region with a separate, detailed model.

Early in the model design stage, one should assess the level of accuracy needed in modeling individual well behavior to achieve the desired results. For example, if the ultimate objective is to design production facilities for an offshore platform in an undeveloped field, forecasting well capacity and GOR and WOR performance can be an important study objective. Alternatively, if one is studying the effect of pressure maintenance on ultimate recovery in a well-developed field with considerable well performance history, forecasting individual well behavior is less important and a rate boundary condition based on historical well performance may be adequate. It is important to assess how accurately well performance must be calculated to meet study objectives, because the gridblock size in most reservoir models normally is too large to simulate a well directly. The consequence is that well performance in a gridblock must be derived from the calculated gridblock cumulative production, pressure, and fluid saturations using well models. These well models can be derived from (1) empirical curves of rate, WOR, and GOR vs. cumulative well production, (2) simple, analytic, multiphase, steady-state flow models,[13] (3) correlations developed from separate, detailed, individual well models,[14,15] or (4) built-in, detailed numerical well models.[16,17] A combination of Options 2 and 3 is generally used. The techniques are discussed below.

Individual well capacity (Fig. 7.4) is governed by such factors as the following.

1. *Instantaneous well inflow performance relationship (IPR).* This relationship is a function of reservoir rock properties, near-well saturation, relative-permeability effects, and wellbore conditions (e.g., formation damage, paraffin deposition, and perforation condition).

2. *Completion details.* Three of the most commonly encountered factors that must be accounted for in developing well functions are the effective completion interval, partial penetration, and the position of the water/oil contacts (WOC's) and gas/oil contacts (GOC's). The *effective completion interval* may be different from the mechanical completion interval because of plugged or damaged perforations and flow channels in cement. *Partial penetration* can reduce the well productivity.[18,19] The *position of fluid contacts* relative to the completion interval influences the rates at which wells can be produced without cusping or coning of water or gas into wells.

3. *Wellbore and surface system hydraulics.* Backpressure on a producing well is determined by pump and compressor capacities and pressure drops in tubing, flowlines, surface and subsurface chokes, and separators.[7,8]

4. *Well stimulation.* Hydraulic fracturing, acidizing, or naturally occurring matrix fractures increase the effective permeability of the well drainage area.[20-22]

7.4.1 Well Inflow Rates and Pressures. When wellhead or BHP boundary conditions are applied to a model well, the well rate, q, must be replaced in the model equations with an analytic expression for rate, stated in terms of BHP and producing-block pressure. In such an expression, individual well production capacity is governed by the drop in reservoir pressure and the PI, J, which is related to the parameters previously mentioned. Assuming steady-state flow in the near-well region, the relationship between well rate and reservoir pressure drop can be expressed as

$$q_p = J_p(p_e - p_{wf}) \quad \text{.......} (7.1)$$

where

q_p = well flow rate of a produced phase,
J_p = phase PI,
p_e = pressure at outer boundary of well drainage area, and
p_{wf} = flowing BHP of well.

When near-well conditions are not changing with time, it is often adequate to determine J_p from well tests. In a radial drainage area where saturation is uniform over the drainage region, J_p can be determined from Darcy's law[23]:

$$J_p = \frac{0.00708 k k_{rp} h}{B_p \mu_p [\ln(r_e/r_w) + s + c]}, \quad \text{.......} (7.2)$$

where

k = absolute permeability,
k_{rp} = relative permeability to Phase p,
h = effective reservoir thickness,
B_p = phase FVF,
μ_p = viscosity of Fluid Phase p,
r_e = external drainage radius,
r_w = effective well radius,
s = skin factor, incorporating well damage or stimulation, perforation effects, inclined wellbore, and partial penetration effects, and
c = 0 for steady-state flow, -0.50 for pseudosteady-state flow,[4] -0.75 if J_p is based on average well drainage volume pressure instead of on p_e,[4] and $-\pi/2$ if J_p is based on gridblock pressure and r_e is set to block size, Δx (see Eq. 7.4).[24]

Odeh[13] developed geometric factors for applying Eq. 7.2 to 21 noncircular drainage shapes for pseudosteady-state flow. In Odeh's equation, r_e is replaced by a characteristic length expressed as a geometric factor multiplied by the square root of the drainage area.

7.4.1.1 Gridblock Effects. In a reservoir model, the producing-block pressure is not normally the well drainage boundary pressure.[24-28] Peaceman[28] addressed this problem by interpreting the block pressure as a flowing pressure at an equivalent radius from the block center. Assuming isotropic permeabilities, square gridblocks, single-phase flow, and a well at the center of an interior block, he showed that the equivalent radius, r_{eq}, is about

$$r_{eq} = 0.2\Delta x, \quad \text{.......} (7.3)$$

where Δx is the length of the block edge.

Kuniansky and Hillestad[24] validated Peaceman's result with potential flow theory. They showed that

$$r_{eq} = \Delta x \exp(-\pi/2) = 0.208\Delta x. \quad \text{.......} (7.4)$$

They also derived equivalent-radius factors for off-center, block-edge, and block-corner wells and for multiple producing wells in a block (Chaps. 3 and 8). Peaceman also derived solutions for non-square blocks and anisotropic permeability. Thus, PI's derived from field tests or calculated from Eq. 7.2 should be adjusted as follows for application in the reservoir model:

$$J_{pm} = \left(\frac{q_p}{p_b - p_{wf}}\right)_m = J_p \frac{\ln(r_e/r_w)}{\ln(r_{eq}/r_w)}, \quad \text{.......} (7.5)$$

where

J_{pm} = model PI,
p_b = gridblock pressure, and
r_{eq} = equivalent radius at which p_b is flowing pressure.

7.4.1.2 Multiple Wells in Grids. A number of authors address the problem of representing several wells in a single gridblock.[23,24,29] This requires use of the principle of superposition, which has seen wide use in well-test analysis.[30] Williamson and Chappelear[23] describe two cases.

1. If the wells always maintain the same relative production ratio, they can be represented by a single pseudowell.

2. If a more accurate representation is required, then pressure interference effects between the wells must be computed.

Equations that describe the performance of a ring cluster of gas wells and that account for mutual interference between the wells are discussed by Lingen.[29]

7.4.1.3 Allocation of Production Rates in Multiblock Well Completions. When a well penetrates several vertical blocks in a model, a specified well rate must be allocated to each of the blocks in the column containing the well[12,31] (Fig. 7.5). Well rates can be specified as total oil rate, q_{ot}, total liquid rate, $q_{ot}+q_{wt}$, or total fluid rate, $q_{ot}+q_{wt}+q_{gt}$.

If the *total oil rate* is specified, oil rates for individual gridblocks in the column representing the well are given by

$$q_{oi} = q_{ot} \frac{J_{oi}\Delta p_i}{\sum_{i=1}^{n} J_{oi}\Delta p_i}, \quad \text{.......} (7.6)$$

where

J_{oi} = PI of well Gridblock i (Eq. 7.2),
Δp_i = $p_{bi} - p_{wfi}$ (pressure drawdown at the well in Gridblock i),
p_{bi} = pressure in Gridblock i,
p_{wfi} = flowing pressure in wellbore in Gridblock i, and
n = number of gridblocks in well.

Note that

$$p_{wf} = p_w + \bar{\rho}_w g \Delta z, \quad \text{.......} (7.7)$$

where

p_w = wellbore pressure at some reference depth,
$\bar{\rho}_w$ = average wellbore fluid density in completion interval (estimated from wellbore hydraulics calculation, see Sec. 7.4.2),
g = gravitational constant, and
Δz = vertical distance from gridblock center to reference depth.

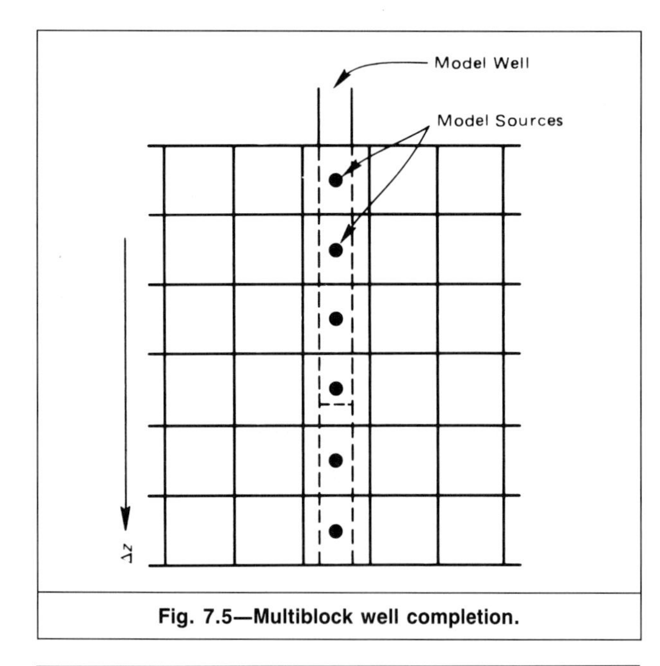

Fig. 7.5—Multiblock well completion.

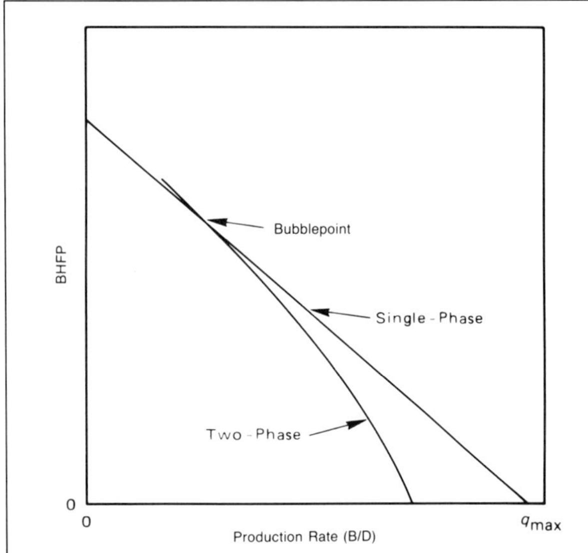

Fig. 7.6—Single-zone IPR.[4] (From *Principles of Oil Well Production*, by T.E.W. Nind. ©1981, McGraw-Hill Publishing Co. Reproduced with permission.)

To avoid the complication of accounting for differences in hydrostatic head in the wellbore, it is sometimes assumed that pressure drawdown, $(p_b - p_{wf})_i$, and skin factor, s, are the same at all well gridblocks.[31] On the basis of these assumptions, Eq. 7.6 can be simplified to

$$q_{oi} = \frac{(kh)_i(k_{ro}/\mu_o B_o)_i q_{ot}}{\sum_{i=1}^{n}(kh)_i(k_{ro}/\mu_o B_o)_i} \qquad (7.8)$$

Calculations of *total liquid rate* are analogous to those for oil rate. In Eqs. 7.6 and 7.8, oil rate, q_o, is replaced by total liquid rate, $q_L = q_o + q_w$. And in Eq. 7.8, $(k_{ro}/\mu_o B_o)$ is replaced by $(k_{ro}/\mu_o B_o + k_{rw}/\mu_w B_w)$.

To calculate *total fluid rate*, q_o in Eqs. 7.6 and 7.8 is replaced with $q_f = q_o + q_w + q_g$, with all rates expressed in consistent units. $(k_{ro}/\mu_o B_o)$ in Eq. 7.8 is replaced with $[k_{ro}(1+R_s)/\mu_o B_o + k_{rw}/\mu_w B_w + k_{rg}/\mu_g B_g]$, with R_s, B_o, B_w, and B_g expressed in consistent units.

When bottomhole pressure, p_{wf}, is specified as a producing-well boundary condition, an appropriate gravity gradient is used to relate this pressure to the individual wellblock pressures, and Eq. 7.6 or 7.8 can be used to calculate oil rates. Total liquid rates can be calculated in a similar manner.

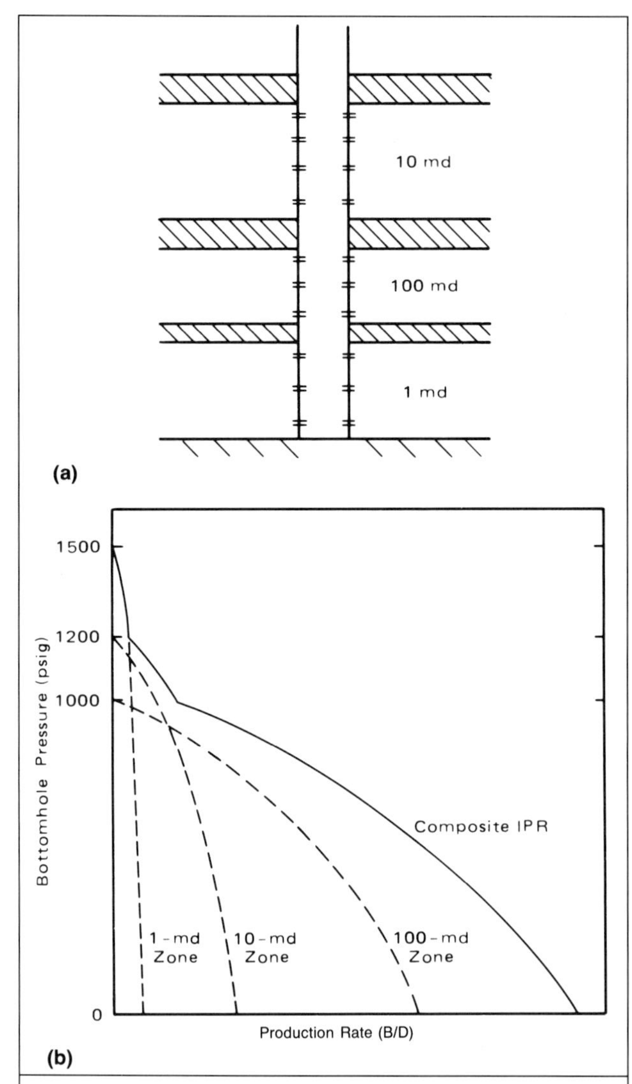

Fig. 7.7—Multiple-zone IPR[4]: (a) example reservoir with production commingled, and (b) composite IPR for the reservoir. (From *Principles of Oil Well Production*, by T.E.W. Nind. ©1981, McGraw-Hill Publishing Co. Reproduced with permission.)

7.4.1.4 Near-Wellbore Effects. The effect of near-wellbore factors on well productivity or injectivity can be handled by introducing a nonzero skin factor into Eq. 7.2 or by using a skin factor to calculate an apparent wellbore radius. Effects that can be handled in this way include well damage,[30] perforation effects,[32,33] partial penetration,[18,19,34,35] fracturing,[21] acidizing,[22] and inclined (deviated) wells.[36,37] The well skin factor for these effects is additive; i.e.,

$$s_t = \sum_{j=1}^{k} s_j, \qquad (7.9)$$

where s_t is total skin factor and s_j is individual skin factors caused by damage, partial penetration, etc.

Total skin factor, s_t, can also be obtained by pressure-buildup analysis methods and from estimates of flow efficiency or damage ratio.[30] If desired, an effective (pseudo, equivalent, or apparent) wellbore radius, r_{pw}, can be calculated from skin factors, s, for use in Eq. 7.2 as follows:

$$r_{pw} = r_w e^{-s}, \qquad (7.10)$$

because $\ln(r_e/r_w) + s = \ln(r_e/r_w e^{-s})$.

Other near-wellbore effects that may require consideration in the well model are saturation changes, coning, and the presence of fluid contacts (fluid segregation or dispersion) in a model block.[12] For gas wells, factors such as turbulence[5,6,29] and retrograde condensation during wet-gas production[3,38] may require consideration.

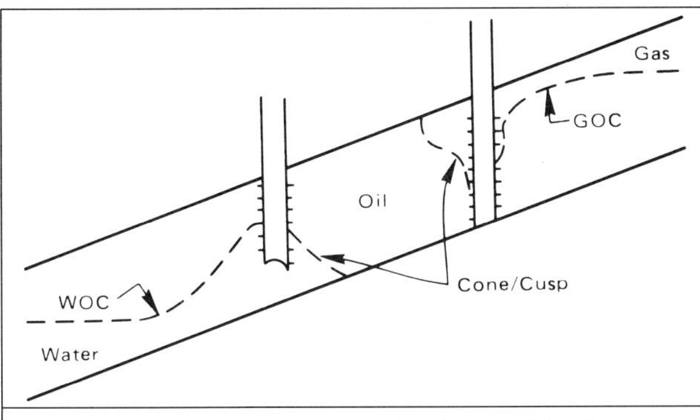

Fig. 7.8—Near-well saturation distribution resulting from coning or cusping.

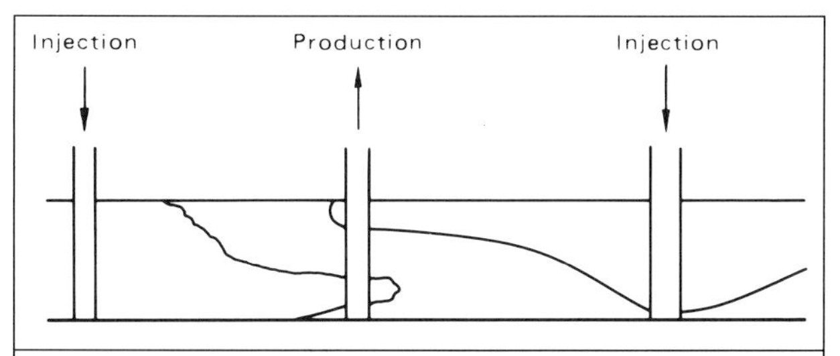

Fig. 7.9—Near-well saturation distribution resulting from stratification.

7.4.1.5 Saturation Effects. Generally, the PI, J, must be related to changes in near-wellbore saturations. The relationship can be expressed analytically for wells in a solution-gas-drive reservoir. For most other types of wells, well pseudofunctions must be used.

7.4.1.6 Inflow Performance Relationships. Kazemi[39] provides an excellent discussion of IPR for wells in solution-gas-drive reservoirs. Analytic IPR concepts were developed by several authors[1-4,40-44] and are demonstrated in Figs. 7.6 and 7.7 for single- and multizone reservoirs. Golan and Whitson[40] presented a generalized form of Vogel's[1] present-time IPR.

The present and future values of J are related by

$$J_F = J_P \frac{(k_{ro}/B_o\mu_o)_F}{(k_{ro}/B_o\mu_o)_P}. \qquad (7.11)$$

Eq. 7.11 can be used to determine the productivity at any future flow efficiency of the completion and at any stage of depletion in a well drainage pattern undergoing solution gas drive or in a reservoir in which pressure is being maintained below the bubblepoint. The same methods can be used with minor errors if the bubblepoint is below the reservoir pressure but above the bottomhole flowing pressure (BHFP).

7.4.1.7 Well Pseudofunctions. Coning, cusping, stratification, and normal floodout of the producing zone (Figs. 7.8 and 7.9) differ in their effects on well productivity. Well pseudofunctions can account for these effects and can allow the simulator to model well performance realistically.

Well pseudofunctions relate near-wellbore fluid mobilities to gridblock saturations; hence, they permit the simulator to calculate WOR and GOR at a model well on the basis of the producing gridblock saturations.[10,14,15] These functions are used only in well performance calculations; they are not used to control multiphase flow between gridblocks.

Well pseudofunctions are derived by running a fine-grid well model separately from the reservoir model. The well model is a

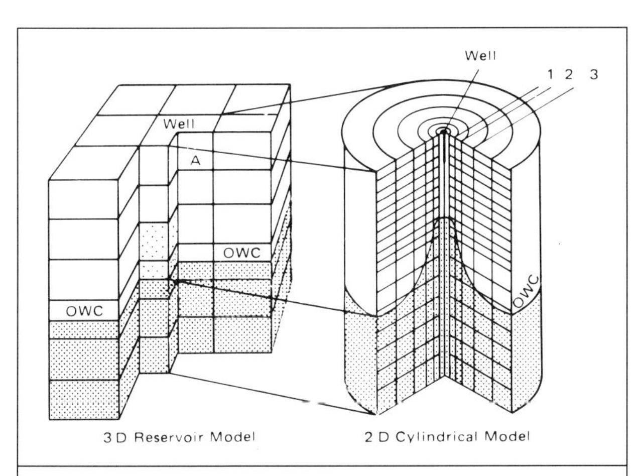

Fig. 7.10—Relationship of well models to reservoir models for pseudofunction development.[15]

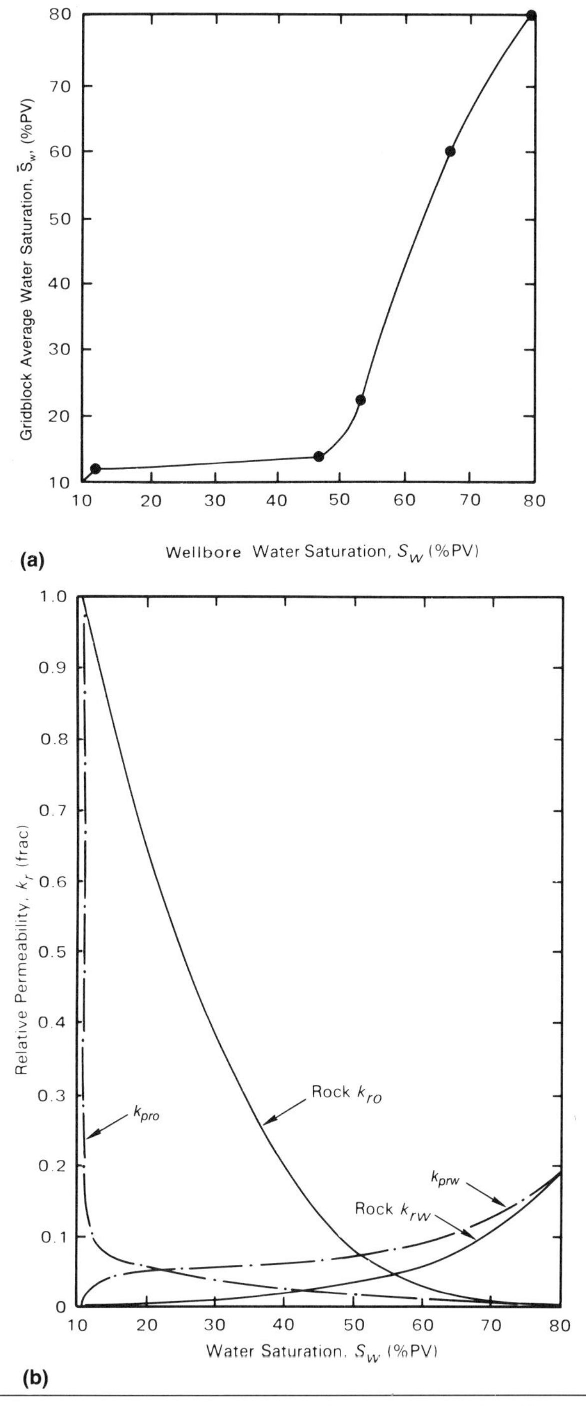

Fig. 7.11—Production-well saturation pseudofunctions[15]: (a) wellbore vs. gridblock saturations and (b) rock and pseudo-relative-permeability functions.

detailed subdivision of the producing blocks in the reservoir model (Fig. 7.10) and simulates near-wellbore flow in much greater detail. Gridding in the well model should be fine enough to simulate the influence of near-wellbore relative permeabilities on the distribution of fluids that flow into the well. It may be necessary to represent the wellbore with one column of blocks in the well model. Boundary conditions imposed on the well model should be realistic and may need to be taken from a preliminary run of the full reservoir model. Sometimes flow conditions in the reservoir change so much that the full model and the well model must be run sequentially a number of times.

For a particular set of conditions imposed on the well model, there will be a unique relationship between relative permeabilities near the wellbore and the overall average saturation of the blocks in the well model that represents the gridblock (or blocks) containing the well in the full reservoir model. This relationship can be expressed with pseudofunctions (Chaps. 2 through 4). An example relationship between wellbore and average block saturation obtained from a well model is illustrated in Fig. 7.11. The rock relative permeability and the well pseudofunctions that result from combining these two relationships are also shown.

Obviously, there is no generally applicable set of well functions. The pseudofunctions assigned to a well in a reservoir model should account for the producing mechanism and the geometric distribution of fluid saturations that can be expected at that model well; i.e., the pseudofunctions should reflect the well completion interval, the reservoir description around the well, and whether multiphase flow into the well is to occur by coning, cusping, or stratified flow. If conditions change—e.g., during a simulated recompletion of a model well—it may be necessary to use a different set of well functions.

With well pseudofunctions, the PI of a model well is updated to time t as follows:

$$J_{p,t}=J_{p,i}\left(\frac{k_{prp}}{\mu_p B_p}\right)_t\left(\frac{\mu_p B_p}{k_{prp}}\right)_i, \quad (7.12)$$

where

t = current model time,
i = initial condition, and
k_{prp} = pseudo-relative permeability of Phase p.

Well pseudofunctions are also used to calculate WOR and GOR, by the following relationships:

$$F_{wo}=\frac{k_{prw}/\mu_w B_w}{k_{pro}/\mu_o B_o} \quad (7.13)$$

and

$$R=\frac{k_{prg}/\mu_g B_g}{k_{pro}/\mu_o B_o}+R_s, \quad (7.14)$$

where R_s is solution GOR.

7.4.1.8 Coning Functions. Three-dimensional (3D), multiphase flow can occur in the near-wellbore region because of water[14,45,46] or gas[47] coning. For these cases, the derivation of an appropriate source representation of a well requires that the steady-state, near-well flow be analyzed and the resultant solution be connected with the finite-difference solution.[23] The most direct way to analyze coning is to use a numerical coning model. Several studies have found that the resultant modification to the source representation can be expressed in terms of pseudo-relative permeability and pseudo-capillary pressure.[14,15]

Three classes of models are used to represent water or gas coning in a field-scale numerical model: analytic solutions,[46] correlations based on numerical coning models,[47] and pseudofunctions.[14,15,45]

The analytic solution by Chappelear and Hirasaki[46] gives a critical coning rate for water-free production in an oil/water system and relates WOR to average oil-zone thickness when viscous forces dominate gravity forces. They also give a more general equation for cases in which viscous forces do not dominate gravity forces.

The second method of developing coning functions was demonstrated by Addington,[47] who used numerical simulator results to correlate gas coning behavior and one critical parameter—the average oil-column height above the perforated interval of the well. Addington was able to relate gas breakthrough-time data to average oil-column height, reservoir properties, oil rate, and well spacing. The second major parameter was the slope of the GOR curve, which allowed GOR to be related to the same factors.

A third way of developing coning functions involves the development of pseudofunctions (pseudo-relative permeability and pseudo-capillary pressure).[14,15,45] Pseudo-relative permeabilities and pseudo-capillary pressures can be derived from a detailed numerical well model as discussed in Chaps. 2, 3, 5, and 8. The appropriate set of pseudofunctions will yield the correct sum of the viscous, capillary, and gravity forces applicable to the field-scale model. These coning pseudofunctions govern flow between gridblocks and serve a different function from well pseudofunctions discussed in the previous section.

Woods and Khurana[15] discussed the case in which viscous forces dominate gravity forces (i.e., coning performance is independent of rate) and described the use of pseudo-relative-permeability and pseudo-capillary-pressure functions.

Emanuel and Cook[14] and Stright[45] took a similar approach in deriving pseudo-relative permeabilities for use as well functions to represent coning well performance in two-dimensional (2D) areal models. Akbar *et al.*[16] and Ridings and Mrosovsky[17] took the more sophisticated approach of incorporating detailed numerical well models in the reservoir-model grid.

7.4.1.9 Injection-Well Rates and Pressures. Replacing simulator injection-well source terms with analytic equations is analogous to the procedure used for producing wells in the preceding section. The implementation is simpler, however, because normally only a single-phase fluid is injected into a reservoir (except in the case of steam-injection wells). The equation analogous to Eqs. 7.2 and 7.5 is

$$i_p=I_{pm}(p_{wf}-p_b), \quad (7.15)$$

where the injectivity index, I_{pm}, is field-measured and converted to a model value or is derived for a radial injection region as

$$I_{pm}=\frac{0.00708kk_{rp}h}{B_p\mu_p[\ln(r_{eq}/r_w)+s+c]}, \quad (7.16)$$

where i_p is injection rate and I_{pm} is model injectivity index.

Other considerations that were mentioned in the discussions of producing wells, such as the relation of model and field-measured injectivity index, multiple wells in grids,[23] and allocation of rates in multiblock well completions, also hold for injection wells. In addition, because injection can occur into model blocks where the injected phase saturation is zero, a special procedure may be required to estimate injected-phase mobility, k_{rp}/μ_p. Common practice in this case is to equate injected-phase mobility to total mobility in the block,[23] giving

$$I_p=\frac{0.00708k(k_{ro}/\mu_o+k_{rw}/\mu_w+k_{rg}/\mu_g)}{B_p[\ln(r_{eq}/r_w)+s+c]}. \quad (7.17)$$

When there is a single displaced fluid phase, an analytic, radial, two-phase displacement model of the Buckley-Leverett type (Fig. 7.12) can be used with the steady-state pressure equation[48] to model more accurately saturation distribution and pressure drop within the injection gridblock as injected-phase saturation increases.

Another factor that can affect injection-well performance is the injection of surface water or seawater into a reservoir of much higher temperature. Because the viscosity of the injected water is higher than it would be at reservoir temperature, the well injectivity will decline.[49,50] The time variation of I_p for one such case is shown in Fig. 7.13. One way to account for the gradual warming of the injected water with time is to run a multiphase thermal model, to derive a relationship between injectivity index and cumulative fluid injected, and to use this relationship in Eq. 7.16. Another, less-rigorous approach is to use the injected-water viscosity at the injection temperature in Eq. 7.17. This method, however, will underestimate injectivity because it does not account for in-situ heating of injected water or for that part of the water bank that is interstitial water at reservoir temperature.

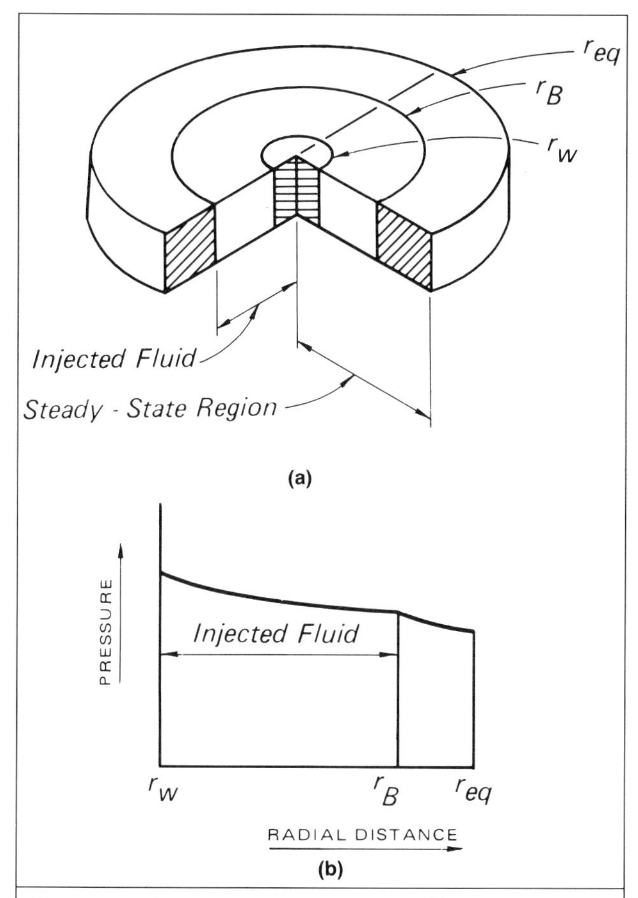

Fig. 7.12—Two-phase injection model[48]: (a) conceptual model and (b) typical pressure distribution.

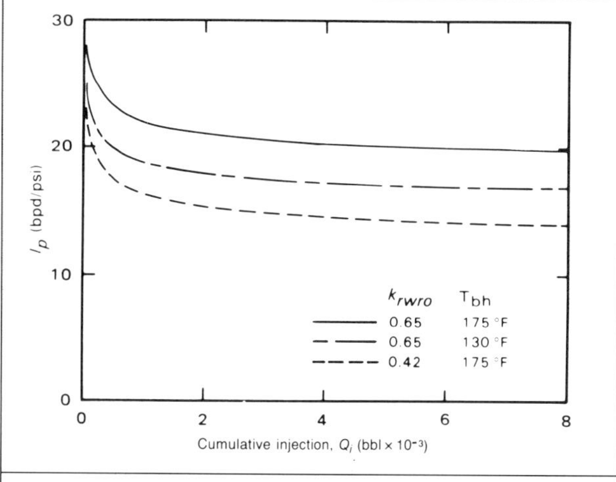

Fig. 7.13—Decline in injectivity resulting from cooling.[49]

7.4.2 Well Outflow Performance. It is frequently desirable to specify a rate or pressure boundary condition at the wellhead or some other point in the surface facilities. To do so, it is necessary to use a hydraulics model to account for single-, two-, or three-phase flow in pipes. Such a model can be derived theoretically from either an energy or a pressure balance, or empirically from experimental data.[4,51] The result is an equation of the form

$$p_{in}-p_{out}=\Delta p_f+\Delta p_h+\Delta p_{ke}+\Delta p_w, \quad (7.18)$$

where

Δp_f = pressure drop caused by irreversible work resulting from friction losses,
Δp_h = pressure drop caused by head or specific weight loss resulting from fluid in tubing,
Δp_{ke} = pressure drop caused by kinetic energy change or acceleration loss resulting from velocity changes, and
Δp_w = pressure drop caused by external work loss, such as driving a turbine (a pump would introduce a $-\Delta p_w$).

The frictional pressure gradient is related to the friction factor and velocity, and the gravity pressure gradient is related to changes in hydrostatic head.

The kinetic energy term is negligible except when flow is through critical flow provers or two-phase chokes. Nind[4] gives theoretical relationships between pressure and rate for two-phase flow through knife-edged chokes.

The pressure drop caused by external work, Δp_w, normally does not appear in the system defined for reservoir simulation. Common practice is to set boundary conditions at the sandface, at the pump suction in the case of pumping wells, or at the wellhead or separators in the case of flowing or gas lift wells. If one chooses to include pumps and compressors in the model system, the appropriate manufacturer's head-capacity curves for centrifugal pumps and rate-efficiency curves for plunger pumps should be included. Several authors[29,52-57] have discussed the modeling of interfaced reservoir/piping network systems.

The problem of multiphase flow under oilfield conditions has been the subject of much research.[7-9,51,58-65] But because a large part of this research was conducted with unrealistically smooth pipes, it is important to calibrate pressure drops derived analytically with actual field data whenever possible. Discrepancies between predicted and field-measured data should be compared in terms of absolute pressure drop in the well rather than as a percentage of BHP. This comparison usually will indicate the range of errors to be expected when predicting well flow rates.

The next few subsections present an overview of single-phase water and gas flow and multiphase gas and liquid flow.

7.4.2.1 Water Injection. For water-injection wells, the wellhead pressure and BHP, p_{wh} and p_{wf}, can be related through Eq. 7.18. The result is

$$p_{wf}=p_{wh}-\Delta p_f+\Delta p_h. \quad (7.19)$$

Eq. 7.19 can also be used for horizontal or inclined flow where Δp_h is the hydrostatic head for an elevation change, Δz, over length L, and p_{wh} and p_{wf} are the inlet and outlet pressures, respectively.

For single-phase flow modeling, it is often adequate to express Eq. 7.18 or 7.19 in the Hazen-Williams format by using an analytic expression for friction factor in terms of the Reynolds number. This results in an equation of the form

$$\Delta p=Kq^a-\Delta p_h, \quad (7.20)$$

where K is a coefficient that is determined experimentally or is derived from an analytic expression for friction pressure gradient and a is an experimentally determined exponent normally ranging from 1.75 to 1.85 for water.

7.4.2.2 Gas Production and Injection. Because gas is highly compressible, an equation of state that relates density to pressure must be introduced into the flow equations for gas before integration over length. The result is an equation of the form[51]

$$p_{wf}^2=Ap_{wh}^2+Bq^2(A-1), \quad (7.21)$$

where A is a function of temperature, gas gravity, compressibility factor, and length, and B is a function of temperature, compressibility factor, diameter, and friction loss.

Eq. 7.21 is valid for vertical flow through a circular conduit, assuming a linear temperature distribution, constant gas deviation factor, and negligible acceleration effects. For injection, the injection rate, i_g, must be a negative quantity.

For horizontal flowlines with constant gas deviation factor, Z, temperature, T, and negligible acceleration effects, the form of Eq. 7.21 reduces to[51]

$$p_{in}^2-p_{out}^2=Cq^2, \quad (7.22)$$

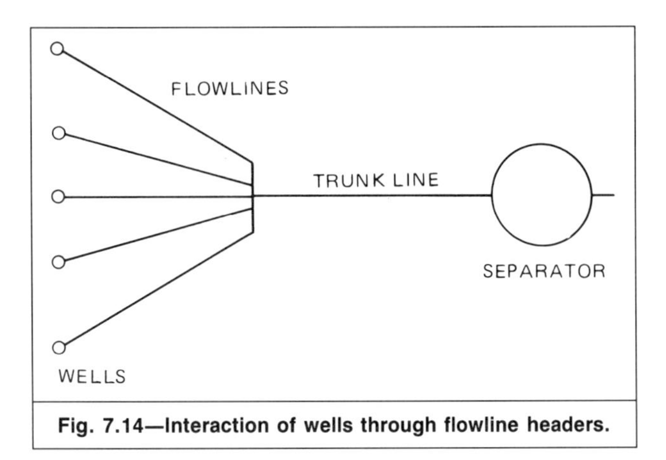

Fig. 7.14—Interaction of wells through flowline headers.

where C is a function of temperature, gas gravity, compressibility factor, diameter, and friction loss.

7.4.2.3 Gas/Liquid Production. The use of multiphase gas/liquid production as a reservoir-model boundary condition is discussed by Williamson and Chappelear.[23] They summarize this topic succinctly:

> "We first describe some salient points for three important types of wells. For injection wells, either the surface pumping pressure or rate generally is known and controlled. At formation level, the pressure distribution usually can be determined from single-phase pipe flow theories. We show. . .that the pressure distribution along the sandface closely approximates a hydrostatic pressure distribution in many cases. Thus, injection well flow is relatively easy to model. In production wells, the situation is more complicated. Ultimately, production wells deliver reservoir fluids into a surface gathering system. In a typical flowing or gas-lift well, the choke design and the operation of the (first) separator fix the pressure on the upstream side of the choke. Further upstream (i.e., moving to the wellhead and then downbore to formation levels), the fluid pressure increases according to the multiphase flow pressure gradient. At formation level, the pressure distribution in the well closely approximates a hydrostatic pressure distribution in many cases of practical interest. However, determination of the mean density of the wellbore fluid requires consideration of flow regimes and phase slip or holdup. In pumping wells, the casinghead pressure often is controlled as part of a gas gathering system. The annulus pressure then increases down the wellbore with a gradient approximately equal to the gas static-pressure gradient until the gas/liquid interface is reached. When the liquid level is relatively stationary, the casinghead pressure is the effective controlling agency. For producing intervals above the liquid level, the wellbore pressure gradient is the hydrostatic gas gradient, while below the liquid level, a multiphase flow calculation is required." (Pages 328–29.)

Williamson and Chappelear provide equations in their paper for implementing these concepts.

7.5 Operating Conditions

Prerequisites to realistic modeling of field operating conditions are a knowledge of well histories, information on equipment in use in the field and its operating characteristics, and data on historical rates and pressures. It is also important to be concerned with common operating problems, such as sanding up of completions, downhole asphalt or paraffin deposition, and the effect of these problems on reservoir producibility. The best way to gain the necessary knowledge is to examine well-history files and to communicate with field operating and reservoir description personnel.

When examining well files and discussing operations with field personnel, look for the basic reasons why rates or pressures were maintained or changed with time. The following are examples.

1. Production or injection rates will be constant when flow is controlled by surface or subsurface chokes, flow regulators, or critical flow provers, or by subsurface volumetric pumps—e.g., constant-speed, constant-displacement, sucker-rod pumps, or turbine pumps operating under constant head.

2. Production or injection pressures will be constant when producing wells are pumped off, when injection wells are fed through wellhead flow regulators, or when injection pumps have controlled discharge pressures.

TABLE 7.4—TYPICAL WELL-MANAGEMENT ROUTINE DATA

Well Level
WOR constraint
GOR constraint
Maximum gas- and water-injection rates
Maximum oil or gas well rates
Minimum oil rate
Wellhead pressure
Ratio of well true vertical depth to measured depth for directionally deviated wells
Tubing size
Group Level
WOR constraint
GOR constraint
Maximum rates of oil, water, and gas
Number of drilling rigs available
Number of workover rigs available
Drilling time for injectors and producers
Workover/recompletion time per well
Operating factors
Separator pressure
Minimum allowable reservoir pressure
Drilling priority list
Workover priority list
Recompletion priority list
Artificial lift availability
Drilling well criteria
Maximum and minimum pressure
Maximum gas or water saturation
Work backlog required before workover or drilling rig mobilization can be justified
Field/Reservoir Level
Oil-production target
Dry (sales) gas target

Rates and/or pressures will vary if there are any of the following.

1. Deliberate changes—e.g., installation of artificial lift or changes in pump or compressor size, choke size, tubing size, system backpressure, or water-handling capacity.

2. Changes induced by relative-permeability effects, sanding up of perforations or of the wellbore, asphalt or paraffin problems, pressure interference between wells, or in the case of gas wells, turbulent flow.[1,3-7,66]

3. Changes in well characteristics resulting from workovers to exclude or reduce gas or water production, increasing or decreasing the completion interval by reperforating or squeeze cementing, increasing the effective near-well reservoir permeability by hydraulic fracturing or acidizing.

4. Changes caused by interaction between separate elements in the production system that are induced by the configuration of surface facilities. An example is interaction between flowing wells producing into flowline headers (Fig. 7.14). A change in rate or pressure of one well affects all wells on the common header.

5. Multiple completions in zones that deplete at different rates.[30]

6. Either pressure depletion or startup of pressure maintenance.

7.6 Data Requirements

Typical data for a well-management routine that are entered at the well, group, and field/reservoir control levels are listed in Table 7.4.

7.7 Summary

The well-management routine is, in effect, an executive routine for implementing logical, orderly operating decisions during the course of a simulation run with a minimum of manual intervention. To be effective, a well-management routine should be designed with the following considerations in mind.

1. *Objectives of the simulation in general and of well management in particular.* First determine what factors are likely to affect reservoir performance and what business decisions may be made from model results. Then select or develop an appropriate well-management routine.

2. *Simplicity of design and ease of implementation.* The structure of the routine should allow it to be customized to the field being

modeled. For some cases, specification of constant or stepwise constant rates or well potentials is adequate. For more complicated cases, the management routine will be more sophisticated and may be difficult and time consuming to use and to monitor.

3. *Efficiency of Computation.* Well-management routines that are overly complex or poorly structured can consume more computer time than the solution of the flow equations. Take care to ensure that the logic of the routine leads to convergent solutions and that mathematical procedures will converge rapidly.

Selecting the features of the well-management routine that are to be activated during a model run involves important decisions. Adding features normally means that additional data must be prepared and validated. Use those features that contribute necessary realism to the problem but be judicious in adding features to enhance aesthetics or to avoid criticism.

Finally, monitor the actions taken by the well-management routine during a modeling run to ensure that these actions are logical, appropriate, and consistent with the anticipated operating philosophy for the reservoir under study.

Nomenclature

a = experimentally determined exponent in Hazen-Williams equation (Eq. 7.20)
A,B,C = coefficients in simplified equation of state for gas (Eqs. 7.21 and 7.22), dimensionless
B_p = phase FVF, RB/STB [res m^3/stock-tank m^3]
F_{wo} = WOR, dimensionless
g = gravitational constant, ft/sec^2 [m/s^2]
h = effective reservoir thickness, ft [m]
i_g = injection rate of gas, scf/D [std m^3/d]
i_p = injection rate of Phase p, bbl/D [m^3/d]*
I_{pm} = model injectivity index of Phase p, bbl/(psi-D) [m^3/(kPa·d)]*
J = PI, bbl/(psi-D) [m^3/(kPa·d)]*
J_{oi},J_{wi},J_{gi} = oil, water, and gas PI's of well in Gridblock i, bbl/(psi-D) [m^3/(kPa·d)]*
J_{pm} = model PI of Phase p, bbl/(psi-D) [m^3/(kPa·d)]*
k = absolute permeability, md
k_{prp} = pseudo-relative permeability of Phase p, dimensionless
k_r = relative permeability, dimensionless
k_{rp} = relative permeability of Phase p, dimensionless
k_{rwro} = relative permeability to water at residual oil, dimensionless
K = coefficient determined experimentally or derived from analytic expression
L = length, ft [m]
n = number of gridblocks in well
p = pressure, psi [kPa]
p_b = gridblock pressure, psi [kPa]
p_e = pressure at outer boundary of well drainage area, psi [kPa]
p_{in} = pressure at entry to wellbore/facilities system (usually $p_{in}=p_{wf}$), psi [kPa]
p_{out} = pressure at some point defining the limit of the wellbore/facility system to be considered by the simulator, psi [kPa]
p_w = wellbore pressure, psi [kPa]
p_{wf} = BHFP, psi [kPa]
p_{wh} = wellhead pressure, psi [kPa]
Δp_f = pressure drop caused by irreversible work resulting from frictional losses, psi [kPa]
Δp_h = pressure drop caused by head or specific weight loss resulting from fluid in tubing, psi [kPa]
Δp_i = pressure drawdown at well in Gridblock i, psi [kPa]
Δp_{ke} = pressure drop caused by kinetic energy change or acceleration loss resulting from velocity changes, psi [kPa]
Δp_w = pressure drop caused by external work loss, psi [kPa]
q = production well flow rate, STB/D [stock-tank m^3/d]
q_{gt} = total gas rate of production, scf/D [std m^3/d]
q_{ot} = total oil rate of production, STB/D [stock-tank m^3/d]
q_{wt} = total water rate of production, STB/D [stock-tank m^3/d]
Q_i = cumulative injected fluid, STB [stock-tank m^3]
r_B = radial distance from wellbore to leading edge of injected fluid front, ft [m]
r_e = external drainage radius, ft [m]
r_{eq} = equivalent radius, ft [m]
r_{pw} = effective well radius, ft [m]
r_w = well radius, ft [m]
R = producing GOR, scf/res bbl [std m^3/res m^3]
R_s = solution GOR, scf/res bbl [std m^3/res m^3]
s = skin factor, dimensionless
s_j = individual skin factors, dimensionless
s_t = total skin factor, dimensionless
S_w = water saturation, % PV
t = time, days
T = temperature, °F [°C]
T_{bh} = bottomhole temperature, °F [°C]
Δx = block size, ft [m]
Δz = vertical distance or vertical block size, ft [m]
Z = gas deviation factor, dimensionless
μ_p = viscosity of Fluid Phase p, cp [Pa·s]
$\bar{\rho}_w$ = average wellbore fluid density, lbm/ft^3 [kg/m^3]

Subscripts

e = outer (external)
f = fluid
F = future model time
g = gas
i = index denoting gridblock number
j = index denoting individual components of total skin factor
L = liquid
m = model
max = maximum permitted
o = oil
p = phase
P = present model time
t = current model time
w = water

*STB [stock-tank m^3] for oil and water and scf [std m^3] for gas.

References*

1. Vogel, J.V.: "Inflow Performance Relationships for Solution-Gas Drive Wells," *JPT* (Jan. 1968) 83–92; *Trans.*, AIME, **243.**
2. Patton, L.D. and Golan, M.: "Generalized IPR Curves for Predicting Well Behavior," *Pet. Eng. Intl.* (Sept. 1980) 74–82.
3. Fetkovich, M.J.: "The Isochronal Testing of Oil Wells," paper SPE 4529 presented at the 1973 SPE Annual Meeting, Las Vegas, Sept. 30–Oct. 3.
4. Nind, T.E.W.: *Principles of Oil Well Production,* second edition, McGraw-Hill Book Co., New York City (1981), 48, 52, 53.
5. Holditch, S.A. and Morse, R.A.: "The Effects of Non-Darcy Flow on the Behavior of Hydraulically Fractured Gas Wells," *JPT* (Oct. 1976) 1169–79.
6. Tek, M.R., Coats, K.H., and Katz, D.L.: "The Effect of Turbulence on Flow of Natural Gas Through Porous Reservoirs," *JPT* (July 1962) 799–806; *Trans.*, AIME, **225.**

*References may be grouped accordingly: well-management routines (Refs. 10 and 11); well performance (Refs. 1 through 6, 12, 13, 18 through 22, 30 through 44, 49, 50, and 66); well functions (Refs. 14, 15, and 45 through 48); wells in grids (Refs. 16, 17, and 23 through 28); hydraulics (Refs. 7 through 9, 51, and 58 through 65); and facilities (Refs. 29 and 52 through 57).

7. Brown, K.E.: *The Technology of Artificial Lift Methods,* Petroleum Publishing Co., Tulsa (1977).
8. Brown, K.E.: *Gas Lift Theory and Practice,* Prentice-Hall Publishing Co., Englewood Cliffs, NJ (1967).
9. Chierici, G.L., Ciucci, G.M., and Sclocchi, G.: "Two-Phase Vertical Flow in Oil Wells—Prediction of Pressure Drop," *JPT* (Aug. 1974) 927–38; *Trans.,* AIME, **257.**
10. Stackel, A.W. and Brown, H.M.: "An Example Approach to Predictive Well Management in Reservoir Simulation," *JPT* (June 1981) 1087–94.
11. Fentor, D.J.: "A Multi-Level Well Management Program for Modeling Offshore Fields," paper SPE 12964 presented at the 1984 SPE European Petroleum Conference, London, Oct. 22–25.
12. *Reservoir Simulation Manual,* Scientific Software Corp. (PB-250-821), USGR-CD-75-005, Natl. Technical Information Service, U.S. Dept. of Commerce (1975).
13. Odeh, A.S.: "Pseudosteady-State Flow Equation and Productivity Index for a Well with Noncircular Drainage Area," *JPT* (Nov. 1978) 1630–32.
14. Emanuel, A.S. and Cook, G.W.: "Pseudo-Relative Permeability for Well Modeling," *SPEJ* (Feb. 1974) 7–9.
15. Woods, E.G. and Khurana, A.K.: "Pseudofunctions for Water Coning in a Three Dimensional Reservoir Simulator," *SPEJ* (Aug. 1977) 251–62; paper SPE 5525 presented at the 1975 SPE Annual Technical Conference and Exhibition, Dallas, Sept. 28–Oct. 1.
16. Akbar, A.M., Arnold, M.D., and Harvey, A.H.: "Numerical Simulation of Individual Wells in a Field Simulation Model," *SPEJ* (Aug. 1974) 315–20.
17. Ridings, R.L. and Mrosovsky, I.: "Two-Dimensional Radial Treatment of Wells Within a Three-Dimensonal Reservoir Model," *SPEJ* (April 1974) 127–31.
18. Brons, F. and Marting, V.E.: "The Effect of Restricted Fluid Entry on Well Productivity," *JPT* (Feb. 1961) 172–74; *Trans.,* AIME, **222.**
19. Odeh, A.S.: "Steady-State Flow Capacity of Wells with Limited Entry to Flow," *SPEJ* (March 1968) 43–51; *Trans.,* AIME, **243.**
20. Crafton, J.W. and Harris, C.D.: "A Direct Finite Difference Simulation of a Gas Well With a Finite Capacity Vertical Fracture," paper 5736 presented at the 1976 SPE Numerical Simulation Symposium, Los Angeles, Feb. 19–20.
21. Prats, M. and Levine, J.S.: "Effect of Vertical Fractures on Reservoir Behavior—Results on Oil and Gas Flow," *JPT* (Oct. 1963) 1119–26; *Trans.,* AIME, **228.**
22. Novotny, E.J.: "Prediction of Stimulation From Acid Fracturing Treatments Using Finite Fracture Conductivity," *JPT* (Sept. 1977) 1186–94; *Trans.,* AIME, **263.**
23. Williamson, A.S. and Chappelear, J.E.: "Representing Wells in Numerical Reservoir Simulation: Part 1—Theory; Part 2—Implementation," *SPEJ* (June 1981) 323–44.
24. Kuniansky, J. and Hillestad, J.G.: "Reservoir Simulation Using Bottomhole Pressure Boundary Conditions," *SPEJ* (Dec. 1980) 473–86.
25. van Poollen, H.K., Breitenbach, E.A., and Thurnau, D.H.: "Treatment of Individual Wells and Grids in Reservoir Modeling," *SPEJ* (Dec. 1968) 341–46.
26. van Poollen, H.K., Bixel, H.C., and Jargon, J.R.: "Individual Well Pressure in Reservoir Modeling," *Reservoir Modeling,* Petroleum Publishing, Tulsa (1971) 44.
27. Abou-Kassem, J.H. and Aziz, K.: "Analytical Well Models for Reservoir Simulation," *SPEJ* (Aug. 1985) 573–79.
28. Peaceman, D.W.: "Interpretation of Well-Block Pressures in Numerical Reservoir Simulation," *SPEJ* (June 1978) 183–94; *Trans.,* AIME, **265.**
29. Lingen, P.L.: "Description of Groningen Gas Well Performance Suitable for Medium and Long Term Planning," paper SPE 4816 presented at the 1974 SPE European Spring Meeting, Amsterdam, April 7–9.
30. Matthews, C.S. and Russell, D.G.: *Pressure Buildup and Flow Tests in Wells,* Monograph Series, SPE, Richardson, TX (1967) **1.**
31. Crichlow, H.B.: *Modern Reservoir Engineering—A Simulation Approach,* Prentice-Hall, Englewood Cliffs, NJ (1977).
32. Harris, M.H.: "The Effect of Perforating on Well Productivity," *JPT* (April 1966) 518–28; *Trans.,* AIME, **237.**
33. Locke, S.: "An Advanced Method for Predicting the Productivity Ratio of a Perforated Well," *JPT* (Dec. 1981) 2481–88.
34. Odeh, A.S.: "An Equation for Calculating Skin Factor Due to Restricted Entry," *JPT* (June 1980) 964–65.
35. Odeh, A.S.: "Pseudosteady-State Flow Capacity of Oil Wells with Limited Entry and an Altered Zone Around the Wellbore," *SPEJ* (Aug. 1977) 271–80.
36. Cinco, H., Miller, F.G., and Ramey, H.J. Jr.: "Unsteady-State Pressure Distribution Created by a Directionally Drilled Well," *JPT* (Nov. 1975) 1392–1400; *Trans.,* AIME, **259.**
37. Roemershauser, A.E. and Hawkins, M.F. Jr.: "The Effect of Slant Hole, Drain Hole, and Lateral Hole Drilling on Well Productivity," *JPT* (Feb. 1955) 11–14.
38. Fussell, D.D.: "Single-Well Performance Predictions for Gas Condensate Reservoirs," *JPT* (July 1973) 860–70; *Trans.,* AIME, **255.**
39. Kazemi, H.: "A Reservoir Simulator for Studying Productivity Variation and Transient Behavior of a Well in a Reservoir Undergoing Gas Evolution," *JPT* (Nov. 1975) 1401–12; *Trans.,* AIME, **259.**
40. Golan, M. and Whitson, C.H.: *Well Performance,* Intl. Human Resources Development Corp., Boston (1986) 40.
41. Handy, L.L.: "Effect of Local High Gas Saturations on Productivity Indices," *Drill. and Prod. Prac.,* API (1957).
42. Standing, M.B.: "Concerning the Calculation of Inflow Performance of Wells Producing From Solution Gas Reservoirs," *JPT* (Sept. 1971) 1141–44.
43. Al-Saadoon, F.T.: "Predicting Present and Future Well Productivities for Solution-Gas-Drive Reservoirs," *JPT* (May 1980) 868–70.
44. Rosbaco, J.A.: "Discussion of Predicting Present and Future Well Productivities for Solution-Gas-Drive Reservoirs," *JPT* (Dec. 1980) 2265–66.
45. Stright, D.H. Jr.: "Grand Forks—Modelling of Three-Dimensional Reservoir with Two-Dimensional Reservoir Simulators," *J. Cdn. Pet. Tech.* (Oct.-Dec. 1973) 46–52.
46. Chappelear, J.E. and Hirasaki, G.J.: "A Model of Oil-Water Coning for Two-Dimensional, Areal Reservoir Simulation," *SPEJ* (April 1976) 65–72; *Trans.,* AIME, **261.**
47. Addington, D.V.: "An Approach to Gas Coning Correlations for a Large Grid Cell Reservoir Simulator," *JPT* (Nov. 1981) 2267–74.
48. Woods, E.G. and Comer, A.G.: "Saturation Distribution and Injection Pressure for a Radial Gas-Storage Reservoir," *JPT* (Dec. 1962) 1389–93; *Trans.,* AIME, **225.**
49. Weinstein, H.G., Wheeler J.A., and Woods, E.G.: "Numerical Model for Thermal Processes," *SPEJ* (Aug. 1977) 65–78; *Trans.,* AIME, **263.**
50. Rubinstein, L.: "Influence of Cold Water Injection on Residual Oil Saturation of Multilayered Oil Reservoir," paper SPE 5555 presented at the 1975 SPE Annual Meeting, Dallas, Sept. 28–Oct. 1.
51. Smith, R.V.: *Practical Natural Gas Engineering,* PennWell Publishing Co., Tulsa (1983).
52. Dempsey, J.R. *et al.*: "An Efficient Model for Evaluating Gas Field Gathering System Design," *JPT* (Sept. 1971) 1067–73.
53. van Beek, F. and Troost, P.J.P.M.: "The Groningen Gas Field: A Case History of the Development of a Giant Gas Field," *JPT* (July 1979) 815–20.
54. Simlote, Y.N. and Hearn, C.L.: "Paddle River Gas Field, Alberta, Canada—Evaluation of Gas Reserves and Future Operating Strategy," paper SPE 7466 presented at the 1978 SPE Annual Technical Conference and Exhibition, Houston, Oct. 1–3.
55. Startzman, R.A. *et al.*: "Computer Combines Offshore Facilities and Reservoir Forecasts," *Pet. Eng.* (May 1977) 65–74.
56. Emanuel, A.S. and Ranney, J.C.: "Studies of Offshore Reservoirs With an Interfaced Reservoir-Piping Network Simulator," *JPT* (March 1981) 399–406.
57. Mohamed, D.A. and Steffensen, R.J.: "An Efficient Reservoir-Coupled Gas Gathering System Simulator," paper SPE 8333 presented at the 1979 SPE Annual Technical Conference and Exhibition, Las Vegas, Sept. 23–26.
58. Gould, T.L., Tek, M.R., and Katz, D.L.: "Two-Phase Flow Through Vertical, Inclined, or Curved Pipe," *JPT* (Aug. 1974) 915–26; *Trans.,* AIME, **257.**
59. Mandhane, J.M., Gregory, G.A., and Aziz, K.: "Critical Evaluation of Friction Pressure-Drop Prediction Methods for Gas-Liquid Flow in Horizontal Pipes," *JPT* (Oct. 1977) 1348–58; *Trans.,* AIME, **263.**
60. Beggs, H.D. and Brill, J.P.: "A Study of Two-Phase Flow in Inclined Pipes," *JPT* (May 1973) 607–17; *Trans.,* AIME, **255.**
61. Aziz, K. *et al.*: *Gradient Curves For Well Analysis and Design,* Monograph, Cdn. Inst. of Mining, Montreal (1979).
62. Gaither, O.D., Winkler, H.W., and Kirkpatrick, C.V.: "Single and Two-Phase Fluid Flow in Small Vertical Conduits Including Annular Configurations," *JPT* (March 1963) 309–20; *Trans.,* AIME, **228.**
63. Fancher, G.H. Jr. and Brown, K.E.: "Prediction of Pressure Gradients for Multiphase Flow in Tubing," *SPEJ* (March 1963) 59–69; *Trans.,* AIME, **228.**
64. Payne, G.A. *et al.*: "Evaluation of Inclined-Pipe, Two-Phase Liquid Holdup and Pressure-Loss Correlations Using Experimental Data," *JPT* (Sept. 1979) 1198–1208; *Trans.,* AIME, **267.**
65. Orkiszewski, J.: "Predicting Two-Phase Pressure Drops in Vertical Pipe," *JPT* (June 1967) 829–38; *Trans.,* AIME, **240.**
66. Patton, L.D. and Abbott, W.A.: "Part 5—Pseudodamage," *Pet. Eng. Intl.* (Oct. 1979) 81–92.

SI Metric Conversion Factors

bbl	× 1.589 873	E−01	=	m^3
°F	(°F−32)/1.8		=	°C
psi	× 6.894 757	E+00	=	kPa

Chapter 8
History Matching: Testing the Validity of the Reservoir Model

The goal of a numerical-model study is the prediction of reservoir performance in more detail and with more accuracy than is possible with simple techniques such as extrapolation. It is intuitively evident that for a model to behave like the reservoir it must be conceptually similar to the reservoir.* Significant differences between the data defining the reservoir in the numerical model and the actual values of the parameters governing reservoir performance will cause correspondingly significant errors in the simulation. Unfortunately, we seldom know enough about a reservoir to develop an acceptably accurate model without testing it in some way and altering its properties until it passes the test. The most useful—and usually the only available—way to test the model is to simulate past performance of the reservoir and to compare the simulation with actual, historical performance. Modeling past performance will identify weaknesses in data, suggest modifications that are needed to improve the model, and demonstrate the quality of the reservoir description that is eventually accepted. If the changes that are made in the model to force it to simulate historical performance are consistent with a comprehensive and rational description of the reservoir, this process of matching history can be an especially useful and powerful reservoir-description technique.

History matching can be time-consuming, expensive, and frustrating because reservoir performance can be complex with numerous interactions that, as a whole, may be difficult to comprehend. To make the process manageable, it is useful to separate it into a number of specific, individual steps. While there is no approach to history matching that is universally applicable, there are a few techniques that lend some structure to the matching process.

This chapter outlines a few of the techniques that can be used to obtain a match and illustrates their use by describing some typical problems. Procedures used in automatic as well as manual history matching will be discussed, and the utility of the two approaches will be compared. A series of special problems will be mentioned, including the problem of relating field-measured pressures to calculated block pressures.

8.1 Objectives of Matching Historical Reservoir Performance

It is clear from the introductory remarks that the primary objectives of history matching are to test and to improve the reservoir model. There are also secondary objectives, some of which may become apparent only as history matching proceeds. For example, history matching will contribute to an understanding of the current status of the reservoir, including fluid distribution and fluid movement and, perhaps, to verification or identification of the current depletion mechanism. It will allow one to infer a reservoir description, including oil and gas in place, in parts of the reservoir where there are no data, and will supply details needed to justify plans and to establish objectives for obtaining data. Sometimes, history matching can lead to discovery of a major operating problem—casing leaks, improper allocation of fluids to wells, etc. In addition, a well-matched model that is kept current can be an excellent reservoir-surveillance tool.

*Within the limits of accuracy of available data, two or more sets of reservoir description data may produce equally acceptable results. Even after history matching, it likely will not be possible to describe a reservoir uniquely.

8.2 Strategy and Plans for History Matching

Chaps. 3 and 4 discuss the data needed to construct a reservoir model. In brief, core analysis and log data can define porosity and initial fluid distribution if the data are available in sufficient quantity and quality. Permeability data usually are too limited in quantity, both areally and vertically, to describe the reservoir adequately. Analysis of the transient behavior of individual wells (a form of history matching) is a standard technique for determining permeability in the region around the well. For developing improved definition of the permeability distribution of the reservoir as a whole, history matching is the method most commonly used. Aquifer data are always extremely sparse, and it is frequently necessary to use history matching to define aquifer porosity, transmissibility, and extent.

8.2.1 Performance Data To Be Matched. In general, the data that are matched are pressure, water/oil ratios (WOR's), gas/oil ratios (GOR's), water/gas ratios (WGR's), water and gas arrival times, and fluid saturations from cores, well logs, and chemical tracer tests.

Periodic observations of shut-in bottomhole pressures are almost always available. Bottomhole flowing pressures (BHFP's) are also available at times, but these data are usually less reliable than shut-in pressures for history-matching purposes. Shut-in surface pressures can be useful if accurate fluid levels and gradients are available to correct pressures to bottomhole conditions. Pressure interference data can be especially useful if they are accurate enough to yield independent estimates of between-well permeability-thickness.

Matching historical WOR's, GOR's, or WGR's is usually the best way to confirm the validity* of estimates of effective zonation and zonal continuity. If the reservoir being studied is in an early stage of depletion, or if for other reasons there are no direct data defining water or gas movement, one must rely heavily on core analysis, logs, and knowledge of the depositional environment to develop zonation and to estimate continuity. Interference tests, pulse tests, and single-well pressure-transient data can also be helpful. These data usually do not, by themselves, give a sufficient picture of the complexity of the reservoir to provide an adequate basis for accurate prediction of water and gas arrival and eventual water- and gas-production rates. As a consequence, most studies of young fields predict first arrival of water or gas later than it actually occurs. If reliable production- and injection-well flow profiles are available, the accuracy with which water or gas arrival can be predicted will be improved. Often these data are not available, but when they are, they should be used to improve permeability zonation and to allocate fluid injection and withdrawal. In general, unless there is some history of water or gas production to match, simulation will not predict abandonment conditions of a reservoir accurately.

*History matching may not identify zones that are not being swept effectively.

Field-measured production and injection rates are normally used without alteration. There are some special situations, however, where it may be appropriate to assume that historical production or injection rates are in error and to adjust them.

Oil production rates are usually the most accurate data available. Gas production in older fields may not have been measured accurately, especially if gas has been flared. Injection data tend to be less accurate than production data, either because of measurement errors or because fluids are lost to other intervals as a result of casing leaks or flow behind pipe. Errors in production data may occur for the same reasons, but they are usually discovered and corrected. If volumes are measured at central sites and not at individual wells, allocation back to wells will be a potential source of error. Where production or injection is commingled, allocation to individual zones will be a source of error.

8.2.2 Action Steps in a History Match. The steps one would normally follow in conducting a match include the following.

1. Assemble data on performance history.
2. Screen the data and evaluate their quality. (For example, one should determine whether correct fluid gradients have been used to adjust observed pressures to datum.)
3. Define the specific objectives of the history match.
4. Develop a preliminary model based on the best available data.
5. Simulate history with the preliminary model and compare simulated performance with actual field history.
6. Decide whether the model is satisfactory. If not—as is most probable—analyze results with simplified models or "hand" calculations to identify changes in model properties that are most likely to improve the agreement between observed and calculated performance.
7. Decide whether an automatic matching program should be used.
8. Make adjustments to the model. Consult with geologic, drilling, and production operations personnel, as necessary, to confirm the realism of proposed changes.
9. Again, simulate part or all of past performance data to improve the match. Analyze results as in Step 6.
10. Repeat Steps 6, 8, and 9 until a satisfactory match of observed data is obtained.

8.2.3 General Strategy for History Matching. Although each reservoir study will supply its own unique set of problems during a history match, the following general strategy is usually effective.

1. Match volumetric-average pressure levels. This is a first step toward confirming the overall compressibility of the reservoir system. Work quickly at this time, using hand calculations and simple models as guides. A rough match is adequate at this stage.
2. Complete a gross match of pressure gradients to establish flow patterns. Work with large areas of the reservoir and aquifer and be aggressive in changing the permeability distribution. Use simple models and hand calculations when they are cost-effective, but balance manpower and computer costs.
3. Match pressure more precisely, making changes in small groups of blocks. Significant changes in reservoir description may occur at this time, so be sure changes are reasonable.
4. Match contact movements, saturations, and WOR, GOR, or WGR on an area basis.
5. Match individual well behavior.

It frequently is wise to obtain a history match for a complex reservoir in two stages, which could be categorized roughly as a "gross phase" and a "detailed phase." In the gross phase, all the history-matching dependent variables, including pressures, saturations, water or gas arrival times, and any other field data, should be brought within reasonable but not tight tolerances. In this phase, a more coarsely gridded model may sometimes be used to reduce overall study costs. After this first phase has been completed, matches of pressure, contact movement, and fluid arrival times should be brought to closer tolerances.

It is always good strategy to maintain close ties with geologists and reservoir and production engineers involved in describing and managing the reservoir. The objectives, of course, are to avoid making changes that are inconsistent with geological and engineering data and to facilitate discovery of errors in field data.

8.2.4 Judging the Acceptability of a Model. A general comment has been made, and not entirely in jest, that "a good history match is obtained when you run out of either time or money." A much better guideline is to judge the quality of the match by whether the reservoir model is good enough to permit the objectives of the study to be met.

Quality tests of a match of pressure history are generally applied at the field level, at some areal subdivision of the field, and at individual wells. In general, the best match is expected at the field level; average field pressures may differ from average model pressures by only a few pounds per square inch. The quality of the match will generally be poorest at the subregion or individual well level.

Pressure matches for individual wells are often acceptable if model and well pressures agree to within ±50 psi [±345 kPa] on the average. In some reservoirs, of course, such as most gas reservoirs and many high-permeability reservoirs, a match must be much better than ±50 psi [±345 kPa] to be acceptable.

One way matching criteria can be developed is to estimate the accuracy with which a specific parameter—e.g., pressure—must be predicted if the study is to satisfy its objectives. The accuracy of the history match should be better than, or at least comparable to, the accuracy required in predictions. This same approach can be used to evaluate whether an improved match would affect predictions enough to make the extra work worthwhile.

In cases where there is little field history, especially for reservoirs in relatively early stages of development, it is possible that a variety of reservoir descriptions will permit a match of the existing data. Model studies of these types of reservoirs should include sensitivity cases to evaluate reservoir performance with two or more equally probable descriptions of the reservoir.

8.3 Manual Adjustment of History-Matching Parameters

Making changes by guessing or by following one's intuition can be expensive and usually will prolong the history-matching phase of a study. The decision to use such an unstructured approach may result from the impression that experienced reservoir engineers develop a "feel" for the "art" of history matching. Experience is valuable, of course, but only because it increases one's understanding of reservoir mechanics. Using that understanding to improve the accuracy of a reservoir's description should not be viewed as an art.

There are numerous papers on automatic history matching. Nevertheless, the majority of engineers engaged in reservoir simulation use manual rather than automatic methods of history matching because of the limitations and expense of currently available automatic methods. In fact, in most large reservoir studies some manual adjustment is almost always required, even if automatic methods are used.

This section describes a structured approach for matching pressure history, fluid contact movements, gas and water arrival times, and GOR and WOR behavior.

8.3.1 Parameters That Can Be Changed To Match History. Those reservoir and aquifer properties appropriate for alteration, in approximate order of decreasing uncertainty, are (1) aquifer transmissibility, kh, (2) aquifer storage, $\phi h c_t$, (3) reservoir kh (including vertical restrictions and directional variations), and (4) relative-permeability and capillary-pressure functions.

The following additional properties must sometimes be altered, but they usually are known with acceptable accuracy: (5) reservoir porosity and thickness, (6) structural definition, (7) rock compressibility, (8) reservoir oil and gas properties (and their geographic distribution within the reservoir, if properties are not uniform), (9) water/oil contacts (WOC's) and gas/oil contacts (GOC's), and (10) water properties.

8.3.2 Matching Pressure History. The following steps normally will produce a successful pressure history match.

1. List those properties of the reservoir and the aquifer that are most likely to affect the pressure history match.

2. Estimate the bounds of uncertainty for the properties listed above.

3. Develop criteria by which to judge the acceptability of a pressure history match.

4. Complete a trial simulation of reservoir history and decide whether the volumetric average pressure of the entire reservoir is satisfactorily matched by the model.

5. If not, use material-balance, pressure-transient theory, and geologic information to estimate changes that should be made to model values of fluids in place in the oil zone and gas cap, average aquifer properties, and aquifer size. At this stage, reconsider concepts of the current depletion mechanism and, in particular, ascertain whether water influx is playing a major role in performance history.

6. Adjust properties until a satisfactory match of overall average reservoir pressure history is achieved.

7. Refer to criteria previously established and decide whether more detailed matching is needed to satisfy study objectives. If so, evaluate the quality of the match of average pressures in major segments of the reservoir. At this time, also evaluate the match of pressure distribution in the reservoir at selected times.

8. If the match is not satisfactory, analyze pressure distribution in and near the reservoir to find evidence for heterogeneous aquifer properties and nonuniform water influx. Also look for differences in pressure distributions between the model and the field that imply the presence of sealing faults, pinchouts, poor communication between zones, and migration to or from other reservoirs.

9. Change reservoir and aquifer properties (storage and transmissibility) areally with use of the pressure-transient theory. Pressure errors that appear shortly after production or injection rates change can be reduced by altering properties in or near the reservoir. Errors that are delayed in time can be reduced by changing properties in regions more remote from the reservoir. Use the depth-of-investigation concept to estimate where changes should be made.

10. Locate regions in which pseudosteady-state conditions exist. In these areas, correct errors in pressure gradients by adjusting transmissibility.

11. Reconsider criteria established in Step 3 and decide whether study objectives justify matching pressure histories of individual wells. If so, continue the matching process with concepts mentioned in Steps 9 and 10.

12. Be alert for situations in which matches in pressure gradients are satisfactory for early history but become poorer as production continues. In simulations of reservoirs producing by waterdrive or water injection, this behavior may indicate errors in fluid mobilities. In this case, it may be necessary to modify rock or pseudo-relative permeabilities. Note also that a drop in the quality of a match after startup of water or gas injection can be evidence of loss of injected fluids to other formations or erroneous allocation of injected fluids to wells or zones.

In general, permeability is the principal reservoir variable used to obtain a match of pressure behavior. Porosity values derived from log and core data should not be changed unless the data are sparse and of poor quality or changes in other, more uncertain, properties do not provide a satisfactory match. Fluid contacts and fluid properties are usually established before history matching begins and, in many cases, may be better defined than porosity. Porosity-thickness in the aquifer is usually less well known than in the reservoir itself and, within limits, aquifer porosity-thickness or the areal extent of the aquifer may be varied to achieve a match. In general, however, permeability is the least well defined and most effective reservoir parameter to vary. Some permeability values may be considered relatively certain, especially those measured by a well test. Even these values may be inaccurate, however, if an overly simplified reservoir model is used in interpreting the well test data.

8.3.3 Matching Gas and Water Movement. Matching fluid movement usually is the strongest verification of the validity of assumptions concerning reservoir description and reservoir mechanics. It is seldom possible to match water and gas movement adequately without having a model of the reservoir that is reasonably complete and is almost entirely consistent with both the assumed reservoir description and observed production history.

The best approach to use in matching fluid-contact movement, gas and water arrival times, and subsequent GOR and WOR behavior will be very specific to the reservoir being studied. The following steps summarize a very general approach that can be tailored to most reservoirs.

1. List those properties of the reservoir and the aquifer that are most likely to influence movement of water or gas.

2. Estimate the bounds of uncertainty of the properties listed above.

3. Develop criteria by which to judge the quality of a match of gas and water movement. Decide whether matching the behavior of groups of wells rather than individual wells is sufficient.

4. Analyze the reservoir-depletion process to determine whether coning or cusping has influenced arrival times of gas and water and subsequent GOR or WOR behavior. If so, well functions may be needed to carry out the history-matching process, particularly on full-field models. For example, well functions are almost always needed for representing partially penetrating wells in two-dimensional (2D) areal models. (See Chap. 7.)

5. Analyze simulations conducted when matching pressure history to determine whether gas and water arrival times and GOR and WOR behavior were matched satisfactorily.

6. If not, look for evidence that permeability stratification is more or less severe than previously indicated. If so, it will be necessary to adjust permeability distribution in the producing section to match water and gas arrival and produced gas and water volumes.

7. Ascertain whether the areal permeability distribution and/or the continuity of selected zones in the reservoir and aquifer should be adjusted. If so, work with geologists to determine what should be adjusted. (For example, the influence of faulting may be more pronounced than was anticipated.)

8. Decide whether relative-permeability data should be modified. Try to avoid changing these data if they were obtained in measurements at reservoir conditions on representative core samples whose wettability had been preserved. If the relative-permeability data are not considered to be reliable, both the shapes of the curves and end-point saturation can be changed. However, extreme changes that move relative-permeability data outside the range observed in other reservoir studies should be avoided. Keep in mind that pseudo-relative permeabilities must be rederived if there are changes in rock relative permeability, stratification, or vertical permeability.

9. Before completing the history match, evaluate the sensitivity of the match to errors in vertical permeability. Vertical-permeability values can be important in calculating displacement efficiency and vertical sweep efficiency and, thus, can affect calculated gas and water arrival times. Unfortunately, effective vertical permeability is usually not available from field measurement and cannot be estimated reliably from core measurements. (See Chap. 4 for more discussion.)

10. Analyze performances of selected wells to see whether grid-block definition is a major problem. Coarse gridding can create apparent differences in model and field behavior because gridblock centers may be too far from actual well locations, or because poor definition causes errors in calculated displacement efficiency or sweep efficiency.

11. Recognize that incorrect allocation of injected and produced fluids in the field may make precise agreement between field and model individual well behavior impossible to achieve.

12. As changes in model properties are made to match gas and water movement, continue to compare calculated and actual pressure behavior. Make further adjustments in model properties to maintain a pressure match, if matching fluid movement has caused major changes in the quality of the pressure history match.

Matching performance of a well in which water underlies (or gas overlies) the completion interval almost always requires use of a coning model. The model is adjusted to match history by varying the permeability levels in a key layer(s) such as a tar-bearing zone, where permeability is not well known, or in a low-permeability zone, which severely limits vertical flow. Vertical permeability between the completion interval and WOC or GOC is almost always a critical matching parameter. But it is also important to model horizontal permeability correctly so that pressure drawdown is matched accurately.

In the absence of coning, cusping, and severe stratification, models may predict water production that is not observed in the field. This behavior is sometimes difficult to explain.* Obviously, water relative permeability is not properly defined, but exactly why may not be understood. Possible explanations include (1) saturation change in the field is following a hysteresis loop, and drainage rather than imbibition water relative permeabilities should be used at low water saturations, (2) water relative permeabilities at low water saturations are incorrect (laboratory measurements at low saturations are difficult and relative permeabilities at saturations up to about 20% PV above irreducible water saturation probably will not have been measured), or (3) the initial water-saturation distribution in the model is incorrect. Laboratory experiments may be necessary to evaluate whether one of the explanations should be accepted for a specific reservoir system.

8.4 Examples of Adjustments Required in History Matching

This section will discuss a few typical kinds of adjustments in reservoir description that are needed to match historical performance. In the examples, we will illustrate a problem (mismatch), show the final match, and indicate what data were changed to obtain the final match. Where special techniques were involved in making this model adjustment, they will be illustrated.

Three of the examples were developed with a hypothetical reservoir to illustrate the effect on calculated pressure level of changes in reservoir permeability, aquifer permeability, and aquifer porosity. Three additional examples, taken from actual reservoir studies, summarize results of matching an actual pressure distribution by changing permeabilities and illustrate some of the techniques that can be used when matching water arrival time and WOR's. A final example, also from an actual reservoir study, illustrates one approach for matching a log-derived water-saturation profile.

8.4.1 Adjustments to Match Pressures.

8.4.1.1 Pressure Levels. General guidelines for matching observed pressure response can be obtained by analysis of the single-phase, transient-pressure-response equation,**

$$p=p_i+70.6\frac{q\mu B}{kh}[\mathrm{Ei}(-1/4t_D)], \quad (8.1)$$

where

p = pressure at radius r from producing well, psi,
p_i = initial pressure, psi,
q = well rate, STB/D,
k = permeability, md,
μ = viscosity, cp,
B = fluid FVF, RB/STB,
h = formation thickness, ft,
t_D = dimensionless time, or

$$t_D=0.00632\frac{kt}{\phi c \mu r^2}, \quad (8.2)$$

t = time, days,
ϕ = porosity, fraction,
c_t = total compressibility, psi^{-1},
r = radius from producing well, ft, and
Ei = exponential integral function; solution to point or line-source radial diffusion equation.

The timing of the pressure response is controlled by the ratio $k/\phi c \mu$ (Eq. 8.2), while the level of the response is controlled by $kh/\mu B$

*We assume in the discussion that adequate attention will have been given to numerical dispersion; the error discussed is not an error in computation but in the description of the physics of the system being modeled.

**Eq. 8.1 provides a good approximation for wellbore pressure, p_w, except at very early times (usually times of less than 1 hour). Note that $p=p_w$ when $r=r_w$.

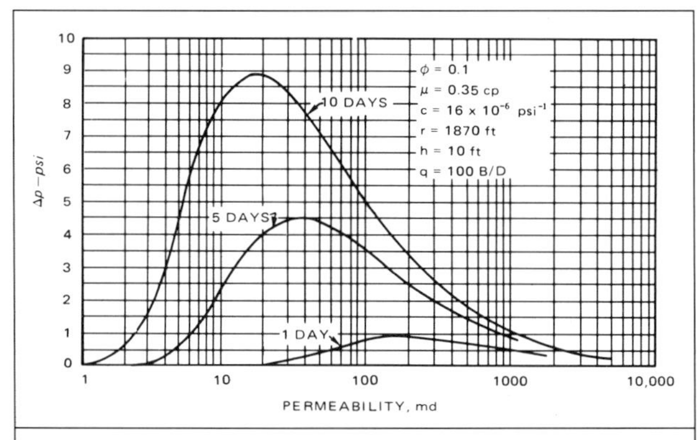

Fig. 8.1—Variation in pressure response with permeability and time as calculated by Eq. 8.1.

(Eq. 8.1). The time at which a heterogeneity, such as a permeability discontinuity, influences the pressure at a well is proportional to the square of the distance from the heterogeneity to the well.

Fig. 8.1 illustrates the influence of permeability on the timing and level of pressure response (calculated from Eq. 8.1) between a producing well and an observation well on a nominal 80-acre [32-ha] spacing. A high-permeability system creates little pressure drawdown to be transmitted to the observation well. A low-permeability system requires a long time to transmit large pressure variations to the observation well. Furthermore, under a given set of conditions, there is one value of permeability that will result in a maximum pressure drop from initial pressure at a given time and distance. For the case presented in Fig. 8.1, at a time of 10 days the maximum pressure drop of 9 psi [62 kPa] will occur for a permeability of 17.7 md. (If, for this same set of conditions, a pressure drop greater than 9 psi [62 kPa] is observed at a time of 10 days, then the assumed values of reservoir parameters are in error.) Fig. 8.1 also demonstrates that an attempt to calculate formation permeability from a single data point can result in two possible values of permeability. In the case under discussion, an observed pressure drop of 7 psi [48 kPa] at 10 days could imply a permeability of either 7.5 or 51 md.

The conclusions to be drawn from such relationships as Fig. 8.1 are overly simplified. In a producing reservoir, there are multiple points of withdrawal and injection, an aquifer and/or a gas cap may be contributing support, the wellbore may be damaged or stimulated, and well rates may be changing. Nevertheless, pressure-transient theory is a useful tool for developing initial estimates of changes to be made when history matching.

Fig. 8.1 demonstrates that it is helpful when history matching to have pressure data during transient periods (well or field shutdowns, new wells turned on, etc.) when pressure changes are more rapid. Pressures that change slowly are not sensitive indicators of reservoir permeabilities.

Figs. 8.2 and 8.3 were taken from a simulation-workshop problem that deals with a single-well reservoir surrounded by a large aquifer. For both parts of the problem, the students assumed that the permeability of the reservoir was 10 times that of the aquifer and obtained the "first pass" pressure prediction shown in the figures. The problem was to find what properties of the system had been changed by the instructor to obtain the "observed" performances illustrated. In Fig. 8.2, the calculated pressures are below the observed trend but almost parallel to it. This is typical of a system in which the permeability of nearby regions (the oil reservoir in this case) is limiting support. A 1.5-fold increase in the reservoir permeabilities was required to achieve the final match shown. (It is common practice, at least initially, to adjust the level of permeability by a uniform multiplying factor over a designated portion of the reservoir, or the entire reservoir in this example, rather than to attempt different amounts of change on a block-by-block basis.)

In Fig. 8.3, the calculated pressure fell below the observed pressure and continued to diverge. This is typical of a system in which support is limited by permeabilities or porosities distant from the well. In this case, the reservoir permeability was not altered.

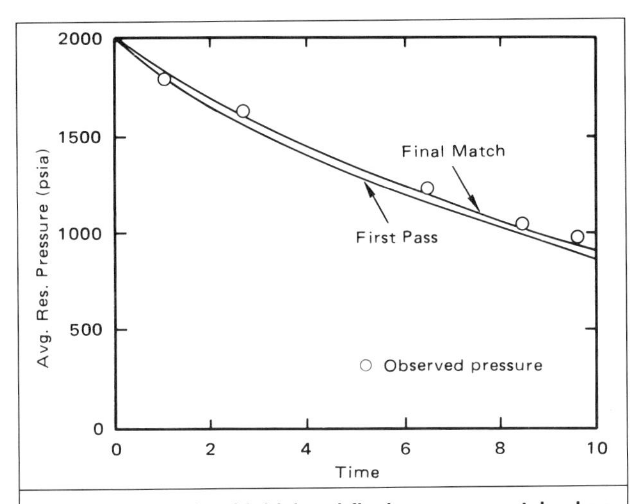

Fig. 8.2—Example of initial and final pressure match when estimate of reservoir permeability is low.

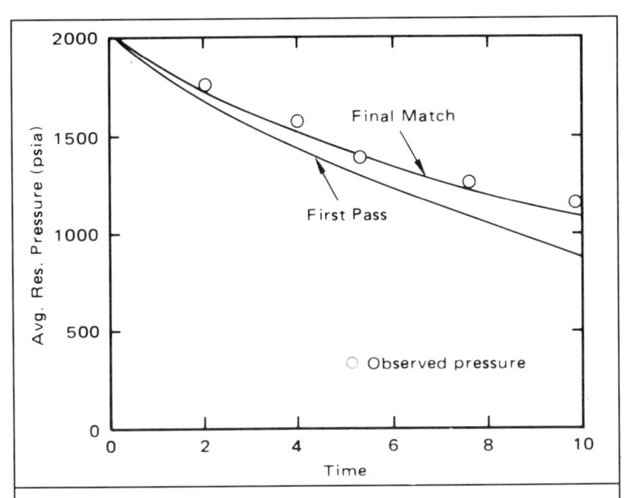

Fig. 8.3—Example of initial and final pressure match when estimate of aquifer permeability is low.

The match was achieved by raising the aquifer permeability level uniformly by 1.5-fold. A fair match could have been achieved by increasing aquifer porosity-thickness. Unless there is evidence that aquifer porosity-thickness has been underestimated, however, porosity-thickness is not an acceptable matching parameter. That there are two possible solutions to the problem of Fig. 8.3 illustrates a point that can be considered to be a general rule: *matching pressure data alone will not produce a unique reservoir description.*

8.4.1.2 Pressure Gradients. The previous discussions concerned only the simple case of matching average pressure of a reservoir in which pressure is declining. Matching average pressure is adequate only for a reservoir in which pressure gradients are low and, hence, pressures of all wells are about the same at any given time. For such cases, it is possible to calculate an accurate aquifer porosity-thickness and permeability-thickness with classic methods. In these cases, final matching of history requires only a few simulations to verify the calculated values of reservoir and aquifer properties.

In the more general case, there are pressure gradients in a reservoir that must be matched. If parts of the reservoir are reasonably close to a steady-state or pseudosteady-state pressure condition (and if reservoir geometry is not overly complex), the approach described below may be useful in adjusting calculated

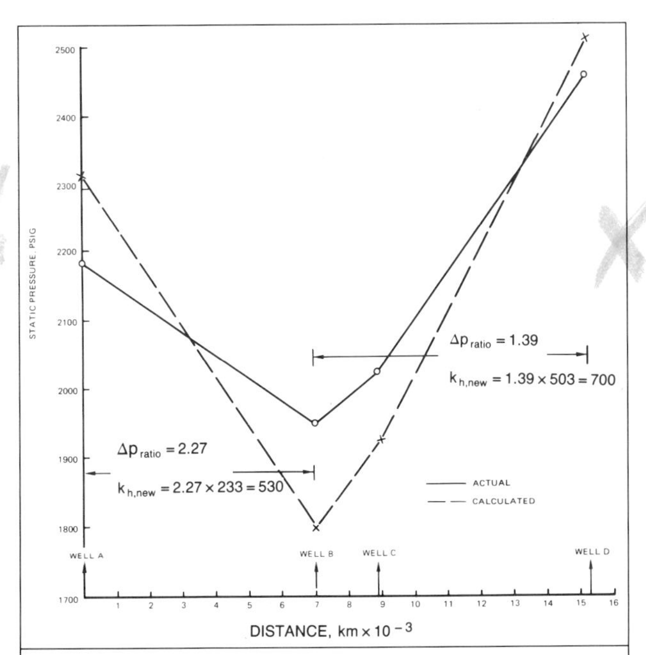

Fig. 8.4—Actual and calculated pressure gradient indicating that between-well permeability is low.

pressure gradients. The approach will be illustrated by describing a matching problem during a reservoir study of a large reservoir producing primarily by aquifer influx. Fig. 8.4 shows plots of actual and calculated pressures near the end of the history on a line parallel to the main direction of flow in the reservoir. Calculated pressures at this time were too high at the reservoir edge and too low at the center. The calculated pressure gradient on the west flank (the region between Wells A and B) was too large by a factor of 2.27. On the east flank (between Wells B and D), the gradient was too large by a factor of 1.39. An increase in model permeabilities by factors of 2.27 on the west flank and 1.39 on the east flank solved the problem. As anticipated, the adjustments did not produce a perfectly matched model because the overall pressure level was affected and further adjustments to aquifer permeabilities had to be made to restore the match of the average pressure level. In general, when calculated pressures "straddle" observed pressures, as in Fig. 8.4, this procedure can be used successfully.

8.4.2 Adjustments To Match Water and Gas Arrival, GOR, and WOR Behavior. It is important to match GOR's and WOR's, because eventual reservoir performance and the design of surface facilities may be more critically affected by gas or water production than by pressure behavior.

One of the most common causes of early water production is coning into a partially penetrating well open to an oil column overlying water. A matching problem involving coning in an actual reservoir study is illustrated in Fig. 8.5 and Tables 8.1 and 8.2. The coning model used was a radial model having 15 layers. Table 8.1 gives the depth, thickness, k_h, k_v, and ϕ assigned to these layers on the basis of core analysis data. The original WOC was located at a depth of 6,735 ft [2053 m]. In the first simulator run, water arrived late and the WOR rose too slowly. Preliminary simulations showed that the level of vertical permeability assigned to the low-k_v layers would have the most effect on time of water arrival at the producing interval (Layers 1 through 7). In Trial 1,

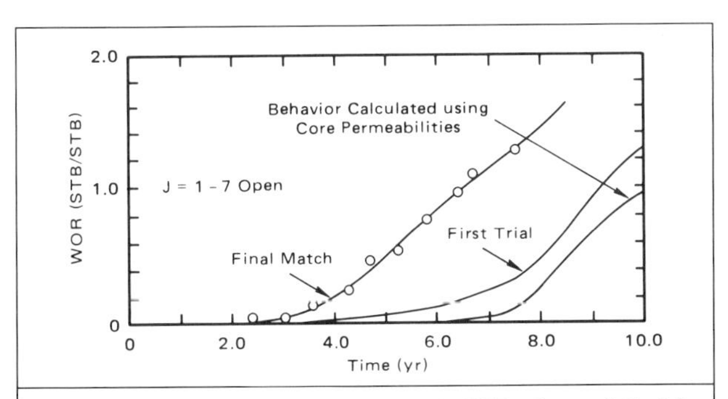

Fig. 8.5—Initial and final matches of WOR of a well that is coning water.

TABLE 8.1—RESERVOIR ZONATION*

Layer**	Depth (ft subsea)	Δh (ft)	k_h (md)	k_v (md)	ϕ (%)
1	6,337	32	226.5	0.1	16.7
2	6,369	60	165.7	15.2	26.4
3	6,429	26	526.0	7.9	30.9
4	6,455	20	314.6	10.4	28.2
5	6,475	20	68.4	3.6	20.0
6	6,495	23	342.8	1.05	18.9
7	6,518	28	1,094.3	229.2	28.7
8	6,546	25	997.0	239.0	31.0
9	6,571	10	684.0	1.9	26.5
10	6,581	18	725.5	144.3	29.0
11	6,599	19	769.8	37.9	27.6
12	6,618	14	114.3	0.13	18.8
13	6,632	20	65.6	51.4	25.0
14	6,652	20	282.3	9.7	24.8
15	6,672	20	701.6	10.1	23.2
16	6,692	20	400.7	41.0	23.7
17	6,712	20	228.0	2.4	16.5
18	6,732	40	436.4	18.7	19.5
—	6,735 original WOC		—	—	—
19	6,772	41	158.6	31.6	19.4

*Based on core analysis used originally in coning model (Fig. 8.5).
**Layers 1 through 7 are producing interval.

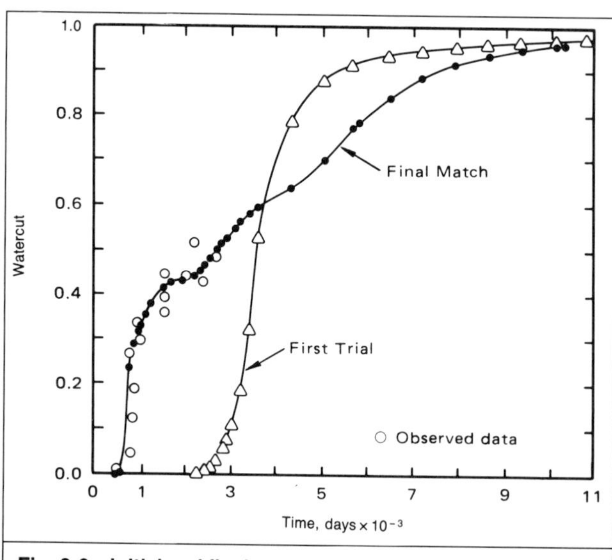

Fig. 8.6—Initial and final matches of WOR of a well in a highly stratified reservoir.

the calculated time of first water arrival was improved by increasing vertical permeability in Layers 9 and 12 to 150 and 4 md, respectively. The predicted breakthrough time was still 2.5 years too late, however, and the calculated water cut did not increase rapidly enough with time. In the final trial, it was found that extension of these increased values to a radial distance of 2,000 ft [610 m] (Model Rings 1 through 7) and use of the original core analysis values beyond that point (Model Rings 8 through 15) gave the best match of the well's WOR history. The presence of the outlying tight streaks increased both horizontal and vertical pressure gradients. As a result of the elevated pressure differentials, coning was more rapid and occurred at a time that agreed with observed behavior.

Vertical permeability is not always the dominant variable in coning. The horizontal permeability and its effect on pressure drawdown (and equilibrium cone height) is sometimes of key importance. Parameter studies for coning problems are available in the literature.[1,2]

Fig. 8.6 illustrates watercut behavior for a well not underlain originally by water. A 2D cross-sectional model was used to match this well. Actual water arrival was much earlier than could be predicted in a model in which zonation was based solely on core analysis. To match the observed data (including data from logs that identified zones producing water), it was necessary to raise horizontal permeability by a factor of 21 in Layer 4 (see Table 8.3), the zone through which water was observed to be entering the producing well. It was not necessary to change vertical-permeability distribution in this model.

Wells sometimes are available to define WOC or GOC movement. Saturation logs taken at different times can give useful data to match before water-arrival data are available. Fig. 8.7 illustrates a sequence of matching runs in a model that first predicted channeling of water higher and in a narrower zone than was indicated by well logs. Table 8.4 compares "first trial," "second trial," and "final match" k_h and k_v values used in the various cross-sectional layers. In Trial 1, the higher permeability was placed in Layer 2. Harmonic averaging of k_v values entered on block centers was used, resulting in the rather low k_v values shown.

The exceptionally low k_v values above and below Layer 2 caused the water to remain in that layer and produced a water saturation anomaly in that zone. Eliminating low vertical permeability except at the base of Layer 5 and modifying permeability values of Layers 2 and 5 moved the saturation anomaly to the correct zone (Layer 5 as indicated by the induction-electric log), but the anomaly was of insufficient amplitude. In the final match, the permeability of Layer 5 was increased by 400 md while that of Layer 6 was decreased by 400 md.

Although these examples are not complex, they are typical of problems that must be solved, and the approaches described are typical of techniques normally used to resolve differences between model and field data. Other examples of history matching are presented in Refs. 3 and 4, which describe the use of history matching to improve estimates of reservoir PV and to evaluate the influence of flow barriers on performance history.

8.5 Special Considerations in History Matching

Several of the special issues that will confront engineers during history matching are described in this section.

8.5.1 Evaluating the Quality of Field Data. Good rate and pressure data from the field are essential to obtaining a good reservoir model. These data should be plotted on a well-by-well basis to identify and to remove any obvious data inconsistencies.

When beginning a history-match phase, it is useful to get as close as possible to the source of the data. If timing will permit, personally collect the data in the field office. Screen the data, but do not discard data that may appear to be anomalous. These data may provide valuable information for the history match because anomalies are often the key to discovery of unique reservoir features.

In general, be aware of the quality and relative accuracy of the rate and pressure data. Gas and oil production rates from gas/oil separation plants or by lease are usually quite accurate. However, allocation of these rates to the individual wells is generally much less accurate. Further inaccuracies exist in the information on zonal production rates that are necessary for three-dimensional (3D) studies. Water-injection rates are often less accurate than oil-production rates. Casing leaks or leaks through bad cement jobs can sometimes reduce or increase the rates of water flowing into

TABLE 8.2—VARIATION OF RESERVOIR DESCRIPTIONS USED IN THE CONING MODEL (Fig. 8.5)

	k_v, md	
Model Layer $j=9$	$i=1$ through 7	$i=8$ through 15
Original based on core analysis	1.9	1.9
First trial	150	150
Final match	150	1.9
Model Layer $j=12$		
Original based on core analysis	0.13	0.13
First trial	4	4
Final match	4	0.13

TABLE 8.3—DIFFERENCE IN HORIZONTAL PERMEABILITIES ASSUMED IN FIG. 8.6—FIRST TRIAL AND FINAL MATCH

Layer	Depth (ft subsea)	Layer Thickness (ft)	Horizontal Permeability (md)	
			First Trial	Final Match
1	5,811.2	22.38	954.3	318.1
2	5,825.0	5.28	48.0	16.0
3	5,838.7	22.00	1,053.6	351.2
4	5,856.4	13.50	237.9	5,000.0
5	5,871.6	16.83	872.1	290.7
6	5,885.8	11.57	998.7	332.9
7	5,897.0	10.83	102.6	34.2
8	5,907.3	9.83	247.8	82.6
9	5,914.7	5.00	204.0	68.0
10	5,922.1	9.86	1,536.9	512.3
11	5,941.9	29.73	187.2	62.4
12	5,968.5	23.49	164.4	54.8
13	5,998.9	37.17	6.3	2.1
14	6,025.0	15.10	57.3	19.1
Total *kh*, darcy-ft			104.48	101.26

TABLE 8.4—k_h AND k_v VALUES (md) USED IN CROSS-SECTIONAL MODEL (Fig. 8.7)

Layer*	Trial 1		Trial 2		Final Match	
	k_h	k_v	k_h	k_v	k_h	k_v
1	182.0	0.23	182.0	14.0	182.0	14.0
2	4,172.0	0.23	891.0	519.0	891.0	519.0
3	2,061.0	447.0	2,061.0	694.0	2,061.0	694.0
4	1,612.0	1.28	1,612.0	130.0	1,612.0	130.0
5	891.0	0.37	4,172.0	0.46	4,572.0	0.46
6	908.0	0.53	908.0	5.76	508.0	5.76
7	105.0	16.4	105.0	29.4	105.0	29.4
8	357.0	22.6	375.0	32.7	357.0	32.7
9	139.0	8.95	139.0	10.6	139.0	10.6
10	230.0	3.59	230.0	4.48	230.0	4.48
11	88.0	1.51	88.0	1.81	88.0	1.81
12	37.0	0.68	37.0	0.79	37.0	0.79
13	17.0	0.10	17.0	0.26	17.0	0.26
14	2.0		2.0		2.0	

*At Column $I=32$ corresponding to the observation-well location.
k_v values in Table 8.4 refer to those at the boundary with the next lower block.

a formation; the existence of such things is often detected when history matching. Note also that it is usually necessary to confirm that measured pressures have been corrected to datum properly.

Equally important are data on WOC's, GOC's, and original oil in place (OOIP) or original gas in place. Initial values of these quantities should be compared with existing estimates. If there are differences, they should be resolved before a simulation goes beyond the initialization stage. Generally, in a field with a long history, there will be values, especially for OOIP, that have been established by prior studies and that should not be changed without adequate reason. For young reservoirs, there may not be a good estimate of OOIP. In this case, care must be taken to make sure that simulator values are consistent with whatever data are available.

8.5.2 Correcting Observed Pressures to Model Conditions. Pressure data for active production and injection wells normally will not correspond directly to calculated pressure in the gridblocks containing the wells. For example, calculated pressure in a gridblock containing a producing well may be above the BHFP but less than the pressure measured after a 72-hour shut-in period. The reason for the apparent discrepancy, of course, is that the horizontal dimensions of a gridblock are much larger than the radius of the well and, hence, the gridblock pressure corresponds to an actual pressure some distance from the wellbore. For adequate comparison, it is necessary to adjust either the calculated or measured pressure so that the two pressures represent conditions at the same location in the reservoir. In practice, it usually is more convenient to adjust the measured pressures.

Under steady-state flow in a homogeneous reservoir in which a production or injection well is completed in the entire productive interval, a pressure distribution will be established that can be described by a straight-line plot of p vs. $\ln r$, where r is the radial

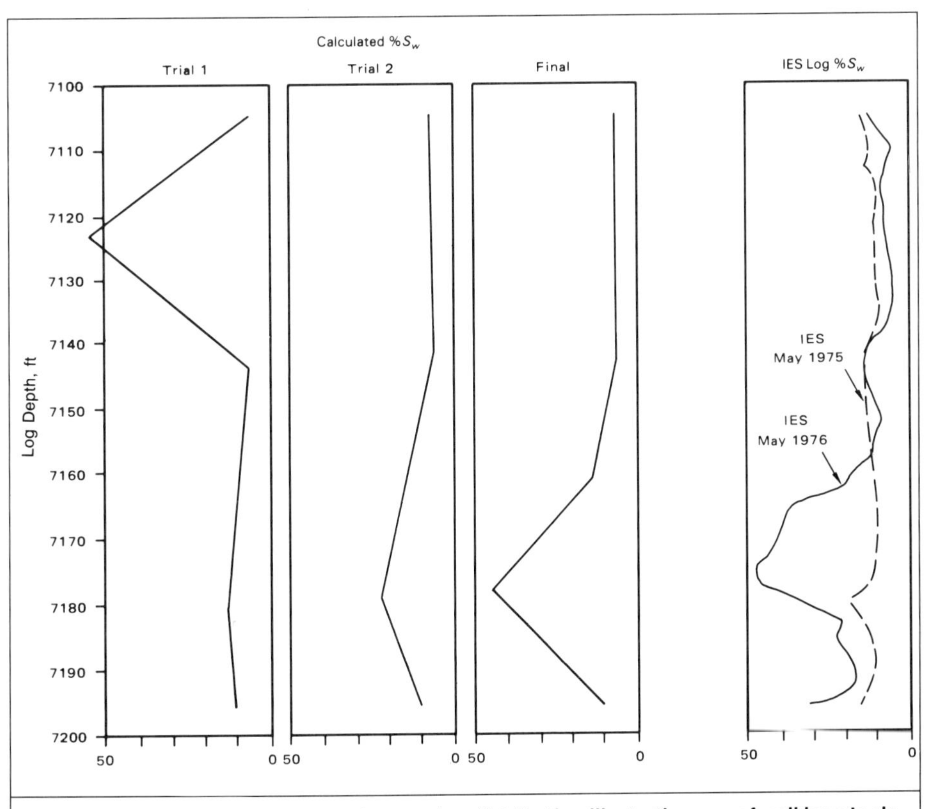

Fig. 8.7—Calculated and measured saturation distribution illustrating use of well logs to develop zonation.

distance from the wellbore. In Fig. 8.8, p_f is the BHFP at a steady-state condition for a flow rate q. When the well is shut in for a period, the pressure at the wellbore will change. For the case of a square grid, and uniform and equal k_x and k_y, Peaceman[5] showed that the model will calculate a pressure equivalent to the flowing pressure at $r_o=0.2\Delta x$, where Δx is the block width.* In Fig. 8.8, a shut-in time was used that allowed the pressure (at a production well) to build up to a measured value of $p=p_m$. Hence, the measured pressure, p_m, must be corrected by the difference p_m-p_o to obtain the value p_o that would correspond to the model-calculated value. To estimate this correction, p_m-p_o, the theory of Miller *et al.*[9] together with the relationship $r_o=0.2\Delta x$ gives the shut-in time to build up to p_o as**

$$t_o=1{,}687\frac{\phi\mu c_t r_o^2}{k}, \quad (8.3)$$

where c_t is the total compressibility of the rock and fluid system (psi^{-1}) and the pressure correction (if $t_m \neq t_o$) is

$$p_o-p_m=\frac{162.6\ q\mu B}{kh}(\log_{10} t_o/t_m), \quad (8.4)$$

where t_m is the time at which the well shut-in pressure is measured (days).

Thus, if a single value of shut-in pressure is measured, Eq. 8.4 can be used to correct the measurement for comparison with model pressures. If permeability at the well is not known from previous tests, the value of kh to use in Eq. 8.4 is the average of the edge values of the model wellblock. The oil-production rate, q, should be the average sustained rate for the period immediately before shut-in for pressure measurement.

Eq. 8.4 may not provide an accurate correction for very short or very long shut-in times. For very short shut-in times, afterflow or other "early-time" effects may be important; for very long shut-in times, interference or reservoir limits may influence pressure behavior. If a buildup or falloff curve is available, p vs. $\log_{10} t$ should be plotted to ensure a "middle-time" region for which the straight-line relationship implied by Eq. 8.4 exists and that t_o is in the region. If so, pick p_o at Time t_o. If t_o is in the early-time region, there will be effects that are not represented in the model; in this case, select a value of t_m in the middle-time region and use Eq. 8.4 to calculate p_o from p measured at t_m. If t_o is in the late-time region, if an unknown amount of interference is suspected, and if buildup (or falloff) data are not available, it is sometimes possible to incorporate the actual shut-in time into the simulation itself. If reservoir pressure is not changing too rapidly with time, and shut-in times are reasonably uniform at the wells being matched, it is appropriate to approximate the shut-in period as occurring at the middle or end of the month for all wells measured during that month. This permits modeling the shut-in period with a single timestep or only a few shut-in timesteps each month. The pressure correction will be largest for high-rate wells in low-permeability formations and is frequently important for water-injection wells.

8.5.3 Treating Wells Remote From Block Centers. It is frequently not possible to prepare a grid without some of the wells being remote from block centers. For these wells, it may be necessary to compare the observed data with interpolated model pressure. For example, on successive model runs, the model well in question can be moved to an adjacent block to obtain an alternative calculation of pressure. Then, the appropriately interpolated value would be compared with the observed value. If the above approach is not adequate for the particular model being used, an alternative adjustment to the model data must be developed to put calculated and observed pressures on a comparable basis. If the adjustment seems excessive and the well is a key well, the model probably should be redesigned.

If a large number of wells are involved, it is often adequate, and frequently preferable, to compare an average of the pressures of a group of wells rather than individual well pressures. In any case, of course, pressure gradients in the model must match field gradients adequately.

*van Poollen *et al.*[6] and Coats *et al.*[7] have contended that the block pressure occurs at the radius $r_o=r=0.32\Delta x$, which would be the *average* pressure integrated over the area of the block. Kuniansky and Hillestad[8] support the $0.2\Delta x$ equivalent radius derived by Peaceman for central wells in an interior gridblock and conclude that it is a good approximation for edge and corner blocks as well. The relationship is different, however, when the well is displaced from the block center to the block corner or block edge, when the gridblocks are nonsquare, or when permeability is anisotropic.

**In Eqs. 8.3 and 8.4, t_o and t_m are time in days, μ is viscosity in centipoise, r_o is radial distance in feet, k is formation permeability in millidarcies, q is well rate before shut-in in STB/D, B is FVF for the produced fluid in RB/STB, and h is formation thickness in feet. For an injection well, rate is a negative quantity.

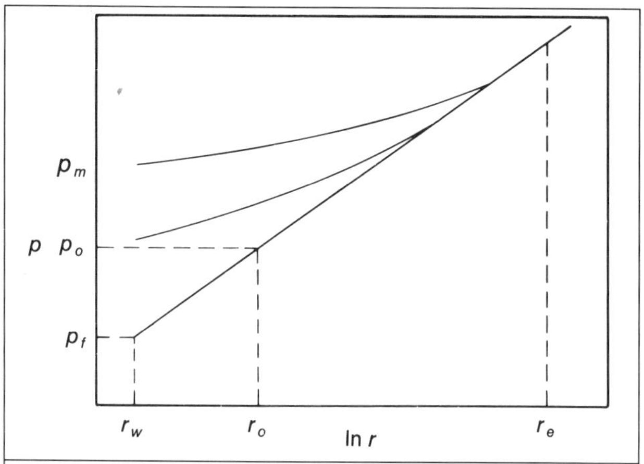

Fig. 8.8—Pressure distributions to consider in comparing measured and calculated shut-in pressures.

8.5.4 Relating Block Saturations to Contact Positions. Data on the positions of WOC's and GOC's as indicated by logs are sometimes available for matching. In some instances, these types of data may be more abundant than post-breakthrough WOR and GOR data. Comparison of actual and calculated contact locations cannot be made directly, however, even in a 3D model, because model blocks will be too large for accurate definition of contact depths. The best way to make a comparison is to develop correlations with results from a detailed cross-sectional model. The cross section obviously must model the region involved in reasonable detail. An areal or 3D model block will correspond to all or part of a column (or group of columns) in the cross section. Contact depths, as indicated in the calculated cross-sectional saturation array, are plotted vs. the PV-weighted average saturation of the cross-sectional blocks corresponding to specific areal or 3D model blocks. Contact depths are read from the plot at times corresponding to those times when contact measurements were made in the field. These types of correlations are approximate, of course, and should be used with caution.

8.5.5 Coping With Simulator Difficulties During Matching. It is not uncommon to have simulator difficulties during history matching. For example, water or gas saturation at a producing well in a block near a WOC or GOC may occasionally rise to a value so high that oil relative permeability falls to zero and oil cannot be delivered by the model well even though the actual well is still producing oil. Correction of the problem on a future run might involve modification of the model-block depth, WOC, GOC, or porosity-thickness to place more oil in the block so that water or gas saturation does not build up to such a high value during the history period. Alternatively, relative permeability or stratification may be modified to retard the time oil relative permeability falls to near-zero values.

The simulator sometimes will fail to converge or will cut timesteps severely if historical well rates change rapidly. This problem can usually be circumvented by averaging rates over longer time periods, thereby reducing the frequency with which rates change.

8.6 Automatic History Matching

Numerous techniques have been described that have used the computer with various degrees of success to achieve a match of historical data.[10-23] These techniques generally use nonlinear optimization methods to achieve a best or "least-squares" fit of the observed data. In the terminology of operations research, these procedures seek to minimize an "objective function" Q, defined as

$$Q=\sum_{i=1}^{n} R_i^2, \quad \text{(8.5)}$$

where R_i is a residual that may be defined in various ways depending on the data to be matched. Expressed in general terms,

$$R_i=W_i(X-X_o)_i, \quad \text{(8.6)}$$

where
X = calculated data,
X_o = actual data (adjusted to model conditions—spatially and timewise), and
W_i = weighting factor.

W_i is normally unity, but W_i could be greater than one if it is desired to weight certain data points more heavily than others. This may occur when sparse data regions (areally or timewise) must have their data emphasized to exert an appropriate influence on reservoir description.

X is usually a calculated pressure, but it can be calculated GOR or WOR, cumulative water or gas production, or any other quantity to be matched. Defining X as the cumulative gas production has been described by Rossen[24] as useful in determining gas reserves.

Most automatic history-matching methods do not permit simultaneous matching of two or more kinds of data. In practice, pressure normally would be matched first. Then GOR or WOR would be matched by automatic modification of either rock or pseudo-relative-permeability functions. Most experience to date has been on matching pressure data, but the selection of the type of data to vary is an option. For a match of pressure, the model grid generally will be divided into arbitrary areas and the simulator will modify multiplying factors—one value for each area—that will raise or lower all permeabilities and/or porosities uniformly for each area. Hence, the reservoir variables or parameters that are automatically changed to achieve a match are the multiplying factors rather than the permeabilities or porosities themselves. It is generally not feasible to have a multiplying factor for every permeability or porosity value in the model.*

To make the objective function, Q, become as small as possible, most techniques calculate the amount of change in Q resulting from a change in each reservoir parameter to be varied. These partial derivative values of Q are used to improve estimates of the reservoir parameters that ultimately will be varied to reduce Q to its lowest possible value. Q must be evaluated not only for a base set of conditions but also for a number of additional sets corresponding to the number of reservoir variables to be altered. The ratio of the change in Q to the change in the variable—all other variables held at base value—is the numerical approximation of the partial derivative of Q being evaluated. New techniques[14,18,19,25,26] have sought to reduce the computer work required to calculate the partial derivative of Q. Different methods proceed at different rates to this optimal value of Q; some methods require many trials and make numerous successive approximations before converging on the lowest Q or best fit of the data. Initial estimates of reservoir parameters can be obtained with simplified models before proceeding to the final matching stage with the full simulation model.

8.6.1 Procedures. The procedure for automatic history matching will depend somewhat on the characteristics of the computer program, but generally will include the following steps.

1. Devise a numerical model of the reservoir. If waterdrive is significant, the model should simulate the aquifer in addition to the reservoir. The model should run relatively rapidly on the computer because numerous reruns of history will be required. To accomplish this, the model might have a simplified or coarse grid and, if the history period is short enough to assume that fluid contacts have not moved, a single-phase representation of the system might be used. Of course, the model must represent the real system adequately; e.g., a single-phase model will not be sufficient if there is much water or gas encroachment.
2. Select the variables to be modified by the automatic history-matching package. It is important to be judicious in the selection of variables and to select only those variables that have the strongest effect on the objective function. Variables having little effect should be avoided or eliminated as soon as that fact is discovered. Elimination of weak variables is aided by rotational discrimination methods.[24,25] Normally, no more than 50 variables should be selected. Select an appropriate number of areas of the grid that the program can modify with uniform multiplying factors. For example, if there are five areas in which permeability is to be modified, five multiplying factors will be modified simultaneously by the automatic history-matching package. The regions or areas can be adjusted, if necessary, to improve the eventual match. Experience indicates that the number of areas in which permeabilities and porosities are to be varied with uniform multiplying factors should not exceed the number of observation points in the reservoir/aquifer system and each area should contain at least one observation point.
3. Set constraints so that the automatic history-matching program will not be allowed to produce wild or unrealistic values of reservoir parameters. Variables that have only a weak effect on the objective function may drift aimlessly as a best fit is approached. Unrealistic final values may be assigned to these variables if reasonable constraints are not applied.
4. Assign the best current reservoir description to the model.
5. Set up the observed data (observed pressures, WOR's and GOR's, and cumulative production) in a format acceptable to the automatic history-matching program.
6. Assign scaling factors to the observed data. Frequently, all data are given the same weight. It may be necessary or desirable, however, to weight sparse data more heavily to obtain an adequate match of those data.
7. At any stage of the history-matching process, make judicious changes in variables and variable areas or regions on the basis of experience and understanding of reservoir mechanics. No automatic history-matching method can be used blindly.

An example application described below will illustrate use of automatic history matching. The example field is the Khursaniyah field in Saudi Arabia, which presented a difficult problem for manual history matching, but which lent itself well to the application of automatic history matching.[27]

8.6.2 Example Application of an Automatic History-Matching Method. This example, taken from a paper by Boberg *et al.*,[27] involved use of 2D radial and 3D models to simulate a complex, intercommunicating reservoir system. Other examples in the literature illustrate use of various automatic history-matching methods with 2D areal models.[10-22]

8.6.2.1 Reservoir Description. Oil is produced in the Khursaniyah field from four separate overlying calcareous limestone reservoirs. The structure is an elliptical anticline trending southwest/northeast. The reservoirs are separated by anhydrite, which, while impermeable on the reservoir flanks, is fractured in the vicinity of the structural crest. The fractures provide vertical communication between the four reservoirs and with an underlying aquifer. The reservoirs will be referred to here as Reservoirs A through D in order of increasing depth; the underlying aquifer is designated H. Because Reservoirs A and B are thin and separated from the rest of the system by anhydrite, they are considered as a unit for model purposes; this unit is designated Reservoir AB. Reservoir D is modeled as two zones—an upper zone having the better reservoir characteristics and a lower, less productive zone. The upper zone is designated Reservoir D(MP), or "main porosity" Reservoir D; the lower zone is referred to as Reservoir D(JL). Pressure measurements show that Reservoirs D(MP) and D(JL) do not communicate vertically except in the oil zone.

*Chen *et al.*[14] report that history matching with optimal-control theory avoids this restriction. It should be understood that for some problems, optimal-control methods may not be useful because of limitations to single-phase flow or limited multiphase-flow assumptions. Optimal-control methods are described in Refs. 10, 14, and 18 through 20.

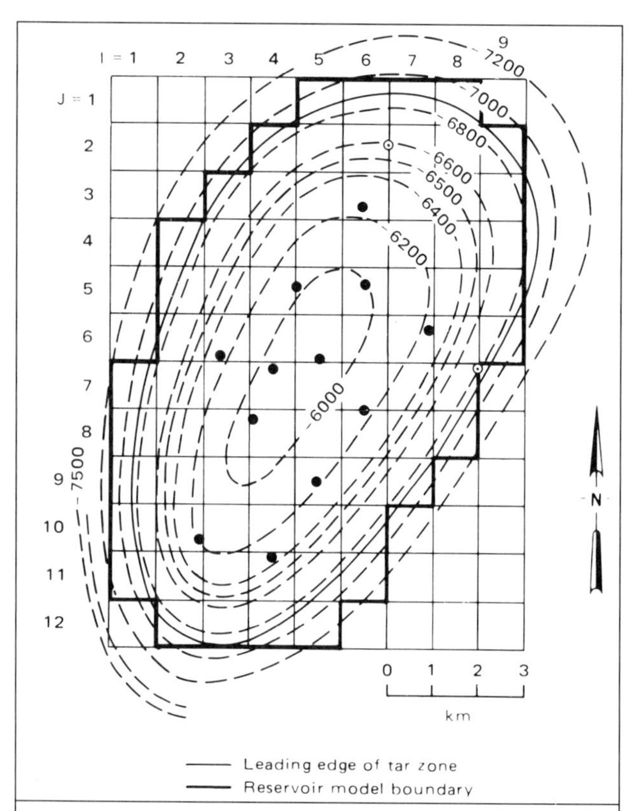

Fig. 8.9—Structure contour map showing model grid—top of Reservoir A, Khursaniyah field.[27]

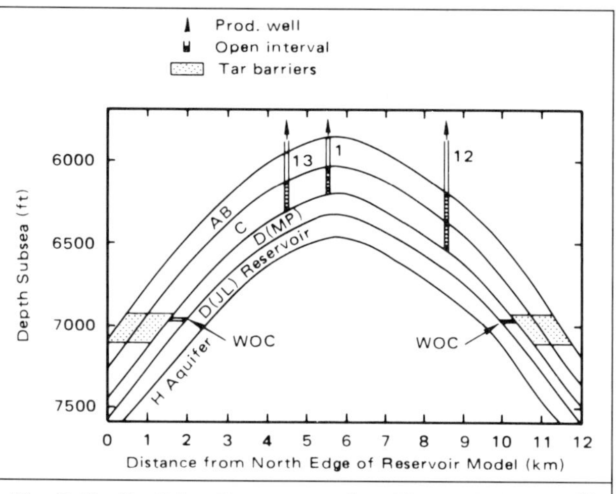

Fig. 8.10—North/south cross section, Khursaniyah field.[27]

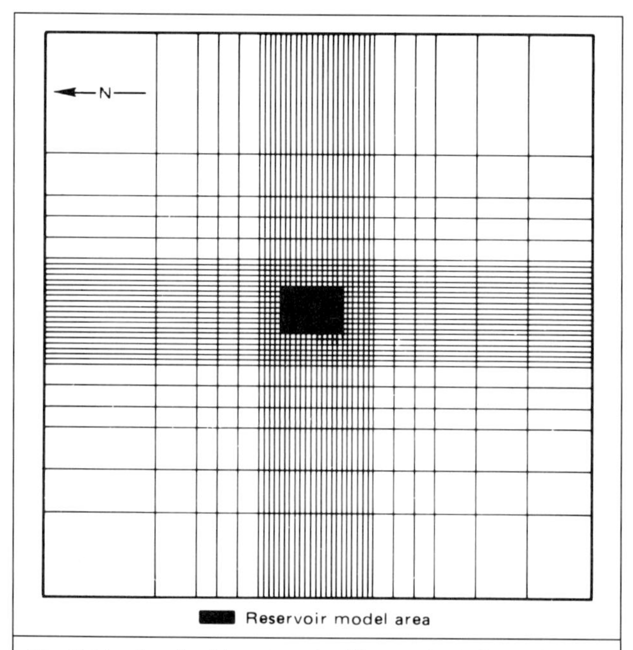

Fig. 8.11—Areal grid system for Khursaniyah field 3D aquifer model.[27]

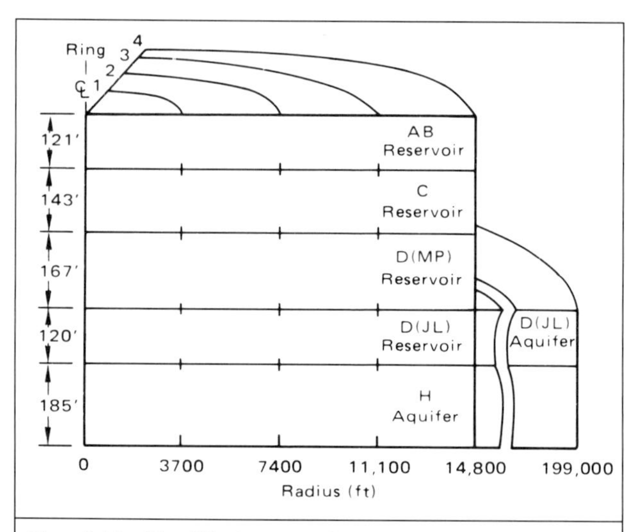

Fig. 8.12—Simplified regression model of Khursaniyah field.[27]

Fig. 8.9 (also Fig. 3.17) is a structure contour map of the top of Reservoir A showing the 0.6-mile [1-km] model grid used for the study. Reservoirs AB, C, and D(MP) are underlain with tar, which prevents communication with the aquifers on their respective flanks. The reservoir system is shown schematically in north/south cross section in Fig. 8.10. Pressure support for the reservoirs comes only from the underlying Aquifer H through a fracture system and from the aquifer contiguous with Reservoir D(JL) on the flank. The reservoir pressures are well above the bubblepoint.

8.6.2.2 3D Aquifer Model. A five-layer, 3D, single-phase aquifer model was developed to provide water-influx data to a $9 \times 12 \times 20$, 3D, two-phase window model (Chap. 3) having the areal grid shown in Fig. 8.9. The grid for the aquifer model encompassed a large area and is shown in Fig. 8.11. The smallest blocks of this grid are 0.39 sq miles [1 km^2]; the shaded portion coincides with the reservoir window model grid. The five layers represent the four reservoirs [AB, C, D(MP) and D(JL)] and the underlying Aquifer H. No well was open to more than one of these layers. The reservoir simulator used in this work is described in Ref. 28.

8.6.2.3 Simplified Regression Model. To provide improved estimates of reservoir and aquifer parameters, a five-layer, radial, two-phase model[27] shown in Fig. 8.12 was used. The five layers corresponded to the four reservoirs and underlying aquifer as described for the 3D, one-phase aquifer model.

The reservoirs were represented by the internal four rings of the upper four layers. Because vertical communication between reservoirs occurs mainly through vertical fractures in anhydrite beds near the center of the structure, only the center three rings (of each layer) were assigned nonzero values of vertical permeability. The tar barrier was assumed to prevent flow between the reservoir and aquifer for Reservoirs AB, C, and D(MP) at the outer boundary of Ring 4. No interaquifer communication was assumed.

The primary advantage of the simplified regression model over the 3D aquifer model is its size; it contained only 225 gridblocks, whereas the aquifer model contained 5,115 gridblocks.

8.6.2.4 First Regression Trial. Twenty variables were selected with the simplified regression model.

1. Vertical permeability values between all reservoirs for Rings 1 through 3 (12 variables).

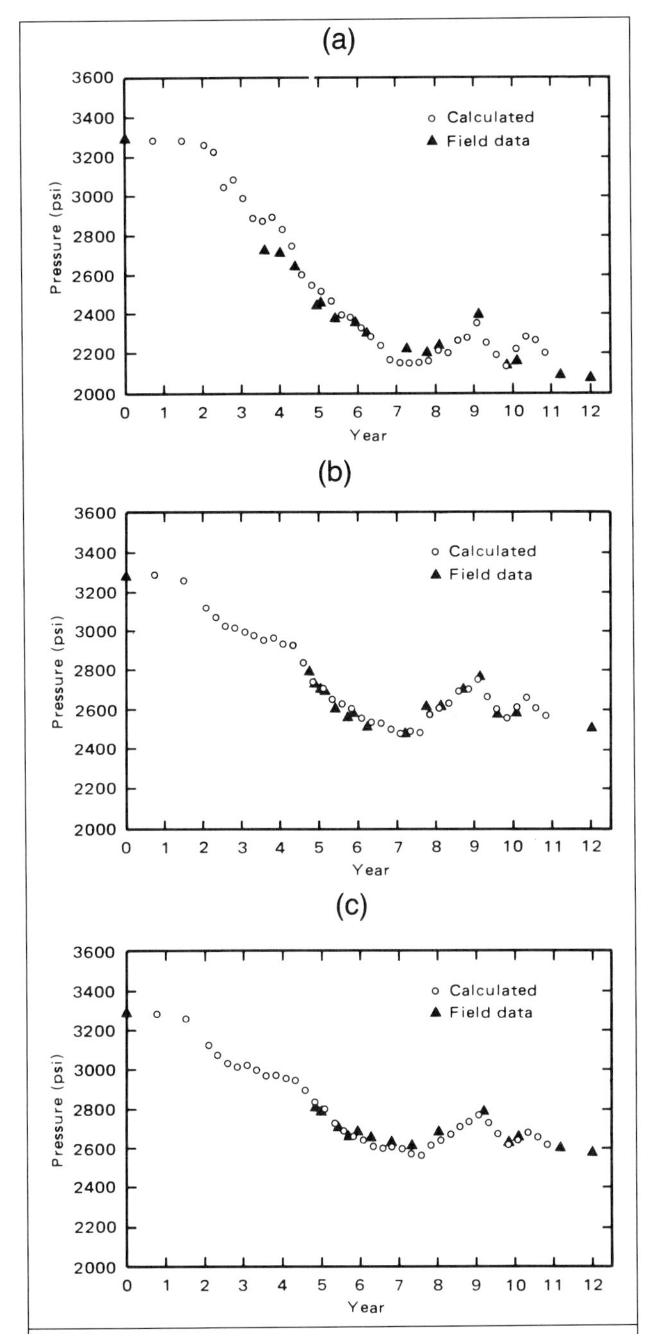

Fig. 8.13—Final pressure matches of typical Khursaniyah field wells[27]: (a) Reservoir AB, (b) Reservoir C, and (c) Reservoir D(MP).

2. A factor, $k_h/k_{h(\mathrm{map})}$, to multiply original field map values of horizontal permeability. Average values of k_h were assigned to Rings 1 through 4 [four variables—one each for Reservoirs AB, C, D(MP), and D(JL)].

3. Single horizontal permeability and porosity values for Aquifers D(JL) and H (four variables).

A uniform rock compressibility of 4.0×10^{-6} psi^{-1} [0.58×10^{-6} kPa^{-1}] was used during this trial.

Pressure matches obtained from the first trial were excellent for Reservoirs C and D but were poor for Reservoir AB (calculated pressures were 75 to 130 psi [517 to 896 kPa] low at 10 years).

8.6.2.5 Second Regression Trial. The simplified regression model was again used with the following regression variables selected.

1. $\phi h/\phi h_{(\mathrm{map})}$ multiplying factors for each reservoir. These were constrained to change no more than $\pm15\%$ for Reservoir AB and $\pm10\%$ for the other reservoirs. The $k_h/k_{h(\mathrm{map})}$ factor for Reservoir D(JL) was also a variable (five variables).

2. Average values of vertical permeability between each reservoir and between Reservoir D(JL) and Aquifer H (four variables).

3. Horizontal permeability and porosity for Aquifers D(JL) and H (four variables).

4. Formation compressibility constrained to the range 2×10^{-6} to 4×10^{-6} psi^{-1} [0.29×10^{-6} to 0.58×10^{-6} kPa^{-1}] (one variable).

Thus, 14 variables were modified in the second trial.

The horizontal permeabilities and aquifer porosities obtained during this trial were accepted without further modification. In general, there was only marginal improvement in the pressure match over that achieved in the first trial.

8.6.2.6 Third Regression Trial. It appeared that an improved match could not be obtained with the simplified regression model and that a more detailed model was required. Hence, the 3D, one-phase aquifer model (Fig. 8.11) was used directly in this trial. To minimize computer expense, only five variables were selected.

1. Uniform porosity multiplying factors for the AB, C, and combined D reservoirs (three variables).

2. Uniform multiplying factors for interreservoir vertical permeabilities between Reservoirs AB, C, and D(MP) (two variables).

The third regression trial differed from the previous two in other important respects.

1. Scaling factors other than unity were used to weight the pressure data. Scaling factors for each reservoir were inversely proportional to the number of wells in each reservoir and proportional to the individual reservoir OOIP estimates. In addition, pressure data for the last 3 years of the history period were weighted twice as heavily as earlier data.

2. The wells were located more accurately with respect to both area and depth than in the simplified model.

Fig. 8.13a through 8.13c compares the actual and calculated pressure histories for typical wells in Reservoirs AB, C, and D(MP). The match for all 24 wells was good to excellent. The reservoir description provided by this approach permitted matching the undulating pressure behavior experienced as a result of sporadic water injection into Reservoirs AB and C.

Field observations over the years since this study was made continue to support the regression-derived reservoir description.

In the study discussed here, it was possible to match pressure performance with a single average value for k_h and porosity for each of the two aquifers. Further, it was not necessary to impose additional areal variations on any of the arrays describing the permeability and porosity distributions for a given reservoir.

8.6.3 When To Use Automatic Matching Programs. In the example just discussed, an automatic history-matching technique was used throughout. The same study could have been conducted manually. Which technique would have been better in this instance is a matter of conjecture. Probably for this particular problem, a better match—at lower cost—was obtained by automatic matching than could have been obtained manually. Manpower costs and total elapsed time to obtain the match were likely somewhat less while computer costs were probably greater.

Currently, automatic history matching is not widely used and probably should not be the method of choice for most problems. Automatic matching should be considered, however, if manual matching is not proceeding satisfactorily. If automatic matching is considered, the following general guidelines may be useful.

1. Use automatic history matching only after making a number of manual history-matching trials to identify important matching variables. Then use the automatic matching program to identify remaining "weak" variables that have little effect on the quality of the match.

2. Make careful estimates of computing costs before embarking on an automatic matching phase. If the reservoir model must be simplified to control costs, ensure that the simplified model still represents the reservoir adequately.

3. Above all, do not proceed blindly when using an automatic history-matching simulator. Closely follow the progress of regression as a match is approached and be well aware of the value of the sum of squared differences of each new trial. If little or no progress is being made toward a match, change the selection of

matching variables, the areas to which they apply, or the limits to which they are being constrained.

Nomenclature

B = fluid FVF, RB/STB [res m^3/stock-tank m^3]
c_t = total compressibility, psi^{-1} [kPa^{-1}]
Ei = exponential integral function
h = formation thickness, ft [m]
Δh = layer thickness, ft [m]
k = permeability, md
k_h = horizontal permeability, md
$k_{h(\text{map})}$ = initial k_h from map, md
$k_{h,\text{new}}$ = new value of k_h, md
k_v = vertical permeability, md
k_x = permeability in x direction, md
k_y = permeability in y direction, md
n = total number of observations
p = pressure at radius r from producing well, psi [kPa]
p_f = BHFP, psi [kPa]
p_i = initial pressure, psi [kPa]
p_m = measured pressure, psi [kPa]
p_o = measured shut-in pressure corrected to be comparable with calculated model pressure, psi [kPa]
p_w = wellbore pressure, psi [kPa]
Δp = pressure drop, psi [kPa]
Δp_{ratio} = calculated Δp divided by observed Δp, fraction
q = well flow rate, STB/D [res m^3/d]
Q = objective function
r = radius from producing well, ft [m]
r_e = external radius, ft [m]
r_o = radial distance from the well location at which pressure calculated at production or injection block applies, ft [m]
r_w = wellbore radius, ft [m]
R_i = residual value
S_w = water saturation, fraction
t = time, days
t_D = dimensionless time
t_m = time at which well shut-in pressure is measured, days
t_o = shut-in time for well to build up to p_o, days
W_i = weighting factor
Δx = gridblock width, ft [m]
μ = viscosity, cp [Pa·s]
ϕ = porosity, fraction

Subscript

map = initial value taken from a map

References

1. Miller, R.T. and Rogers, W.L.: "Performance of Oil Wells in Bottom Water Drive Reservoirs," paper SPE 4633 presented at the 1973 SPE Annual Meeting, Las Vegas, Sept. 30–Oct. 3.
2. Chappelear, J.E. and Hirasaki, G.J.: "A Model of Oil-Water Coning for Two-Dimensional, Areal Reservoir Simulation," paper SPE 4980 presented at the 1974 SPE Annual Meeting, Houston, Oct. 6–9.
3. Brummett, W.M. Jr., Emanuel, A.S., and Ronquille, J.D.: "Reservoir Description by Simulation at SACROC—A Case History," *JPT* (Oct. 1976) 1241–55.
4. Harpole, K.J.: "Improved Reservoir Characterization—A Key to Future Reservoir Management for the West Seminole San Andres Unit," *JPT* (Nov. 1980).
5. Peaceman, D.W.: "Interpretation of Well-Block Pressures in Numerical Reservoir Simulation," *SPEJ* (June 1978) 183–94; *Trans.*, AIME, **265.**
6. van Poollen, H.K., Breitenbach, E.A., and Thurnau, D.H.: "Treatment of Individual Wells and Grids in Reservoir Modeling," *SPEJ* (Dec. 1968) 341–46.
7. Coats, K.H. *et al.*: "Three-Dimensional Simulation of Steam Flooding," *SPEJ* (Dec. 1974) 573–92; *Trans.*, AIME, **257.**
8. Kuniansky, J. and Hillestad, J.G.: "Reservoir Simulation Using Bottomhole Pressure Boundary Conditions," *SPEJ* (Dec. 1980) 473–86; *Trans.*, AIME, **269.**
9. Miller, C.C., Dyes, A.B., and Hutchinson, C.A. Jr.: "Estimation of Permeability and Reservoir Pressure from Bottomhole Pressure Build-up Characteristics," *Trans.*, AIME (1950) **189,** 91–104.
10. Jacquard, P. and Jain, C.: "Permeability Distribution from Field Pressure Data," *SPEJ* (Dec. 1965) 281–94; *Trans.*, AIME, **234.**
11. Jahns, H.: "Rapid Method for Obtaining a Two-Dimensional Reservoir Description from Well Pressure Response Data," *SPEJ* (Dec. 1966) 315–27; *Trans.*, AIME, **237.**
12. Slater, G.E. and Durrer, E.J.: "Adjustment of Reservoir Simulator Models to Match Field Performance," *SPEJ* (Sept. 1971) 295–305; *Trans.*, AIME, **251.**
13. Carter, R.D. *et al.*: "Performance Matching With Constraints," *SPEJ* (April 1974) 187–91; *Trans.*, AIME, **257.**
14. Chen, W.H. *et al.*: "A New Algorithm for Automatic History Matching," *SPEJ* (Dec. 1974) 593–608; *Trans.*, AIME, **257.**
15. Veatch, R.W. Jr. and Thomas, G.W.: "A Direct Approach for History Matching," paper SPE 3515 presented at the 1971 SPE Annual Meeting, New Orleans, Oct. 3–6.
16. Coats, K.H., Dempsey, J.R., and Henderson, J.H.: "A New Technique for Determining Reservoir Description from Field Performance Data," *SPEJ* (March 1970) 66–74; *Trans.*, AIME, **249.**
17. Thomas, L.K., Hellums, L.J., and Reheis, G.M.: "A Nonlinear Automatic History Matching Technique for Reservoir Simulation Models," *SPEJ* (Dec. 1972) 508–14; *Trans.*, AIME, **253.**
18. Wasserman, M.L., Emanuel, A.S., and Seinfeld, J.H.: "Practical Applications of Optimal-Control Theory to History-Matching Multiphase Simulator Models," *SPEJ* (Aug. 1975) 347–55; *Trans.*, AIME, **259.**
19. Gavalas, G.R., Shah, P.C., and Seinfeld, J.H.: "Reservoir History Matching by Bayesian Estimation," paper SPE 5740 presented at the 1976 SPE Numerical Simulation Symposium, Houston, Feb. 20.
20. Wasserman, M.L. and Emanuel, A.S.: "History Matching Three Dimensional Models Using Optimal Control Theory," paper 7611 presented at the 1976 CIM Annual Technical Meeting, Calgary, June 7–11.
21. Bishop, K.A. *et al.*: "The Application of Sensitivity Analysis to Reservoir Simulation," paper SPE 6102 presented at the 1976 SPE Annual Technical Conference and Exhibition, New Orleans, Oct. 3–6.
22. Dorsey, J.B., Jones, L.D., and Bencheikh, A.: "Numerical Simulation of the Zarzaitine Devonian F4 Reservoir, Algeria," paper SPE 4281 presented at the 1973 SPE Numerical Simulation Symposium, Houston, Jan. 11–12.
23. Welty, D.H. and Miller, W.C.: "Automated History Matching of Well Tests," paper SPE 7695 presented at the 1979 SPE Reservoir Simulation Symposium, Denver, Feb. 1–2.
24. Rossen, R.H.: "A Regression Approach to Estimating Gas in Place for Gas Field," *JPT* (Oct. 1975) 1283–89; *Trans.*, AIME, **259.**
25. Fariss, R.H. and Law, V.J.: "Transformational Discrimination for Unconstrained Optimization," *Ind. and Eng. Chem. Fund.* (1972) **11,** 154–61.
26. Chavent, G., Dupuy, M., and Lemonnier, P.: "History Matching by Use of Optimal Theory," *SPEJ* (Feb. 1975) 74–86; *Trans.*, AIME, **259.**
27. Boberg, T.C. *et al.*: "Application of Inverse Simulation to a Complex Multireservoir System," *JPT* (July 1974) 801–08; *Trans.*, AIME, **257.**
28. Spillette, A.G., Hillestad, J.G., and Stone, H.L.: "A High-Stability Sequential Solution Approach to Reservoir Simulation," paper SPE 4542 presented at the 1973 SPE Annual Meeting, Las Vegas, Sept. 30–Oct. 3.

SI Metric Conversion Factors

bbl	×	1.589 873	E−01	=	m^3
cp	×	1.0*	E+00	=	mPa·s
ft	×	3.048*	E−01	=	m
miles	×	1.609 344*	E+00	=	km
psi	×	6.894 757	E+00	=	kPa
psi^{-1}	×	1.450 377	E−01	=	kPa^{-1}

*Conversion factor is exact.

Chapter 9
Forecasting Future Performance

Most reservoir simulation studies require that forecasts of future performance be made under different operating conditions or with two or more equally probable reservoir descriptions. This chapter describes concepts and procedures used in making these predictions and analyzing the results. It discusses planning of the prediction cases to be run, determining input data requirements, making a smooth transition from history to predictions, checking data and results, and evaluating predicted performance.

Running predictions is the most interesting part of a simulation study. Predictions give the engineer a chance to visualize the future performance of a well or of a reservoir under different operating strategies. The engineer can examine a variety of scenarios and select a strategy that likely will result in the most desirable performance. The engineer also has an opportunity to demonstrate the potential benefits of new ideas and to generate results of high interest to the client or company.

There are a number of excellent references on the use of numerical simulation to predict future performance. Applications range from urgent studies to assist in controlling a blowout by injecting water into a relief well,[1] to more deliberate research studies needed to clarify interpretation of laboratory corefloods.[2] The primary use, however, has been in evaluating reservoir depletion plans.[3] The literature focuses on example results of simulator predictions and usually does not discuss procedures involved in actually running predictions. A notable exception is Crichlow's work.[4]

The material in this chapter is oriented toward predictions made with conventional multidimensional, multiphase, black-oil simulators using fairly complex well-management routines, such as those described in Refs. 5 through 7. This emphasis reflects an industry trend to use simulation for the more complex reservoir problems whose solutions require detail and realism in the treatment of wells and other factors expected to influence performance. The discussions are applicable primarily to models of an entire reservoir or a major fraction of a large reservoir. The intent is not to minimize the importance of single-well models, vertical cross-sectional models, or models of typical segments of a reservoir but rather to concentrate on predictions involving the most difficult well-management and production controls. Parts of the discussion are applicable to models that may not need a complex well-management routine. Such models are frequently used to provide a cost-effective way to examine detailed displacement behavior and to evaluate effects of various reservoir descriptions and operating alternatives on predicted performance.[8-14]

9.1 Planning the Prediction Cases To Be Run

Planning for predictions should start at the outset of the study, even though the actual running of predictions is one of the last phases of a simulation study. Early planning is needed to ensure that the reservoir model and the well-management routine include all the features that will be needed to meet the study objectives. Early planning is also needed to identify any data required for predictions that are not readily available and may require long lead times to obtain. For example, it may be necessary to schedule field tests to obtain reliable data on current well potentials or the fluid-handling capacities of facilities.

In initial plans, it is usually sufficient to include a general description of the cases to be run, special data requirements, and special features needed in the simulator. As noted in Chap. 3 and in Ref. 8, the guiding philosophy should be to use the simplest approach that will satisfy the objectives of the study and provide the information needed to select the best course of action. This approach will save time and manpower and reduce total costs, as well as minimize the errors and unexpected difficulties that are more apt to occur as the degree of complexity increases. Some special features may be desirable specifically to increase credibility and understanding, especially when outside parties are involved. The added cost of these features should be recognized and their value should be carefully assessed if, indeed, they are expected to have little impact on the technical aspects of the final result.

The number of prediction cases that are to be run usually will be constrained by time and money. Results are often needed on or before a specified time if they are to be useful in influencing important operating or budget decisions. In such situations, the most important prediction cases should be identified so that they may be scheduled first.

It is important to establish a realistic project time schedule for completing priority cases. Some planning experience and judgment are needed, because time distribution will be highly dependent on the size and complexity of the model, the well-management routine, and the number of cases to be run. Prediction runs can be made in 1 to 2 days with simple models but may require more than 1 month with large, three-dimensional (3D) models. As discussed later in this chapter, the first prediction usually takes several times longer than subsequent cases because input data and initial results need to be closely checked before proceeding further. Crichlow[4] states that predictions normally involve about one-fourth of the total study time. This estimate, however, depends on the individual study, the degree of complexity, and the amount of history to be matched.

When scheduling predictions, allow for such contingencies as program bugs, computer availability and downtime, and in-depth analysis of unexpected results from the simulation. Ideally, the schedule should be flexible enough to allow time to optimize predicted performance, to resolve questions that arise during analysis of initial cases, and to investigate promising alternative approaches to reservoir management. There may also be a need for sensitivity cases to establish likely ranges of potential future behavior.

9.1.1 Selecting the Prediction Cases. Most simulation predictions involve evaluation of alternative operating plans using a complete prediction case for each alternative. For example, waterflooding and natural depletion might both be potentially viable depletion schemes. Individual case results can be compared to select the most favorable alternative. One case, often representing continuation of existing operating strategies, will be designated the *base case,* and results of other cases with alternative strategies will be compared with this base plan.

In other studies, the prediction cases will cover a range of values for some specific operating variable to determine its impact on reservoir performance. For example, the potential influence of producing rate on ultimate recovery might be evaluated by running high-, medium-, and low-rate cases. The cases should bracket the "best" answer to cover operating conditions likely to be encountered in the future.

9.1.2 Sensitivity Cases. Many studies[10,11,15] include "sensitivity" cases to evaluate ranges of behavior for different values of key reservoir or operating parameters. Such cases are valuable to both the reservoir engineer and management to help assess the impact of major uncertainties on predicted performance. For example, cases might be run for a range of reasonable values of aquifer size.

Sensitivity cases can help identify critical parameters, define probable ranges of behavior, and aid in designing programs for gathering more data or for monitoring key aspects of reservoir performance. Coats[8] cites a sensitivity study in which a cross-sectional model demonstrated that predicted performance was entirely dependent on oil relative permeability. After the study isolated the critical nature of this parameter, considerable laboratory work was undertaken to provide reliable values of oil relative permeability for use in subsequent runs to evaluate the effect of rate on oil recovery.

It sometimes can be shown that computed results are only slightly affected by reasonable variations in much of the reservoir description. This may prove useful in deciding where to allocate resources to acquire the most important reservoir rock and fluid data.[8] In studies where two different reservoir model descriptions yield history matches of equal quality, one of the two models will be selected for use in making the prediction runs. The base-case prediction can then be repeated in the second model to demonstrate the effect of the differences in properties on predicted results. In a study of the Kuparuk River field,[11] sensitivity studies showed that pseudo-relative permeabilities generated for one set of conditions were valid for use with a variety of development scenarios.

Sensitivity studies will be needed if parts of the model cannot be validated by history matching. In the early stages of depletion of a flank waterdrive field, for example, water/oil pseudo-relative permeabilities and well functions assigned to upstructure areas that have not yet been invaded by water cannot be evaluated by matching history. In this case, a sensitivity prediction should be run with pessimistic values for these functions to evaluate the effect of less-efficient water advance on such key items as drilling requirements, water-disposal volumes, and the length of time for which the plateau oil-production rate can be sustained.

9.1.3 Prediction Guidelines and Constraints. The general guidelines and physical constraints imposed on model predictions need to be carefully selected, because they can have a significant impact on calculated results. *Guidelines,* as used in this text, relate to the general policies and strategies that are to be followed in determining overall operation of the field and model. Guidelines are usually self-imposed to set acceptable limits for good practices. For example, guidelines can govern field or well target producing rates and minimum operating pressures, set criteria for determining when and where to drill new wells, and define the earliest acceptable timing for installation of new facilities or artificial lift. *Constraints* deal mainly with physical and external limits of the system—e.g., maximum and minimum fluid-handling capacities, allowable operating pressures, statutory controls, and market constraints (Chap. 7). The distinction between guidelines and constraints is not always clear-cut nor does it need to be; it is the use of these controls that is significant.

Table 9.1 shows an example listing of prediction guidelines and constraints. Because of their importance, guidelines and constraints should be carefully selected and agreed upon by all study participants. They must be realistic and must be applied uniformly to the various prediction cases to allow direct comparison of results. For example, in a study to evaluate the effect of the distribution of withdrawals on performance, guidelines for producing-area pressure levels must not change from one case to another. Otherwise, in some cases wells could flow to higher water cuts than in others, with the result that drilling requirements could be reduced and, perhaps, the target rate could be maintained for a longer time. These effects might dominate results and outweigh the other differences in performance that were under investigation.

TABLE 9.1—EXAMPLE PREDICTION GUIDELINES AND CONSTRAINTS

Facility Capacities

	Production		Injection	
Facility	Oil (STB/CD)	Water (bbl/CD)	Water (bbl/CD)	Maximum Pump Pressure (psig)
A	30,000	30,000	35,000	2,700
B	20,000	30,000	25,000	2,500
Total	50,000	60,000	60,000	

General Producing Guidelines and Constraints

Producing Facilities	
Minimum average reservoir pressure, psig	2,000
Separator pressure, psig	150
Maximum GOR, scf/STB	600
Producing Well Constraints	
Maximum GOR, scf/STB	750
Maximum WOR, bbl/bbl	99
Maximum total liquid rate, STB/CD	5,000
Minimum oil production rate, STB/CD	100
Operating factor, OD/CD	0.95
Drilling New Producing Wells	
Maximum wells drilled per year	12
Maximum allowable water cut, %	25
Minimum allowable pressure, psig	2,100
Minimum oil capacity, STB/CD	1,000
Minimum well spacing, acres	80
Workovers	
Number of recompletions per well	1
Success ratio	0.5
Other	
Earliest date to start artificial lift	Jan. 1, 1997
Earliest date to decrease separator pressure to 50 psig	Jan. 1, 1994
Maximum allowable pressure at new injection-well locations, psig	6,000

Some constraints influence relatively short-term performance. For example, guidelines for drilling, operating pressures, gas/oil ratio (GOR), and water/oil ratio (WOR) will be implemented in the well-management routine and may immediately alter predicted phase rates or drilling activity.

Guidelines and constraints may vary with time. Target production rates may change periodically to reflect seasonal variations in offtake or the addition of new facilities. Restrictions on water production may be relaxed when water-handling facilities are installed. The reservoir engineer might want to downgrade maximum injection pressure over a period of time to simulate gradual deterioration of the mechanical integrity of the injection system. Similarly, he might degrade well productivity indices (PI's) or injectivity indices (II's) with time to simulate well damage trends that have been observed in past reservoir performance.

It may be desirable to eliminate some constraints in the actual simulation run but to incorporate them indirectly in final economic evaluations. For example, limits on water production could be set sufficiently high in the simulation to negate the constraint effectively. When predicted water production exceeds certain levels, appropriate investments could be included to reflect addition of facilities to handle increased volumes of water.

Guidelines should allow flexibility for incorporating reasonable changes that will improve predicted performance. For example, guidelines should allow transfer of production and injection between areas if initial results indicate that the transfer can improve pressure distribution, balance depletion rates, or minimize migration. Changes in guidelines should be clearly highlighted so that all changes, the reasons for making them, and benefits to be derived from them will be obvious to those who review the results.

9.2 Preparation of Input Data for Predictions

Preparation of the input data required for simulator predictions can be relatively easy for simple models or can require a sizable effort

TABLE 9.2—EXAMPLE DATA REQUIRED FOR INDIVIDUAL WELLS
Well sequence number in simulator
I, J, K location in model grid
Actual well name/number in the field
Reservoir or field to which well is assigned
Well group (facility, platform, lease) to which well is assigned
Well type (producer, water or gas injector, new location, etc.)
Multiwell trunkline number to which well is assigned (if any)
Water/oil well function number assigned to well
Gas/oil well function number assigned to well
PI or II
Outflow performance coefficients
Maximum oil or gas producing rate
Minimum oil or gas producing rate
Maximum total liquid rate for producers or water or gas rate for injectors
Well groups (up to three) to which new well can be assigned
Workover status (can well be recompleted)
Well status (active, shut-in wet, abandoned, etc.)

for complex models with many wells. The amount of effort required is a function of the number of wells, the complexity of the model, the study guidelines, and the well-management features being implemented. As mentioned earlier, plans should be made at the start of the study to have the required data available by the time the prediction phase of the study starts. In a large study, it may be necessary to assign one engineer solely to assembly and testing of prediction data even while the history-matching phase is still in progress.

Ideally, one should use actual field-measured data, or correlations based on observed behavior, for input to predictions. It will often be necessary, however, to use theoretical procedures or to run separate models to develop estimates of such key parameters as well PI's, well functions, and wellbore/flowline hydraulics. Numerous references here[4-7,16-19] and in Chap. 7 discuss the treatment of individual wells. Preparation and calibration of the input data to describe inflow/outflow performance for individual wells can take substantially more time and effort than development of all remaining input data for predictions.

9.2.1 Input Data for Individual Wells. In relatively uncomplicated predictions, input data for a well may involve only a grid location, the well number, well type (producer, injector, etc.), and specification of either a constant rate or constant pressure for the well. In two-dimensional (2D) cross-sectional and 3D models, the well-management routine must include a procedure for allocating the total rate to the individual gridblocks that make up the well. In simple studies, if there is more than one mobile phase in blocks representing a well, the distribution of production or injection between phases will generally be based on the interblock relative permeabilities or pseudo-relative permeabilities, rather than on special well pseudofunctions.

In more-complex studies, well input requirements become detailed and lengthy. Table 9.2 gives an example of the types of information that must be supplied for each well. Such items as well status, platform/facility assignment, and multiwell trunkline numbers are easily selected or obtained. Other items—e.g., the current PI or II, well function assignments, and data to describe wellbore hydraulics (outflow performance)—can be difficult to gather or to develop for input into the well-management routine.

Most individual well data usually can be obtained from well files, recent well test results, and discussions with field production engineers and operating personnel. Data from these sources include current well status (type), PI's and II's, GOR, WOR, maximum producing capability, well depth, completion interval, description of the well tubulars (for use in calculating wellbore and flowline pressure drops), and any operating restrictions placed on the well rate to improve reservoir management by controlling coning, cusping, or regional frontal advance. PI is usually calculated with measured pressures and rates and an estimated drainage radius. PI should be adjusted (Chap. 7) if the equivalent radius corresponding to the well gridblock pressure is different from the drainage radius. In 3D models, the total PI must be allocated to the gridblocks open to flow. The allocation is usually in proportion to block permeability-thickness (Chap. 7) or to the *kh* distribution measured by production logs.

Well pseudofunctions that relate near-wellbore phase mobilities to the average gridblock saturation and pressure may be developed from single-well models or vertical cross-sectional models. They may also be obtained from analysis of historical field data by relating observed WOR's or GOR's to block saturations or to such parameters as time or cumulative production.

Where empirical relationships are used, they should be based on actual data covering the entire range of WOR's or GOR's to be forecast, or they should be extrapolated beyond existing data in a manner consistent with results from analytic or single-well models. Well pseudofunctions should be carefully extrapolated to higher saturations because the resultant GOR or WOR inferred from the well function can have a major impact on predicted ultimate recovery from wells (and hence the reservoir). Chap. 7 contains an extensive discussion of well functions and cites a number of references describing different techniques that have been used. Adjustment of well functions to match observed WOR or GOR is discussed later in this chapter.

Where cross-sectional models are used to generate dynamic interblock pseudo-relative permeabilities, it is usually a simple matter to edit the same results to generate well pseudofunctions. Experience indicates that well pseudofunctions developed from vertical cross sections are reliable for use in areal models in all cases except those involving severe coning or cusping.

Specifications for hypothetical new wells that will be "drilled" during the simulation must be as complete as those for existing wells. Gridblock locations need to be defined, and the well group or facility to which the well will be assigned for bookkeeping and rate-control purposes must be specified. Because the PI's or II's of hypothetical wells will not be known, they must be estimated from the gridblock permeability-thickness or determined by mapping or averaging values from existing wells in the surrounding area. Well pseudofunctions assigned to these wells should be consistent with those of nearby wells suitably adjusted to account for assumed differences in stratification and for changes in future completion practices.

To describe multiphase well outflow performance, it may be necessary to use wellbore flow models to generate data relating wellbore and flowline pressure drops to liquid flow rate and gas/liquid ratio.[4,5,16,17] If so, information will be needed on fluid properties, well tubulars, flowline sizes and lengths, well depths, and typical operating pressures at the wellhead or separator. The data required to calculate individual well outflow performance will be specific to a particular well-management routine and may be customized to the particular field and reservoir being studied. Whatever technique is used should provide a reasonable estimate of pressure drops through the system. The well-management routine can then define well potential through simultaneous calculation of the inflow and outflow performance. Emanuel and Ranney[18] discuss interfacing of a reservoir simulator with a piping network simulator to improve forecasts of reservoir deliverability.

9.2.2 Input Data for Well Constraints. Table 9.1 gives the general constraints placed on production or injection wells in studies that use well-management routines similar to the one described by Stackel and Brown.[5] The input data for these constraints apply to all wells. The constraints are checked in the well-management routine against the oil capacity, GOR, and WOR calculated by inflow/outflow performance and well pseudofunctions. If the calculated values fall outside the specified ranges, the well will be shut in, worked over, or restricted as demanded by the guidelines of the well-management routine.

Note that the constraints imposed on rates have been specified in stock-tank barrels per calendar day (STB/CD). In this case, the well-management routine will first calculate capacity rates for the well, then reduce the rates by an operating factor that represents the ratio of the average number of actual operating days (OD's) to CD's. The operating factor takes into account downtime as a result of such factors as well testing, mechanical problems, facility maintenance, and weather. The factor may be different for injection systems than for production systems. If an operating factor is used, input data dealing with target rates or rate constraints must be specified on the basis of CD's.

Other general constraints that may be imposed on producing wells might include criteria on minimum allowable gridblock or datum pressures. Such criteria could be used to keep well pressures from declining below the bubblepoint, for example. If a producing gridblock drops below the minimum pressure, it is shut in until the pressure increases to a specified level above the minimum pressure before the well is allowed to return to production. There should be an appropriate increment between the minimum and the reactivation pressure levels so that the well will not cycle on and off production. In large gridblocks that receive good pressure support from the surrounding area, this increment might be 50 to 100 psi [345 to 700 kPa]. A large increment may be needed if there are steep pressure gradients into the block when it is producing. In some cases, this procedure will not prevent cycling and it may then be necessary to reduce individual well rates or to restrict the number of wells that are allowed to come back on production at each timestep. To manage injection wells, one may wish to specify a maximum pressure limit so as not to exceed equipment limitations or the formation fracture pressure.

9.2.3 Input Data for Drilling New Wells. The well-management routine must have some basis for determining when and where to drill new wells. The drilling schedule may be (1) automatically controlled by the well-management routine as required to maintain a specified production or injection rate for a field or well group until all future well locations have been used, (2) predetermined by current plans, rig availability, and the time required to drill and to complete each well, (3) specified as a set number of wells per year based, perhaps, on budgetary limitations, or (4) manually controlled, external to the simulator.

The locations of new wells may be (1) preselected with well locations specified in sequence to maintain a desired well spacing or to balance withdrawals, (2) automatically selected by the well-management routine from locations having the highest datum pressure while still having acceptable WOR's or GOR's, or (3) automatically selected by the well-management routine from remaining locations that have the highest potential oil rates. Care should be taken if Option 3 is selected because there will be a tendency to concentrate drilling and withdrawals in some areas while neglecting other, less productive, areas of the reservoir. Option 2, drilling at locations in the highest-pressure areas, can also concentrate drilling in one area and create localized pressure sinks or an imbalance in withdrawals. Problems with Options 2 and 3 are most apt to occur when the well-management routine automatically selects several new locations during a single timestep and the model has no opportunity to react to changes in pressure and productivity caused by production from the new wells.

In addition to control of the timing and locations of new wells, the well-management routine may have the capability to require that new wells satisfy other criteria specified in the study guidelines. Example criteria are minimum acceptable pressure level for producers, maximum acceptable pressure for injectors, minimum acceptable oil saturation for new producers, minimum water or gas saturations or maximum oil cuts for new injectors, minimum total oil capacity, and eligibility for connection to the proper well group or facility. In 3D models, the well-management routine must have some basis for determining the completion interval—perhaps by excluding only those gridblocks in the vertical direction that exceed specified maxima for WOR or GOR. The intent of imposing these additional criteria is to prevent drilling in undesirable locations where constraints would be exceeded in a short time and the well would be shut in with uneconomical recovery or unrealistic well life. Appropriate checks should be made to ensure that the final drilling program in the model is compatible with optimal sweep and recovery efficiencies.

9.2.4 Input Data for Facilities. Facility data requirements generally deal with desired target rates, maximum and minimum capacities (on a CD basis), and allowable operating pressures. Typical constraints might include maximum oil-, gas-, and water-handling capacities, maximum rates and pressures for injection systems, and dates for placing new facilities in operation. The target rates are usually agreed upon when study guidelines are determined. Development of maximum and minimum rates may require discussion with the engineers and operating personnel responsible for facilities.

It is helpful to have some understanding of the reasons for imposing constraints on facilities. If constraints result from relatively minor problems—e.g., a bottleneck in piping or a small pump that can be readily replaced—it may be more realistic to assume that the problem will be eliminated than to constrain maximum capacity. If major new equipment or facilities are to be added, the simulation should allow necessary lead time for design, fabrication, and installation.

Facility constraints may change with time to reflect planned addition of new equipment or changes in operating pressure. Changes in separator pressure with time, installation of artificial lift facilities, etc., can be simulated by switching to new outflow performance data at the time changes are to become effective.

If new operating strategies (such as gas-cap blowdown) are to be studied, their effect on the capacity of separators or other parts of a facility must be considered. For this reason, it is helpful to review planned prediction cases with facilities personnel who might provide information that otherwise might be overlooked.

9.2.5 Other Input Data for Predictions. If the reservoir model includes a surrounding aquifer containing other producing fields, it is necessary to enter a forecast of rates or pressures in the other fields to model interference effects properly. Forecasts of rates and pressures of outlying fields are also needed for predictions with a linked aquifer/reservoir simulator such as that described by Graham and Smart.[20] If boundary conditions for a "windowed" reservoir model require flux rates from a window area in an associated coarse-grid aquifer/reservoir model (Chap. 3), it will be necessary first to forecast coarse-grid model performance so that flux rates or pressure boundary conditions can be calculated. Calculated flux rates or pressures, as functions of time, are then entered into the detailed model. Rates and withdrawal distributions predicted by the detailed model likely will differ from the preliminary coarse-grid forecast. If so, the coarse-grid forecast should be repeated, using rates from the detailed model to obtain better values of flux rates. One such iteration usually produces flux rates that are consistent with the performance predicted by the detailed model. A second iteration may be necessary when there are sizable changes in rates or withdrawal distributions.

The well-management routine may include provisions to simulate workovers when a well exceeds constraints on rate, GOR, or WOR. The levels for these constraints need to be defined in accordance with current operating strategy or regulatory requirements.

It is realistic to assume that some workovers will not be successful because of completion difficulties or adverse reservoir properties. One way to implement recognition by the model of potential workover failures is to reduce the PI of the recompletion by a factor representing the anticipated success rate for the workovers (e.g., multiply PI by 0.5 for a 50% success ratio). This procedure maintains a reasonable estimate of producing capacity after a workover and spreads the success uniformly over all workover attempts. Arbitrary assignment of workover failures on a well-by-well basis can result in unexpected and unusual success/failure patterns in different areas of the field. Furthermore, the pattern could then vary from case to case, making it difficult to compare case results directly.

After all input data are assembled, they should be checked carefully before a prediction run is made. Be sure the data satisfy and are compatible with well-management requirements. Arrays should be computer contoured, or at least be printed or displayed on a terminal, to check for missing or erroneous values. Well-function tables should be plotted and scanned to ensure that values are in the proper order. Finally, as a continuing check on the data, thoroughly analyze model performance in a few selected timesteps in each prediction run to make certain all data and constraints are being implemented correctly.

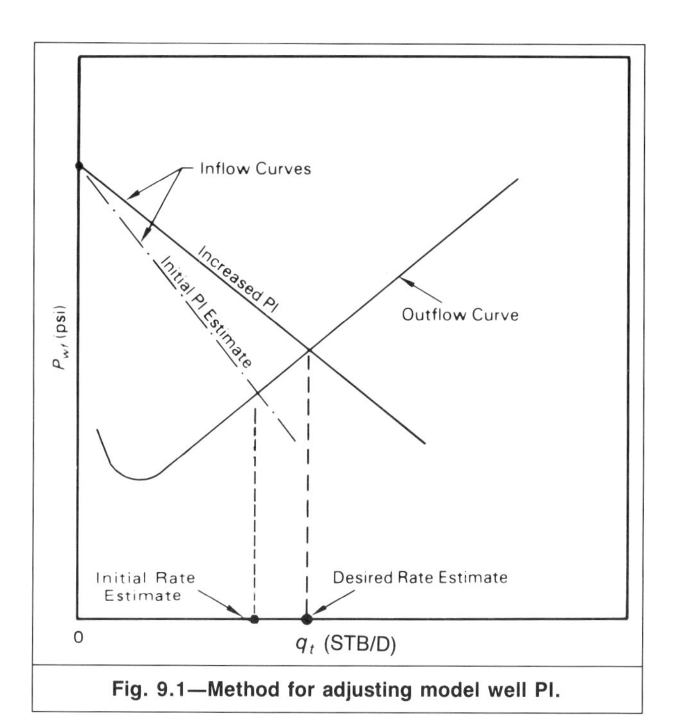

Fig. 9.1—Method for adjusting model well PI.

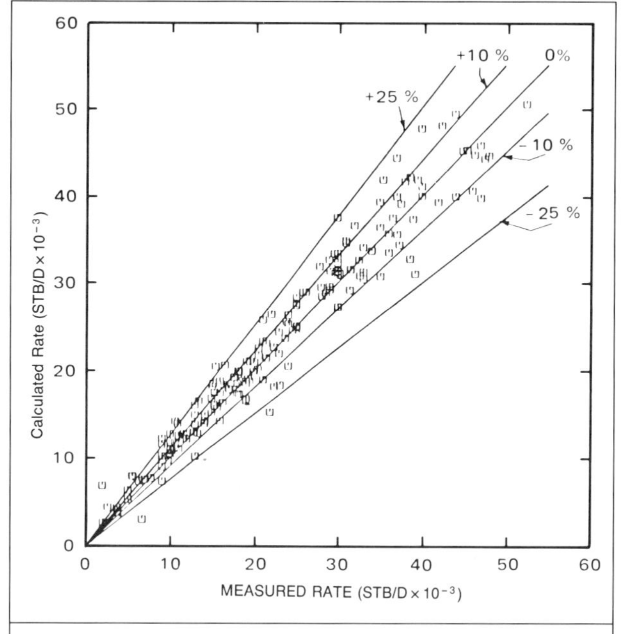

Fig. 9.2—Typical match of well rates in a large areal model at the beginning of predictions.

9.3 Making a Smooth Transition From History to Predictions

Calculated performance during the change from the history-match mode to the predictive mode should be smooth and without marked discontinuities in well capacities, pressures, or well activity (unless, of course, there is a major change in reservoir operating strategy at the time predictions start). The ability of the model to switch smoothly from specified historical well rates to phase rates predicted by well-management procedures is another test of the quality of the reservoir model and the well-management routine.

Adjustments in input data may be required to bring predicted well capacities, GOR's, or WOR's in line with those observed in the field. If major discrepancies are not rectified at this stage, the reliability and credibility of predicted results may suffer. Resolution of obvious discrepancies is especially important when dealing with individuals who are not familiar with reservoir simulation or who may be skeptical when predicted results are reviewed. It is easier to resolve discrepancies between the simulator and field at this early stage than to take time later to convince others that the discrepancies "really do not affect" the final results and conclusions.

It is not realistic to expect every well to be matched exactly to field-measured well capacities and gas and water production. There are simply too many variables and unknowns. The objective at this stage is to develop a model whose near-term performance, on balance, matches current totals and field trends with no localized areas where performance is consistently better or worse than the field.

One procedure for evaluating the switch from history to predictions is to restart at the end of history and simulate several short timesteps with output at each time. Dummy values should be used for operating factors, target rates, and facility constraints so that unrestricted well capacities that have not been modified by the well-management routine are available for comparison with field values. Alternatively, one may develop an edit to calculate capacities in the same manner as the well-management routine, then print out the calculated well capacities, GOR's, WOR's, and any well-status changes for comparison and review with field data. As noted below, it may also be necessary to use model pressures and saturations during the last few years of history to aid in calibrating well pseudofunctions for predictions. It is important that conditions under which field well capacities are measured be known so that the proper conditions are modeled in the well-management routine.

9.3.1 Evaluation of Predicted Well Capacities. Ideally, predictions of current well capacities should be comparable to the quality of the overall match of recent reservoir history. For any specific study, however, a deliberate decision should be made on the level of accuracy that will be acceptable. If establishing credibility is an issue, special attention should be given to modeling well performance. If a predicted well rate falls outside acceptable ranges, it will be necessary to determine the cause and to make reasonable adjustments in the least certain of the parameters affecting the calculated rates. Typically, the most uncertain parameter will be either PI, outflow data, or the well pseudofunctions; it usually will be clear which of these should be changed to bring calculated rates more in line with field data.

Fig. 9.1 illustrates one method for changing the predicted rate by adjusting the PI of a model well. If outflow performance is suspect, new parameters can be developed to shift the outflow curve. If the well-management routine uses relatively simple analytical expressions to define outflow performance (e.g., Stackel and Brown[5]), it may be easy to change a term in the expression for any particular well to yield a rate that will agree with the observed data and still maintain the slope of the rate/pressure relationship for that well. Care should be exercised in keeping such adjustments minimal, or outflow performance can become distorted at higher water cuts. A change in well pseudofunction assignment or in the relative permeabilities used in the well function may also be required to improve the match of field well capacities and GOR or WOR. Any arbitrary adjustments should be kept as small as possible and should be used with caution because they may bias the results or cause unrealistic behavior later in the predictions as pressures and saturations change.

Fig. 9.2 shows an example of the final agreement between predicted and reported well capacities in a typical large, 2D, areal model study. Most of the predicted rates fall within 10% of the reported values, with no bias toward either high or low predicted rates. The results in Fig. 9.2 were obtained by reviewing each well individually, ensuring that outflow performance coefficients were consistent with actual wellbore and flowline dimensions, using PI's that were within the range of certainty in measured values, and selecting well functions that gave the best match of historical water cuts. For a few wells, the reported well capacities fell outside the range that was reasonable for the well tubulars and PI. Discussion of these cases with engineers in the field led to development of improved capacity estimates for the wells from new well tests run specifically for this purpose. No arbitrary adjustments were made to the input data used for generating the match shown in Fig. 9.2. The overall match is acceptable in view of the uncertainties in reported field pressures and rates, and in the parameters describing inflow and outflow performance of the wells.

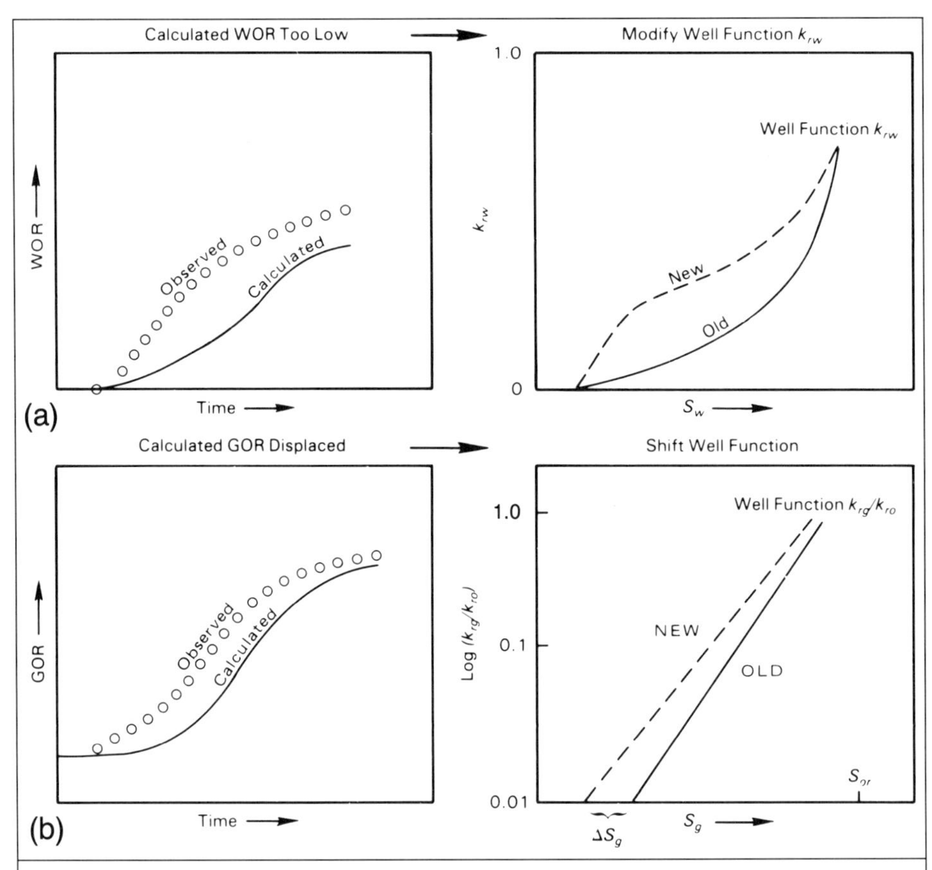

Fig. 9.3—Typical actions needed to adjust model well performance: (a) modify water relative permeability in the well function to adjust WOR and (b) shift relative-permeability ratios in the well function to match GOR.

An alternative to adjusting individual well capacities is to multiply all capacities in a well group by an adjustment factor based on the ratio of observed to calculated total well capacity for the group. This approach spreads the adjustments over a larger number of wells in proportion to their individual capacities.

9.3.2 Evaluation of Predicted GOR's and WOR's. In many studies, calculated GOR's and WOR's will be matched to reported well test values during the history-matching process and no further calibration will be needed. If this procedure cannot be followed, it will be necessary to check the consistency of calculated and historical GOR and WOR performance. Well GOR's and WOR's in the last few years of history should be calculated with the model gridblock pressures and saturations developed during the history match and the well-management techniques to be used in the predictions. These "calculated" GOR's and WOR's should be similar to those observed in the field, especially during the last 1 to 2 years of history.

Fig. 9.3a is an example in which the calculated WOR's do not have the same trend with time as the observed data. In this case, an adjustment of the water relative-permeability curve in the assigned well function might be needed to improve the match. Because the well functions are usually developed from cross-sectional, single-well, or analytical models that are based on a specific reservoir description, any adjustments in the well pseudo-relative permeabilities should be smoothed back into the original values at higher saturations. This will maintain a degree of consistency with the original endpoint saturation of the well function and will invoke abandonment at the proper saturation in the gridblock.

An alternative to adjusting values of pseudo-relative permeabilities in the well functions is to shift the saturation scale. The saturation used by the well functions is normally the saturation in the gridblock containing the well. Fig. 9.3b illustrates a case in which the calculated GOR based on gridblock gas saturation parallels field performance but is offset by a fairly constant amount. The match could be improved if the GOR were calculated from the same well pseudo-relative permeabilities but with an adjusted saturation equal to the block saturation plus an increment, ΔS_g. A different value for ΔS_g, or ΔS_w in the case of a water/oil system, can be determined for each well if desired. This approach requires that the well-management routine include provisions to store the value of ΔS_g or ΔS_w for each well. Also, as the block saturation increases, the value of ΔS_g or ΔS_w should be proportionately decreased so that it becomes zero before the block saturation reaches the value where the well pseudo-relative permeability to oil becomes zero. Otherwise, future performance may become too optimistic or too pessimistic at higher saturations.

A third method for adjusting GOR or WOR is to change the well pseudofunction. In most studies, several different well functions will be available to reflect alternative reservoir descriptions or variations in coning or cusping. The approach in this case is to select the particular well function that best matches observed well performance and is consistent with the general description and displacement mechanics of the reservoir in the region containing the well.

There are occasional instances when an actual well is producing at an elevated GOR or WOR, but the model well is not because the gas or water is not yet in the gridblock containing the well. This might be the case if there is channeling or cusping that is not adequately modeled with existing grid definition. In this case, it might be necessary either to improve the history match until fluids move into the well block or to accept some delay in the start of two-phase production. Such a compromise might be reasonable if the delay is offset by higher-than-observed two-phase production in other model wells.

9.3.3 Evaluation of Other Input Data. If the model is reasonably well history-matched, model gridblock pressures usually do not create significant problems in the transition to the prediction mode. Sizable pressure discrepancies, however, can cause problems when well-management routines are switched from history matching to predictions. For example, if the model pressure is too low, the

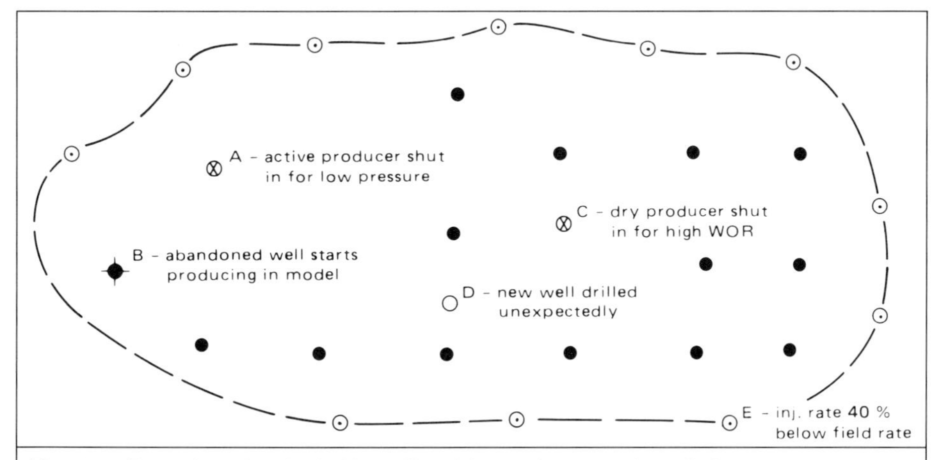

Fig. 9.4—Examples of undesirable well activity at the start of predictions:
A = pressure constraint set too high for near term or the pressure history match needs to be improved. To correct, relax minimum pressure constraint or increase block pressure in new history match.
B = Error in input data for well status. Correct input to show this well is abandoned.
C = Wrong well function assigned to well or flood-front history match needs to be improved. Reassign to well function that will show dry production or improve history match.
D = Well may have been drilled to replace lost potential under Items A and C. Correcting Items A and C may eliminate this drilling. Otherwise target may be too high or predicted potentials too low for the well group.
E = Calculated wellbore pressure losses too high, surface pressure too low, or incorrect II. Correct outflow performance or II.

minimum-pressure constraint in the well-management routine may be invoked, causing the model well to be shut in even though the real well is still producing.

Unusual well activity—e.g., wells being shut in, worked over, or cut back in rate for violating well-management constraints during the first few prediction timesteps—is indicative of errors in specifications for wells or descriptions of some areas in the model. The unusual behavior may be a result of errors in input data, overly restrictive guidelines or constraints, nonrepresentative well data, or incorrect model properties. Causes of the behavior should be identified and decisions reached on corrective action before proceeding with the prediction.

Fig. 9.4 illustrates some of the types of unusual performance that might be encountered immediately after shifting from history to predictions. Comments on possible corrective actions that might be taken are noted in the figure caption.

9.4 Review and Analysis of Predicted Performance

The previous section dealt primarily with obtaining reasonable and realistic performance following the change in control from history to prediction mode in the well-management routine. The focus was on calibrating input data and eliminating data errors so that near-term predictions would follow trends in observed performance. This section extends these concepts to long-range performance predictions. During this phase of a simulation, results must be reviewed continually for reasonableness and accuracy. Some of the techniques for accomplishing this are discussed.

The first prediction case normally will be a base case to which results of subsequent prediction runs are compared. The base case should be designed to be as realistic as possible and, within the guidelines defining the case, should represent the best possible operation of the reservoir. It is important to eliminate errors and oversights when running the base case to reduce the probability of having to repeat cases to correct mistakes.

Review of subsequent runs can be less thorough and can rely on periodic spot checks supplemented by detailed review when new depletion practices or well-management features are invoked for the first time. The need for careful review of the input data and results and the effort required to select and, perhaps, to develop the appropriate output displays usually cause the first prediction run to take much more time and effort than the predictions that follow.

9.4.1 Mechanics of Reviewing and Analyzing Results. In making the base-case prediction, it is generally advisable to complete a short prediction of 2 to 5 years and to review the results before proceeding. Unexpected behavior and errors in input data frequently will be noted in these initial runs, and problems can be resolved before wasting time and computer costs. Required data changes can then be incorporated and the prediction rerun for the initial time period plus a few more years. Again, results and any required changes to improve performance are reviewed before continuing. During the review process, there may be opportunities to improve performance by changing guidelines. For example, changes in such things as injection/withdrawal distributions can be made and incorporated in the restart run.

This leap-frogging process is repeated, usually extending the run for longer time increments after each review, until the prediction has covered the desired time period for study. Each extension may be made either by starting at the beginning of the prediction or, more often, by restarting at the end of the last valid time on the previous attempt. Once the base case is well on its way, other predictions can be started following a similar process. The procedure will become easier as one becomes more familiar with what to expect and focuses on the unique aspects of each new case.

At the end of each new extension of a prediction, one should review four key areas: predicted rates, predicted well activity (shutting in, drilling, recompleting, etc.), predicted saturations and frontal movements, and calculated pressure performance. In addition, of course, summaries indicative of the performance of the simulator should be checked to ensure that there are no problems in solving the fluid-flow equations for the reservoir.

One suggested approach for reviewing results is to (1) start with summary plots and printed output showing the production and injection rates, the number of wells, and average datum pressure vs. time for the field, (2) work backward reviewing similar data down the hierarchy of control (reservoir, well group, and individual wells), and (3) review saturation movements and pressure behavior.

The goals of this review process are to detect when and where rates depart from desired levels, to spot undesirable trends in well activity, and to confirm that operating constraints are properly implemented. Once a problem area is identified by this process, more detailed attention can be directed to find the cause of the problem in that area and to take corrective action when appropriate. In models with a simple well-management routine and straightforward calculations of well performance, concern will be mainly with reviewing the predicted pressures and saturations rather than with well activity.

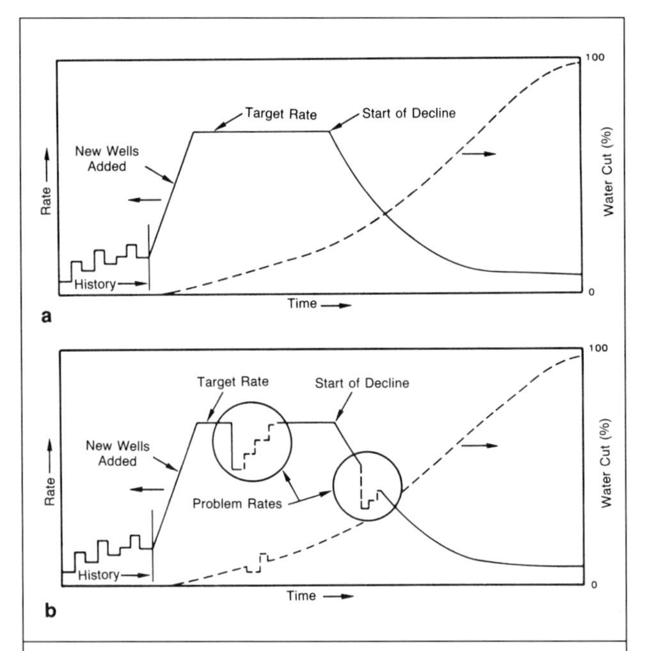

Fig. 9.5—Predictions of oil-production rate: (a) anticipated smooth rate/time curve and (b) unexpected, erratic rate curve, indicating a problem in the rate calculation.

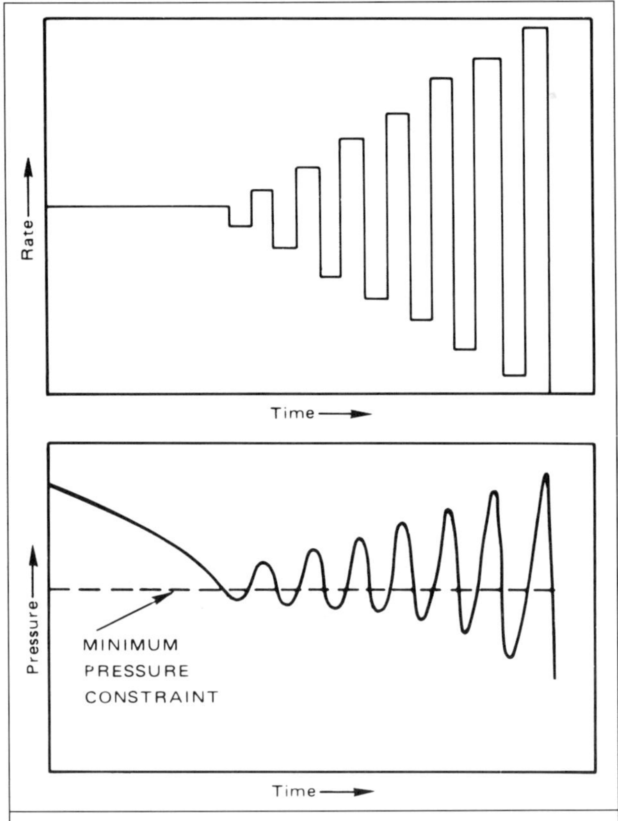

Fig. 9.6—Example of unrealistic oscillations in pressure and rate of model wells when reservoir pressure declines.

The following list indicates, in approximate order of priority, edits that are most helpful for obtaining an overview of the reservoir performance predicted in the simulation. (See Chap. 10.)

1. Graphic displays and/or tabular summaries, as a function of time, of production and injection rates, GOR, water cuts, well counts, and average pressure by field and well group (lease, separation facility, or platform).
2. Chronological summaries of model well status changes (number of wells drilled, worked over, and shut in for low pressure, high GOR or WOR, or low rate).
3. Contour maps of pressure, saturations, water cut, etc., at selected times.
4. Graphic or tabular summary of individual well rates, cumulatives, and pressures at selected times.
5. Printed arrays of pressures and saturations at selected times.
6. Interactive terminal displays of well status, undrilled locations, or grid data.

Items 1 and 2 provide a quick overview of when and where rates and well activity are changing and indicate areas with possible problems that should be investigated further. Item 3 allows the user to review pressure gradients and frontal movements to ensure that no undesirable trends are developing. Items 4 through 6 provide more detailed information to isolate anomalies or to check calculated performance. This suggested approach is flexible and can vary to meet individual study needs. There are, of course, no set rules and one will usually develop a preferred approach and favorite edits for reviewing and analyzing predicted results.

9.4.2 Reviewing Predicted Rates and Well Activity. Predicted production and injection rates generally will follow a fairly smooth and expected trend (e.g., Fig. 9.5a). Marked changes in rates will signal a problem unless the changes are attributable to a desired change that has been specified. Examples of specified changes that alter rates are the addition (or shutdown) of facilities, relaxation of group or well constraints, or the addition of artificial lift.

An unexpected trend in rate can occur during a plateau-rate period when wells are worked over and new wells are drilled to sustain a level target rate. If pressure in the producing area falls below the minimum pressure required for drilling at new locations and below the pressure at which wells are shut in, the predicted rate will drop below the specified target for a short period and then return to the target level, as illustrated in Fig. 9.5b. The return to target will occur as reservoir pressure begins to increase as a result of the lower offtake rates, permitting the well-management routine to reactivate wells or to drill new wells. The predicted rate may oscillate under some conditions.

Pressure decline can also cause unrealistic oscillations in the performance of single wells or a small group of wells. Fig. 9.6 illustrates pressure and rate behavior when wells cycle on and off as they are shut in for low pressure and then are returned to production after pressure increases in the model block containing the well. Oscillations can be reduced or eliminated by raising the minimum pressure level at which wells can be reactivated, by increasing pressure support to the area, by reducing the rate, or by calculating well rates implicitly or semi-implicitly.

Oscillations might also be the result of gas coning or cusping into a well. After a well is shut in because of high GOR, gravity segregation may cause the gas saturation in the well block to decrease to below the minimum value specified in the well-management routine and the well can be returned to production. Restricting the well's rate to a value below the critical rate (Chappelear and Hirasaki[19]) helps relieve this problem until the gas or water front actually invades the well.

Low reservoir pressure can also affect rates during the decline phase of reservoir life. If so, it will be necessary to decide what, if anything, should be done either to raise the reservoir pressure or to relax well-management constraints.

If a prediction is run with specified phase-withdrawal rates (i.e., specified oil and/or water rates), a phase saturation should not be allowed to fall below the irreducible saturation at which its relative permeability becomes zero. In some simulators, the well-management routine will stop production of that phase. Others will stop the simulation and give an error message. In extreme cases, the simulator may continue to withdraw that phase and allow its saturation to become negative.

If only an oil rate is specified with no checks on outflow performance, total fluid production may rise to unrealistic levels as water or gas saturations increase in the well block. If this occurs, it is best to switch to a specified total rate and let relative permeabilities, saturations, and pertinent flow relationships control the producing rate for each phase, especially when the predictions will cover a time period long enough to allow large changes in saturation to occur.

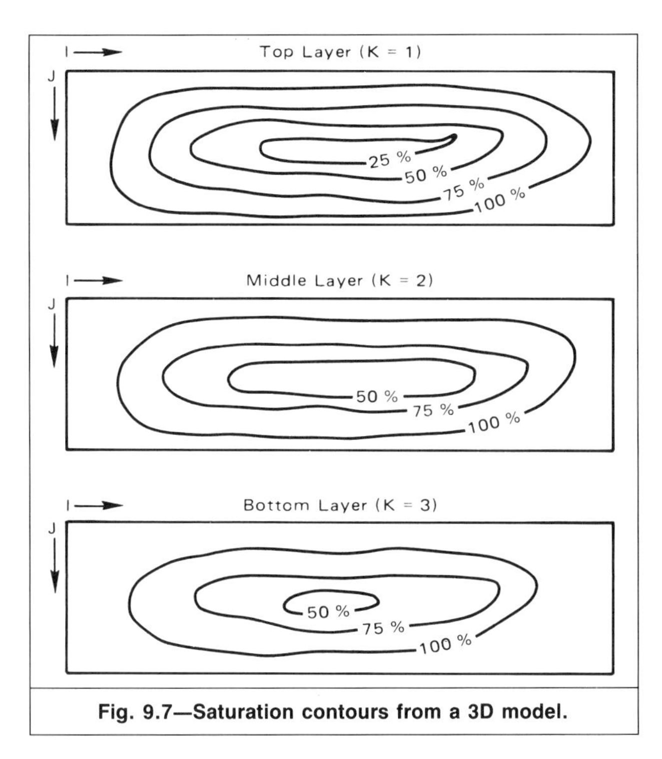

Fig. 9.7—Saturation contours from a 3D model.

Sometimes predicted rates seem reasonable, but predicted well workover and drilling activity seem unrealistic, indicating that a problem exists. Well activity is the result of the corrective action by the well-management routine when pressure, GOR, or WOR constraints are violated. Any unusual increase in wells being worked over, put on artificial lift, or shut in can be spotted easily by edits that show chronological summaries of well-status changes.

Low-pressure shut-in of several wells in an area indicates that withdrawal rates are too high, injection rates are too low, or that wells cannot receive adequate pressure support with the existing injection/production pattern. Wells being shut in or recompleted because of high GOR may be caused by offstructure movement (overriding) of a gas cap or by gas coming out of solution as a result of declining pressure. An area in which an increasing number of wells are being shut in for low rate (dying) or high water cuts may be experiencing an advance of the water front that is too rapid relative to that in other areas. High rates and high pressure drops may cause coning or cusping of gas or water that can cause the well-management routine to shut in the well. In all these examples, it will be necessary to check further into the predicted pressures and saturations to confirm the causes of problems and to decide on corrective action.

In some cases, high levels of well activity may indicate that constraints in the well-management routine are too severe for the reservoir properties and the case being studied. If so, a less-aggressive depletion plan should be developed.

Sometimes, of course, high activity levels are realistic and indicate that the operator must be prepared to accept increased activity to achieve the desired production rate. For example, an increase in well activity, especially drilling of new wells, is normal near the end of the plateau-rate period while the well-management routine tries to maintain the desired target rate during the time total fluid withdrawals approach their highest levels. Then, as the reservoir reaches more advanced stages of depletion, the total number of wells shut in for high GOR, high WOR, or low rate will steadily increase.

It is desirable to plot or to tabulate rates, pressure, and cumulative oil, gas, and water production of individual wells as a function of time. This will reveal unusual behavior and identify changes in the well's performance resulting from workovers or implementation of new well-management constraints. In a study involving a large number of wells, it is usually possible to keep informed about well activity by monitoring the behavior of a few key wells. Performance of key wells will indicate when it is advisable to conduct a complete review of individual well data.

9.4.3 Reviewing Predicted Saturations. Contour maps of oil, gas, and water saturations at selected times, and maps of changes in saturation from initial values, provide one way of overviewing where and how fluids are moving. The maps are useful in evaluating whether gas or water frontal advance is reasonable and consistent with good reservoir engineering practice. They can reveal areas where oil is not being swept efficiently and can be helpful in selecting locations for new wells that may be needed to improve sweep efficiency.

Analysis of results of 3D simulation requires displays of vertical, as well as areal, distributions of fluids. One approach is to develop a contour map for each layer of interest and to display them all on one page, as in Fig. 9.7. Corresponding figures can be developed to show saturations in selected vertical cross sections. Alternatively, saturations can be averaged vertically with porosity-thickness weighting to produce a 2D areal map of the areal distribution of each phase. Generous use of color displays and maps can greatly facilitate visualization and interpretation of results of 3D model studies. It is very helpful to have assistance from someone experienced in mapping and displaying simulator results when dealing with these large, complex models.

Contour intervals of most saturation maps are too large to show saturation reversals or anomalies. Printed arrays are useful in monitoring this type of anomaly, particularly if saturations are unrealistic (greater than one or less than zero). There may be legitimate causes[8] for saturation reversals but, infrequently, reversals may be the result of the simulator obtaining a poor solution of the flow equations. Whenever reversals are encountered, one should take the time to determine the cause.

In 2D areal models, saturations in the direction of flow should be checked to be sure they are consistent with those determined in the cross-sectional model used to derive the areal model pseudorelative permeabilities. If they do not agree, the areal model pseudofunctions need to be rechecked and revised to match more closely the displacement observed in the cross-sectional model.

If nested or windowed models (Chap. 3) are used in a study, saturations and pressures in the window area of the coarse-grid model should track those in the edge blocks of the fine-grid model. If they diverge, boundary flux data will become erroneous and will distort predicted behavior in the detailed model.

As noted before, review of saturation data can help locate areas of the reservoir that are not being adequately swept or drained and may be candidates for infill drilling. These data can also be used to spot movement of oil into a gas-cap area, distortions in areal or vertical sweep, regional coning, offstructure movement of gas, and the formation of secondary gas caps in areas below the bubblepoint. Once problems have been detected, appropriate action can be taken to improve predicted performance in the simulator model.

9.4.4 Reviewing Predicted Pressure Performance. Generally, predicted pressures are reviewed first with contour maps, printer maps, or color displays showing the oil or gas potential (gridblock pressures corrected to a common datum) at selected times. Such displays reveal the potential gradients that are controlling fluid movement in the reservoir. Analyzing potential gradients provides early insight into the development of undesirable trends—e.g., movement of oil across lease boundaries or into a gas cap or aquifer—that might not show up until several model years later in a review of the predicted saturations. Changes in the distribution of injection and production can then be made to improve reservoir performance.

Maps of calculated gridblock pressures, rather than potentials, are used infrequently because these pressures include the fluid head resulting from differences in gridblock depths and thus do not show actual potential gradients and flow patterns. Maps of block pressures are sometimes needed, however, to show areas in which pressures may be higher or lower than desired (e.g., when approaching the formation overburden pressure or nearing the bubblepoint).

In analyzing 3D model results, it may be necessary to review the pressure behavior of each model layer individually if there is

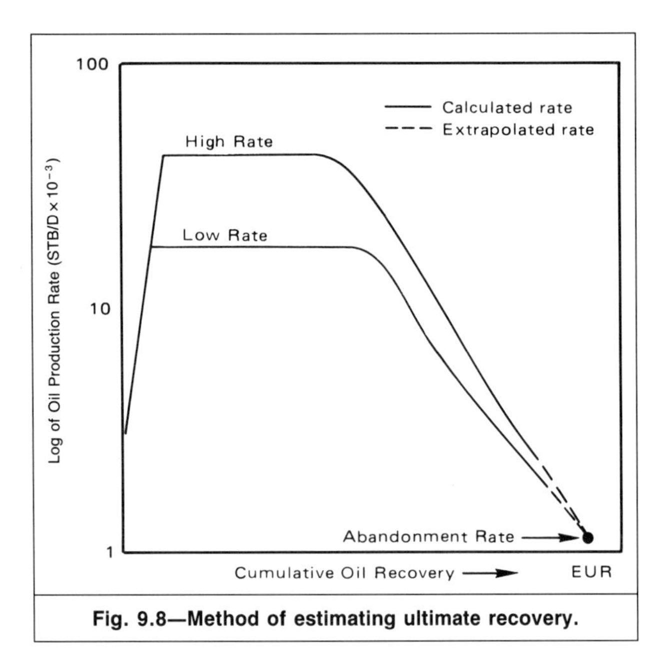

Fig. 9.8—Method of estimating ultimate recovery.

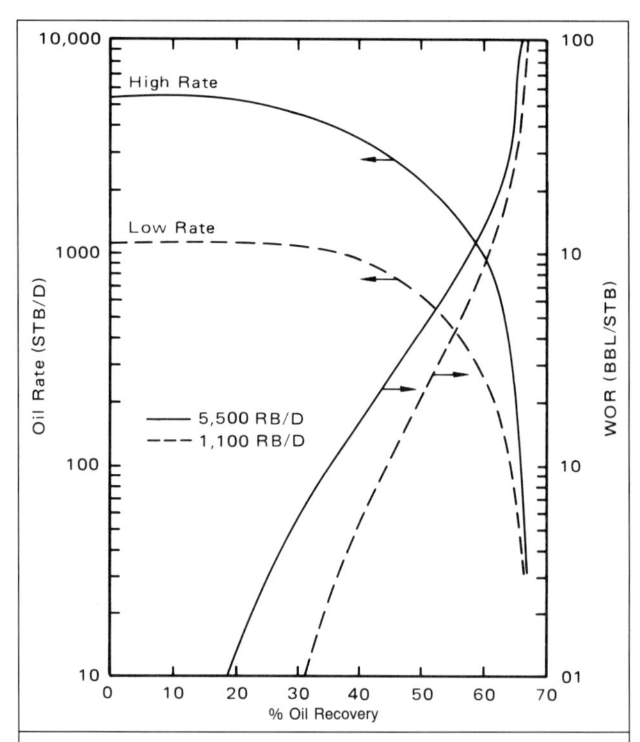

Fig. 9.9—Effect of peak rate on WOR behavior and on ultimate recovery.[3]

restricted vertical communication between the layers. This helps point out areas within individual layers that need additional injection wells or recompletions in producing wells to achieve maximum recovery.

Oscillating pressures in a well block or in an area of the model usually result from well-management constraints that cause wells to alternate on and off production or injection. Refer to Sec. 9.4.

A pressure-related problem that is often encountered is the estimation of future water-injection rates to maintain constant pressure in a field undergoing production decline. One satisfactory solution is to incorporate procedures in the well-management routine to calculate the net injection rate for specified areas at each timestep and to modify this rate by a correction factor whenever the area pressure goes above or below the target pressure level. Wijesinghe *et al.*[6] describe another approach for reservoir pressure maintenance in their well-management program. Wallace and van Spronson[7] describe an approach to implement pressure maintenance in distinct reservoir zones.

An excellent study demonstrating the continuing review of predicted pressures is that of Henzell *et al.*,[21] who describe a 3D single-phase model of Australia's Gippsland basin aquifer that has been used since 1975 to predict pressures throughout the aquifer/reservoir system. Results are used to calculate external boundary pressures for detailed window models around individual reservoirs. The model is also used to forecast the effect of declining reservoir pressure on gas deliverability, to help define the water/oil contact in exploration wells, and to estimate the degree of hydraulic communication between the aquifer and reservoir sands encountered in new wells.

9.4.5 Estimating Ultimate Recovery. One of the objectives of many reservoir studies is estimation of ultimate recovery from each of several alternative operating plans. It is necessary first to select appropriate criteria for defining reservoir abandonment conditions. The criteria might be based on an anticipated minimum producing rate from the field, maximum water cut, minimum pressure (for gas fields), or other factors that determine the economic limit. Once the criteria are defined, predictions can be run until abandonment conditions are reached or until the results can be extrapolated to that point. Fig. 9.8 shows a typical semilog plot of oil rate vs. cumulative recovery. This type of plot usually can be extrapolated to a specified abandonment rate without difficulty.

When using simulator predictions to guide reservoir-management decisions, one should be aware that an estimate of ultimate recovery from any single simulation is subject to considerable uncertainty, especially if it is developed early in the life of a reservoir. On the other hand, differences in ultimate recoveries resulting from differences in reservoir depletion strategy can be very meaningful and can be an excellent basis for choosing between possible alternative methods of field operation. This is especially true when results of a comparison can be corroborated with sensitivity cases covering a range of possible reservoir descriptions.

As mentioned previously, sensitivity cases can be run to evaluate the effects of reasonable changes in reservoir description on ultimate recovery. If results are highly sensitive to such changes, either additional effort should be devoted to improving the reservoir description or little credence should be given to the estimate of ultimate recovery.

In addition to uncertainties in reservoir description, factors that can be categorized as "operator controlled" may influence estimates of ultimate recovery. Factors that are operator controlled include recovery mechanism (i.e., natural depletion or waterflooding), operating constraints (rate, GOR, water-cut limits, artificial lift, and well spacing), and abandonment conditions, which depend on producing rates, costs, and revenues.

It is important that the operator-controlled parameters be consistent in comparative cases so that any differences in ultimate recovery will be attributable only to the particular variable that was deliberately changed.

The effect of rate on ultimate recovery has been reported by several investigators.[3,22-24] These studies generally conclude that recovery either is independent of the peak producing rate or increases as rate increases. An implicit assumption in this conclusion is that the rates are within a practical operating range and that the basic displacement mechanism does not change (for example, from pressure maintenance to solution-gas drive). Using such plots as the one in Fig. 9.9, Coats[3] illustrated that "Water/oil displacements are rate-sensitive if an economic limit of maximum water cut is used, and are not rate-sensitive if an economic limit of a minimum oil rate is used." This points out the need to define the relative weights of these two limits in adopting the abandonment conditions for determining ultimate recovery. Even in Coats' examples, however, any rate-sensitivity effects tend to be minor at realistic abandonment conditions.

Ultimate recovery values calculated by simulation should be reviewed to confirm that they are reasonable. Buckley-Leverett or other simplified models[13] can be used to provide a qualitative

TABLE 9.3—SUMMARY TABLE COMPARING CASE* RESULTS

	Case A	Case B	Case C
Average oil rate, STB/D	9,100	13,700	12,400
Cumulative oil recovery,			
STB × 10^{-6}	40	90	100
% OOIP	20	45	50
Average GOR, scf/STB	1,000	500	500
Cumulative water produced,			
STB × 10^{-6}	5	70	80
New wells drilled	10	15	20
Number of workovers	2	10	12
Project life, years	12	18	22

*Case A = natural depletion.
Case B = peripheral water injection.
Case C = peripheral water injection and closer spacing.

check on the simulator recoveries. In some instances, data may be available from a ''look-alike'' reservoir that is at an advanced stage of depletion and can be used as a guide for estimating ultimate recovery.

9.5 Evaluating and Monitoring Predicted Performance

The previous section discussed procedures for running and analyzing results of individual prediction cases in terms of predicted well activity, saturations, and pressures. The objective was to obtain reasonable results, from both the reservoir engineering and operational viewpoints, for the base-case prediction and for the other cases that usually represent some variation of the base case. This section comments on techniques for evaluating overall results of the different predictions. Some limitations and common weaknesses of predicted results are mentioned and the need to monitor predicted performance is highlighted.

9.5.1 Evaluating Predicted Performance. If the review process previously described has been followed, most of the work required to evaluate predicted performance will already have been completed. Results of each case will have been thoroughly checked, and needed improvements will have been incorporated to help optimize predicted performance within the limits outlined by study objectives and guidelines. The engineer will also have developed an understanding of the reservoir mechanics and some idea of the relative merits of each prediction case.

The next steps are to compare the case results, to identify and run any new cases that may be needed to answer unresolved questions, and then to report the results of the study.

The simplest method of comparing case results is to construct a summary table (e.g., Table 9.3). This type of summary highlights the main results at a glance. Another common method for comparing results of several cases is to plot such key parameters as predicted oil rates, cumulative recovery, or the number of wells vs. time. Predicted rates are sometimes shown as a function of cumulative recovery (Fig. 9.9).

In many instances, study objectives include economic evaluation of the various prediction cases. Many of the data needed to make cash-flow calculations are available from simulator results. Annual volumes of individual phase production and injection, the number of active wells, wells drilled, workovers performed, wells producing on artificial lift, and other pertinent performance data can easily be extracted in a format needed for input to an economics program. It is then necessary to supply only the needed revenue, investment, and operating-cost data to analyze economics.

A further step in performance evaluation is the comparison of predicted saturations and recovery efficiencies to determine whether further improvement in reservoir management is possible. During the analysis and review of a particular prediction, ideas for new ways to improve performance may become apparent. If these ideas merit further investigation, this is the best time to evaluate them by making a new prediction run—assuming, of course, that the necessary time and money are available to do the work. It is cheaper and faster to run sensitivity cases or to evaluate alternative strategies at this time than later. If the cases are delayed several months, additional time and effort may be needed for personnel to regain peak efficiency.

9.5.2 Common Areas of Weakness. Well-conceived and carefully executed reservoir simulations constitute the most reliable method available for estimating future reservoir performance. Simulators are based on established laws of fluid flow and have been tested and improved over a period of years. Other limitations external to the simulator, however, introduce various degrees of uncertainty[25] into predictions of reservoir performance. One should remain aware of these limitations and of the need for continued improvement.

Reservoir description is usually the area of greatest uncertainty in all simulator models, for reasons that are obvious from previous discussions. The importance of uncertainties in reservoir description when predicting future well performance can be evaluated by running sensitivity cases. The parameters of concern are varied over reasonable ranges in the simulator model, and the impact on predicted performance is calculated and compared with the base case.

Another area of uncertainty is in the effect on individual well performance of future changes in conditions. The effects of changing pressures and saturations on future PI, GOR, water cuts, and well outflow performance are all subject to a degree of error. This error decreases as data are obtained on wet or high-GOR wells used to calibrate model well performance.

Some optimistic bias in predicted reservoir performance may be introduced by well-management decisions. Drilling locations may be selected and well-operating decisions may be made that cannot be realized in actual practice. The reason, of course, is that the well-management routine uses logic based on precise knowledge of model pressures and saturations at all times in the predictions, whereas such precision and timing is unattainable when dealing with a real producing reservoir. Another minor optimistic bias may also be present if predictions do not include a realistic allowance for new wells to replace wells lost through corrosion or mechanical problems.

An important question to be addressed when considering the above uncertainties is, will model weaknesses make any difference in the investment and operating decisions that will be based on this study? If the effects of uncertainties do not mask the relative values of alternative operating strategies, performance predictions can be used with confidence when making reservoir-management decisions.

Predictions of reservoir performance are most reliable for the first few years into the future; longer-term predictions tend to be less reliable because errors resulting from uncertainty in reservoir characteristics become more significant with time. As a consequence, predictions of the absolute values of recovery, well counts, etc., will change with time as knowledge of the reservoir improves. On the other hand, relative differences between similar prediction cases are less likely to change. Hence, comparison of alternative plans provides a reliable basis for planning investments and operating strategies. Similarly, comparison of selectively different prediction cases is a reliable method for investigating the sensitivity of reservoir performance to values of such hard-to-define reservoir parameters as permeability heterogeneity.

9.5.3 Monitoring Predicted Results. Once predictions have been completed and results reported, procedures should be established for comparing predicted and actual field performance periodically. The model will usually track field pressures and well behavior reasonably closely for a few years and then gradually diverge as effects of uncertainties start to develop. It is important to be alert to differences between predicted and actual performance that are large enough to suggest that the prediction is seriously in error and that operating strategies recommended from the study should be reconsidered.

The monitoring process can be as simple as posting observed field rates, average pressures, and well activity on plots of prediction performance. Contour maps of observed and predicted pressures and frontal positions can also be compared to detect anomalies. Direct comparisons, such as those just mentioned, become more difficult as time passes, because the field is almost never operated in the exact manner assumed in the model predictions. To maintain their reliability, models should be brought up to date from time to time through history matching of the period that has elapsed since the previous match was completed. The need for frequent re-evaluation of the utility of existing models is substantiated by an increasing number of papers[15,21,26-33] that discuss the evolution of models used to improve reservoir-management strategy.

Nomenclature

h = formation thickness, ft [m]
k = permeability, md
k_{rg} = relative permeability to gas
k_{ro} = relative permeability to oil
k_{rw} = relative permeability to water
p_{wf} = bottomhole flowing pressure, psi [kPa]
q_t = total flow rate, STB/D [stock-tank m^3/d]
S_g = gas saturation
ΔS_g = gas saturation increment
S_{or} = residual oil saturation
S_w = water saturation
ΔS_w = water saturation increment

References

1. Miller, R.T. and Clements, R.L.: "Reservoir Engineering Techniques Used to Predict Blowout Control During the Bay Marchand Fire," *Numerical Simulation,* Reprint Series, SPE, Richardson, TX (1973) **11,** 200–14.
2. Huppler, J.D.: "Numerical Investigation of the Effects of Core Heterogeneities on Waterflood Relative Permeabilities," *SPEJ* (Dec. 1970) 381–92; *Trans.,* AIME, **249.**
3. Coats, K.H.: "Reservoir Simulation: State of the Art," *JPT* (Aug. 1982) 1633–42.
4. Crichlow, H.B.: *Modern Reservoir Engineering—A Simulation Approach,* Prentice-Hall Inc., Englewood Cliffs, NJ (1977).
5. Stackel, A.W. and Brown, H.M.: "An Example Approach to Predictive Well Management in Reservoir Simulation," *JPT* (June 1981) 1087–94.
6. Wijesinghe, A.M. *et al.*: "A Comprehensive Well Management Program for Black Oil Reservoir Simulation," paper SPE 12260 presented at the 1983 Reservoir Simulation Symposium, San Francisco, Nov. 15–18.
7. Wallace, D.J. and van Spronson, E.: "A Reservoir Simulation Model with Platform Production/Injection Constraints for Development Planning of Volatile Oil Reservoirs," paper SPE 12261 presented at the 1983 Reservoir Simulation Symposium, San Francisco, Nov. 15–18.
8. Coats, K.H.: "Use and Misuse of Reservoir Simulation Models," *Numerical Simulation,* Reprint Series, SPE, Richardson, TX (1973) **11,** 183–90.
9. Christian, L.D. *et al.*: "Planning a Tertiary Oil-Recovery Project for Jay/LEC Fields Units," *JPT* (Aug. 1981) 1535–44.
10. Kempthorne, R.H. and Irish, J.P.R.: "Norman Wells—A New Look at One of Canada's Largest Oil Fields," *JPT* (June 1981) 985–91.
11. Johnson, J.B. *et al.*: "The Kuparuk River Field: A Regression Approach to Pseudo-Relative Permeabilities," paper SPE 10531 presented at the 1982 Reservoir Simulation Symposium, New Orleans, Feb. 1–3.
12. McCulloch, R.C., Langton, J.R., and Spivak, A.: "Simulation of High Relief Reservoirs, Rainbow Field, Alberta, Canada," *Numerical Simulation,* Reprint Series, SPE, Richardson, TX (1973) **11,** 215–24.
13. Richardson, J.G. and Blackwell, R.J.: "Use of Simple Mathematical Models for Predicting Reservoir Behavior," *JPT* (Sept. 1971) 1145–54; *Trans.,* AIME, **251.**
14. Wendschlag, D.D., Stephenson, R.E., and Clark, T.J.: "Fieldwide Simulation of the Anschutz Ranch East Nitrogen Injection Project with a Generalized Compositional Model," paper SPE 12257 presented at the 1983 SPE Reservoir Simulation Symposium, San Francisco, Nov. 15–18.
15. Harpole, K.J.: "Improved Reservoir Characterization—A Key to Future Reservoir Management for the West Seminole San Andres Unit," *JPT* (Nov. 1980) 2009–19.
16. Aziz, K. and Settari, A.: *Petroleum Reservoir Simulation,* Applied Science Publishers Ltd., Wilmette, IL (1979) 303–48.
17. Williamson, A.S. and Chappelear, J.E.: "Representing Wells in Numerical Reservoir Simulation: Part 1—Theory; Part 2—Implementation," *SPEJ* (June 1981) 323–44; *Trans.,* AIME, **271.**
18. Emanuel, A.S. and Ranney, J.C.: "Studies of Offshore Reservoirs with an Interfaced Reservoir/Piping Network Simulator," *JPT* (March 1981) 399–406.
19. Chappelear, J.E. and Hirasaki, G.J.: "A Model of Oil-Water Coning for Two-Dimensional, Areal Reservoir Simulation," *SPEJ* (April 1976) 65–72; *Trans.,* AIME, **261.**
20. Graham, M.F. and Smart, G.T.: "Reservoir Simulation Employing a Fine-Grid Model Nested in a Coarse-Grid Model," paper SPE 9372 presented at the 1980 SPE Annual Technical Conference and Exhibition, Dallas, Sept. 21–24.
21. Henzell, S.T., Young, A.A., and Khurana, A.K.: "Reservoir Simulation of the Gippsland Basin," *The Australian Pet. Expl. Assn. J.* (1984) 170–79.
22. Beveridge, S.B. *et al.*: "A Study of the Sensitivity of Oil Recovery to Production Rate," paper SPE 5129 presented at the 1974 SPE Annual Meeting, Oct. 6–9.
23. Lee, J.E. *et al.*: "The Effect of Rate on Recovery for Canadian Carbonate Reservoirs," paper SPE 5128 presented at the 1974 SPE Annual Meeting, Oct. 6–9.
24. Stright, D.H., Bennion, D.W., and Aziz, K.: "Influence of Production Rate of the Recovery of Oil from Horizontal Waterfloods," paper SPE 5127 presented at the 1974 SPE Annual Meeting, Oct. 6–9.
25. Brush, R.M. and Marsden, S.S.: "Bias in Engineering Estimation," *JPT* (Feb. 1982) 433–39.
26. Aron, D., Ashbourne, T.J., and Oloketuyi, D.O.: "The Secondary Recovery Project at Ogharefe Field, Nigeria," *JPT* (April 1984) 671–77.
27. Bradford, R.N. and Hrkel, E.J.: "Evaluation of a Reservoir Simulation Study: West Civit Dykeman Sand Unit," *JPT* (Dec. 1979) 1599–1604.
28. Brinkman, F.P.: "Increased Gas Recovery from a Moderate Water Drive Reservoir," *JPT* (Dec. 1981) 2475–80.
29. DesBrisay, C.L. *et al.*: "Review of Miscible Flood Performance, Intisar "D" Field, Socialist People's Libyan Arab Jamahiriya," *JPT* (Aug. 1982) 1651–60.
30. Holst, P.H. and Zadick, T.W.: "Compositional Simulation for Effective Reservoir Management: The Brady South Weber Pressure-Maintenance Project," *JPT* (March 1982) 635–44.
31. Mann, L. and Johnson, G.A.: "Predicted Results of Numeric Grid Models Compared with Actual Field Performance," *Numerical Simulation,* Reprint Series, SPE, Richardson, TX (1973) **11,** 191–99.
32. Thakur, G.C. *et al.*: "G-2 and G-3 Reservoirs, Delta South Field, Nigeria: Part 2—Simulation of Water Injection," *JPT* (Jan. 1982) 148–58.
33. Thu, G.S., Heacock, D.W., and Loveless, D.E.: "Exploration, Development, and Reservoir Engineering Studies for the Tapis Field Offshore Peninsular Malaysia," *JPT* (June 1983) 1051–60.

SI Metric Conversion Factors

acre	× 4.046 873	E−01	=	ha
bbl	× 1.589 873	E−01	=	m^3
psi	× 6.894 757	E+00	=	kPa
scf/bbl	× 1.801 175	E−01	=	std m^3/m^3

Chapter 10
Editing

The data used and generated by most numerical models are so numerous that they are virtually impossible to proof, understand, analyze, and discuss without first being reduced to summaries that are presented as tables, graphs, or pictorial displays. The computational process involved in preparing the summaries is known as *editing*. Broadly defined, the term "editing" encompasses almost any computational activity that is not an integral part of the simulation and that reorganizes, summarizes, or analyzes either input to or output from simulation.

The type and quality of edits have evolved from crude printer maps and iteration summary tables to quality multicolor displays, perspective drawings, and motion pictures. The evolution has been driven by the need to interpret ever larger and increasingly complex models. Because continuing evolution in editing can be expected, we will not attempt to present in this chapter a comprehensive discussion of all the types of edits that are currently used. Instead, we will list those that are most useful, with some occasional comments on their utility.

The choice of edits to use is dictated by both need and timing. Most edits are working tools and must be available soon after—and sometimes during—a simulation run. In these cases, simple, easily obtained edits are more useful than complex edits that are difficult to obtain. On the other hand, displays for reporting purposes are usually selected primarily for their effectiveness in explaining results and with less regard for the calendar time or difficulty involved in obtaining them.

The relative ease with which data in a simulator can be accessed for editing can influence the efficiency with which a study can be conducted. If data access is difficult or clumsy, calendar time and computing time can be wasted. This is particularly true if special edits are needed that must be developed on an *ad hoc* basis.

10.1 Preliminary Comments

The variables that must be followed most closely in all stages of a simulation are pressure or potential, saturation, and production and injection rates. Many of the most useful edits deal with these variables. At least one time during a study, however, values of every parameter that influences reservoir behavior or serves as a measure of reservoir performance should be reviewed. A few general comments on edits that facilitate such reviews follow.

Chap. 4 mentions the usefulness of computer programs that generate rock-property arrays for reservoir flow models from digitized geologic data. An edit to display and to validate the arrays is a useful addition to these programs, although most simulators will contain equivalent editing capability.

To facilitate visualization and interpretation of flow behavior, it is usually best to express pressures as potentials or pressures at a reference depth. Otherwise, pressure variations resulting solely from changes in the gravity head with structural position may make it difficult to interpret pressure data. When communicating results of a study, of course, it may not be appropriate to express pressures as potentials.

Contour maps are useful, but their quality may be disappointing. This is true especially of maps drawn by automatic contouring programs with insufficient data. For example, large potential gradients that may occur near faults are difficult for most automatic contouring programs to handle. In these cases, maps displaying values in each gridblock according to a color or "shades of gray" code may be more useful than conventional contour maps.

10.2 The Most Useful Edits

10.2.1 During Construction of a Model. Edits are used when a model is under construction to verify the accuracy with which input data were entered and to discover inconsistencies in data. At this stage, data are sometimes screened for irregularities that can cause problems later; e.g., a large increase in the slope of a capillary-pressure/saturation function at low wetting-phase saturations can be troublesome but might not be noticed when data are entered into the model. An edit that evaluates the derivatives of saturation and pressure functions would detect this irregularity.

Useful edits during this phase of a study include: (1) contour maps and cross-sectional plots of k, ϕ, and depth assigned to the gridblocks; (2) drawings of the grid system made with data taken directly from the gridblock dimension arrays; (3) areal and cross-sectional maps of lithologic types (for use in assigning saturation functions); (4) plots of saturation and pressure functions and derivatives of the functions with respect to saturation and pressure (functions may be pseudofunctions); and (5) contour maps of initial saturations, pressures, and potentials that may be specified by the user.

10.2.2 After Construction and Initialization of Model, but Before History Matching Begins. Just before spending computing time on the first history-match run, it is advisable to confirm that the model was initialized properly and that the well-management routine for historical production is functioning correctly. In these edits, principal emphasis will be on saturation and pressure distribution and on data related to the location and timing of injection and production.

In almost all studies, six types of edits will be needed before history matching should be started: (1) maps of saturation and potential distribution, (2) summaries of fluids in place by model subregions, (3) map of the grid system showing well locations, (4) cross-sectional plots showing historical completion intervals, (5) plots of specified well rates as functions of time, and (6) plots and maps of historical data that are to be matched (pressures, water cuts, fluid-contact positions, etc.).

10.2.3 During a History Match. As mentioned in earlier chapters, history matching can be the most time-consuming and costly phase of a simulation study. It is imperative, therefore, that both model performance and computational efficiency be monitored with timely and adequate edits. The objective of monitoring model performance, of course, is to supply information needed for efficient modification of model parameters to force the model to match historical reservoir performance. The objective of monitoring computational efficiency is to ensure that calculations are proceeding without undue difficulty and are producing accurate answers.

Edits to monitor the performance of the model include the following.

1. Contour maps of calculated and historical regional distributions of potential and saturation at selected times in reservoir history. (Maps of differences between calculated and historical data can also be useful.)

2. Plots of calculated and measured potentials (or pressures as appropriate) vs. time for individual wells, and similar plots of average potentials for preselected groups of wells and for preselected areas of the reservoir. When comparing measured well pressures with calculated pressures (potentials), it is usually necessary to adjust one of the sets of pressures so that the two sets represent conditions at the same locations in the reservoir. See Chaps. 2, 7, 8, and 9.

3. Maps of regions in which selected reservoir parameters have reached predetermined values (e.g., pressure below the bubblepoint or water saturation above a set value).

4. Tables, maps, and plots of regional and boundary fluxes, especially those between the reservoir and its aquifer.

5. Tables, maps, and plots comparing historical and model values of cumulative oil, water, and gas production by well, well group, and reservoir.

6. Plots of calculated and measured gas/oil ratios (GOR's) and water/oil ratios (WOR's) as a function of time for each well, well group, and reservoir.

7. Maps or plots comparing calculated pressures (potentials) obtained in different history-match runs.

8. Maps or plots similar to Edit 7, but comparing saturation.

9. Plots comparing the performance (pressure, rate, etc.) of specified wells with that of surrounding wells.

10. Plots comparing historical and computed water or gas arrival times.

11. If a large number of wells are involved, it is useful to use an edit that prepares miniature plots of measured and calculated performances of individual wells and arranges the plots into a composite map or montage in which the locations of the plots indicate relative well locations.

Edits to monitor simulator performance usually will be specific to the simulator being used. In almost all cases, however, the following types of edits will be useful.

1. Listings of maximum, minimum, and average timestep size.

2. For iterative-solution techniques, the average, maximum, and minimum number of iterations required to achieve a solution.

3. Maps or listings showing locations of gridblocks in which maximum changes in saturation or pressure occurred during a timestep.

4. Listings of gridblocks in which tolerances imposed on the computation were approached (see Chap. 5).

5. A tabulation of information, including frequency and causes of failure, concerning timesteps that were attempted but not completed successfully.

6. Other edits, specific to the simulator being used, that give an indication of the quality of the computations (e.g., maximum and cumulative material-balance errors are useful in monitoring many iterative solutions).

10.2.4 After History Matching but Before Predictions. Before proceeding with the first prediction run, it is desirable to review the properties of the matched model and to decide whether further modification is needed for a smooth transition between history and predictions. The principal change in operation of the model is a shift to a prediction-mode well-management routine that calculates rather than specifies well rates.

Some of the edits used at this time are similar to those used earlier. The following edits are normally required.

1. Contour, color, or shaded maps displaying the absolute and relative changes in k and ϕ between the initial geologic description and that in the final matched model.

2. Maps showing saturation changes that occurred during the period covered by the history match.

3. Maps, plots, bar charts, or tables showing the status of wells at the end of history (shut in, flowing, artificial lift, workover candidate, etc.).

4. Plots showing locations of well completions relative to gas/oil and water/oil contacts.

5. Lists and plots displaying individual well rates as a function of time.

6. Graphs that compare calculated well rates at the start of predictions with those at the end of history (refer to Chap. 9 for more discussion of these useful graphs).

7. Contour, color, or shaded maps showing the areal distribution of injection and production and the areal distribution of GOR's and WOR's.

8. Maps showing potential drilling sites.

9. Plots, maps, or tables, as appropriate, summarizing production guidelines that are entered into the well-management routine for wells, areas, reservoirs, and the field.

10.2.5 During Predictions. Prediction runs are edited at frequent intervals to check results of the simulation for reasonableness and accuracy, to detect when and where rates depart from target levels, to spot undesirable trends in well performance, to confirm that operating constraints are being followed, and to identify opportunities for improving performance. Chap. 9 discusses some of the edits used to review and to analyze results.

The types of edits that are most useful at this time will depend on the objectives of the study. Most of the following edits will usually be needed.

1. Contour or shaded maps of pressure (potential).

2. Contour or shaded maps of saturation.

3. Plots of average potential vs. time for well groups, reservoir, and field.

4. Plots and tables of production rates, GOR, or WOR by well, well group, reservoir, and field.

5. Plots and tables of cumulative production (oil, water, gas) by well, well group, reservoir, and field.

6. Plots and tables similar to Edits 4 and 5 of injection and cumulative injection rates.

7. Plots, bar charts, tables, and/or maps of well status (wells drilled, worked over, shut in, etc.) at selected times.

8. Same as Edit 7, but showing changes in well status over specified time intervals.

9. Contour or shaded maps of changes in saturation between the end of history and selected times in the future.

10. Contour or shaded areal and/or cross-sectional maps of recovery efficiency.

Chapter 11
Simulating Special Processes

Up to this point, this monograph has dealt with "black-oil" simulation, which models immiscible flow under conditions such that fluid properties can be treated either as functions of pressure only or as functions of pressure and solution gas/oil ratio. Black-oil simulators can handle more than three-fourths of all simulator applications adequately. They are inadequate, however, for studies that must account for mixing of fluids having significantly different properties, displacement of oil by miscible or conditionally miscible fluids, displacements involving chemicals that can affect fluid properties, nonisothermal flow, or combustion reactions. This chapter addresses the simulation of such special processes. Its objective differs from those of previous chapters in that emphasis is on factors involved in modeling each process rather than on practical information and techniques the reader can readily apply to existing simulators. The previous approach is not practical for most of the special processes discussed here because the technology is not sufficiently advanced.*

Table 11.1 is presented to convey an impression of state-of-the-art modeling for these processes. In general, these special processes tend to be less understood than those modeled with black-oil simulators. They pose modeling difficulties, not all of which have been satisfactorily solved, and industry has had less experience in attempting to model them.[1]

In general, each process is treated as follows. A process and its underlying physics are described, and the basic governing equations and difficulties associated with solving them are presented. Problems that may arise in applications—e.g., special gridding considerations, the number of components required in compositional simulators, and unusual computing time requirements—are discussed. Finally, simplified methods applicable in certain cases are described and, in the last section of the chapter, input data requirements specific to each process are discussed.

11.1 Compositional Simulation

In reservoirs containing light oils—e.g., gas condensates or volatile oils—vapor/liquid equilibrium depends on composition as well as pressure. Rigorous flash calculations must be made with equilibrium K values or an equation of state (EOS) to determine hydrocarbon phase compositions. Viscosities and densities can then be calculated from phase compositions.

In principle, compositional simulation should be useful whenever compositional effects are important. In practice, however, accuracy problems arise in compositional modeling of miscible displacement. These are particularly severe if miscibility is achieved through multiple contacts. These problems are discussed further in the section on miscible displacement.

The compositional reservoir flow equations were originally presented by Collins,[2] but here we use notation similar to that of Kazemi *et al.*[3]

The water equation is unchanged from the black-oil formulation (see Appendix B):

$$\nabla\cdot\left(\frac{\lambda_w}{B_w}\nabla\Phi_w\right)+q_w=\frac{\partial}{\partial t}\left(\frac{\phi S_w}{B_w}\right). \quad (11.1)$$

*In this chapter, we use a consistent set of units and do not provide the equivalent oilfield units.

The hydrocarbon equation accounts for flow (of Component ν) in both the oil and gas phases:

$$\nabla\cdot(x_\nu\xi_o\lambda_o\nabla\Phi_o+y_\nu\xi_g\lambda_g\nabla\Phi_g)+q_\nu$$
$$=\frac{\partial}{\partial t}[\phi(x_\nu\xi_oS_o+y_\nu\xi_gS_g)] \quad (11.2)$$

In the above equations,

λ = phase mobility $=kk_r/\mu$,
Φ = phase potential,
ξ = molar density,
x_ν = mole fraction of Component ν in liquid phase,
y_ν = mole fraction of Component ν in vapor phase, and
q_ν = injection or production rate of Component ν.*

Note that no provision is made for the transport of components other than water in the water phase. This limitation can be severe, particularly in modeling processes that involve such highly water-soluble components as CO_2. Nothing about the model precludes including such transport; however, it is not usually included within the context of a general program, because transport would only be needed for certain components.

The production rate of Component ν is the sum of its production rates in the oil and gas phases:

$$q_\nu=\hat{x}_\nu\hat{\xi}_oq_o+\hat{y}_\nu\hat{\xi}_gq_g, \quad (11.3)$$

where $\hat{x}_\nu$, $\hat{\xi}_o$, $\hat{y}_\nu$, and $\hat{\xi}_g$ apply to the well stream.

A number of approaches to solve these equations are described in the literature.[3-10] For the most part, they differ primarily in how they handle the right side of Eq. 11.2. The term $x_\nu\xi_oS_o+y_\nu\xi_gS_g$ is a nonlinear function of pressure and the overall mole fractions. It must be computed on the basis of new time-level values of these quantities, or material balance will not be preserved. In general, this must be done iteratively. Kazemi *et al.*[3] and Nghiem *et al.*[10] use direct substitution iteration. Coats[5] and Young and Stephenson[9] use Newton-Raphson iteration. Coats iterates on the transport terms as well, resulting in fully implicit solutions for the equations. Young and Stephenson organize their calculations to yield a very efficient method. Through a different approach, Ács *et al.*[4] and Watts[8] obtain a procedure similar in some ways to that of Young and Stephenson. Their method differs from the others in that it avoids the nonlinear iteration. Also, Watts describes a way to treat the saturation-dependent terms semi-implicitly.

Thele *et al.*[11] compared the performances of the Nghiem *et al.*,[10] Coats,[5] and Young and Stephenson[9] formulations. They chose these three as representing the state of the art at the time of their study. They reported that the Young and Stephenson formulation generally requires the least computer time of the three, and they prefer it overall. There has been no published comparison including the Ács *et al.*[4] and Watts[8] formulations, which were published more recently than the others.

*Note that q_w and q_ν are positive for injection and negative for production. This convention is followed throughout this chapter.

TABLE 11.1—SIMULATION OF SPECIAL PROCESSES—STATE OF THE ART

Process	Stability Characteristics	Numerical Accuracy Problems	Model Complexity	Relative Computing Cost	Amount of Industrial Experience
Compositional without CO_2	Generally stable	Numerical dispersion	Fairly complex	Moderate	Fairly extensive
Compositional with CO_2	Occasional problems	Numerical dispersion	Complex	Expensive	Moderate
Miscible	Stable	Numerical dispersion	Simple	Inexpensive	Moderate
Chemical	Occasional problems	Numerical dispersion; bank definition; grid-orientation effect	Complex	Moderate	Limited, but growing
Steam	Strong tendency to instability	Grid-orientation effect	Complex	Expensive	Extensive
Combustion	Very strong tendency to instability	Grid-orientation effect; bank definition	Very complex	Very expensive	Very little

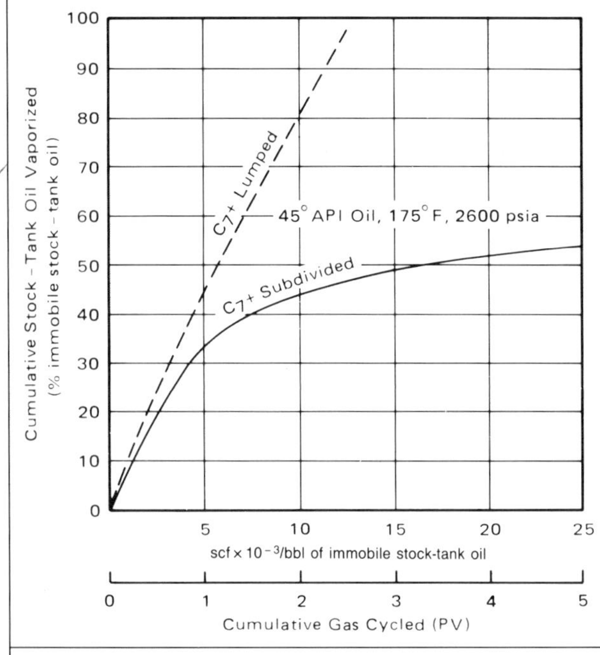

Fig. 11.1—Effect of subdividing C_{7+} fraction on calculated vaporization of volatile oil.[14]

Ensuring that compressibility will be positive can be more difficult in compositional than in black-oil simulation. Values for total system compressibility in a multiple-phase system cannot be assigned until equilibrium compositions and phase densities have been calculated because interphase mass transfer takes place as pressure changes. If the densities and equilibrium calculations are inconsistent, small errors, which would normally be acceptable, can lead to negative compressibilities. If these occur, the simulation will become unstable.

This problem is particularly severe near the critical point, where all physical properties of the two phases should be identical. If consistency is not ensured, computational problems will result. Nolen[6] recommends avoiding the problems by using the same density correlation for both phases.

Recently, the trend has been to sidestep this entire issue by using EOS's to correlate fluid properties. The most popular of these are the cubic EOS's—e.g., the Peng-Robinson[12] and the Redlich-Kwong.[13]

Existing correlations cannot accurately predict phase behavior and properties of complex reservoir fluids, particularly when significant amounts of nonhydrocarbon components—e.g., CO_2, N_2, and H_2S—are present. It is common practice to calibrate the correlations by matching them with data from laboratory experiments. Nolen[6] discusses a procedure for calibration using regression analysis.

The number of components that must be used for adequate simulation depends on the process being modeled and the level of detail desired. CO_2-flooding behavior can be approximated with only three components (oil, gas, and CO_2) plus water if the main effects of interest are swelling and viscosity reduction of the oil. If more-elaborate behavior is to be modeled, such as the formation of multiple liquid phases made of hydrocarbons or the deposition of asphaltenes, more components are needed. Relatively few components are needed to model hydrocarbon miscible floods, particularly first-contact miscible floods. Multiple-contact miscibility can be predicted accurately, however, only if intermediate hydrocarbon components are included.

According to Wattenbarger,[7] modeling the depletion of volatile-oil or gas-condensate reservoirs requires that all components through hexane be included, with the heptane-plus fraction being lumped. If depletion is by gas cycling, the model must include a breakdown of the composition of the heptane-plus fraction, because an important part of the process is vaporization of heavy components. If this detailed breakdown is not used, the model will eventually compute that all the oil has vaporized, which is physically unrealistic. Fig. 11.1, taken from Cook *et al.*,[14] illustrates the problem. The figure shows the computed percent of immobile oil vaporized as a function of cumulative gas cycled. Computations were performed both with the heptane-plus fraction lumped and with it subdivided. The two computations agree fairly well when only a small amount of gas cycling has occurred, but they start to deviate later in the computation. Taylor[15] discusses similar behavior.

The best way to determine how many components are required is through simulation of laboratory experiments that mimic the behavior expected in the reservoir. The level of hydrocarbon characterization adequate to model laboratory behavior should also be adequate in the reservoir simulator.

Initializing the simulator also poses some difficulties. Saturations are inferred from phase pressures by the procedure discussed in Chap. 4—i.e., pressures in all phases are specified at some reference or "starting" point, then densities of all phases are computed at selected locations (e.g., block centers) throughout the reservoir volume so that pressure differences (capillary pressures) and, hence, saturations can be calculated. The problem is what compositions to use in computing densities. Kazemi *et al.*[3] use a single base composition representing a fluid at its bubblepoint at the pressure at the gas/oil contact (GOC), which they define as the location of the first nonzero gas saturation. All other pressures are then based on this. Oil pressures below the GOC are easily computed. Those above the GOC are computed with approximate densities. Then the bubblepoint fluid is flashed at these pressures to obtain oil- and gas-phase compositions. Saturations are calculated from capillary-pressure relationships. It is necessary to iterate when this scheme is used, however, because the densities used in determining the pressures are only approximate.

Allocation of production is also difficult in compositional simulation. It is desirable to define production in terms of stock-tank barrels and standard cubic feet, but, internally, the simulator computes pound-moles of individual hydrocarbon components. As a result, models of the surface separation facilities must be included in the simulator. But the separators will operate at different temperatures and at pressures much lower than those in the reservoir. Hence, reservoir fluid properties cannot be used in modeling facilities and another element of complexity must be addressed. Kazemi *et al.*[3] discuss this in more detail.

Several approximate methods are used in compositional simulation; the crudest method is the variable-bubblepoint calculation. It is used in black-oil models where variable bubblepoints are created when pressure falls below the bubblepoint and then later increases (see Chap. 3). The next step up in accuracy involves models that include a volatile oil component, as well as solution gas.[16] Finally, there is the approach of Cook *et al.*,[17] intended for modeling gas injection in volatile oil or condensate reservoirs. They correlate parameters describing fluid properties with cumulative gas invasion. These parameters are then estimated in one-dimensional (1D) compositional simulations. This approach is often adequate, but Henry[18] shows that it loses accuracy when K values are functions of concentration.

Taylor[15] provides a fairly thorough treatment of the practical considerations associated with modeling condensate reservoirs. He discusses both the modified black-oil and fully compositional approaches and when each should be used. He also describes input data requirements with emphasis on issues specific to modeling condensates. Fluid-sampling concerns are also covered briefly. Coats[16] discusses several issues involved in modeling condensates. His primary focus is on describing the reservoir fluid behavior and the use of pseudocomponents in doing so.

11.2 Miscible Displacement

The discussion of simulation of miscible displacement that follows is rather brief. A considerably broader treatment is given by Stalkup in his monograph *Miscible Displacement,*[19] which includes six examples of field simulations taken from the literature.

For the sake of discussion, miscible displacements can be considered one of two types: first-contact miscible or multiple-contact miscible. Stalkup[19] discusses these in detail. (Actually, Stalkup describes three types of multiple-contact miscible displacements: condensing gas drive, vaporizing gas drive, and CO_2 miscible displacement. The major modeling difficulties for the three processes are similar. Certain phenomena occur in the CO_2 miscible process, however, that do not occur in the other multiple-contact processes.)

Modeling multiple-contact miscible displacement is difficult. There are troublesome vapor/liquid equilibrium calculations in the region near the critical point where miscibility is achieved. In addition, there are serious accuracy problems resulting from numerical dispersion and other discretization errors. The computational difficulty is illustrated by Fig. 11.2, taken from Coats.[5] The figure shows gas saturations generated during a 1D condensing gas drive calculation. The results have not converged, despite the fact that up to 80 gridblocks are used between wells. Results summarized in this figure suggest that about 200 gridblocks between wells are needed to get accurate results in this problem. Thus, it appears that rigorous multiple-contact miscible-displacement calculations can be made only in one dimension, and then with difficulty.

As a result, the most common approach in modeling field-scale, multiple-contact miscible displacements is to assume miscibility. A slight elaboration of this procedure is sometimes made by assuming that the displacement is miscible above a specified pressure and immiscible below some lower pressure, with some sort of smooth transition in behavior occurring between the two. In either case, only three components are typically used, with the three components representing initial in-place hydrocarbon, injected solvent, and drive fluid. The result is a model that is simplified in two ways: fewer components are used and rigorous vapor/liquid equilibrium calculations are avoided. It runs much faster than a fully compositional model, making it possible to use a finer grid.

The applications of such a model are limited. Obviously, it cannot be used to determine whether miscibility is obtained in the reservoir; its primary use is in modeling fluid flow. Such a model could be used, for example, to estimate how injection and production rates, reservoir layering, and shale barriers affect gravity segregation and ultimate oil recovery. The model is generally not useful in defining the size of a miscible bank because numerical dispersion limits its accuracy.

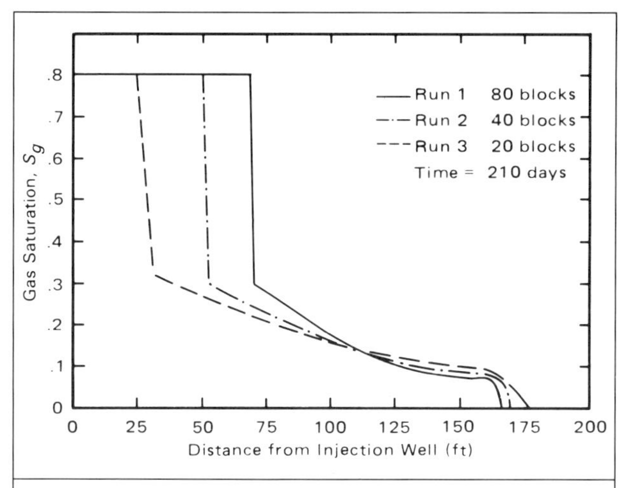

Fig. 11.2—Influence of numerical dispersion on calculated frontal advance during a miscible displacement.[5]

Simplified miscible-displacement calculations of this sort are often made with a modified black-oil simulator. The modifications required were first described by Lantz,[20] who considered the analogy between miscible and immiscible displacement. In this analogy, bulk immiscible flow becomes bulk miscible flow, and flow driven by capillary pressures becomes diffusive flux. Relative permeabilities must be varied to maintain the correct total mobility while equating fractional flow to saturation. The analogy becomes more complicated when gravitational effects are included; Lantz's treatment of this situation is incorrect.*

Another modification of a black-oil simulator is the model of Todd and Longstaff.[21] The model assumes four components in two phases. The wetting phase contains only water, whereas the nonwetting phase contains gas, solvent, and oil. For computational convenience, a relative permeability is calculated for each component in the nonwetting phase. These relative permeabilities are proportional to the corresponding components' concentrations and must sum to the relative permeability of the nonwetting phase. Viscous fingering is accounted for by use of a mixing coefficient. This approach is adequate in an areal grid but can break down in cross-sectional or three-dimensional (3D) grids. The appropriate value of the mixing parameter is a function of grid size. Because the vertical gridding is usually relatively fine, a value of the mixing parameter that is satisfactory for areal flow can be unacceptable for vertical flow.

Chase and Todd[22] describe a model that combines the approach discussed in the last paragraph with descriptions of phenomena believed important in miscible CO_2 flooding. These phenomena include CO_2 transport in the aqueous phase, water blocking of oil from contact by the invading solvent, and asphaltene deposition and resultant mobility reduction.

As discussed previously, it is usually necessary to assume miscibility in field-scale modeling of miscible-displacement processes. Here, numerical dispersion is the chief remaining accuracy problem (see Chaps. 5 and 6). Somewhat simplistically, one can consider numerical dispersion to be caused by the use of upstream weighting in the finite-difference equations. It follows that one way to reduce the problem is to use midpoint weighting, but this results in oscillations in the solution. In general, it is necessary to accept a tradeoff between diffusion and oscillations; the best solution is obtained when just enough diffusion is present to damp out the oscillations. This condition can be achieved by varying the amount of upstream weighting used,[23] by using midpoint weighting and introducing diffusion in the form of a diffusion coefficient,[24] or by using full upstream weighting and introducing "negative" diffusion.[25,26] Other approaches are the two-point upstream method of Todd *et al.*[27] and the variably timed flux updating technique of Larson.[28,29]

A good bit of work has also been done on alternative mathematical techniques such as finite-element methods[30-32] and the compact implicit method.[33] Although impressive results have been

*From personal communication with M.E. Rose, March 1980.

presented for these methods, they have not seen widespread practical use, perhaps because of their complexity.

An entirely different approach is Garder *et al.*'s[34] method of moving points. This technique is based on the method of characteristics and introduces no numerical dispersion at the displacement fronts, but it is difficult to apply in complex flow geometries.

Actually, numerical dispersion may not be the insurmountable problem it was once thought to be. Laboratory displacements in homogeneous cores yield longitudinal dispersivities on the order of several millimeters. In the past, many workers assumed that these small values would apply in the field; hence, they assumed that little mixing would occur and that fronts would remain sharp. In the field, however, mixing is dominated by heterogeneities of a much larger scale than can be seen in the laboratory. As a result, field longitudinal dispersivities appear to be on the order of a meter or more. Lake and Hirasaki[35] discuss this in more detail. Accurate calculation of diffusion resulting from a longitudinal dispersivity of 1 meter would require use of block lengths of no more than several meters. These are too small to be used in fieldwide models, but they could be used in models of pattern elements.

11.3 Chemical and Polymer Flooding

In the chemical-flooding process, a bank of fluid containing a multicomponent, surface-active agent—or *surfactant slug*—is injected into the formation. The slug may contain surfactant, cosurfactant, oil, water, and other chemicals. The function of the surfactant is to reduce oil/water interfacial tension (IFT), but it may also cause interphase mass transfer of reservoir oil and water. Both the interphase mass transfer and reduction of IFT increase recovery of oil.

The chemical-flooding process uses a sequence of banks, possibly including a preflush, surfactant, viscous drive water, and finally, ordinary drive water. The purpose of a preflush, if it is used, is to precondition the formation. In some concepts, one function of the preflush is to provide sacrificial ions that adsorb on the reservoir rock, reducing later adsorption of surfactant. The preflush is followed by a surfactant bank that, in turn, is driven by a bank of water containing polymer. The viscosity of the drive bank is designed to prevent viscous fingering of drive water into the surfactant bank. The polymer-drive water bank is driven by brine.

The physics of chemical flooding is quite complicated. More than two liquid phases can form, chemical constituents can adsorb on reservoir rock, part of the rock PV is inaccessible to the polymer, relative permeability is no longer a function of saturation only, and mixing effects can be important.

Phase behavior of the oil/brine/surfactant system and of the polymer/oil/brine/surfactant system is particularly complex. At least three liquid phases can form in the oil/brine/surfactant system. A "lower" phase contains primarily water; a "middle" phase is a mixture of oil, water, and surfactant; and an "upper" phase contains primarily oil. Any of these phases may be missing; the phase state depends on the composition of the mixture present. All component concentrations are important, including those of dissolved salts and polymer.

Adsorption can be especially detrimental in surfactant floods because it contributes to loss of both surfactant and polymer. In addition, ion exchange between injectant and the rock can change the composition of the injectant enough to influence the phase behavior of the system. Adsorption is history dependent. The first species to arrive is adsorbed and tends to block later-arriving species from the adsorbing sites. Limited desorption occurs as the solution concentration declines.

The polymer molecules are quite large and cannot fit into some of the smaller pore channels. As a result, the effective porosity is smaller for the polymer than for the other species. As a consequence, the polymer may move through the porous medium faster than the other components. Polymer may also be mechanically trapped in the rock.

To complicate the fluid mechanics further, relative permeability is a function of saturation, IFT, and fluid velocity. The effects of IFT and fluid velocity can be combined through use of the capillary number. It appears that hysteresis effects are at times important and that oil flow can be in one of two regimes—in the form of an emulsion or as a coalesced phase.

The surfactant bank involved in the process may be relatively small, with the result that mixing is very important. By far the most important cause of mixing is dispersion, resulting from movement of the fluids through the porous medium. Molecular diffusion is probably relatively unimportant. Mixing is characterized by longitudinal and transverse mixing dispersivities, which are multiplied by fluid velocities to give local dispersion coefficients. Because fluid motion is normally not parallel to one of the coordinate directions, the dispersion terms actually form a tensor. This introduces cross derivatives into the differential equation, requiring the inclusion of points not in the normal five-point finite-difference representation. The importance of these cross-derivative terms is uncertain; Todd and Chase[36] chose not to include the cross derivatives to avoid the additional terms in their finite-difference equations.

The continuity equation for Component ν can be written

$$\nabla\cdot(\vec{\vec{K}}_\ell\cdot\nabla C_{\ell\nu}+\vec{\vec{K}}_m\cdot\nabla C_{m\nu}+\vec{\vec{K}}_u\cdot\nabla C_{u\nu})$$

$$-\nabla\cdot(u_\ell C_{\ell\nu}+u_m C_{m\nu}+u_u C_{u\nu})+q_\nu=\frac{\partial}{\partial t}(C_{t\nu}), \quad \text{(11.4)}$$

where

ℓ,m,u = lower, middle, and upper phases, respectively,
$\vec{\vec{K}}_p$ = dispersion tensor for Phase p,
$C_{p\nu}$ = concentration of Component ν in units of moles per unit volume of Phase p,
u_p = Darcy velocity of Phase p, and
$C_{t\nu}$ = total concentration of Component ν in units of moles per unit bulk reservoir volume.

$$C_{t\nu}=\phi_\nu(S_\ell C_{\ell\nu}+S_m C_{m\nu}+S_u C_{u\nu}+A_\nu), \quad \text{(11.5)}$$

where ϕ_ν is porosity accessible to Component ν and A_ν is adsorption of Component ν in units of moles per unit PV accessible to Component ν.

Let v_ν be the specific volume of Component ν and be assumed constant; i.e., a certain mass of Component ν will occupy the same volume, regardless of which phase it is in and what the pressure is. In other words, it is assumed that the fluids are incompressible and that no volume change accompanies mixing.

Then the volume fraction of Component ν in Phase p will be $v_\nu C_{p\nu}$, and

$$\sum_\nu v_\nu C_{p\nu}=1. \quad \text{(11.6)}$$

Similarly,

$$\sum_\nu v_\nu C_{t\nu}=\phi. \quad \text{(11.7)}$$

If formation compressibility is neglected, ϕ will be constant with time. Then, if Eq. 11.4 is multiplied by v_ν and the resultant equation is summed over all components, the following total continuity equation results.

$$-\nabla\cdot(u_\ell+u_m+u_u)+q_t=0, \quad \text{(11.8)}$$

where

$$q_t=\sum_\nu v_\nu q_\nu. \quad \text{(11.9)}$$

The Darcy velocity of Phase p is given by

$$u_p=-\lambda_p(\nabla p+\nabla P_{cp}-\rho_p g\nabla D), \quad \text{(11.10)}$$

where

$$\rho_p=\sum_\nu C_{p\nu}. \quad \text{(11.11)}$$

When Eq. 11.10 is substituted into Eq. 11.8 for the phase velocities, the pressure equation results:

$$\nabla\cdot[(\lambda_\ell+\lambda_m+\lambda_u)\nabla p]=\nabla\cdot[(\lambda_\ell\rho_\ell+\lambda_m\rho_m+\lambda_u\rho_u)g\nabla D]$$

$$-\nabla\cdot(\lambda_\ell\nabla P_{c\ell}+\lambda_m\nabla P_{cm}+\lambda_u\nabla P_{cu})-q_t. \qquad (11.12)$$

Here, p is the pressure in an arbitrary phase. Actually, p does not have to correspond to the pressure in a phase, but if it does, capillary pressures involving that phase will be identically zero.

Combining Eqs. 11.5 and 11.7 yields

$$\sum_\nu \phi_\nu v_\nu(S_\ell C_{\ell\nu}+S_m C_{m\nu}+S_u C_{u\nu}+A_\nu)=\phi. \qquad (11.13)$$

As mentioned previously, ϕ_ν is the porosity accessible to Component ν. It is smaller than ϕ for components exhibiting an inaccessible PV effect. Usually, the only such component is polymer. As a result, it is convenient to ensure that Eq. 11.13 is satisfied by assuming that the specific volume, v_ν, for polymer is zero. This is equivalent to assuming that the polymer occupies no volume; while this is not precisely true, it is a good approximation. By using this assumption in combination with Eq. 11.6, remembering that the three saturations plus the volume fraction occupied by adsorbed components must sum to one, one can show that Eq. 11.13 is inherently satisfied. If the assumption of zero polymer volume were not made, satisfying the equation would require a nonlinear iteration of some kind.

These equations can be solved with an implicit pressure, explicit saturation (IMPES) procedure, as follows.

1. Discretize Eq. 11.12 and use the resultant equation to solve for pressures at the new time level.
2. Discretize Eq. 11.4 and use the resultant equations to solve for total concentrations at the new time level.
3. Use these concentrations as input to a phase-behavior package to get new time-level values for the concentrations in each phase, the saturations, and the adsorption levels.

Herein lies the importance of the assumption of no volume change during a phase change. Had the assumption not been made, the volume that a given component would occupy at the end of a timestep would not be known until the phase calculation had been made. As a result, this IMPES procedure could not have been used without introducing material-balance error.

This computational procedure should be fairly stable because it does not contain the stability difficulties inherent in simulating high-velocity processes like coning. Rather abrupt changes in properties can occur, however, causing timestep-size difficulties. In modeling laboratory corefloods, capillary-pressure effects can also be important and may limit the timestep sizes.

Chemical-flood simulators are used to model performance both in the field and in the laboratory. Corefloods are simulated primarily to verify a model and to calibrate it for use in predicting field performance.

Todd *et al.*[37] used simulation to perform an interesting study whose objective was to decide between two chemical-flood processes—a soluble oil process and a high-water-content process. They first modeled the performances of both processes in a suite of laboratory corefloods. They divided their data into two categories—common data that applied to both processes and process-dependent data unique to one process or the other. Common data included basic rock relative permeability and capillary pressure, the correlation of relative permeability with capillary number, the polymer inaccessible volume, the adsorption behavior of the polymer, and the mixing lengths to use in dispersion calculations. The process-dependent data included IFT's, phase behavior, aqueous viscosity, and surfactant adsorption data. By varying certain of the input data, they were able to match the laboratory corefloods as shown in Fig. 11.3. All things considered, the match was good enough to encourage them to attempt to predict field performance with the model.

Because their simulator was limited to two dimensions, they used a combination of a two-dimensional (2D) areal model and a 2D cross-sectional model to evaluate areal and vertical sweep efficiencies. The cross-sectional model included gravity segregation but, unfortunately, did not model the effects of stratification, which are potentially more serious than the effects of gravity segregation. They multiplied laboratory coreflood recovery by areal sweep and by vertical sweep to obtain a composite 3D tertiary recovery efficiency of 54% for one process and 36% for the other.

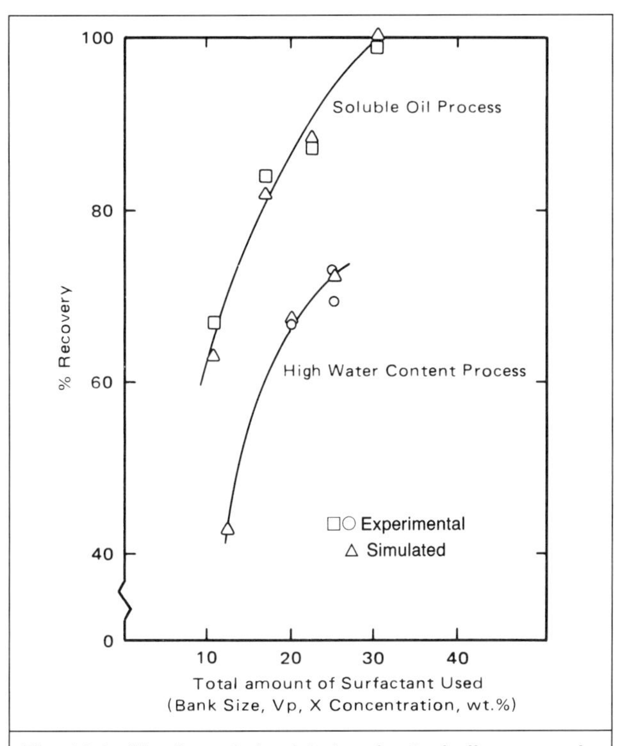

Fig. 11.3—Matches of simulated and actual oil recovery in corefloods of two surfactant-flooding processes.[37]

Van Quy and Labrid[38] used a simulator to analyze the behavior of laboratory chemical floods. They validated their model by comparing the computed and observed oil recoveries as functions of time. All input data used to describe the chemical system's behavior were determined independently—i.e., the model was not calibrated in any way. The comparison was quite good. Unfortunately, the only comparisons reported were of oil recoveries. Camilleri *et al.*[39] conducted similar, but more complete, work. In addition to oil recoveries, they compared simulated and experimentally produced concentrations of surfactant, alcohol, sodium, and calcium. They presented these comparisons for two laboratory systems. The reported agreement was generally good, and essentially all the experimentally observed phenomena were at least qualitatively present in the computed results. It is not completely clear from the paper how much parameter adjustment was required to get this agreement.

Up to this point, no mention has been made of polymer flooding. Polymer flooding is a part of any chemical-flooding process, and as a result, any simulator capable of modeling chemical flooding will be able to model polymer flooding as well. Even so, several simulators have been developed specifically for modeling polymer flooding.

Bondor *et al.*'s[40] work is interesting because it describes simulation of polymer flooding with a straightforward modification of a black-oil simulator. Polymer is represented as a fourth "phase" that is always miscible with water; resistance-factor effects are characterized by varying the aqueous-phase viscosity. Adsorption and the effect of adsorbed polymer on water mobility are included. The authors use Todd and Longstaff's[21] empirical mixing parameters to describe the mixing caused by viscous fingering at the back of the polymer bank, and they approximate non-Newtonian flow effects around injection wells with an apparent skin factor.

Vela *et al.*[41] use an entirely different approach. They use a simulator in which regions of the reservoir can be assigned individual fluid properties. The boundaries between these regions are defined by chains of moving points that have velocities proportional to but not necessarily equal to the local aqueous-phase velocity.

One chain of points represents the front of the polymer bank, another the rear. To represent the effect of adsorption, points denoting the front of the bank move more slowly relative to the aqueous velocity than do those at the rear. This method avoids the accuracy problems caused by numerical dispersion.

Alkaline flooding is another recovery process that involves the injection of chemicals. Alkaline oil recovery is believed to result primarily from emulsification induced by surfactants created by reaction of the injected alkaline solution with organic acids in the crude. Alteration of the wettability of the reservoir rock and precipitation caused by mixing of the injected chemicals with ions in the formation water may also be involved. Mayer *et al.*[42] describe the process in more detail.

Alkaline flooding is a very complex process and many of the considerations involved in simulating it resemble those associated with surfactant flooding. There is not much interest in alkaline flooding, however, and little work has been done on simulation of the process. One simulator that takes a macroscopic approach has been described by Breit *et al.*[43,44] and by Mayer and Breit.[45]

11.4 Steam Stimulation and Steamdrive

Steam stimulation and steam flooding (or steamdrive) are the most successful EOR processes. Both depend primarily on transfer of thermal energy to the oil to reduce its viscosity and thereby increase recovery. These processes are briefly described in this section. More detail is given in the review by Matthews[46] and in Prats' monograph.[47]

In its simplest concept, *steam stimulation* is a process whereby steam is used to heat the section of a reservoir adjacent to the wellbore, securing increased production rates through reduced oil viscosities and the corresponding reduced resistance to flow in this critical area. Other factors, such as thermal expansion and wettability changes, may play roles in providing increased oil recovery. As might be inferred from the name, however, increased production rates and the associated generation or maintenance of economic producing conditions have been the chief incentives for this process.

The process usually consists of a steam-injection phase, a brief shut-in or "soak" phase, and a production phase. The primary objective is to get thermal energy into the formation and to allow the heated rock to act as a heat exchanger to heat the flowing oil and to reduce its viscosity.

Condensed steam causes the water/oil ratio to be high when the well is returned to production, but the ratio declines rapidly. The oil-production rate passes through a maximum and then declines as the reservoir cools. After the reservoir temperature approaches its original value, the production rate will fall to a value suggested by the original decline curve unless wellbore cleanup has occurred or the heating has resulted in alteration of relative permeabilities. In practice, a subsequent steam-injection cycle is usually begun at some point before the reservoir returns to its original temperature. The response from the first or second cycle is usually best, with a declining oil/steam ratio on succeeding cycles.

The usual mechanism for increased oil-production rates during steam stimulation is viscosity reduction. Additional stimulation is often achieved, however, because of removal of certain types of near-wellbore damage, such as fine solids and asphaltic and paraffinic deposits. If viscosity reduction is the dominant mechanism, optimum steam treatments are moderately large. Small steam treatments can be quite effective for damage removal. Other mechanisms affecting steam-stimulation recovery include thermal expansion and wettability changes.

The usual procedure for applying steam-injection processes to a reservoir is first to steam-stimulate and then to begin flooding after stimulation response has declined to the point that flooding is commercially more attractive than stimulation. In some reservoirs containing extremely viscous oils, an extended sequence of stimulation cycles is necessary before sufficient viscosity reduction is achieved to make flooding possible.

The economic success of a steamflood operation depends on both the efficiency with which oil is recovered and the efficiency with which steam is used. Oil recovery depends on displacement efficiency (the degree to which oil is displaced from the contacted rock pores) and volumetric sweep efficiency (the fraction of the total reservoir volume actually contacted).

11.4.1 Displacement Efficiency. Oil displacement during steamflooding is achieved through a number of different mechanisms. Oil is contacted in sequence by cold water, hot water, and steam. Steam distillation of the oil and the solvent drive provided by the distilled light ends as they condense ahead of the steam front contribute to oil recovery. To these mechanisms must be added the effects of thermal expansion and changes in the relative-permeability characteristics of the rock with temperature.

Energy is transported in the reservoir by convection and conduction. Convection is strongest in the directions parallel to the bedding plane. Frequently, most of the convection energy is the latent heat of the steam and is yielded to the reservoir as the steam condenses. Conduction is important in the direction perpendicular to the bedding plane, because it is the mechanism by which energy is lost to the overburden and underburden. To account for these energy losses, it is necessary to include the overburden and underburden in the model in some form.

The primary effects that must be modeled in a simulator are the temperature increase and the resultant reduction in the oil viscosity. If distillation of lighter components is thought to be important, multicomponent representation of the reservoir oil will be needed, in effect making the steam process simulator a nonisothermal compositional model. A simplified treatment usually can be used because of the relatively low pressures at which steamflooding normally takes place.

Three-phase relative-permeability effects are important in steam displacements, as are the effects of hysteresis. As previously implied, there is evidence that relative permeability and capillary pressure vary with temperature, but the importance of these effects is in dispute and they are not usually modeled.

From the modeling standpoint, the chief difficulty with steam processes is computational stability. The mass- and energy-balance equations are strongly nonlinear and closely coupled. This causes severe stability problems, particularly for IMPES-type methods. The physical process leading to these computing problems is as follows. As steam moves through the reservoir, it condenses, greatly changing in volume. This volume change affects the mass balance, which in turn determines how fluids, including steam, move through the reservoir. Hence, the volume change also affects the energy balance, which determines how much steam condenses. In other words, movement of fluids strongly affects the movement of energy and vice versa. This close coupling of energy and fluid movement means that the equations that represent them must be solved simultaneously.

Nonlinearity is generally handled by iterating over each timestep. The nonlinear terms are approximated by first-order Taylor-series expansions, permitting pressures and temperatures at the end of the timestep to be estimated. These values are then used to reapproximate the nonlinear functions in terms of new Taylor-series expansions, and the process is repeated until it converges.

In addition to the numerical difficulties just described, it is difficult to model steam processes because they are so complex. Fluid properties depend on composition, pressure, and temperature. Phase behavior at various temperatures must be computed, and the heat loss to the underburden and overburden must be accounted for in some way.

If multicomponent representation of the reservoir oil is required, the appropriate hydrocarbon material-balance equation is the same as that used in compositional simulation (Eq. 11.2).

The water material-balance equation must reflect the fact that water can be in either the aqueous or the vapor phase:

$$\nabla\cdot(\xi_w\lambda_w\nabla\Phi_w+y_w\xi_g\lambda_g\nabla\Phi_g)+q_w$$

$$=\frac{\partial}{\partial t}[\phi(\xi_wS_w+y_w\xi_gS_g)]. \qquad (11.14)$$

The energy equation is

$$\nabla\cdot(k_h\nabla T+H_o\xi_o\lambda_o\nabla\Phi_o+H_w\xi_w\lambda_w\nabla\Phi_w+H_g\xi_g\lambda_g\nabla\Phi g)+q_H$$

$$=\frac{\partial}{\partial t}[(1-\phi)\rho_fC_fT+\phi(U_o\xi_oS_o+U_w\xi_wS_w+U_g\xi_gS_g)], \qquad (11.15)$$

where

k_h = thermal conductivity of rock and contained fluids,
T = temperature,
H = specific enthalpy,
U = specific internal energy,
ρ_f = rock density corresponding to zero porosity,
C_f = heat capacity of rock, and
q_H = rate of injection or production of enthalpy.

By definition,

$$H=U+pv. \quad (11.16)$$

The saturations and mass fractions must add up to one, providing three more equations:

$$S_o+S_g+S_w=1, \quad (11.17)$$

$$\sum_{\nu=1}^{N_c} x_\nu=1, \quad (11.18)$$

and

$$\sum_{\nu=1}^{N_c} y_\nu+y_w=1. \quad (11.19)$$

If the oil can be treated as nonvolatile, it can be represented as a single component, and the hydrocarbon material-balance equation (Eq. 11.2) reduces to

$$\nabla\cdot(\xi_o\lambda_o\nabla\Phi_o)+q_o=\frac{\partial}{\partial t}(\phi\xi_oS_o). \quad (11.20)$$

The assumption does not affect the water material-balance equation, except that the mass fraction of water in the vapor phase becomes unity. The energy-balance equation is unaffected.

Coats[48] discusses the solution of the equations resulting from a three-hydrocarbon-component steamflood model. The simulator must solve seven simultaneous equations, the unknowns being three mass fractions, two saturations, temperature, and pressure. Solving this many equations at each gridpoint would make modeling quite expensive, and Coats describes a sequential solution procedure that greatly reduces the per-timestep computing cost. In later work, Coats[49] describes a simultaneous solution procedure that is more stable than the sequential procedure but requires more computing time per timestep.

As mentioned previously, energy is lost to the overburden and underburden by conduction. Conductive transport is predominantly perpendicular to the bedding plane; conduction in the overburden and underburden parallel to the bedding plane can almost always be ignored. As a result, heat-loss overburden calculations can be made as a number of individual 1D calculations, one for each column of gridblocks. When making this calculation within a finite-difference model—e.g., a steamflood simulator—the most obvious approach is to solve the 1D conduction equation with finite differences. Coats *et al.*[50] did so, using six points to represent the conduction occurring away from each column of cells. They found that the accuracy obtained was quite acceptable and that the computing cost was almost negligible.

Chase and O'Dell[51] and Weinstein[52,53] use a different approach. They approximate the temperature distribution in the overburden, obtaining the coefficients required by their approximations using a variational principle. Weinstein's approximation is more elaborate than that of Chase and O'Dell and also includes the effect of heat conduction parallel to the bedding plane. As a result, this approach is the more accurate of the two. Because Weinstein's approach requires very little computer time, it seems to be the best technique available for representing the overburden.

Steam stimulation is normally simulated with radial single-well models. Successive cycles of injection, soak, and production are modeled to optimize treatment sizes, soak times, and production periods. The model used is geometrically similar to that used in coning calculations and has all the problems normally associated with small gridblocks around the wellbore. As a result, the timestep sizes are sometimes quite small during the injection and production periods. During the soak periods, not much fluid movement or energy transfer takes place and the timestep sizes can be larger.

When steamfloods are simulated, adequate representation of steam overrunning is essential. The density difference between steam and oil is the primary cause of overrunning; a secondary cause is unfavorable mobility ratio. To model overrunning, the top row or rows of gridblocks must be thin enough to permit the steam to move across the top of the reservoir. Similarly, thin, high-permeability strata should be represented accurately because heat conduction from these strata to the surrounding formation is important.

As Coats *et al.*[50] point out, orientation of the model grid can markedly affect the results of a simulation of an unfavorable mobility ratio displacement such as a steamflood. They modeled one element of a repeated five-spot pattern using diagonal and parallel grids and found that, as they refined the grids, the simulations converged to two different solutions. The difference was quite significant, with breakthrough times differing by a factor of three. Chu[54] found that this effect could be alleviated by using the nine-point difference method proposed by Yanosik and McCracken.[55] Grid-orientation effects are discussed in more detail in Chap. 5.

Steamflood simulation is currently expensive. Consequently, most models are quite small, seldom exceeding several hundred gridblocks. The computing requirements result partly from the complexity of the problems being solved and partly from stability difficulties that limit timestep size. In addition, the matrix equations can be difficult to solve with iterative methods. Direct solution can become impractical with large models, however, because these formulations must solve several simultaneous equations per gridpoint. In consequence, steamflood models usually simulate performance of only a single pattern. Although this is primarily because of the computing expense, it is also justified by the nature of the process. Because of poor fluid mobility, the effects of steam injection tend to be localized. There is no large-scale fluid migration as would be associated with, for example, a flank water-injection process.

In modeling single patterns, excessive pressure buildup sometimes occurs upon steam injection. Chu and Trimble[56] introduced the concept of "spongy" rock to overcome this problem. They assumed that there was a small, noncondensable gas saturation in the reservoir before the start of steam injection, and they modified the rock compressibility to include the effects of the compressibilities of both rock and gas. They then varied the assumed gas saturation as a history-matching parameter. The final spongy-rock compressibility that they obtained was within the reasonable range for rock compressibilities of unconsolidated sands.

11.5 In-Situ Combustion

In-situ combustion involves the injection of air (or oxygen) into the reservoir, usually in combination with water. A combustion front is formed at which the injected air burns a small portion of the reservoir oil. Hot flue gas and steam resulting from combustion and water vaporization displace the oil ahead of the combustion front. Vaporization of the light ends and thermal cracking also occur. Ahead of the combustion front, the vaporized light ends condense, providing some assistance to displacement by solvent dilution of the virgin crude.

An adequate combustion simulator must describe reactions that occur. Crookston *et al.*[57] include four reactions in their model: (1) oxidation of a light-hydrocarbon component; (2) oxidation of a heavy-hydrocarbon component; (3) cracking of the heavy-hydrocarbon component to form the light-hydrocarbon component, coke, and inert gas; and (4) oxidation of the coke formed by cracking.

The rates of these reactions are described by Arrhenius-type rate expressions, which are very strongly temperature-dependent. This introduces the possibility of severe stability problems in simulations of the reactions. To illustrate the oxidation reaction for a light hydrocarbon, consider the oxidation of methane,* which is expressed as

$$2O_2+CH_4 \rightarrow CO_2+2H_2O.$$

This can be rewritten in terms of stoichiometric coefficients:

$$-(s_{O_2}O_2+s_{CH_4}CH_4) \rightarrow (s_{CO_2}CO_2+s_{H_2O}H_2O).$$

The compounds on the right side of the equation are being created by the reaction and have positive stoichiometric coefficients; those on the left side are being consumed by the reaction and have negative coefficients. For instance, the stoichiometric coefficient for oxygen in this reaction is -2.

Many different reactions take place during in-situ combustion, but only a few need to be considered. The rate of creation of Component ν in the most significant reactions is

$$\sum_{\ell} s_{\ell\nu} r_{\ell}.$$

Here, $s_{\ell\nu}r_{\ell}$ is the rate of creation of Component ν in Reaction ℓ.

The mass-conservation equation for all components that can be present in the oil phase is given by

$$\nabla \cdot (x_\nu \xi_o \lambda_o \nabla \Phi_o + y_\nu \xi_g \lambda_g \nabla \Phi_g) + q_\nu + \sum_{\ell} s_{\ell\nu} r_{\ell}$$

$$= \frac{\partial}{\partial t}[\phi(x_\nu \xi_o S_o + y_\nu \xi_g S_g)]. \quad \text{(11.21)}$$

Note that a term accounting for the creation of Component ν is included. Otherwise, this equation is similar to the hydrocarbon-continuity equation used in steamflooding (Eq. 11.2).

The water-continuity equation is written as

$$\nabla \cdot (\xi_w \lambda_w \nabla \Phi_w + y_w \xi_g \lambda_g \nabla \Phi_g) + q_w + \sum_{\ell} s_{\ell w} r_{\ell}$$

$$= \frac{\partial}{\partial t}[\phi(\xi_w S_w + y_w \xi_g S_g)]. \quad \text{(11.22)}$$

The constraint equations are

$$S_o+S_g+S_w=1, \quad \text{(11.23)}$$

$$\sum_{\nu=1}^{N_c} x_\nu = 1, \quad \text{(11.24)}$$

and

$$\sum_{\nu=1}^{N_c} y_\nu + y_w = 1. \quad \text{(11.25)}$$

When this process is modeled, the solid phase must be included because of the creation and disappearance of coke. The mass-conservation equation for coke is

$$\sum_{\ell} s_{\ell c} r_{\ell} = \frac{\partial n_c}{\partial t}, \quad \text{(11.26)}$$

where n_c=coke concentration.

The energy-balance equation is similar to that for steamflooding, with the addition of terms corresponding to heats of reaction.

*There is seldom much methane present in a reservoir being fireflooded, but the oxidation reaction for methane is typical of those for light hydrocarbons.

There are two types of *in-situ* combustion models. Using the terminology of Coats,[58] in a *reactant-controlled* model, oxygen is assumed to react instantaneously with oil on contact; in a *kinetic-controlled* model, rates of oil oxidation and all other reactions that may be considered can be defined by Arrhenius rate expressions. The model of Crookston *et al.*[57] is kinetic controlled. Youngren[59] describes a reactant-controlled model that is somewhat simpler than the Crookston model. Coats[60] describes a kinetic-controlled model that is more general than Crookston's. In the same paper, Coats gives a detailed discussion comparing his model with those of Crookston and of Youngren. In later work, Coats[58] describes a model that treats oil oxidation as being reactant-controlled but retains kinetic-controlled coke oxidation and thermal cracking. Another approach is that of Hwang *et al.*,[61] who represent the combustion zone as a moving front.

The kinetic-controlled model is adequate for simulation of laboratory-scale experiments, but it is less satisfactory for solving field-scale problems. The energy released by oxidation is spread over the relatively large gridblocks used in a field-scale model, and an unrealistically small rise in temperature results. Depending on the activation energies used in the Arrhenius rate expressions, the computed temperatures may not be high enough to sustain reaction at a reasonable rate. The apparent remedy is to decrease the block sizes, but this normally leads to unacceptable computing costs. Another possibility is to use arbitrarily low activation energies but, of course, in the extreme, the reactions then are no longer kinetic controlled. As a consequence, the reactant-controlled model is generally used for simulating field-scale forward combustion. This model is satisfactory for some purposes but it is unable to predict spontaneous ignition. Furthermore, because it assumes that oxygen reacts with the first oil contacted, it cannot simulate reverse combustion.

The computing cost associated with modeling combustion is high. On the basis of computing times provided by Crookston *et al.*[57] and Coats,[60] it seems that kinetic-controlled combustion simulations take roughly 20 to 40 times as much time per gridblock per timestep as "equivalent" black-oil simulations. In addition, several times as many timesteps are required. Thus, in very round numbers, combustion models consume about 100 times as much computing time as equivalent black-oil models. Youngren's reactant-controlled model[59] is faster on a per-gridblock-per-timestep basis; however, it needs more timesteps, and the overall cost seems to be somewhat higher.

11.6 Special Data Requirements

Simulation of the processes described in this chapter demands that the user specify more data than are normally required for simulation of conventional depletion processes. This section summarizes these additional data requirements. For the most part, they can be discussed only in a general way because of the variability in modeling approaches and, in some cases, in the processes themselves.

11.6.1 Compositional Simulation. The additional data required are phase-equilibrium information, phase densities, and phase viscosities. Also needed are the compositions of the reservoir hydrocarbons and of any injected hydrocarbons. Finally, separator conditions through which hydrocarbons are produced are needed.

The first practical compositional simulators used equilibrium K values to determine phase equilibrium. Generally, the K values were obtained by correlations of the Natural Gas Producers Society of America (NGPSA) type, and using them required the computation of convergence pressures. A procedure is discussed by Nolen.[6]

More recently, the trend has been toward using EOS's, with the Peng-Robinson[12] and Redlich-Kwong[13] equations being the most popular. The data requirements for use of the two equations differ slightly. Specific data requirements depend to some extent on how the EOS is used.[5] Typical data for each component include (1) critical pressure, temperature, and specific volume, (2) molecular weight, and (3) acentric factor. In addition, binary interaction coefficients for all combinations of pairs of components must be specified, although most of the coefficients are zero. Phase densities are computed using the EOS, so no additional density data are needed.

It is not possible to represent every hydrocarbon component individually, so some component lumping is necessary. Some of the considerations in doing this are mentioned in Sec. 11.1. For each lumped pseudocomponent, the data described in the preceding paragraph are needed. Generally, pseudocomponent data are derived by matching laboratory data, as discussed later.

In general, EOS's are not accurate enough to use without some fine-tuning of parameters by matching laboratory data. The particular laboratory data to be matched must be appropriate to the reservoir process being modeled. Matching constant-composition expansion, constant-volume depletion, and differential liberation is usually adequate if the reservoir is to be produced by a pressure-depletion process. Additional laboratory data may be needed for comparison if other processes are to be modeled. For example, if gas cycling below the dewpoint is to be simulated, the laboratory data must in some way involve the mixing of liquid hydrocarbon with dry gas. One example of such a procedure is described by Cook *et al.*[14] Nolen[6] briefly discusses the quantities that should be matched and the parameters that should be varied during the matching process.

Viscosities are normally determined with one of several correlations. Generally, viscosities do not need to be as accurate as pressure/volume data, so coefficients used in these correlations often need little or no adjustment.

The composition of the reservoir fluid needs to be known to set the simulator's initial conditions. Also, the reservoir temperature is needed, perhaps as a function of location. The information required and the procedure used are discussed by Kazemi *et al.*[3]

Separator conditions must be specified to permit computation of surface volumes and compositions of produced streams. Generally, the EOS used in the reservoir simulation can also be used to simulate surface separations. Whatever method is used must be calibrated by matching data from laboratory tests in which the reservoir hydrocarbons are flashed through the specified separation conditions.

11.6.2 Miscible Displacement. As discussed in Sec. 11.2, there are several ways to model miscible displacement, and the data requirements depend on the approach taken. If the simulation is fully compositional, the data needed are essentially those described in the preceding section. If the modified black-oil approach is used, data needs are entirely different. If CO_2 is to be injected, some additional data may be needed.

If the modified black-oil approach of Lantz[20] is used, special relative-permeability curves need to be constructed with the procedure described by Lantz. Stalkup[19] also discusses the construction of these curves. The fluid-property data needed are FVF's and viscosities. In general, the reservoir pressure is kept within a fairly narrow range during conduct of a miscible-displacement project, simplifying the specification of the fluid-property data.

If the Todd-Longstaff[21] mixing model is used, the mixing parameter must be specified. There is no firm theoretical basis and little published material to use in determining an appropriate value. Values of 0.6 and 0.625 have been used in modeling field performance.[22] Stalkup[19] states that, lacking any other information, the value should range from 0.5 to 0.7.

As mentioned in Sec. 11.2, the transition from miscible to immiscible displacement as pressure falls must sometimes be considered. In this case, a set of immiscible-displacement relative-permeability curves must be provided and the pressures at which the displacement is fully miscible and fully immiscible must be specified. The transition calculation is discussed by Chase and Todd.[22]

For any of several reasons, some of the oil may not be displaced even by a fully miscible displacement. If this effect is to be included, the residual saturation in the miscibly swept region must be specified. If oil is left behind by waterblocking, the residual is a function of water saturation, and this functionality must be specified. Chase and Todd[22] present a way of computing this.

If breakdown of the miscible bank as a result of mixing in the reservoir is to be modeled, dispersive mixing lengths must be specified. There is no accepted, standard way of measuring mixing lengths in the field. All that seems to be known with certainty is that, because of macroscopic heterogeneities, field mixing lengths are much larger than laboratory mixing lengths. Lake and Hirasaki[35] present an approach for estimating the mixing length.

As mentioned previously, additional data are required if a CO_2 miscible process is being modeled. Obviously, loss of CO_2 to brine must be considered, so data on CO_2 solubility in the brine must be provided, normally as a function of pressure.

Another phenomenon that is at times thought to be important is precipitation of heavy ends, possibly resulting in reduction of the mobility of the hydrocarbon phase or phases. If this phenomenon is to be modeled, the conditions under which these heavy ends precipitate, the amount of precipitation, and the reduction in phase mobilities as a function of the amount precipitated must be provided. Chase and Todd[22] discuss this effect.

11.6.3 Chemical and Polymer Flooding. Chemical flooding is extremely complex. It involves many processes, most of which must be described in some detail if the overall process is to be modeled accurately. The data required are extensive and many of the parameters that should be specified are difficult to measure. For a detailed discussion of data requirements, see Dogru *et al.*[62]

The most complex property to describe quantitatively probably is phase behavior, because it is influenced by temperature and the concentration of each component in the system. IFT's are also complex functions of the composition and conditions of the system; indeed, they are functions of "just about everything." Although some simplification of the descriptions of both phase behavior and IFT is possible, each must be described with a number of parameters that must be determined from extensive laboratory experiments.

The viscosity of a given phase is a function of the composition of that phase. The functionality can be represented by a multidimensional table. Viscosity may also be a function of shear rate. Viscosity must be evaluated in the laboratory under appropriate conditions.

The capillary number, which is in turn used in computing relative permeabilities and residual oil saturations, is computed from IFT and viscosity data. The "shift" in relative permeability that occurs as capillary number increases must be described with data from corefloods. Functional forms to describe this performance are given by Hirasaki *et al.*[63]

The influence of polymer on performance of the system must be determined in laboratory experiments. The polymer-related effects that are important in chemical flooding include adsorption of polymer and the effect of adsorbed polymer on the resistance factor, the inaccessible-PV effect, and the effect of polymer concentration, salinity, shear rate, and temperature degradation on the aqueous-phase viscosity. Data describing these phenomena must be entered into the simulator.

Note that much of the "polymer adsorption" included in simulators is actually physical entrapment. Under most conditions, trapped polymer will remain trapped and, as a consequence, adsorption and desorption must be treated separately. Once again, the data required must be measured in the laboratory.

11.6.4 Steamdrive and Steam Stimulation. By comparison with the data needed to describe the processes just discussed, the data requirements for steamflooding are straightforward. The thermal properties of the productive formation and of the overlying and underlying rocks must be described. Thermal properties include the initial temperature, vertical and horizontal thermal conductivities, and heat capacities of rock and fluids. Generally, the heat capacities of the under- and overlying rocks include the contribution of any fluids they contain. Thermal conductivities in all cases include conduction through any fluids present.

The energy content of injected steam must be specified. Injection temperature and pressure must be specified, or steam quality and either temperature or pressure must be specified. These must be specified for downhole conditions, so surface values must be corrected for energy losses in the injection lines and tubing.

Thermodynamic properties of steam and water are usually taken from steam tables built into the simulator. Water and steam FVF's (or densities, depending on the simulator being used), heat capacities, and the latent heat of vaporization must be provided as functions of pressure and temperature. Water and steam viscosities are also needed; these are functions of both temperature and pressure, but the pressure dependency can usually be ignored.

If the hydrocarbon is treated as a single nonvolatile oil component, its FVF (or density), viscosity, and heat capacity are needed. In the most general case, these are functions of temperature and pressure. It is commonly assumed that the FVF can be expressed as a linear function of temperature and pressure. Viscosity is generally treated as the product of a temperature-dependent viscosity and a pressure-dependent correction factor. Heat capacity is usually treated as being constant.

If distillation effects are being considered, the simulator must treat one or more volatilizable hydrocarbon components in addition to the nonvolatile oil. In general, the internal energy of a mixture of components is assumed to be equal to the sum of the internal energies multiplied by the amounts of the components present. This, in effect, means that the only data required are the heat capacities of individual components, which are treated as being constant. For components that can volatilize, heat capacities must be provided for both liquid and vapor phases. Equilibrium K values must also be provided. Effects of composition are customarily neglected, so K values are treated as functions of temperature and pressure only.

Viscosity of the liquid hydrocarbon phase is frequently assumed to be a function only of viscosity and concentration of the nonvolatile oil component.[48] Vapor-phase viscosity can be treated as a function of the steam and hydrocarbon gas viscosities.[48] As a result, the only viscosity data that need to be supplied are the hydrocarbon gas viscosity as a function of temperature and pressure, the liquid viscosity as a function of temperature, and a liquid-viscosity correction as a function of the concentration of the nonvolatile component.

All data required for simulation of conventional water/oil and gas/oil displacement must be supplied. The conventional data frequently are used without modification. Relative permeability and capillary pressure are sometimes considered to be functions of temperature. If so, the curves usually are normalized on the basis of residual saturations at the initial temperature. Then residual saturation is computed as a function of temperature with a table or simple functional form. Once residual saturations at the new temperature are known, the corresponding relative permeabilities and capillary pressures are computed with the normalizing equations. The only additional data required are those specifying the variation of the residual saturations with temperature.

11.6.5 In-Situ Combustion. All thermal properties specified for steamflooding must also be specified for in-situ combustion. In addition, data are required to describe the combustion reactions and to specify the properties of reactants and products. If a reactant-controlled model is being used, nothing more than heats of reaction are needed to describe the reactions. If a kinetic-controlled model is being used, rate constants and activation energies are needed. If an activation temperature[58] is being used, it must be specified. The same types of data must be provided for oxygen, coke, and such inert gases as nitrogen and gaseous reaction products as for the components of a steamflood.

Nomenclature

A = adsorption, moles per unit of accessible PV, kmol/m^3
B = FVF, res m^3/kmol
C = concentration, moles per unit volume, kmol/m^3
C_f = heat capacity of rock, J/kg·K
C_t = total concentration, moles per unit bulk reservoir volume, kmol/m^3
D = depth, m
g = gravitational constant, m/s^2
H = specific enthalpy, J/kmol
k = permeability, m^2
k_h = thermal conductivity of rock and contained fluids, J/m·s·K
k_r = relative permeability, dimensionless
$\vec{\vec{K}}$ = dispersion tensor, m^2/s
n_c = coke concentration, kmol/m^3
N_c = number of components excluding water
p = pressure, Pa
P_c = capillary pressure, Pa
q_H = rate of injection or production of enthalpy, J/s·m^3
q_w = injection or production rate of water, kmol/s·m^3
q_ν = injection or production rate of Component ν, kmol/s·m^3
r = reaction rate, kmol/s·m^3
s = stoichiometric coefficients, dimensionless
S = saturation, fraction
t = time, seconds
T = temperature, K
u = Darcy velocity, m/s
U = specific internal energy, J/kmol
v = specific volume, m^3/kmol
V_p = PV, fraction
x_ν = mole fraction of Component ν in liquid phase, dimensionless
y_ν = mole fraction of Component ν in vapor phase, dimensionless
λ = phase mobility, m^2/Pa·s
ξ = molar density, kmol/m^3
ρ = density, kg/m^3
ρ_f = rock density, kg/m^3
ϕ = porosity, fraction
Φ = phase potential, Pa
μ = viscosity, Pa·s

Subscripts

g = gas
ℓ = lower phase
m = middle phase
o = oil
p = phase
u = upper phase
w = water
ν = component

Superscript

$\hat{}$ = well stream

References

1. Coats, K.H.: "Reservoir Simulation: State of the Art," *JPT* (Aug. 1982) 1633–42; *Trans.*, AIME, **273.**
2. Collins, R.E.: *Flow of Fluids Through Porous Materials,* Petroleum Publishing Co., Tulsa (1976) 254.
3. Kazemi, H., Vestal, C.R., and Shank, G.D.: "An Efficient Multicomponent Numerical Simulator," *SPEJ* (Oct. 1978) 355–68.
4. Ács, G., Doleschall, S., and Farkas, E.: "General Purpose Compositional Model," *SPEJ* (Aug. 1985) 543–53.
5. Coats, K.H.: "An Equation of State Compositional Model," *SPEJ* (Oct. 1980) 363–76; *Trans.*, AIME, **269.**
6. Nolen, J.S.: "Numerical Simulation of Compositional Phenomena in Petroleum Reservoirs," paper SPE 4274 presented at the 1973 SPE Symposium on Numerical Simulation of Reservoir Performance, Houston, Jan. 11–12.
7. Wattenbarger, R.A.: "Practical Aspects of Compositional Simulation," paper SPE 2800 presented at the 1970 SPE Symposium on Numerical Simulation of Reservoir Performance, Dallas, Feb. 5–6.
8. Watts, J.W.: "A Compositional Formulation of the Pressure and Saturation Equations," *SPERE* (March 1986) 243–52.
9. Young, L.C. and Stephenson, R.E.: "A Generalized Compositional Approach for Reservoir Simulation," *SPEJ* (Oct. 1983) 727–42; *Trans.*, AIME, **275.**
10. Nghiem, L.X., Fong, D.K., and Aziz, K.: "Compositional Modeling with an Equation of State," *SPEJ* (Dec. 1981) 688–98; *Trans.*, AIME, **271.**
11. Thele, K.J., Lake, J.W., and Sepehrnoori, K.: "A Comparison of Three Equation-of-State Compositional Simulators," paper SPE 12245 presented at the 1983 SPE Symposium on Reservoir Simulation, San Francisco, Nov. 16–18.

12. Peng, D.Y. and Robinson, D.B.: "A New Two-Constant Equation of State," *Ind. Eng. Chem. Fund.* (1976) **15,** 59–64.
13. Redlich, O. and Kwong, J.N.S.: "On the Thermodynamics of Solutions. V. An Equation of State. Fugacities of Gaseous Solutions," *Chem. Reviews* (Feb. 1949) **44,** 233–44.
14. Cook, A.B., Walker, C.J., and Spencer, G.B.: "Realistic K Values of C_{7+} Hydrocarbons for Calculating Oil Vaporization During Gas Cycling at High Pressures," *JPT* (July 1969) 901–15; *Trans.*, AIME, **246.**
15. Taylor, A.J.: "Computer Simulation of Condensate Reservoirs," paper presented at the 1983 OYEZ Science and Technology Services Ltd. North Sea Condensate Reservoirs and Their Development Conference, London, May 24–25.
16. Coats, K.H.: "Simulation of Gas Condensate Reservoir Performance," *JPT* (Oct. 1985) 1870–86; *Trans.*, AIME, **279.**
17. Cook, R.E., Jacoby, R.H., and Ramesh, A.B.: "A Beta-Type Reservoir Simulator for Approximating Compositional Effects During Gas Injection," *SPEJ* (Oct. 1974) 471–81.
18. Henry, R.L.: "Effect of Including Composition-Dependent *K* Values To Generate Data for a Modified Beta-Type Simulator," *JPT* (Oct. 1976) 1180–82.
19. Stalkup, F.I. Jr.: *Miscible Displacement,* Monograph Series, SPE, Richardson, TX (1983) **8.**
20. Lantz, R.B. "Rigorous Calculation of Miscible Displacement Using Immiscible Reservoir Simulators," *SPEJ* (June 1970) 192–202; *Trans.*, AIME, **249.**
21. Todd, M.R. and Longstaff, W.J.: "The Development, Testing, and Application of a Numerical Simulator for Predicting Miscible Flood Performance," *JPT* (July 1972) 874–82; *Trans.*, AIME, **253.**
22. Chase, C.A. and Todd, M.R.: "Numerical Simulation of CO_2 Flood Performance," *SPEJ* (Dec. 1984) 597–605.
23. Huppler, J.D.: "Numerical Investigation of the Effects of Core Heterogeneities on Waterflood Relative Permeabilities," *SPEJ* (Dec. 1970) 381–92; *Trans.*, AIME, **249.**
24. Douglas, J. Jr. *et al.*: "Self-Adaptive Galerkin Methods for One-Dimensional, Two-Phase Immiscible Flow," paper SPE 7679 presented at the 1979 SPE Reservoir Simulation Symposium, Denver, Jan. 31–Feb. 2.
25. Chaudhari, N.M.: "An Improved Numerical Technique for Solving Multi-dimensional Miscible Displacement Equations," *SPEJ* (Sept. 1971) 277–84.
26. Chaudhari, N.M.: "A Numerical Solution with Second-Order Accuracy for Multicomponent Compressible Stable Miscible Flow," *SPEJ* (April 1973) 84–92.
27. Todd, M.R., O'Dell, P.M., and Hirasaki, G.J.: "Methods for Increased Accuracy in Numerical Reservoir Simulators," *SPEJ* (Dec. 1972) 515–30; *Trans.*, AIME, **253.**
28. Larson, R.G.: "Controlling Numerical Dispersion by Variably Timed Flux Updating in One Dimension," *SPEJ* (June 1982) 399–408; *Trans.*, AIME, **273.**
29. Larson, R.G.: "Controlling Numerical Dispersion by Variably Timed Flux Updating in Two Dimensions," *SPEJ* (June 1982) 409–19; *Trans.*, AIME, **273.**
30. Settari, A., Price, H.S., and Dupont, T.: "Development and Application of Variational Methods for Simulation of Miscible Displacement in Porous Media," *SPEJ* (June 1977) 228–46; *Trans.*, AIME, **263.**
31. Spivak, A., Price, H.S., and Settari, A.: "Solution of the Equations for Multidimensional, Two-Phase, Immiscible Flow by Variational Methods," *SPEJ* (Feb. 1977) 27–41.
32. Young, L.C.: "A Finite-Element Method for Reservoir Simulation," *SPEJ* (Feb. 1981) 115–27; *Trans.*, AIME, **271.**
33. Leventhal, S.H.: "The Operator Compact Implicit Method for Reservoir Simulation," *SPEJ* (June 1980) 120–28; *Trans.*, AIME, **269.**
34. Garder, A.O. Jr., Peaceman, D.W., and Pozzi, A.L. Jr.: "Numerical Calculation of Multidimensional Miscible Displacement by the Method of Characteristics," *SPEJ* (March 1964) 26–36; *Trans.*, AIME, **231.**
35. Lake, L.W. and Hirasaki, G.J.: "Taylor's Dispersion in Stratified Porous Media," *SPEJ* (Aug. 1981) 459–68; *Trans.*, AIME, **271.**
36. Todd, M.R. and Chase, C.A.: "A Numerical Simulator for Predicting Chemical Flood Performance," paper SPE 7689 presented at the 1979 SPE Symposium on Reservoir Simulation, Denver, Feb. 1–2.
37. Todd, M.R. *et al.*: "Numerical Simulation of Competing Chemical Flood Designs," paper SPE 7077 presented at the 1978 SPE Symposium on Improved Methods for Oil Recovery, Tulsa, April 16–19.
38. Van Quy, N. and Labrid, J.: "A Numerical Study of Chemical Flooding—Comparison With Experiments," *SPEJ* (June 1983) 461–74; *Trans.*, AIME, **275.**
39. Camilleri, D. *et al.*: "Comparison of an Improved Compositional Micellar/Polymer Simulator with Laboratory Core Floods," paper SPE 12083 presented at the 1983 SPE Annual Technical Conference and Exhibition, San Francisco, Oct. 5–8.
40. Bondor, P.L., Hirasaki, G.J., and Tham, M.J.: "Mathematical Simulation of Polymer Flooding in Complex Reservoirs," *SPEJ* (Oct. 1972) 369–82.
41. Vela, S., Peaceman, D.W., and Sandvik, E.I.: "Evaluation of Polymer Flooding in a Layered Reservoir With Crossflow, Retention, and Degradation," *SPEJ* (April 1976) 82–96.
42. Mayer, E.H. *et al.*: "Alkaline Injection for Enhanced Oil Recovery—A Status Report," *JPT* (Jan. 1983) 209–21; *Trans.*, AIME, **275.**
43. Breit, V.S., Mayer, E.H., and Carmichael, J.D.: "An Easily Applied Black Oil Model of Caustic Waterflooding," paper SPE 7999 presented at the 1979 SPE California Regional Meeting, Ventura, April 18–20.
44. Breit, V.S., Mayer, E.H., and Carmichael, J.D.: "Caustic Flooding in the Wilmington Field, California. Laboratory Modeling and Field Results," *Trans.*, 1981 European Symposium on EOR, Bournemouth, England (Sept. 22–23) 223–36.
45. Mayer, E.H. and Breit, V.S.: "Alkaline Flood Prediction Studies, Ranger VII Pilot, Wilmington Field, California," *SPERE* (Jan. 1986) 9–22.
46. Matthews, C.W.: "Steamflooding," *JPT* (March 1983) 465–71; *Trans.*, AIME, **275.**
47. Prats, M.: *Thermal Recovery,* Monograph Series, SPE, Richardson, TX (1982) **7.**
48. Coats, K.H.: "Simulation of Steamflooding with Distillation and Solution Gas," *SPEJ* (Oct. 1976) 235–47.
49. Coats, K.H.: "A Highly Implicit Steamflood Model," *SPEJ* (Oct. 1978) 369–83.
50. Coats, K.H. *et al.*: "Three-Dimensional Simulation of Steamflooding," *SPEJ* (Dec. 1974) 574–92; *Trans.*, AIME, **257.**
51. Chase, C.A. and O'Dell, P.M.: "Application of Variational Principles to Cap and Base Rock Heat Losses," *SPEJ* (Aug. 1973) 200–10; *Trans.*, AIME, **255.**
52. Weinstein, H.G.: "A Semi-Analytic Method for Thermal Coupling of Reservoir and Overburden," *SPEJ* (Oct. 1972) 439–47; *Trans.*, AIME, **253.**
53. Weinstein, H.G.: "Extended Semianalytic Method for Increasing and Decreasing Boundary Temperatures," *SPEJ* (April 1974) 152–64; *Trans.*, AIME, **257.**
54. Chu, C.: "Pattern Configuration Effect on Steamflood Performance," *JPT* (Sept. 1979) 1101–11.
55. Yanosik, J.L. and McCracken, T.A.: "A Nine-Point, Finite-Difference Reservoir Simulator for Realistic Prediction of Adverse Mobility Ratio Displacements," *SPEJ* (Aug. 1979) 253–62; *Trans.*, AIME, **267.**
56. Chu, C. and Trimble, A.E.: "Numerical Simulation of Steam Displacement—Field Performance Applications," *JPT* (June 1975) 765–76.
57. Crookston, R.B., Culham, W.E., and Chen, W.H.: "A Numerical Simulation Model for Thermal Recovery Processes," *SPEJ* (Feb. 1979) 37–58; *Trans.*, AIME, **267.**
58. Coats, K.H.: "Some Observations on Field-Scale Simulation of the In-Situ Combustion Process," paper SPE 12247 presented at the 1983 SPE Reservoir Simulation Symposium, San Francisco, Nov. 16–18.
59. Youngren, G.K.: "Development and Application of an In-Situ Combustion Reservoir Simulator," *SPEJ* (Feb. 1980) 39–51; *Trans.*, AIME, **269.**
60. Coats, K.H.: "In-Situ Combustion Model," *SPEJ* (Dec. 1980) 533–54; *Trans.*, AIME, **269.**
61. Hwang, M.K., Jines, W.R., and Odeh, A.S.: "An In-Situ Combustion Process Simulator with a Moving-Front Representation," *SPEJ* (April 1982) 271–79; *Trans.*, AIME, **273.**
62. Dogru, A.H., Mitsuishi, H., and Yamamoto, R.H.: "Numerical Simulation of Micellar Polymer Field Processes," paper SPE 13121 presented at the 1984 SPE Annual Technical Conference and Exhibition, Houston, Sept. 16–19.
63. Hirasaki, G.J., van Domselaar, H.R., and Nelson, R.C.: "Evaluation of the Salinity Gradient Concept in Surfactant Flooding," *SPEJ* (June 1983) 486–500.

SI Metric Conversion Factors

°API	141.5/(131.5+°API)		= g/cm^3
ft	× 3.048*	E−01	= m
°F	(°F−32)/1.8		= °C
scf/bbl	× 2.863 640	E−02	= std m^3/m^3
psi	× 6.894 757	E+00	= kPa

*Conversion factor is exact.

Appendix A
A Brief Review of Basic Reservoir Engineering Concepts: Simplified Calculation Methods

The purpose of this appendix is to review basic reservoir engineering concepts and to present simplified calculation methods for applying those concepts in solving problems. Clear understanding of the physical principles involved is necessary for correct application of a particular calculation procedure. The time-honored techniques reviewed here may be applied in reservoir studies when computer facilities are not readily available. They are also extremely useful in designing computer studies and in monitoring output of reservoir simulators.

A.1 Material Balance

Material-balance calculations are based on the principle that an increase or decrease in reservoir space occupied by one fluid must be accompanied by an offsetting change in the space occupied by some other material. Changes in reservoir space occupied by oil result from oil production and changes in volume of the remaining oil as its dissolved gas content and density change with pressure. Materials that replace the oil space are gas evolved from solution, gas expansion from a gas cap, gas injected through wells, water influx from an aquifer, water injected through wells or by expansion of the rock, and interstitial water as pressure declines. Of course, the net change in reservoir space occupied by gas and water must consider their influx minus the produced volumes and expansion of the remaining volume as pressure decreases.

The material-balance equation is (oil production and shrinkage) = (net expansion from solution gas) + (net expansion of gas cap) + (net water influx) + (expansion of rock and interstitial water), or

$$NB_{oi}-(N-N_p)B_o=[NR_{si}-(N-N_p)R_s-G_{ps}]B_{gs}$$
$$+(G_{Fi}+G_i-G_{Fp})B_{gc}-G_{Fi}B_{gci}+W_e+(W_i-W_p)B_w$$
$$+(c_f+c_wS_{wi})(V_p)(p_i-p). \quad \text{(A.1)}$$

In reservoir studies, the material balance is often used to solve for the water-influx volume, W_e, at various times. The material-balance equation may also be used in checking results of computer simulation for accuracy. For example, Eq. A.1 can be solved for W_e for various times. The net water influx, $W_e+(W_i-W_p)B_w$, should check the change in water volume calculated by summing changes in water volumes in the simulator oil-zone blocks,

$$\sum_1^n \Delta S_w V_p.$$

Also, the water-influx volume, W_e, should equal

$$\sum_1^m (c_f+c_w)(V_p)(p_i-p)$$

for simulator blocks in the aquifer. Lack of equality in either case can indicate problems with formulation of the computer program, lack of convergence to valid solutions, round-off errors, or errors in data input. A similar check on oil balances to see whether

$$NB_{oi}-(N-N_p)B_o=\sum_1^n \Delta S_o V_p$$

can indicate similar problems. To apply such checks to the entire reservoir, an accurate value for average pressure must be available for the reservoir.

Material-balance methods can be used to analyze simulator output for the relative importance of the drive mechanisms operating during the life of the reservoir. Understanding which fraction of the oil is replaced by a given drive mechanism and knowledge of its displacement efficiency can lead to increased recovery by, for example, changes in injection and production operations to enhance the importance of the more efficient drive. The fraction of the net change in oil volume replaced by each of the drive mechanisms follows.

Waterdrive Index

$$I_w=\frac{W_e+(W_i-W_p)B_w}{NB_{oi}-(N-N_p)B_o}. \quad \text{(A.2)}$$

Gas-Cap-Drive Index

$$I_{gc}=\frac{(G_{Fi}+G_i-G_{Fp})B_{gc}-G_{Fi}B_{gci}}{NB_{oi}-(N-N_p)B_o}. \quad \text{(A.3)}$$

Solution-Gas-Drive Index

$$I_{sg}=\frac{[NR_{si}-(N-N_p)R_s-G_{ps}]B_{gs}}{NB_{oi}-(N-N_p)B_o}. \quad \text{(A.4)}$$

Rock-Expansion Index

$$I_f=\frac{(c_f+c_wS_{wi})V_p(p_i-p)}{NB_{oi}-(N-N_p)B_o}. \quad \text{(A.5)}$$

A.2 Steady-State Flow

When pressures and flow rate are constant over a period of time, the condition is described as steady-state flow. The concept, which

TABLE A.1—DIMENSIONLESS FLUID INFLUX AS A FUNCTION OF DIMENSIONLESS TIME FOR CONSTANT WELL PRESSURE[1]

	Q_{tD}				
t_D	$r_e/r_w=1.5$	$r_e/r_w=3.0$	$r_e/r_w=6.0$	$r_e/r_w=9.0$	$r_e/r_w=\infty$
1.0×10^{-2}	0.112	0.112	0.112	0.112	0.112
5.0×10^{-2}	0.276	0.278	0.278	0.278	0.278
1.0×10^{-1}	0.395	0.404	0.404	0.404	0.404
2.5×10^{-1}	0.559	0.689	0.689	0.689	0.689
5.0×10^{-1}	0.617	1.020	1.020	1.020	1.020
1.0		1.563	1.570	1.570	1.570
2.5		2.646	2.838	2.838	2.838
5.0		3.491	4.541	4.541	4.541
1.0×10^{1}		3.928	7.293	7.417	7.417
2.5×10^{1}		4.000	12.50	14.40	1.455×10^{1}
5.0×10^{1}			15.95	22.82	2.482×10^{1}
1.0×10^{2}			17.36	32.27	4.301×10^{1}
2.5×10^{2}			17.50	39.30	9.120×10^{1}
5.0×10^{2}			17.50	39.98	16.24×10^{1}
1.0×10^{3}					29.31×10^{1}
5.0×10^{3}					11.88×10^{2}
1.0×10^{4}					21.96×10^{2}
5.0×10^{4}					9.342×10^{3}
1.0×10^{5}					17.56×10^{3}
5.0×10^{5}					7.699×10^{4}
1.0×10^{6}					14.62×10^{4}
5.0×10^{6}					6.544×10^{5}
1.0×10^{7}					12.52×10^{5}
5.0×10^{7}					5.689×10^{6}
1.0×10^{8}					10.95×10^{6}
5.0×10^{8}					5.03×10^{7}
1.0×10^{9}					9.725×10^{7}
5.0×10^{9}					4.510×10^{8}
1.0×10^{10}					8.747×10^{8}
5.0×10^{10}					4.087×10^{9}
1.0×10^{11}					7.948×10^{9}

has become known as Darcy's law for one-dimensional (1D), laminar flow of a single phase through a porous medium, is given by

$$q_o=0.001127\frac{k_oA}{B_o\mu_o}\left(\frac{\Delta p}{L}+\frac{\rho_o \sin\Theta}{144}\right). \quad \text{(A.6)}$$

The various forms of the equation for steady-state flow of a single-phase fluid are given here because of their utility in reservoir calculations.

For horizontal, linear flow of oil,

$$q_o=0.001127\frac{k_oA\Delta p}{B_o\mu_oL}. \quad \text{(A.7)}$$

For horizontal, linear flow of gas,

$$q_g=\frac{0.000112k_gA(p_1{}^2-p_2{}^2)}{Tz_{\bar{p}}\mu_gL}. \quad \text{(A.8)}$$

For horizontal, radial flow of oil,

$$q_o=0.00708\frac{k_oh\Delta p}{\mu_oB_o\ln\left(\dfrac{r_e}{r_w}\right)}. \quad \text{(A.9)}$$

For horizontal, radial flow of gas,

$$q_g=\frac{0.000703kh(p_1{}^2-p_2{}^2)}{\mu_gTz_{\bar{p}}\ln\left(\dfrac{r_e}{r_w}\right)}. \quad \text{(A.10)}$$

For horizontal, five-spot pattern flow of oil (or water),

$$q_o=\frac{0.003541kh\Delta p}{\mu_o\left(\ln\dfrac{d}{r_w}-0.619\right)}. \quad \text{(A.11)}$$

A.3 Unsteady-State Flow

Many practical problems involve transient or unsteady-state flow behavior in which rates and pressures change with time and position. Equations for unsteady-state flow of a single-phase fluid are based on the simple concepts that Darcy's law applies and that mass must be conserved. Combination of a mass balance on an elemental volume containing a slightly compressible fluid, such as water, with Darcy's law results in the equation

$$\frac{\partial^2\rho}{\partial x^2}=\frac{\phi\mu c_t}{0.00634k}\left(\frac{\partial\rho}{\partial t}\right), \quad \text{(A.12)}$$

which can be approximated by

$$\frac{\partial^2 p}{\partial x^2}=\frac{\phi\mu c_t}{0.00634k}\frac{\partial p}{\partial t}, \quad \text{(A.13)}$$

where

$$c_t\left(\frac{\partial p}{\partial x}\right)^2<<\frac{\partial^2 p}{\partial x^2}.$$

Analytic solutions can be obtained for Eq. A.13 for flow of a single-phase, slightly compressible fluid in a medium of constant thickness and constant permeability. Tabular solutions published by van Ever-

TABLE A.2—DIMENSIONLESS PRESSURE CHANGE AS A FUNCTION OF DIMENSIONLESS TIME FOR CONSTANT TERMINAL RATE

	p_{t_D}				
t_D	$r_e/r_w=1.5$	$r_e/r_w=3.0$	$r_e/r_w=6.0$	$r_e/r_w=9.0$	$r_e/r_w=\infty$
1.0×10^{-2}	0.112	0.112	0.112	0.112	0.112
6.0×10^{-2}	0.251	0.251	0.251	0.251	0.251
1.0×10^{-1}	0.322	0.315	0.315	0.315	0.315
2.0×10^{-1}	0.484	0.424	0.424	0.424	0.424
3.0×10^{-1}	0.644	0.503	0.503	0.503	0.503
4.0×10^{-1}	0.804	0.564	0.564	0.564	0.564
5.0×10^{-1}	0.964	0.616	0.616	0.616	0.616
6.0×10^{-1}	1.124	0.662	0.659	0.659	0.659
7.0×10^{-1}		0.703	0.702	0.702	0.702
8.0×10^{-1}		0.740	0.735	0.735	0.735
9.0×10^{-1}		0.776	0.772	0.772	0.772
1.0		0.806	0.802	0.802	0.802
2.0		1.076	1.020	1.020	1.020
3.0		1.578	1.169	1.169	1.169
4.0		1.828	1.275	1.275	1.275
5.0			1.364	1.362	1.362
6.0			1.441	1.436	1.436
7.0			1.511	1.500	1.500
8.0			1.576	1.556	1.556
9.0			1.638	1.604	1.604
1.0×10^{1}			1.698	1.651	1.651
2.0×10^{1}			2.274	1.983	1.960
3.0×10^{1}			2.846	2.244	2.147
4.0×10^{1}				2.496	2.282
5.0×10^{1}				2.746	2.388
6.0×10^{1}					2.476
7.0×10^{1}					2.550
8.0×10^{1}					2.615
9.0×10^{1}					2.672
1.0×10^{2}					2.723
2.0×10^{2}					3.064
3.0×10^{2}					3.263
4.0×10^{2}					3.406
5.0×10^{2}					3.516
6.0×10^{2}					3.608
7.0×10^{2}					3.684
8.0×10^{2}					3.750
9.0×10^{2}					3.809
1.0×10^{3}					3.860

dingen and Hurst[1] for the constant-terminal-pressure case (see Table A.1) and for the constant-terminal-rate case (see Table A.2) are particularly valuable in evaluating the performance of aquifers.

Dimensionless parameters of interest in using data from Tables A.1 and A.2 are dimensionless time, t_D, dimensionless fluid influx, Q_{tD}, dimensionless pressure, p_{t_D}, and dimensionless radius, r_D:

$$t_D=\frac{0.00634kt}{\mu c_t \phi r_w^2}, \quad \text{(A.14)}$$

$$Q_{tD}=\frac{W_e}{1.12\phi c_t h r_w^2(p_i-p_w)}, \quad \text{(A.15)}$$

$$p_{t_D}=\frac{0.00708kh(p_i-p_w)}{q\mu}, \quad \text{(A.16)}$$

and

$$r_D=\frac{r_e}{r_w}. \quad \text{(A.17)}$$

Data from Tables A.1 and A.2 and from Eqs. A.14 through A.17 can be used with the volumetric-balance equation (Eq. A.1) to solve for the pressure/production behavior of a waterdrive reservoir. The tabular data are applied with the principle of superposition. The superposition principle for the data of Table A.1 states that production of fluid across an aquifer/reservoir boundary having terminal pressures that vary with time is the sum of the production that would occur with a succession of constant-terminal-pressure drops for the appropriate time intervals. Similarly, for the data in Table A.2, superposition for a terminal rate that varies with time requires summing the pressure drops calculated from a succession of constant rate changes for the appropriate time intervals.

In hand-calculation procedures, the volumetric-balance equation (Eq. A.1) is solved for water influx, W_e, at various times. Then data in Table A.1 and Eqs. A.14 and A.15 are used to solve for the water efflux from the aquifer. Aquifer properties—e.g., thickness, permeability, porosity, or size—may be adjusted until the water-efflux history by unsteady calculations agrees with the water-influx history calculated from material balances. After matching history, future pressure behavior may be predicted by assuming production schedules of oil, gas, and water for the reservoir. Hand calculations with the previously described volumetric-balance/unsteady-state-flow procedure require several hours or days to achieve a satisfactory history match and forecast of future behavior under various production schedules. Computer programs of the procedure can yield similar results in a few seconds of computer time.

Users of the procedure should make sure that the aquifer properties required for a satisfactory match are consistent with geologic descriptions of the aquifer. Remember that the method assumes

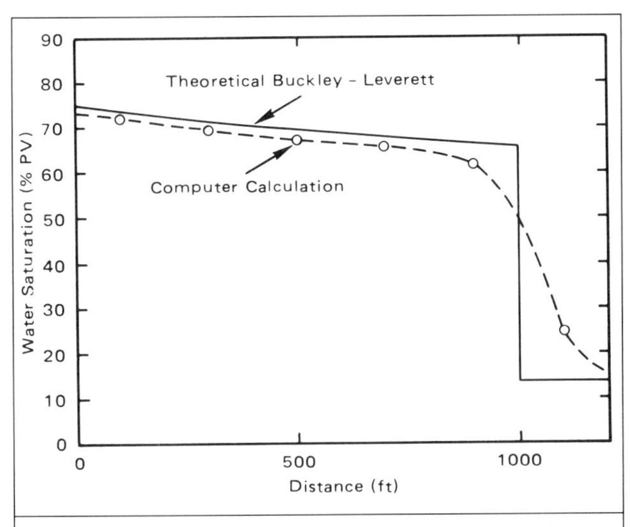

Fig. A.1—Effect of numerical dispersion on calculated saturation profile.

radial flow in an aquifer of constant permeability and thickness. The method also assumes that the average pressure in the oil or gas reservoir is equal to the pressure at the original water/oil or water/gas contact. Further, no pressure interference from other reservoirs in the aquifer is permitted.

A.4 Linear Displacement Behavior

Displacement of oil from a porous medium by such immiscible fluids as water or gas is governed by the relative-permeability characteristics of the rock and by the fluid viscosities and densities. The relative-permeability concept is based on experimental observations that as oil saturation decreases, oil flows less easily and the invading fluid flows more easily. The fractional-flow equation is based on Darcy's law for each fluid flowing at a particular saturation and on the definition of capillary pressure.[2] The fractional-flow equation for water displacing oil is

$$f_w = \frac{1 + \dfrac{0.001127kA}{q_t\mu_o}\left(\dfrac{\partial P_c}{\partial L} - \dfrac{\Delta\rho \sin\Theta}{144}\right)}{1 + \dfrac{k_{ro}\mu_w}{k_{rw}\mu_o}}, \quad \text{(A.18)}$$

where q_t is total flow rate.

Buckley and Leverett presented a procedure for quantifying the efficiency by which oil is displaced in a linear system. The method involves simultaneous solution of the fractional-flow equation and the continuity equation.[3] The continuity equation is based on conservation of mass and is given by

$$\Delta L = \frac{5.615 q_t \Delta t}{\phi A}\left(\frac{df_w}{dS_w}\right). \quad \text{(A.19)}$$

The assumption is usually made that the term $\partial P_c/\partial L$ is negligibly small for linear distances and conditions typical of reservoirs. Values of f_w calculated from Eq. A.18 are plotted vs. saturation. The slope, df_w/dS_w, at a given saturation is used in Eq. A.19 to determine the distance that the particular saturation moves in a given time.

Saturation profiles generated for different times are used to calculate the oil recovery. Integration of the area between saturation profiles yields the oil displaced in that interval, or $\Delta N_p B_o = \Sigma\Delta S\Delta L\phi A$. Generation of saturation profiles with this procedure can also be used to quantify the amount of numerical dispersion occurring in a particular computer-model calculation. An example comparison in Fig. A.1 shows that numerical dispersion has caused the water front to advance several hundred feet too far and the average saturation in the swept zone to be too low by about 2%. Use of smaller blocks will reduce errors from numerical dispersion but will add to costs of calculations.

Welge[4] derived a simplified calculation procedure for 1D displacement of oil using the following relationships:

$$Q_i = \frac{dS_w}{df_w} \quad \text{(A.20)}$$

and

$$\bar{S}_w = \frac{dS_w}{df_w}(1 - f_w) + S_{w2}, \quad \text{(A.21)}$$

where S_{w2} is water saturation at the producing face at or after water breakthrough.

Values of f_w are calculated from relative-permeability data with the fractional-flow equation (Eq. A.18), and plots of f_w vs. S_w are used to measure slopes, df_w/dS_w. Eqs. A.20 and A.21 are then solved for the water throughput and for the corresponding average water saturation. Oil recovery is calculated from the PV and change in average water saturation.

Displacement efficiencies calculated by the previously described 1D procedures are reduced by vertical and areal sweep efficiencies to predict recoveries expected from a reservoir. These hand-calculation methods are very useful in predicting reservoir performance under alternative operating modes. They are also useful in screening cases to study with reservoir simulators. For example, hand calculations can quantify the effect of rate and pressure level on linear-displacement efficiencies to aid in selecting optimum timing and injection volumes for a pressure-maintenance program.

A.5 Three-Dimensional (3D) Flow Behavior

Hand-calculation methods can sometimes be surprisingly effective in analyzing or predicting behavior in 3D reservoirs. The general approach is to combine the results of several simple calculation procedures involving separate flow phenomena into an overall result. The separate calculations may involve use of published correlations of generalized behavior and/or use of simple mathematical models. Some of the most important concepts, correlations, and mathematical models are described in the following sections.

A.5.1 Mobility Ratio. The mobility of a fluid, λ, is defined as the effective permeability to the fluid divided by its viscosity—e.g., oil mobility, $\lambda_o = k_o/\mu_o$. Thus, mobility is a measure of the ease with which a fluid will flow at a particular saturation. The mobility ratio, M, is defined as the mobility of the displacing phase divided by that of the displaced phase, or

$$M = \frac{\lambda_D}{\lambda_d} = \frac{k_w/\mu_w}{k_o/\mu_o} \text{ or } \frac{k_g/\mu_g}{k_o/\mu_o}.$$

The mobility ratio can be considered a point function applying to the saturation of a particular point. Craig *et al.*[5] provide a more useful concept. They defined the mobility ratio in terms of the mobility of the displacing phase at the average saturation in the swept region and of the mobility of the displaced phase at the average saturation in the unswept zone.

A.5.2 Viscous Fingering. When the mobility ratio is greater than 1.0, there is a tendency for the displacing phase to channel, or finger, and to bypass oil even in homogeneous sands. This phenomenon, known as viscous fingering, occurs because once a channel forms, the remaining displacing fluid tends to follow the path of least resistance. In horizontal displacements, viscous fingering can result in poor sweep efficiencies for very unfavorable mobility ratios. In a dipping formation, gravity segregation can effectively prevent viscous fingering if rates are less than a critical rate given by[6]

$$q_c = \frac{7.83 \times 10^{-6} kA\Delta\rho \sin\Theta}{\dfrac{\mu_o}{k_{ro}} - \dfrac{\mu_g}{k_{rg}}}. \quad \text{(A.22)}$$

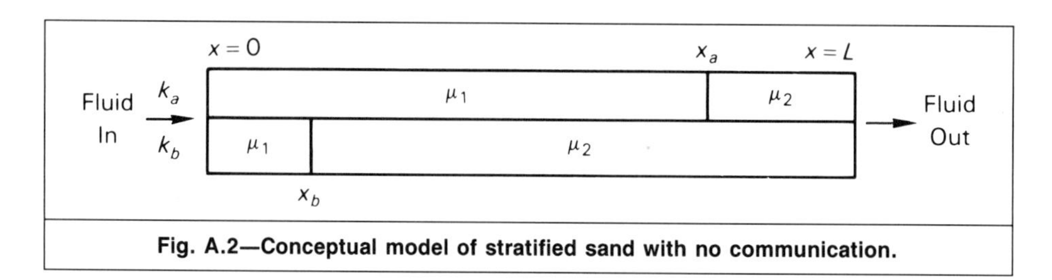

Fig. A.2—Conceptual model of stratified sand with no communication.

At injection rates less than the critical rate, the injected gas will tend to override the oil zone but the gas/oil contact (GOC) will reach a stable angle, β, given by

$$\tan\beta=(1-q/q_c)\tan\Theta. \quad \text{(A.23)}$$

A similar calculation for water/oil displacement will indicate rates at which water will underrun the oil zone when the mobility ratio is unfavorable.

A.5.3 Coning and Cusping. When a gas or water front approaches the producing interval in a well, the pressure drawdown resulting from viscous flow of oil into the well can cause a distortion in the shape of the front. If, for example, the GOC overlies the producing interval at the well, the critical oil-producing rate at which no gas (or water) is produced is given by

$$q_{o_c}=\frac{2.46\times10^{-5}k_o\Delta\rho(h_o^2-h_p^2)}{B_o\mu_o\ln\left(\dfrac{r_e}{r_w}\right)}, \quad \text{(A.24)}$$

in which h_o is thickness of oil zone and h_p is height of top of perforations above the base of oil zone.[7]

If the GOC lies upstructure from the well, the phenomenon that pulls the contact toward the well is known as cusping. The critical rate for *onset of cusping* into the well is given by

$$q_{o_c}=\frac{4.92\times10^{-5}k_o rh\Delta\rho\sin\Theta}{B_o\mu_o}, \quad \text{(A.25)}$$

in which r is radius to the gas front.

If the production rate exceeds the critical coning or cusping rate, free-gas production will ensue. GOR's will be rate-sensitive at rates up to about four times the critical rate, with GOR's increasing as rate increases. Above about four times the critical rate, GOR's will be essentially independent of rate because gravitational forces will become negligibly small compared with the viscous forces. At these higher rates, the GOR's will depend on the relative thicknesses of the oil and gas zones and on fluid mobilities in the oil and gas zones. The ratios will be essentially independent of the location of the perforated interval in a homogeneous formation.

Similar remarks apply to water coning and cusping.

A.5.4 Permeability Stratification. One of the most important but complex problems in production of oil is in calculating flow through stratified sands. In many cases, the degree and kind of stratification controls whether a secondary recovery method will succeed or fail. But, unfortunately, the nature of the stratification is usually not well defined. Some reservoirs are composed of several strata that are laterally continuous and fairly uniform throughout the extent of the pool. Each stratum may have a different permeability than neighboring strata, and they may or may not be in intimate contact. In some cases, layers of very-low-permeability shale separate the sand members, while in other cases there is no shale and free communication exists between sands. Each layer may be fairly homogeneous, or it may vary widely in permeability both laterally and vertically. A seemingly infinite number of kinds and degrees of stratification exist. Only a few of the simpler cases are treated here to illustrate the qualitative effects of stratification on the efficiency with which oil is displaced.

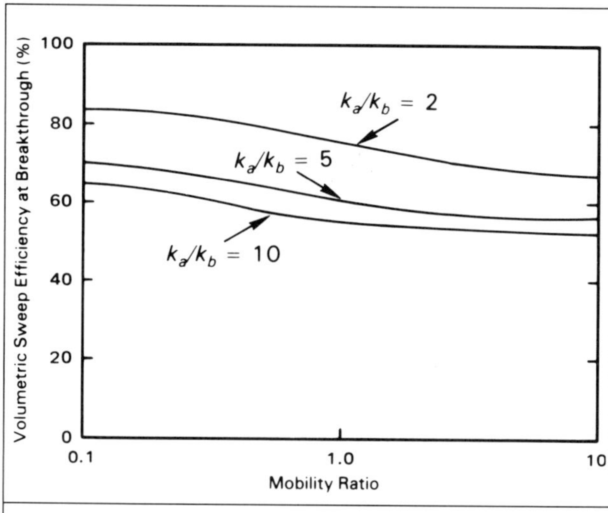

Fig. A.3—Effect of mobility ratio on sweep efficiencies of noncommunicating stratified sands.

A.5.4.1 Noncommunicating Strata. The first type of stratified sands of interest is that in which impermeable members separate the permeable layers into isolated strata that are in communication only at the wellbore. In this type of formation, if the injected fluid has a mobility different from that of the oil, the fraction of injected fluid entering any stratum will vary with time.[8] Initially, when the formation is filled with oil, the fraction of the injected fluid entering any particular stratum will be given by the fraction

$$f_i=\frac{k_ih_i}{\sum_1^n k_ih_i}, \quad \text{(A.26)}$$

in which

f_i = fraction of total fluid entering ith sand,
k_i = permeability of ith sand,
h_i = thickness of ith sand, and
$\sum_1^n k_ih_i$ = sum of k_ih_i products for all n strata.

As the flood progresses, however, water advances farthest in the most-permeable stratum. If the mobility of the water is higher than that of the oil, the fluid conductivity increases faster in the most permeable sand than in the less permeable sands. In this case, the fraction of the total flow entering the most permeable sand increases with time. If the mobility of the water is less than that of the oil, the fraction of the total flow entering the most permeable sand decreases with time. If the mobility of the water and oil are equal, the fraction of water entering each sand does not change with time. The last case has been treated by Stiles.[9]

A simple mathematical model is used to illustrate qualitatively the effects of different permeability ratios of the sand members and the effects of different mobility ratios on recovery. The model consists of two sand members, as shown in Fig. A.2, having permeabilities of k_a and k_b. Flow is assumed to be linear and horizontal with piston-like displacement. Fluid of viscosity μ_1 dis-

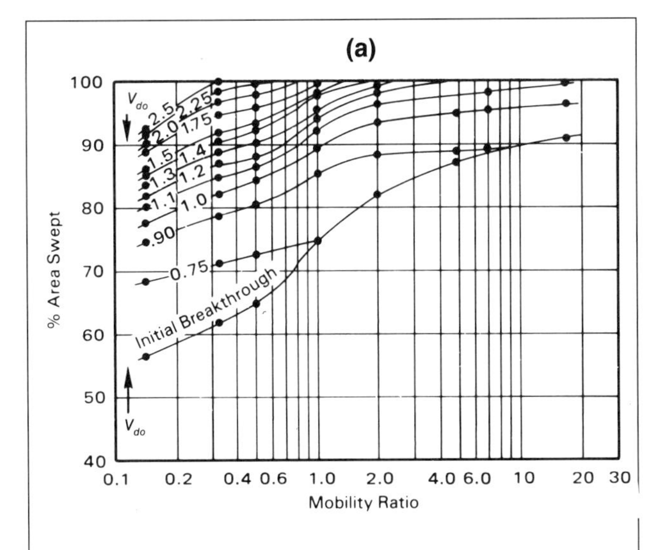

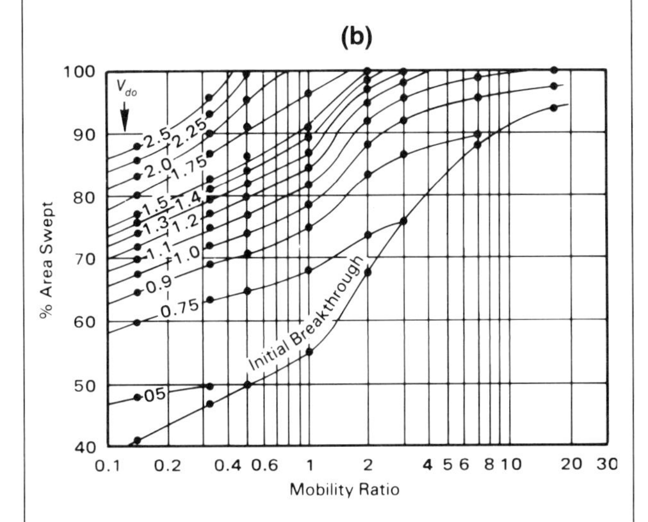

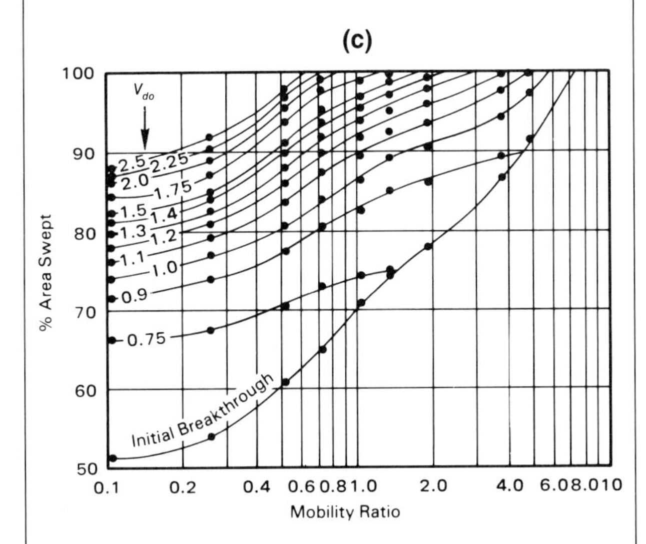

Fig. A.4—Effect of mobility ratio on areal sweep efficiency[10]: (a) five-spot pattern, (b) one-to-one line drive (square pattern), and (c) staggered line drive.

places fluid of viscosity μ_2, and the mobilities behind the flood front, k_{1a}/μ_1 and k_{1b}/μ_1, are assumed to be constant in the two sands. The pressure drop across both sands is Δp, which is constant. The equation relating the position of the front in Sand a, the coarse sand, at times before breakthrough is

$$\frac{\phi_a}{2}\left(\frac{\mu_1}{k_{1a}}-\frac{\mu_2}{k_{2a}}\right)x_a{}^2+\phi_a\left(\frac{\mu_2}{k_{2a}}\right)x_aL=0.00634\Delta pt. \quad \text{. . (A.27)}$$

A similar equation applies to Sand b, the tight sand. At breakthrough in the coarse sand, the position of the front in the tight sand is given by

$$\frac{\phi_b}{2}\left(\frac{\mu_1}{k_{1b}}-\frac{\mu_2}{k_{2b}}\right)x_b{}^2+\phi_b\left(\frac{\mu_2}{k_{2b}}\right)x_bL=\frac{\phi_a}{2}L^2\left(\frac{\mu_1}{k_{1a}}+\frac{\mu_2}{k_{2a}}\right).$$

. . . . (A.28)

Eq. A.28 has been solved for several mobility ratios for permeability ratios of 2, 5, and 10. It was assumed that the strata were of equal thickness and porosity. Results of these calculations are shown in Fig. A.3, in which the volumetric sweep efficiency at breakthrough in the coarse sand is plotted vs. the mobility ratio. It can be seen that when the mobility ratio is unfavorable and the permeability ratio is high, practically none of the tight sand is swept at breakthrough. For example, for an unfavorable mobility ratio of 10 and a permeability ratio of 10, only 51.4% of the sand is swept; this means that only 2.8% of the tight sand is swept. Better sweep efficiencies are obtained for lower mobility ratios and as the ratio of permeabilities approaches 1.0. Sweep efficiencies calculated by this idealized model are too optimistic for unfavorable ratios because of the tendency to finger. When mobility ratios are unfavorable, fingering tends to cause additional channeling in both the more-permeable and the less-permeable strata.

A.5.4.2 Communicating Strata. Determining vertical sweep efficiencies may be quite complex if vertical communication exists between strata. The permeability distribution, the positions of the more-permeable layers relative to those having less permeability, and the interplay among viscous, gravitational, capillary, and diffusional forces all affect vertical sweep of the interval. Problems involving communicating layers are best solved on computers with the use of cross-sectional models. However, a few general comments may be useful. Viscous crossflow improves vertical sweep efficiencies for favorable mobility ratios and reduces them for unfavorable mobility ratios. Gravity segregation may improve sweep efficiencies in waterflooding if the more-permeable layer is on top. The reverse is true in gas-drive operations. Capillary imbibition may be effective in improving sweep, particularly if the formation is water-wet and strata thicknesses are on the order of 10 ft [3 m] or less. Vertical diffusion may improve sweep of an oil reservoir by a miscible gas if strata are less than 5 to 10 ft [1.5 to 3 m] thick. Vertical diffusion is also important in gas-cycling operations if intervals are less than 50 to 100 ft [15 to 30 m] thick.

The role of gravity, capillarity, and diffusion in oil recovery will be discussed further in later sections.

A.5.5 Areal Pattern Efficiencies. Because an operator planning injection programs has control of the location of injection and production wells, it is important to know how the well pattern affects recovery. Figs. A.4a through A.4c show correlations of data from model experiments for five-spot, direct linedrive, and staggered linedrive patterns.[10] The linedrive patterns had the same distances between rows of injectors and producers as the distances between either producers or injectors. Areal sweep efficiencies are plotted vs. the reciprocal of mobility ratio for various volumes of throughput. The throughput is in terms of displaceable oil volume, V_{do}, which is the PV times the saturation change from oil saturation at interstitial water to residual oil saturation.

A.5.6 Recovery Efficiencies. Areal sweep efficiencies read from Fig. A.4 can be combined with displacement efficiencies calculated from 1D Buckley-Leverett or Welge methods and with vertical sweep efficiencies to yield estimates of recovery. Overall recovery efficiency, E_R, is given by

$$E_R = E_D E_I E_P, \qquad \text{(A.29)}$$

in which

E_R = overall recovery efficiency, fraction,
E_D = displacement efficiency, fraction,
E_I = vertical invasion efficiency, fraction, and
E_P = areal pattern efficiency, fraction.

E_R can be determined at various volumes of throughput once the displacement, vertical, and pattern efficiencies are determined separately as functions of throughput.

A.5.7 Gravity Segregation. Gravity segregation can be an effective mechanism in oil recovery by both gas and water displacements if the effective permeability to oil is favorable in the direction parallel to the force of gravity. Favorable permeability to drainage can result from a combination of high dip and high permeability or from a high vertical permeability in formations with moderately low dip. In the latter case, oil drainage will continue vertically downward after a region is invaded by gas; oil will accumulate and flow in a thin layer at the base of the interval. A similar mechanism can be effective in water-invaded regions if conditions are favorable for upward gravity drainage of oil.

Hand-calculation procedures are available from a simple mathematical model for estimating recovery in a reservoir with dip.[11] The model assumes that the displacement occurs in two steps. First, the displacing front moves parallel to the bedding planes and maintains a horizontal attitude. This step is approximated by the 1D Welge calculation procedure described previously to determine the oil saturation at the displacement front. In the second step, oil drains vertically by gravity in the invaded region. This step is approximated by a 1D calculation procedure with an equation derived from Darcy's law and the continuity equation,

$$z = \frac{4.4\times10^{-5} k \Delta p \Delta t}{\phi \mu_o}\left(\frac{dk_{ro}}{dS}\right). \qquad \text{(A.30)}$$

Slopes are measured on a plot of k_{ro} vs. saturation at various saturations. The distance that a particular saturation will move vertically downward from the top of the interval in a given time period after passage of the front is calculated by Eq. A.30. The amount of oil drainage from a given region during a time period can be obtained by graphic integration of a plot of height vs. saturation for times of interest. Oil drainage is given by

$$\Delta N = \Delta S_o h A \phi / 5.615. \qquad \text{(A.31)}$$

Division of the reservoir length along the bedding plane into 10 equal regions usually will provide satisfactory accuracy.

If significant vertical segregation of oil is shown to occur, care should be taken in design of computer models to provide a sufficient number of layers. Improved accuracy in simulation is obtained by using thin layers at the top and bottom of the interval.

The above procedure assumes that the time for oil to flow to the front in a thin layer along the base of the interval can be neglected, as can the volume of oil in this layer. More-accurate calculations may require consideration of the thickness of the capillary transition zone above the oil layer, especially if interval thicknesses are on the order of 10 ft [3 m] or less. Also, at rates above one-half the critical rate (Eq. A.22), oil will tend to accumulate rather than flow away along the base of the interval. Thus, in some cases, the calculation method may require a third step to estimate the shape and volume of the oil layer draining along the base at various times.

Recoveries calculated by the described technique are quite sensitive to values of relative permeability to oil at low oil saturations. Conventional laboratory data for a gas/oil system can be extended to low oil saturations from semilog plots of k_{ro} vs. $(S_o - S_{oir})/(1 - S_{wi} - S_{oir})$. S_{oir} is the irreducible oil saturation for gas/oil displacement in the presence of interstitial water and will usually be nearly zero. If a measured value of S_{oir} is not available, a value is chosen to yield a straight line through the data so that

$$k_{ro} = \left(\frac{S_o - S_{oir}}{1 - S_{wi} - S_{oir}}\right)^n. \qquad \text{(A.32)}$$

The slope of the line, n, should be 4, according to the theory of Corey *et al.*,[12] but may be greater than 6.

Similar extrapolation of conventional laboratory data for a water/oil system is sometimes necessary for rocks of intermediate or mixed wettability because of the tendencies for relative permeability to oil to approach zero asymptotically.

A.5.8 Capillary Imbibition. Capillary imbibition of water can improve the vertical sweep efficiency of water in stratified formations if the rock is water-wet. However, distances over which transport of water by capillary action can occur in reservoir times is usually 10 to 20 ft [3 to 6 m] or less. An equation for the countercurrent flow of oil by water imbibition at one face can be derived using Darcy's law for each phase, definition of capillary pressure, and Leverett's J_{sw} function, and noting that $q_o = -q_w$. The equation is[13]

$$q_o = \frac{0.00519(k\phi)^{1/2} A \sigma f(\theta_c)}{\mu_o}\left(\frac{k_{ro}}{1 + \dfrac{k_{ro}\mu_w}{k_{rw}\mu_o}}\right)\frac{dJ_{sw}}{dS_w}\frac{\partial S_w}{\partial L}, \qquad \text{(A.33)}$$

in which σ is interfacial tension and $f(\theta_c)$ is a function of the contact angle.

Eq. A.33 is combined with the continuity equation,

$$\phi A\left(\frac{\partial S_w}{\partial t}\right)_L = 5.615\left(\frac{\partial q_o}{\partial L}\right)_t \qquad \text{(A.34)}$$

to form

$$\frac{\partial S_w}{\partial t_D} = \frac{\partial}{\partial L_D}\left(\frac{k_{ro}}{1 + \dfrac{k_{rw}\mu_w}{k_{ro}\mu_o}}\right)\frac{dJ_{sw}}{dS_w}\frac{\partial S_w}{\partial L_D}, \qquad \text{(A.35)}$$

in which

t_D = dimensionless time

$$= 0.02916\frac{t\left(\dfrac{k}{\phi}\right)^{1/2}\sigma f(\theta_c)}{\mu_o L_t^2}, \qquad \text{(A.36)}$$

L_D = dimensionless length $= L/L_t$, and
L_t = total length.

Eq. A.35 can be solved numerically to yield recovery and saturation profiles at various times by countercurrent imbibition. Countercurrent imbibition may also be estimated with the experimental recovery data in Fig. A.5 for Berea cores of various lengths correlated vs. t/L^2. Note that imbibition is virtually complete for $t/L^2 = 0.3$ h/cm². For a longer system having the same rock and fluid properties, times for complete recovery by countercurrent imbibition would be $t = 0.3L^2$. For example, for a 20-ft [6-m] distance, $t = 0.3(20 \text{ ft} \times 30.5 \text{ cm/ft})^2 = 1.12\times10^5$ hours, or 12.74 years.

Times for other rock or fluid properties may be estimated with the data in Fig. A.5 and Eq. A.36 for dimensionless time, if the water/oil viscosity ratio is not significantly different from 0.5.

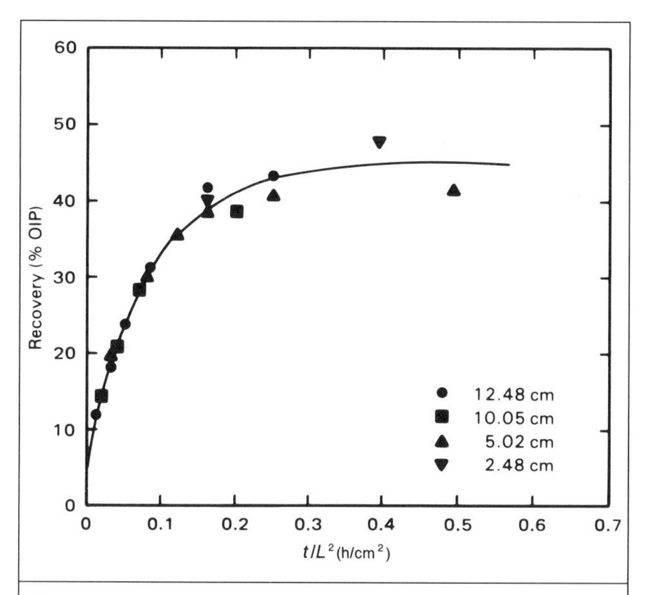

Fig. A.5—Correlation of imbibition data on samples of different lengths.

A.5.9 Diffusion. In miscible displacements, such as displacement of oil by an enriched gas or in gas-cycling operations, diffusion may play a role in improving vertical sweep efficiencies in stratified sands. As with capillary imbibition in immiscible displacements, however, distances over which diffusion can be effective in reservoir times are quite limited.

An estimate of the distance over which diffusion is effective is given by

$$\Delta L_C = 3.62\sqrt{\frac{Dt}{\tau}}, \qquad \text{(A.37)}$$

in which

ΔL_C = length between the 10 and 90% concentration levels, ft [m],
D = diffusion coefficient, ft²/D [m²/d],
τ = tortuosity factor, and
t = time, days.

Values for methane diffusivities in various oils are given in Table A.3. Values for diffusivities of gas in gas may be estimated from the Gilliland equation[14]:

$$D = \frac{3.26T^{3/2}\sqrt{\dfrac{1}{M_a}+\dfrac{1}{M_b}}}{p(V_a^{1/3}+V_b^{1/3})^2}, \qquad \text{(A.38)}$$

in which

D = molecular diffusivity, ft²/D [m²/d],
T = temperature, °R [K],
p = pressure, psia [kPa],
M_a,M_b = molecular weights of gases a and b, and
V_a,V_b = molecular volumes of gases a and b (V=14.8 for each carbon atom, 3.7 for each hydrogen atom, 15.6 for each nitrogen atom, and 12.0 for each oxygen atom).

Diffusivities of gases in gas are usually on the order of 0.1 to 0.2 ft²/D [93 to 186 cm²/d], or roughly 100-fold those of gases in liquids.

For diffusion of dissolved gas in liquids, effective distances on the order of 5 to 10 ft [1.5 to 3 m] are usually observed. For example, for typical values of D and T, Eq. A.37 predicts a ΔL of about 10 ft [3 m] after 10 years:

TABLE A.3—MOLECULAR DIFFUSION COEFFICIENTS FOR METHANE IN CRUDE OILS

Oil Gravity (°API)	Temperature (°F)	Diffusivity* (ft²/D × 10³)
44.5	86	2.81
44.5	140	4.48
32.7	86	1.59
26.9	86	1.09
20.0	86	0.66

*Diffusivities for ethane and propane are about 60 and 40%, respectively, of those shown for methane in oil.

$$\Delta L = 3.62\sqrt{\frac{(4.48\times10^{-3}\ \text{ft}^2/\text{D})(3{,}650\ \text{days})}{2}} = 10.3\ \text{ft}\ [3.1\ \text{m}].$$

Effective distances for diffusion of gas in gas are usually on the order of 50 to 100 ft [15 to 30 m] for reservoir times, or roughly 10 times greater than those for gas in oil.

Nomenclature

A = cross-sectional area, ft² [m²]
B_{gc} = FVF of gas-cap gas, RB/scf [res m³/std m³]
B_{gci} = FVF of injected gas, RB/scf [res m³/std m³]
B_{gs} = FVF of solution gas, RB/scf [res m³/std m³]
B_o = FVF for oil at present conditions, RB/STB [res m³/stock-tank m³]
B_{oi} = FVF for oil at original conditions, RB/STB [res m³/stock-tank m³]
B_w = FVF for water, RB/STB [res m³/stock-tank m³]
c_f = compressibility of formation, psi⁻¹ [kPa⁻¹]
c_t = total compressibility, psi⁻¹ [kPa⁻¹]
c_w = compressibility of water, psi⁻¹ [kPa⁻¹]
d = distance between injection and production wells, ft [m]
D = diffusion coefficient or molecular diffusivity, ft²/D [m²/d]
E_D = displacement efficiency, fraction
E_I = vertical invasion efficiency, fraction
E_P = areal pattern efficiency, fraction
E_R = overall recovery efficiency, fraction
f_i = fraction of total fluid entering ith sand
f_w = fractional flow of water
G_{Fi} = volume of original gas cap, scf [std m³]
G_{FP} = gas-cap gas production, scf [std m³]
G_i = gas injected, scf [std m³]
G_{Ps} = solution gas production, scf [std m³]
h = height, ft [m]
h_i = thickness of ith sand, ft [m]
h_o = thickness of oil zone, ft [m]
h_p = height of top of perforations above base of oil zone, ft [m]
I_f = rock-expansion index, fraction of oil space replaced by expansion of reservoir rock and interstitial water
I_{gc} = gas-cap-drive index, fraction of oil space replaced by gas cap gas
I_{sg} = solution-gas-drive index, fraction of oil space replaced by solution gas
I_w = waterdrive index, fraction of oil space replaced by water
J_{sw} = Leverett's function, dimensionless
k = effective permeability, md

k_i = permeability of ith sand, md
k_{ro} = relative permeability to oil, md
k_{rw} = relative permeability to water, md
L = length, ft [m]
ΔL = distance saturation moves, ft [m]
ΔL_C = length between 10 and 90% concentration levels, ft [m]
L_D = dimensionless length
L_t = total length, ft [m]
M = mobility ratio, dimensionless
M_a,M_b = molecular weights of gases a and b
n = number of blocks in oil zone
N = volume of oil original in place, STB [stock-tank m^3]
ΔN = oil drainage, RB [res m^3]
N_p = oil production, STB [stock-tank m^3]
p = pressure or present pressure, psi [kPa]
Δp = pressure drop, psi [kPa]
p_i = original pressure, psi [kPa]
p_{t_D} = dimensionless pressure
p_w = pressure at wellbore or inner radius of aquifer, psi [kPa]
P_c = capillary pressure, psi [kPa]
q = flow rate, B/D [m^3/d]
q_c = critical flow rate, B/D [m^3/d]
q_g = gas flow rate, Mscf/D [10^3 std m^3/d]
q_o = oil flow rate, STB/D [stock-tank m^3/d]
q_t = total flow rate, B/D [m^3/d]
Q_i = cumulative water injection, PV
Q_{tD} = dimensionless fluid influx
r = radius, ft [m]
r_D = dimensionless radius
r_e = drainage radius of well or outer radius of aquifer, ft [m]
r_w = radius of wellbore or inner radius of aquifer, ft [m]
R_s = solution GOR at present conditions, scf/STB [std m^3/stock-tank m^3]
R_{si} = solution GOR at original conditions, scf/STB [std m^3/stock-tank m^3]
S = saturation, fraction
ΔS_o = oil saturation increment, fraction
S_{oir} = irreducible oil saturation for gas/oil displacement in presence of interstitial water, fraction
S_w = water saturation, fraction
ΔS_w = water saturation increment, fraction
S_{wi} = initial water saturation, fraction
S_{w2} = water saturation at producing face at or after water breakthrough, fraction
t = time, days
Δt = timestep, days
t_D = dimensionless time
T = reservoir temperature, °R [K]
V_a,V_b = molecular volumes of gases a and b
V_{do} = displaceable oil volume, fraction
V_p = PV, bbl [m^3]
W_e = natural water influx, res bbl [res m^3]
W_i = water injected, STB [stock-tank m^3]
W_p = water production, STB [stock-tank m^3]
x = position of front, ft [m]
$z_{\bar{p}}$ = compressibility factor for gas at average pressure, fraction
z = distance in vertical direction, ft [m]
β = stable angle, degrees [rads]
θ_c = contact angle, degrees [rads]
Θ = angle of dip (positive for downdip flow), degrees [rads]
λ = fluid mobility, md/cp [md/Pa·s]
μ = viscosity, cp [Pa·s]
$\Delta\rho$ = density difference, lbm/ft^3 [kg/m^3]
ρ_o = oil density, lbm/ft^3 [kg/m^3]
σ = IFT, dyne/cm [mN/m]
τ = tortuosity factor, dimensionless

Subscripts

d = displaced
D = displacing
g = gas
o = oil
w = water

Superscripts

n = slope of log k_{ro} vs. $(S_o - S_{oir})/(1 - S_{wi} - S_{oir})$

References

1. van Everdingen, A.F. and Hurst, W.: "The Application of the LaPlace Transformation to Flow Problems in Reservoirs," *Trans.*, AIME (1949) **186,** 305–24.
2. Leverett, M.C.: "Capillary Behavior in Porous Solids," *Trans.*, AIME (1941) **142,** 152–69.
3. Buckley, S.J. and Leverett, M.C.: "Mechanism of Fluid Displacement in Sands," *Trans.*, AIME (1942) **146,** 107–16.
4. Welge, H.J.: "Simplified Method for Computing Oil Recoveries by Gas or Water Drive," *Trans.*, AIME (1952) **195,** 91–98.
5. Craig, F.F. Jr., Geffen, T.M., and Morse, R.A.: "Oil Recovery Performance of Pattern Gas or Water Injection Operations from Model Tests," *JPT* (Jan. 1955) 7–14; *Trans.*, AIME, **204.**
6. Dietz, D.N.: "A Theoretical Approach to the Problem of Encroaching and By-Passing Edge Water," *Proc.*, Kon. Neder. Akad. Wetenshappen (1953) Series B-56, No. 1, 83–92.
7. Muskat, M. and Wycoff, R.D.: "An Approximate Theory of Water Coning in Oil Production," *Trans.*, AIME (1935) **114,** 144–63.
8. Dykstra, H. and Parsons, R.L.: "The Prediction of Oil Recovery by Waterflood," *Secondary Recovery of Oil in the United States,* second edition, API, Washington, DC (1950) 160.
9. Stiles, W.E.: "Use of Permeability Distribution in Waterflood Calculations," *Trans.*, AIME (1949) **186,** 9–13.
10. Dyes, A.B., Caudle, B.H., and Erickson, R.A.: "Oil Production After Breakthrough as Influenced by Mobility Ratio," *JPT* (April 1954) 27–32; *Trans.*, AIME, **201.**
11. Richardson, J.G. and Blackwell, R.J.: "Use of Simple Mathematical Models to Predict Reservoir Behavior," *JPT* (Sept. 1971) 1145–54; *Trans.*, AIME, **251.**
12. Corey, A.T. *et al.*: "Three-Phase Relative Permeability," *JPT* (Nov. 1956) 349–51; *Trans.*, AIME, **207.**
13. Richardson, J.G. and Graham, J.W.: "Theory and Application of Imbibition Phenomena in Recovery of Oil," *JPT* (Feb. 1959) 65–70; *Trans.*, AIME, **216.**
14. Gilliland, E.R.: "Diffusion Coefficients in Gaseous Systems," *Ind. & Eng. Chem.* (1934) **27,** 681.

SI Metric Conversion Factors

°API	141.5/(131.5+°API)		=	g/cm^3
ft	× 3.048*	E−01	=	m
ft^2	× 9.290 304*	E−02	=	m^2
°F	(°F−32)/1.8		=	°C
in.	× 2.54*	E+00	=	cm
in.^{2}	× 6.451 6*	E+00	=	cm^2

*Conversion factor is exact.

Appendix B
Mathematical Basis for Numerical Simulation by Finite-Difference Equations

In this monograph, the primary emphasis has been on the capabilities of reservoir simulators and on the considerations necessary to make effective use of them for modeling reservoir performance. Consequently, the mathematics underlying reservoir simulation was not stressed. In Appendices B and C, the mathematics of reservoir simulation is described in some detail to provide the theoretically minded engineer with an understanding of the inside of the "black box" that constitutes a reservoir simulator.*

While reservoir simulators have been characterized variously as computer models, mathematical models, or numerical models, it is useful to make a distinction between these terms. For our purposes, a *mathematical model* of a physical system is a set of partial differential equations, together with an appropriate set of boundary conditions, that we believe adequately describes the significant physical processes taking place in that system.

To use differential equations for predicting the behavior of a reservoir, it is necessary to solve them subject to the appropriate boundary conditions. Only for the simplest cases involving homogeneous reservoirs and very regular boundaries (such as a circular boundary around a single well) can solutions be obtained by the classic methods of mathematical physics. Approximations must be made to put the differential equations into a form (e.g., difference equations) that is amenable to solution by digital computers. Such a set of equations constitutes a *numerical model.* Finally, the computer program or set of programs written to solve the equations of the numerical model makes up the *computer model.*[1,2]

Attention here is restricted to a basic, but very useful, "black-oil" model. More elaborate models, including various EOR models, are discussed in Chap. 11 and in Refs. 2 through 4. Refs. 3 and 4 contain excellent literature surveys for further study.

B.1 Differential Equations

B.1.1 One-Dimensional (1D) Flow. In its simplest form, Darcy's law for horizontal single-phase flow states that the *volumetric* flow rate (expressed as reservoir volume per unit time) through a porous medium of length L and cross-sectional area A is

$$q=-\frac{Ak}{\mu}\left(\frac{\Delta p}{L}\right).$$

If the porous medium is not horizontal, but is tilted to the horizontal at an angle Θ, this equation is modified as follows to include the effect of gravity:

$$q=-\frac{Ak}{\mu}\left(\frac{\Delta p}{L}-\rho g \sin \Theta\right).$$

To derive the differential equation for flow in one dimension, we allow area and depth, D, to vary arbitrarily with distance, x, and replace $\Delta p/L$ by $\partial p/\partial x$ and $\sin \Theta$ by $\partial D/\partial x$ to obtain the single-phase differential form of Darcy's law:

$$q=-\frac{Ak}{\mu}\left(\frac{\partial p}{\partial x}-\rho g\frac{\partial D}{\partial x}\right).$$

For immiscible three-phase flow, relative permeability is included to obtain Darcy's law separately for the volumetric flow rates of oil, water, and gas:

$$q_o=-\frac{Akk_{ro}}{\mu_o}\left(\frac{\partial p_o}{\partial x}-\rho_o g\frac{\partial D}{\partial x}\right), \quad \text{(B.1)}$$

$$q_w=-\frac{Akk_{rw}}{\mu_w}\left(\frac{\partial p_w}{\partial x}-\rho_w g\frac{\partial D}{\partial x}\right), \quad \text{(B.2)}$$

and

$$q_g=-\frac{Akk_{rg}}{\mu_g}\left(\frac{\partial p_g}{\partial x}-\rho_g g\frac{\partial D}{\partial x}\right). \quad \text{(B.3)}$$

These three equations will be combined with material-balance, or continuity, equations to obtain the differential equations governing the flow of oil, water, and gas in a porous medium.

To derive the continuity equation for the oil phase, we carry out a *mass* balance on the small element of volume shown in Fig. B.1. The mass rate (expressed as standard volumes per unit time) at which oil enters the left face of the element is

$$\left(\frac{q_o}{B_o}\right)_x,$$

while the rate at which oil leaves the right face is

$$\left(\frac{q_o}{B_o}\right)_{x+\Delta x}.$$

Here B_o is the oil FVF—i.e., reservoir volume of the oil phase per standard volume of oil.

Because mass must be conserved within the element,

rate in rate out = rate of accumulation.

Now, the PV of the element is $A\Delta x\phi$, and the mass of oil contained in the element is $A\Delta x\phi S_o/B_o$. (Porosity, ϕ, is PV per element volume and may change with time because of the effect of rock compressibility, together with changes in pressure level with time.

*In this appendix we use a consistent set of units and do not provide the equivalent oilfield units.

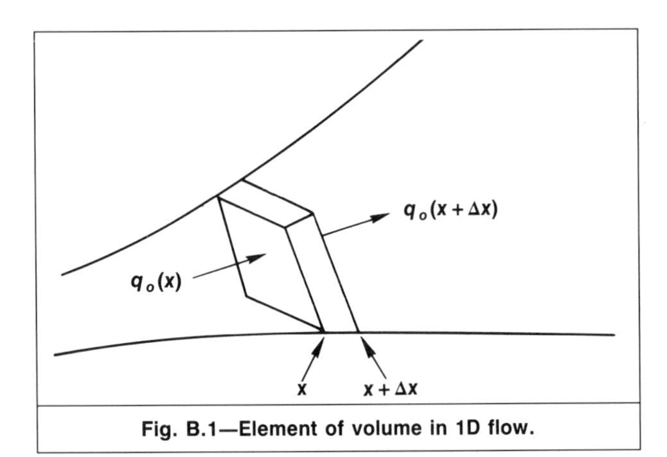

Fig. B.1—Element of volume in 1D flow.

Oil-phase saturation, S_o, is reservoir volume of the oil phase per unit PV.) Hence, the rate of accumulation of oil in the element is

$$A\Delta x \frac{\partial}{\partial t}\left(\frac{\phi S_o}{B_o}\right)$$

and

$$\left(\frac{q_o}{B_o}\right)_x - \left(\frac{q_o}{B_o}\right)_{x+\Delta x} = A\Delta x \frac{\partial}{\partial t}\left(\frac{\phi S_o}{B_o}\right).$$

Dividing by Δx gives

$$-\frac{\left(\frac{q_o}{B_o}\right)_{x+\Delta x} - \left(\frac{q_o}{B_o}\right)_x}{\Delta x} = A\frac{\partial}{\partial t}\left(\frac{\phi S_o}{B_o}\right).$$

Taking the limit as $\Delta x \rightarrow 0$, we obtain

$$-\frac{\partial}{\partial x}\left(\frac{q_o}{B_o}\right) = A\frac{\partial}{\partial t}\left(\frac{\phi S_o}{B_o}\right). \quad \text{(B.4)}$$

Exactly the same approach leads to the continuity equation for water:

$$-\frac{\partial}{\partial x}\left(\frac{q_w}{B_w}\right) = A\frac{\partial}{\partial t}\left(\frac{\phi S_w}{B_w}\right). \quad \text{(B.5)}$$

If there were no mass transfer between phases, a similar continuity equation would also be written for the gas phase. A limited, but very useful, mass-transfer effect can be taken into account by using the so-called "black-oil" model, in which it is assumed that gas dissolves in the oil phase, but that oil does not vaporize into the gas. The gas material balance is therefore altered to include not only the gas in the gas phase but also the gas dissolved in the oil phase:

$$-\frac{\partial}{\partial x}\left(\frac{q_g}{B_g} + \frac{q_o R_s}{B_o}\right) = A\frac{\partial}{\partial t}\left[\phi\left(\frac{S_g}{B_g} + \frac{S_o R_s}{B_o}\right)\right], \quad \text{(B.6)}$$

where R_s is the solution gas/oil ratio (GOR)—i.e., the standard volume of gas dissolved in a standard volume of oil. Note that R_s/B_o is then the standard volume of gas dissolved per unit reservoir volume of oil.

One may allow also for volatilization of the oil into the gas phase by a similar modification of the oil equation, Eq. B.4. This is equivalent to assuming that the hydrocarbon system consists of only *two* components, oil and gas, and ignores the actual effect of composition on the vapor/liquid equilibrium. More realistic modeling of volatile oil systems requires compositional simulators that take into account the effect of composition on the vapor/liquid equilibrium. Discussion of compositional simulators is beyond the scope of this appendix; however, the interested reader can find the derivation of the partial differential equations for compositional simulators discussed in Chap. 11 and in Peaceman.[1] This derivation is based on material balances written for each chemical species included in the model.

For the black-oil model being considered here, the final differential equations for three-phase flow in *one* dimension are obtained by substituting Eqs. B.1 through B.3 into the material-balance equations, Eqs. B.4 through B.6. These differential equations are

$$\frac{\partial}{\partial x}\left[\frac{Akk_{ro}}{B_o\mu_o}\left(\frac{\partial p_o}{\partial x} - \rho_o g\frac{\partial D}{\partial x}\right)\right] = A\frac{\partial}{\partial t}\left(\frac{\phi S_o}{B_o}\right), \quad \text{(B.7)}$$

$$\frac{\partial}{\partial x}\left[\frac{Akk_{rw}}{B_w\mu_w}\left(\frac{\partial p_w}{\partial x} - \rho_w g\frac{\partial D}{\partial x}\right)\right] = A\frac{\partial}{\partial t}\left(\frac{\phi S_w}{B_w}\right), \quad \text{(B.8)}$$

and

$$\frac{\partial}{\partial x}\left[\frac{Akk_{rg}}{B_g\mu_g}\left(\frac{\partial p_g}{\partial x} - \rho_g g\frac{\partial D}{\partial x}\right) + \frac{AR_s kk_{ro}}{B_o\mu_o}\left(\frac{\partial p_o}{\partial x} - \rho_o g\frac{\partial D}{\partial x}\right)\right]$$

$$= A\frac{\partial}{\partial t}\left[\phi\left(\frac{S_g}{B_g} + \frac{S_o R_s}{B_o}\right)\right]. \quad \text{(B.9)}$$

B.1.2 Two-Dimensional (2D) Flow. The extension to two space dimensions, x and y, is straightforward; we divide by $\Delta x\Delta y$ instead of Δx before taking limits. The factor A in the differential equations is replaced by thickness h, which is to be considered a function of x and y. In addition, derivatives accounting for flow in the y direction need to be added. The oil equation becomes

$$\frac{\partial}{\partial x}\left[\frac{hk_x k_{ro}}{B_o\mu_o}\left(\frac{\partial p_o}{\partial x} - \rho_o g\frac{\partial D}{\partial x}\right)\right]$$

$$+\frac{\partial}{\partial y}\left[\frac{hk_y k_{ro}}{B_o\mu_o}\left(\frac{\partial p_o}{\partial y} - \rho_o g\frac{\partial D}{\partial y}\right)\right] = h\frac{\partial}{\partial t}\left(\frac{\phi S_o}{B_o}\right),$$

where the possibility of anisotropic permeability is permitted through the use of the x-direction rock permeability, k_x, and the y-direction rock permeability, k_y.

Note that the left side is a combination of expressions of the form

$$\frac{\partial}{\partial x}\left(f_x\frac{\partial p}{\partial x}\right) + \frac{\partial}{\partial y}\left(f_y\frac{\partial p}{\partial y}\right),$$

where f_x and f_y are some functions of x, y, and t. This is commonly abbreviated as $\nabla\cdot(f\nabla p)$. Thus, the 2D equations can be written in the abbreviated form

$$\nabla\cdot\left[\frac{hkk_{ro}}{B_o\mu_o}(\nabla p_o - \rho_o g\nabla D)\right] = h\frac{\partial}{\partial t}\left(\frac{\phi S_o}{B_o}\right), \quad \text{(B.10)}$$

$$\nabla\cdot\left[\frac{hkk_{rw}}{B_w\mu_w}(\nabla p_w - \rho_w g\nabla D)\right] = h\frac{\partial}{\partial t}\left(\frac{\phi S_w}{B_w}\right), \quad \text{(B.11)}$$

and

$$\nabla\cdot\left[\frac{hkk_{rg}}{B_g\mu_g}(\nabla p_g - \rho_g g\nabla D) + \frac{hR_s kk_{ro}}{B_o\mu_o}(\nabla p_o - \rho_o g\nabla D)\right]$$

$$= h\frac{\partial}{\partial t}\left[\phi\left(\frac{S_g}{B_g} + \frac{S_o R_s}{B_o}\right)\right]. \quad \text{(B.12)}$$

B.1.3 Three-Dimensional Flow. To extend to three space dimensions, x, y, and z, we need merely to add derivatives that account for flow in the z direction. The factor h in the differential equations disappears completely. If we define the abbreviation $\nabla \cdot (f \nabla p)$ by

$$\nabla \cdot (f \nabla p)=\frac{\partial}{\partial x}\left(f_x \frac{\partial p}{\partial x}\right)+\frac{\partial}{\partial y}\left(f_y \frac{\partial p}{\partial y}\right)+\frac{\partial}{\partial z}\left(f_z \frac{\partial p}{\partial z}\right), \quad \text{(B.13)}$$

then we get exactly the same equations as Eqs. B.10 through B.12 for three-phase flow in three dimensions (provided h is taken to be 1).

B.1.4 Auxiliary Relations. In addition to the differential equations, certain auxiliary relations must be provided to complete the description of the mathematical model. First, we note that the sum of the volumes of the three phases must always equal the PV at any point in the system. Hence,

$$S_o+S_w+S_g=1. \quad \text{(B.14)}$$

Obviously, any one saturation can always be expressed in terms of the other two.

At any given position in the reservoir, relative permeabilities are taken to be functions of saturation alone. Thus, we write

$$k_{ro}=k_{ro}(S_o,S_w), \quad \text{(B.15)}$$

$$k_{rw}=k_{rw}(S_o,S_w), \quad \text{(B.16)}$$

and

$$k_{rg}=k_{rg}(S_o,S_w). \quad \text{(B.17)}$$

Because of the lack of adequate data, three-phase relative permeabilities are usually calculated with relative-permeability models and data obtained in two-phase gas/oil and water/oil systems.[5,6] Where saturation reversals occur, relative permeabilities are also history-dependent and hysteresis should be taken into account.

Similarly, at any position in the reservoir, capillary pressures are taken to be functions of saturation alone:

$$P_{c_{ow}}=p_o-p_w=P_{c_{ow}}(S_o,S_w) \quad \text{(B.18)}$$

and

$$P_{c_{go}}=p_g-p_o=P_{c_{go}}(S_o,S_w). \quad \text{(B.19)}$$

Capillary pressure may also be history-dependent if saturation reversals occur. Note that a third capillary pressure is automatically defined by the first two—i.e.,

$$P_{c_{gw}}=p_g-p_w=P_{c_{go}}+P_{c_{ow}}.$$

Again, because data are lacking, three-phase capillary pressures are usually calculated from water/oil and gas/oil two-phase subsystems. $P_{c_{ow}}$ is assumed to be a function of S_w alone, while $P_{c_{go}}$ is assumed to be a function of S_g alone.

Relative permeabilities and capillary-pressure functions are frequently position-dependent, in which case multiple sets of data must be used.

The density, viscosity, and volume factors of each phase are usually taken as functions of phase pressure. Thus, we can write

$$\rho_p=\rho_p(p_p),\ p=o,w,g, \quad \text{(B.20)}$$

$$\mu_p=\mu_p(p_p),\ p=o,w,g, \quad \text{(B.21)}$$

and

$$B_p=B_p(p_p),\ p=o,w,g. \quad \text{(B.22)}$$

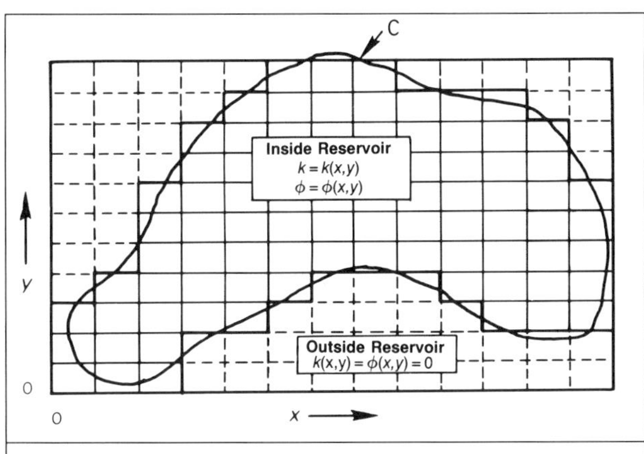

Fig. B.2—Representation of irregularly shaped reservoir.

Gas solubility is expressed as a function of oil pressure:

$$R_s=R_s(p_o). \quad \text{(B.23)}$$

The functions describing density, viscosity, FVF, and gas solubility may also be position-dependent, again requiring the use of multiple sets of data.

Other functions appearing in the differential equations are functions of position alone. Thus we have

$$k_x=k_x(x,y,z), \quad \text{(B.24)}$$

$$k_y=k_y(x,y,z), \quad \text{(B.25)}$$

$$k_z=k_z(x,y,z), \quad \text{(B.26)}$$

and

$$D=D(x,y,z). \quad \text{(B.27)}$$

Porosity is a function of both pressure and position. Thus,

$$\phi=\phi(p_o,x,y,z). \quad \text{(B.28)}$$

Refer to Chap. 4 for a discussion of the selection and assignment of all the data required.

Eqs. B.14 through B.28 constitute a complete list of auxiliary relationships (under the simplifying assumption that pressure does not rise above the bubblepoint, causing the gas phase to disappear). Together with Eqs. B.10 through B.12, these relationships define a system of three partial differential equations in three unknowns: p_o, S_w, and S_g. All the other quantities depend on only these unknowns and the independent variables x, y, z, and t.

B.1.5 Boundary Conditions. A frequent assumption in reservoir simulation is that the reservoir lies within some closed curve, C, across which there is no flow, and that fluid injection and production take place at wells located at points or lines within the interior of the reservoir. Strictly, we should represent the no-flow boundary condition by requiring that the component of flow perpendicular to Curve C be zero. This is relatively difficult to do numerically for an arbitrary curve. However, there usually is little interest in an accurate solution in the neighborhood of the curved boundary; rather, our interest lies mostly within the interior of the reservoir. For this reason, it is adequate to represent the curved boundary in the following crude way. The reservoir is embedded in a gridded rectangle and the functions k and ϕ are set to zero in the gridblocks outside Curve C, as shown in Fig. B.2.

The most important part of the boundary conditions is the specification of fluid injection and production at the wells. At each well, either the pressure or the flow rate for each phase is specified. Because each well has a small diameter relative to the horizontal dimensions of a reservoir, it may be represented mathematically by a point source or sink, or a line source or sink. Because it is difficult

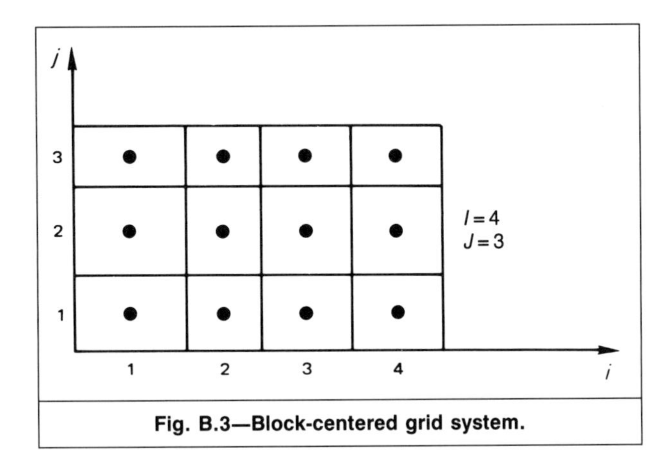

Fig. B.3—Block-centered grid system.

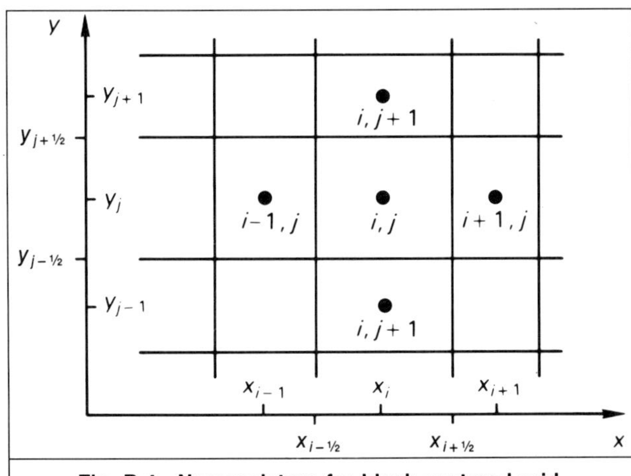

Fig. B.4—Nomenclature for block-centered grid.

to specify properly a point or line source or sink boundary condition without some special notation, we will postpone the discussion of wells until after we begin to consider the numerical solution of the differential equations by finite-difference methods.

B.1.6 Initial Conditions. To complete the mathematical description of the reservoir, it is necessary to specify initial conditions.

It may be possible to specify pressures and saturations at each position at initial time. More commonly, however, phase pressures are specified at a reference depth, and the capillary pressure and density relationships (Eqs. B.18 through B.20) are used to compute pressures and saturations through the ordinary differential equations,

$$\frac{\mathrm{d}p_p}{\mathrm{d}D}=\rho_p(p_p)g,\ p=o,w,g,$$

resulting from the assumption that phase potentials do not vary with position.

B.2 Spatial Discretization

The numerical solution of partial differential equations by finite differences involves replacing the partial derivatives by finite-difference quotients. Then, instead of obtaining a continuous solution, we obtain an approximate solution at a discrete set of gridblocks or points at discrete times. In this section, we discuss the replacement of the spatial derivatives.

To simplify the presentation, only the case of two space dimensions will be considered. For the most part, the extension to three dimensions (or the reduction to one dimension) is quite straightforward.

A discrete set of gridblocks in the x-y plane is obtained by use of a grid system to divide the solution rectangle, as in Fig. B.3. There are I gridblocks in the x direction and J gridblocks in the y direction. The subscript i is used to identify columns of gridblocks and the subscript j to identify rows. Each Point (x_i,y_j), also called Point (i,j), lies at the center of a gridblock. Double subscripts are used to indicate position within the grid. Thus, for example, $S_{i,j}$, refers to the value of S at Point (i,j), and more generally to the average value of S within Gridblock (i,j).

Locations of the gridblocks are defined by locations of their boundaries:

$$x_{½},x_{3/2}\ldots x_{I+½}$$

and

$$y_{½},y_{3/2}\ldots y_{J+½}.$$

The centers of the gridblocks then satisfy

$$x_i=(x_{i-½}+x_{i+½})/2$$

and

$$y_j=(y_{j-½}+y_{j+½})/2.$$

(See Fig. B.4.)

To permit greater definition in some parts of the reservoir relative to other parts, we allow the grid spacing to be variable.

We can now begin the replacement of the space derivatives. For simplicity, we will consider for the moment just one of the three partial differential equations, namely the oil equation (Eq. B.10). Further, we will temporarily ignore the gravity terms. Then the oil equation (Eq. B.10) simplifies to

$$\nabla\cdot\left(\frac{hkk_{ro}}{B_o\mu_o}\nabla p_o\right)=h\frac{\partial}{\partial t}\left(\frac{\phi S_o}{B_o}\right).\ \ldots\ldots\ldots\ldots \text{(B.29)}$$

To simplify the notation further, let

$$M_o=\frac{k_{ro}}{B_o\mu_o}.\ \ldots\ldots\ldots\ldots \text{(B.30)}$$

Then

$$\nabla\cdot(hkM_o\nabla p_o)=h\frac{\partial}{\partial t}\left(\frac{\phi S_o}{B_o}\right).\ \ldots\ldots\ldots\ldots \text{(B.31)}$$

In expanded form, the differential equation (Eq. B.31) is

$$\frac{\partial}{\partial x}\left(hk_xM_o\frac{\partial p_o}{\partial x}\right)+\frac{\partial}{\partial y}\left(hk_yM_o\frac{\partial p_o}{\partial y}\right)=h\frac{\partial}{\partial t}\left(\frac{\phi S_o}{B_o}\right).$$

$$\ldots\ldots\ldots\ldots \text{(B.32)}$$

Note that hk_x and hk_y are time-invariant, while M_o, *the mobility factor*, is time-varying because it is a combination of quantities that depend on the solution variables.

Consider the x derivative first. We can approximate it at Point (x_i,y_j) by

$$\frac{\partial}{\partial x}\left(hk_xM_o\frac{\partial p_o}{\partial x}\right)\sim\frac{\left(hk_xM_o\frac{\partial p_o}{\partial x}\right)_{i+½,j}-\left(hk_xM_o\frac{\partial p_o}{\partial x}\right)_{i-½,j}}{x_{i+½}-x_{i-½}}.$$

In turn, we can make the approximations

$$\left(\frac{\partial p_o}{\partial x}\right)_{i+½,j}\sim\frac{(p_o)_{i+1,j}-(p_o)_{i,j}}{x_{i+1}-x_i}$$

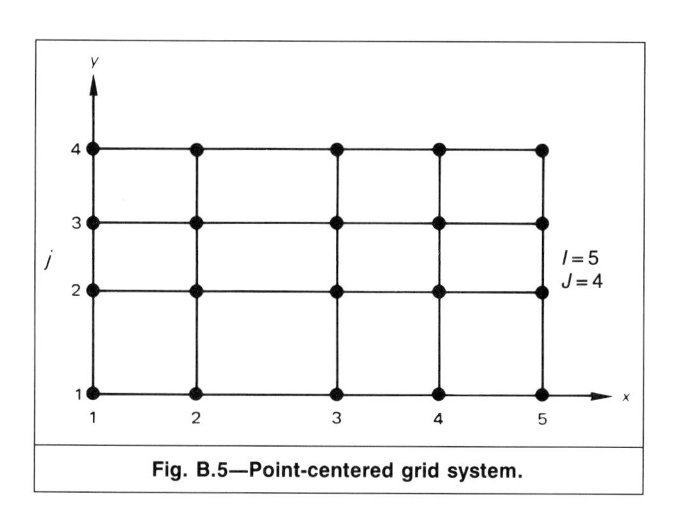

Fig. B.5—Point-centered grid system.

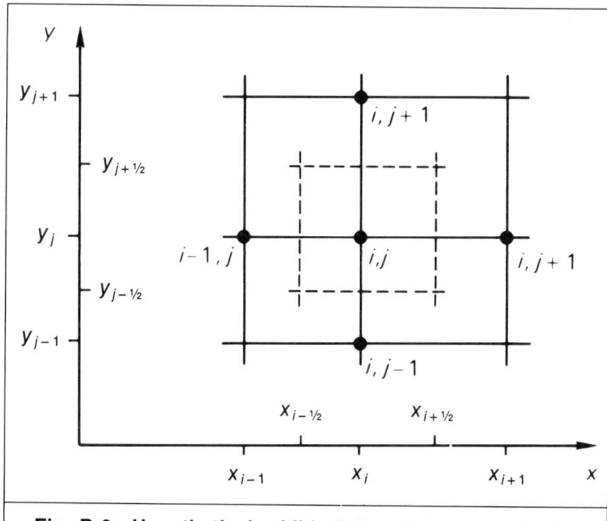

Fig. B.6—Hypothetical gridblock in point-centered grid.

and

$$\left(\frac{\partial p_o}{\partial x}\right)_{i-½,j} \sim \frac{(p_o)_{i,j}-(p_o)_{i-1,j}}{x_i-x_{i-1}},$$

where $(p_o)_{i,j}$ is the *approximate*, or numerical, solution for p_o at Point (i,j). Then

$$\frac{\partial}{\partial x}\left(hk_xM_o\frac{\partial p_o}{\partial x}\right) \sim$$

$$\frac{\dfrac{(hk_xM_o)_{i+½,j}[(p_o)_{i+1,j}-(p_o)_{i,j}]}{x_{i+1}-x_i}-\dfrac{(hk_xM_o)_{i-½,j}[(p_o)_{i,j}-(p_o)_{i-1,j}]}{x_i-x_{i-1}}}{x_{i+½}-x_{i-½}}.$$

Similarly,

$$\frac{\partial}{\partial y}\left(hk_yM_o\frac{\partial p_o}{\partial y}\right) \sim$$

$$\frac{\dfrac{(hk_yM_o)_{i,j+½}[(p_o)_{i,j+1}-(p_o)_{i,j}]}{y_{j+1}-y_j}-\dfrac{(hk_yM_o)_{i,j-½}[(p_o)_{i,j}-(p_o)_{i,j-1}]}{y_j-y_{j-1}}}{y_{j+½}-y_{j-½}}.$$

Note that we have not yet specified how to evaluate properties associated with block boundaries [e.g., $(M_o)_{i\pm½,j}$ and $(M_o)_{i,j\pm½}$]; pressure and saturation are only defined at block centers. Various choices will be discussed in Appendix C. "Upstream weighting" is by far the most common choice. In the absence of gravity,

$$(M_o)_{i+½,j}=(M_o)_{i,j}, \text{ if } (p_o)_{i,j}\geq(p_o)_{i+1,j}$$

and

$$(M_o)_{i+½,j}=(M_o)_{i+1,j}, \text{ if } (p_o)_{i,j}<(p_o)_{i+1,j}.$$

B.2.1 Grid Systems. Two types of grids are in common use in reservoir simulation. Grids of the kind just described are called *block-centered,* because Point (x_i,y_j) is at the center of Block (i,j). The second, less frequently used, kind of grid is called by several names. *Point-centered*[1] is the most popular name, but lattice grid,[7] gridpoint distribution method,[8] and point-distributed grid[9] are also used. (See Fig. B.5.) In this case, locations of the gridpoints are specified directly,

$$x_1,x_2\ldots x_I$$

and

$$y_1,y_2\ldots y_J,$$

and a rectangular block is visualized around each gridpoint with left and right faces at $x_{i-½}$ and $x_{i+½}$, and lower and upper faces at $y_{j-½}$ and $y_{j+½}$, as shown in Fig. B.6, where

$$x_{i-½}=(x_{i-1}+x_i)/2,$$

$$x_{i+½}=(x_i+x_{i+1})/2,$$

$$y_{j-½}=(y_{j-1}+y_j)/2,$$

and

$$y_{j+½}=(y_j+y_{j+1})/2.$$

For interior points, the spatial difference quotients are written the same way for either kind of grid. There are, however, significant differences between the two grid systems. The point-centered system has boundaries that coincide with the exterior calculation points; this is advantageous when wells are to be placed exactly at the outer boundary of the computing rectangle, as in the modeling of a quarter five-spot pattern. On the other hand, in the block-centered system, the boundaries of the computing rectangle coincide with block boundaries; this is consistent with a control-volume approach and is frequently more natural to the engineer. Another difference is that the block-centered system requires no special treatment of the difference equations for the exterior blocks, while the point-centered system requires a slight modification. For these reasons, block-centered grid systems are usually preferred for reservoir simulation.

B.3 Time Discretization

To complete the discretization, we also replace each time derivative by a corresponding difference quotient. Time is divided into discrete points: 0, t^1, $t^2\ldots t^n$, t^{n+1}. . . . (Note that we use superscripts to indicate the time level.) Assume that we have, at time t^n, a solution for each dependent variable at each gridpoint. A numerical procedure consists, then, of a technique for generating a solution for each dependent variable at each gridpoint at the next time, t^{n+1}. Clearly, starting with the initial condition at time zero, repeated application of the numerical procedure will generate the solution at each discrete point in space and time, (x_i,y_j,t^n), for the period of interest.

Let

$$\Delta t=t^{n+1}-t^n.$$

Then a time derivative, such as that on the right side of Eq. B.32, may be approximated at Gridpoint (i,j) by

$$\frac{\partial}{\partial t}\left(\frac{\phi S_o}{B_o}\right) \sim \frac{\left(\frac{\phi S_o}{B_o}\right)_{i,j}^{n+1} - \left(\frac{\phi S_o}{B_o}\right)_{i,j}^{n}}{\Delta t}.$$

B.4 Basic Finite-Difference Equation

Substituting the numerical approximations for the spatial and time derivatives into the differential equation for oil (Eq. B.32) gives, then, the following difference equation:

$$\frac{\frac{(hk_xM_o)_{i+\frac{1}{2},j}[(p_o)_{i+1,j}-(p_o)_{i,j}]}{x_{i+1}-x_i} - \frac{(hk_xM_o)_{i-\frac{1}{2},j}[(p_o)_{i,j}-(p_o)_{i-1,j}]}{x_i-x_{i-1}}}{x_{i+\frac{1}{2}}-x_{i-\frac{1}{2}}}$$

$$+$$

$$\frac{\frac{(hk_yM_o)_{i,j+\frac{1}{2}}[(p_o)_{i,j+1}-(p_o)_{i,j}]}{y_{j+1}-y_j} - \frac{(hk_yM_o)_{i,j-\frac{1}{2}}[(p_o)_{i,j}-(p_o)_{i,j-1}]}{y_j-y_{j-1}}}{y_{j+\frac{1}{2}}-y_{j-\frac{1}{2}}}$$

$$=\frac{h_{i,j}}{\Delta t}\left[\left(\frac{\phi S_o}{B_o}\right)_{i,j}^{n+1} - \left(\frac{\phi S_o}{B_o}\right)_{i,j}^{n}\right]. \quad \text{(B.33)}$$

Note that no superscripts have been used on the left side of this equation. This indicates that, for the time being, we leave undetermined the time level at which various parts of the spatial differences are to be evaluated. There are many numerical procedures whereby we can go from Step n to Step $n+1$, and each numerical procedure is characterized by the way superscripts n and $n+1$ are assigned to the left side. In Appendix C, we shall consider a number of these numerical procedures and the appropriate superscripts will be used. A common choice is to evaluate pressures at Time $n+1$ and all other quantities at Time n.

B.5 Rearranged Finite-Difference Equation

A rearrangement of Eq. B.33 yields a finite-difference equation in which the various terms can be given a physical interpretation in terms of the blocks shown in either Figs. B.3 and B.4 or B.5 and B.6. Multiply through by $(x_{i+\frac{1}{2}}-x_{i-\frac{1}{2}})(y_{j+\frac{1}{2}}-y_{j-\frac{1}{2}})$, which is the area of the block. Then the difference equation (Eq. B.33) becomes

$$(T_{ox})_{i+\frac{1}{2},j}[(p_o)_{i+1,j}-(p_o)_{i,j}]$$
$$-(T_{ox})_{i-\frac{1}{2},j}[(p_o)_{i,j}-(p_o)_{i-1,j}]$$
$$+(T_{oy})_{i,j+\frac{1}{2}}[(p_o)_{i,j+1}-(p_o)_{i,j}]$$
$$-(T_{oy})_{i,j-\frac{1}{2}}[(p_o)_{i,j}-(p_o)_{i,j-1}]$$
$$=\frac{V_{i,j}}{\Delta t}\left[\left(\frac{\phi S_o}{B_o}\right)_{i,j}^{n+1} - \left(\frac{\phi S_o}{B_o}\right)_{i,j}^{n}\right], \quad \text{(B.34)}$$

where

$$(T_{ox})_{i+\frac{1}{2},j}=\frac{(hk_xM_o)_{i+\frac{1}{2},j}(y_{j+\frac{1}{2}}-y_{j-\frac{1}{2}})}{x_{i+1}-x_i},$$

$$(T_{oy})_{i,j+\frac{1}{2}}=\frac{(hk_yM_o)_{i,j+\frac{1}{2}}(x_{i+\frac{1}{2}}-x_{i-\frac{1}{2}})}{y_{j+1}-y_j},$$

and

$$V_{i,j}=h_{i,j}(x_{i+\frac{1}{2}}-x_{i-\frac{1}{2}})(y_{j+\frac{1}{2}}-y_{j-\frac{1}{2}}).$$

Each of these last terms has a physical interpretation. $(T_{ox})_{i+\frac{1}{2},j}$ can be regarded as the transmissibility to oil in the x direction at the right boundary of Block (i,j), $(T_{oy})_{i,j+\frac{1}{2}}$ as the transmissibility to oil in the y direction at the upper boundary of Block (i,j), and $V_{i,j}$ as the volume of Block (i,j).

Each of the transmissibility terms can be factored into a time-invariant and a time-varying portion:

$$(T_{ox})_{i+\frac{1}{2},j}=(T_x)_{i+\frac{1}{2},j}(M_{ox})_{i+\frac{1}{2},j}$$

and

$$(T_{oy})_{i,j+\frac{1}{2}}=(T_y)_{i,j+\frac{1}{2}}(M_{oy})_{i,j+\frac{1}{2}},$$

where

$$(T_x)_{i+\frac{1}{2},j}=\frac{(hk_x)_{i+\frac{1}{2},j}(y_{j+\frac{1}{2}}-y_{j-\frac{1}{2}})}{x_{i+1}-x_i},$$

$$(T_y)_{i,j+\frac{1}{2}}=\frac{(hk_y)_{i,j+\frac{1}{2}}(x_{i+\frac{1}{2}}-x_{i-\frac{1}{2}})}{y_{j+1}-y_j},$$

$$(M_{ox})_{i+\frac{1}{2},j}=\left(\frac{k_{ro}}{B_o\mu_o}\right)_{i+\frac{1}{2},j},$$

and

$$(M_{oy})_{i,j+\frac{1}{2}}=\left(\frac{k_{ro}}{B_o\mu_o}\right)_{i,j+\frac{1}{2}}.$$

These again have a physical interpretation. $(T_x)_{i+\frac{1}{2},j}$ is the *single-phase* transmissibility (for $\mu=1$) in the x direction at the right boundary of the block; $(T_y)_{i,j+\frac{1}{2}}$ is the *single-phase* transmissibility in the y direction at the upper boundary of the block. $(M_{ox})_{i+\frac{1}{2},j}$ and $(M_{oy})_{i,j+\frac{1}{2}}$ may be regarded as the time-varying mobilities (for $k=1$) associated with the right and top boundaries. (Appendix C discusses how these are calculated from block-centered values.)

Furthermore, transmissibility multiplied by pressure drop is rate of oil flow (in standard volumes per unit time). Thus the first term of Eq. B.34, $(T_{ox})_{i+\frac{1}{2},j}[(p_o)_{i+1,j}-(p_o)_{i,j}]$, is the rate of oil flow *into* Block (i,j) across the right boundary *from* Block $(i+1,j)$; the second term (with minus sign) is the rate of oil flow into Block (i,j) across the left boundary from Block $(i-1,j)$; the third and fourth terms are the rates of oil flow into Block (i,j) from the blocks above and below. The right side of Eq. B.34 is the rate of accumulation of oil in the block.

More abbreviations are needed to simplify the representation of the difference terms. Let α be the time level at which the mobilities are evaluated and β be the time level at which pressures are evaluated. For example, if $\alpha=n$ and $\beta=n+1$, "old" mobilities and "new" pressures are used.

Then the difference equation (Eq. B.34) can be written as

$$\Delta T\cdot M_o^{\alpha}\Delta(p_o)_{i,j}^{\beta}=(V_{i,j}/\Delta t)\Delta_t(\phi S_o/B_o)_{i,j}, \quad \text{(B.35)}$$

where

$$\Delta_t(A)=(A)^{n+1}-(A)^n$$

and

$$\Delta B\cdot\Delta A_{i,j}=B_{i-\frac{1}{2},j}(A_{i-1,j}-A_{i,j})$$
$$+B_{i+\frac{1}{2},j}(A_{i+1,j}-A_{i,j})$$
$$+B_{i,j-\frac{1}{2}}(A_{i,j-1}-A_{i,j})$$
$$+B_{i,j+\frac{1}{2}}(A_{i,j+1}-A_{i,j})$$

for any block-center quantities, A, and block-boundary quantities, B.

B.6 Well Injection and Production Rates

We will now discuss well injection and production rates and introduce terms for well rates. Let $(q_o)_{i,j}$ be the rate (in standard volumes per unit time) at which oil is injected into or produced from Block (i,j). $(q_o)_{i,j}$ is negative if oil is produced. Then, because mass must be conserved, the difference equation (Eq. B.35) becomes

$$\Delta T\cdot M_o\Delta(p_o)_{i,j}+(q_o)_{i,j}=(V_{i,j}/\Delta t)\Delta_t(\phi S_o/B_o)_{i,j}. \quad \text{(B.36)}$$

In the case of injection, the rates q_o, q_w, and q_g probably would be specified in advance. In the case of production, however, rates of all phases at a well cannot be specified, because their ratios must satisfy certain mobility conditions. For example, if capillary effects are negligible near the well, then the production of each phase is proportional to its mobility in the block:

$$\frac{(q_o)_{i,j}}{\left(\dfrac{k_{ro}}{\mu_o B_o}\right)_{i,j}}=\frac{(q_w)_{i,j}}{\left(\dfrac{k_{rw}}{\mu_w B_w}\right)_{i,j}}=\frac{(q_g)_{i,j}}{\left(\dfrac{k_{rg}}{\mu_g B_g}\right)_{i,j}}. \quad \text{(B.37)}$$

The user usually specifies one of the rates q_o, q_w, or q_g as a function of time, and the reservoir simulator program will adjust the other two rates to satisfy Eq. B.37. Alternatively, many simulators permit the total rate to be specified, and the program adjusts all three rates to satisfy Eq. B.37, as well as the total.

It is frequently desirable to specify wellbore pressure. In that case, $(q_o)_{i,j}$ is replaced in Eq. B.36 by

$$R_{i,j}\left(\frac{k_{ro}}{\mu_o B_o}\right)_{i,j}[(p_{wf})_{i,j}-(p_o)_{i,j}],$$

where p_{wf} is the desired wellbore pressure and $R_{i,j}$ is a "well transmissibility factor" that depends on permeability and geometry. For square gridblocks, it has been shown[10] that

$$R_{i,j}=\frac{2\pi(kh)_{i,j}}{\ln(0.2\Delta x/r_w)}.$$

B.7 Final Form of Difference Equations

Finally, we bring gravity back into the equations. The final form of the difference equation for oil is

$$\Delta T\cdot M_o[\Delta(p_o)_{i,j}-g\rho_o\Delta D_{i,j}]+(q_o)_{i,j}=(V_{i,j}/\Delta t)\Delta_t(\phi S_o/B_o)_{i,j}. \quad \text{(B.38)}$$

Similarly, the water equation is

$$\Delta T\cdot M_w[\Delta(p_w)_{i,j}-g\rho_w\Delta D_{i,j}]+(q_w)_{i,j}=(V_{i,j}/\Delta t)\Delta_t(\phi S_w/B_w)_{i,j} \quad \text{(B.39)}$$

and the gas equation is

$$\Delta T\cdot M_g[\Delta(p_g)_{i,j}-g\rho_g\Delta D_{i,j}]+\Delta T\cdot R_s M_o[\Delta(p_o)_{i,j}-g\rho_o\Delta D_{i,j}]+(q_g)_{i,j}=(V_{i,j}/\Delta t)\Delta_t[(\phi S_g/B_g)_{i,j}+(\phi S_o R_s/B_o)_{i,j}]. \quad \text{(B.40)}$$

Nomenclature

A = cross-sectional area, m^2
B = FVF, res m^3/stock-tank m^3
D = depth, m
g = acceleration of gravity, m/s^2
h = thickness, m
I = number of gridblocks in x direction
J = number of gridblocks in y direction
k = permeability, m^2
k_r = relative permeability, dimensionless
k_x,k_y,k_z = permeability in x, y, and z directions, respectively, m^2
L = length, m
M = mobility factor, stock-tank m^3/res m$^3\cdot$Pa$\cdot$s
M_x,M_y = mobility factors in x and y directions, respectively, stock-tank m^3/res m$^3\cdot$Pa$\cdot$s
p = pressure, Pa
Δp = pressure drop, Pa
p_{wf} = wellbore pressure, Pa
P_c = capillary pressure, Pa
q = volumetric flow rate, res m^3/s, or standard volume flow rate, stock-tank m^3/s
r_w = wellbore radius, m
R = well transmissibility factor, m^3
R_s = solution GOR, std m^3/res m^3
S = saturation, fraction
t = time, seconds
Δt = length of timestep, seconds
T_x,T_y = single-phase transmissibility factors in x and y directions, respectively, m^3
T_{ox},T_{oy} = oil transmissibility factors in x and y directions, respectively, stock-tank m^3/Pa$\cdot$s
V = volume, m^3
x,y,z = space dimensions, m
$\Delta x, \Delta y$ = block length in x and y directions, respectively, m
Δ = difference operator
Θ = angle of dip, rads
μ = viscosity, Pa$\cdot$s
ρ = density, kg/m^3
ϕ = porosity, fraction

Subscripts

g = gas
i = gridblock number in x direction
j = gridblock number in y direction
o = oil
p = phase
w = water

Superscripts

n = last timestep taken
$n+1$ = next timestep
α = time level at which mobilities are evaluated
β = time level at which pressures are evaluated

References

1. Peaceman, D.W.: *Fundamentals of Numerical Reservoir Simulation*, Elsevier Scientific Publishing Co., Amsterdam (1977).
2. Aziz, K. and Settari, A.: *Petroleum Reservoir Simulation*, Applied Science Publishers Ltd., London (1979).
3. *Numerical Simulation II*, Reprint Series, SPE, Richardson, TX (1986) **20.**
4. Bech, N.: "Classification of Reservoir Simulators," Energiministeriets Energiforskningsprogram, *Olie- og gasreservoirmodeller*, Report No. 6, Riso-M-2421, Riso Natl. Laboratory, Roskilde, Denmark (1984).
5. Stone, H.L.: "Probability Model for Estimating Three-Phase Relative Permeability," *JPT* (Feb. 1970) 214–18; *Trans.*, AIME, **249.**
6. Stone, H.L.: "Estimation of Three-Phase Relative Permeability and Residual Oil Data," *J. Cdn. Pet. Tech.* (Oct.–Dec. 1973) 53–61.
7. Crichlow, H.B.: *Modern Reservoir Engineering—A Simulation Approach*, Prentice-Hall Inc., Englewood Cliffs, NJ (1977) 78.
8. Settari, A. and Aziz, K.: "Use of Irregular Grid in Reservoir Simulation," *SPEJ* (April 1972) 103–14.
9. Abou-Kassem, J.H. and Aziz, K.: "Analytical Well Models for Reservoir Simulation," *SPEJ* (Aug. 1985) 573–79.
10. Peaceman, D.W.: "Interpretation of Well-Block Pressures in Numerical Reservoir Simulation," *SPEJ* (June 1978) 183–94; *Trans.*, AIME, **253.**

Appendix C
Description of Effective Solution Techniques

In Appendix B, basic finite-difference equations that approximate the differential equations for flow of oil, water, and gas in three dimensions were derived, taking into account gravity, capillary pressure, compressibility, and the solubility of gas in the oil phase. These finite-difference equations were left in a general form by not specifying how to evaluate properties associated with block boundaries and not specifying timestep levels in the spatial differences. In this appendix, definitions of the various terms in the space differences are made more specific, thereby leading to specific numerical techniques for proceeding from the current time level, t^n, to the next time level, t^{n+1}. We cannot hope to cover all the various finite-difference methods that have appeared in the literature for solving multiphase flow problems, but the most important types of difference equations will be discussed.*

To simplify the presentation, we restrict the discussion to two dimensions and two phases (oil and gas), omitting solution gas and gravity. With these simplifications, Eqs. B.38 through B.40 become

$$\Delta T\cdot[M_o\Delta(p_o)_{i,j}]+(q_o)_{i,j}=(V_{i,j}/\Delta t)\Delta_t(\phi S_o/B_o)_{i,j} \quad \text{(C.1)}$$

and

$$\Delta T\cdot[M_g\Delta(p_g)_{i,j}]+(q_g)_{i,j}=(V_{i,j}/\Delta t)\Delta_t(\phi S_g/B_g)_{i,j}. \quad \text{(C.2)}$$

C.1 Mobility Weighting

In Appendix B, it was not stated explicitly how one obtains values for block-boundary transmissibilities and mobilities—i.e., for

$$(T_x)_{i+½,j}=\frac{(hk_x)_{i+½,j}(y_{j+½}-y_{j-½})}{x_{i+1}-x_i}, \quad \text{(C.3)}$$

$$(T_y)_{i,j+½}=\frac{(hk_y)_{i,j+½}(x_{i+½}-x_{i-½})}{y_{j+1}-y_j}, \quad \text{(C.4)}$$

$$(M_{ox})_{i+½,j}=(k_{ro}/B_o\mu_o)_{i+½,j}, \quad \text{(C.5)}$$

$$(M_{oy})_{i,j+½}=(k_{ro}/B_o\mu_o)_{i,j+½}, \quad \text{(C.6)}$$

$$(M_{gx})_{i+½,j}=(k_{rg}/B_g\mu_g)_{i+½,j}, \quad \text{(C.7)}$$

and

$$(M_{gy})_{i,j+½}=(k_{rg}/B_g\mu_g)_{i,j+½}. \quad \text{(C.8)}$$

In some simulators, values of $(hk_x)_{i+½,j}$ and $(hk_y)_{i,j+½}$ that correspond to the block boundaries are supplied as data by the user; in others, values of h, k_x, and k_y are supplied for Blocks (i,j), and the program uses average values for each block boundary. In a few simulators, the user may have the option of entering T_x and T_y directly for each block boundary.

*In this appendix we use a consistent set of units and do not provide the equivalent oilfield units.

With regard to the interval mobility factors, $(M_{ox})_{i+½,j}$, $(M_{oy})_{i,j+½}$, $(M_{gx})_{i+½,j}$, and $(M_{gy})_{i,j+½}$, the most intuitively obvious scheme is midpoint weighting. In midpoint weighting, values of $(k_{ro}/B_o\mu_o)$ and $(k_{rg}/B_g\mu_g)$ are computed at each gridblock center point, and average values are used for the boundaries between gridblocks. Thus,

$$(M_{ox})_{i+½,j}=½(k_{ro}/B_o\mu_o)_{i,j}+½(k_{ro}/B_o\mu_o)_{i+1,j}$$

and

$$(M_{oy})_{i,j+½}=½(k_{ro}/B_o\mu_o)_{i,j}+½(k_{ro}/B_o\mu_o)_{i,j+1}.$$

This type of averaging is also referred to as 50/50 weighting.

Unfortunately, it has been found that in many cases midpoint weighting of the mobility factor does not give satisfactory results. As an example, consider Fig. C.1, which shows some typical results obtained by Huppler[1] for one-dimensional (1D), two-phase calculations with several different weighting schemes. Fig. C.1a is for the displacement of oil by water with a favorable mobility ratio; Fig. C.1b is also for the displacement of oil by water but with an unfavorable mobility ratio. (In both cases, capillary pressure is sufficiently small that the Buckley-Leverett solution may be considered to be the correct solution.) In both cases, midpoint weighting gives solutions that are too high behind the front, and the computed front lags the actual front. In fact, in the absence of capillary pressure and compressibility, difference equations with midpoint weighting of mobilities evaluated at the old time level have solutions that tend to oscillate and blow up (see Chap. 4 of Peaceman[2]).

By far the most commonly used mobility-weighting scheme in reservoir simulation is upstream weighting. In this scheme, the direction of flow of *each phase* between each pair of neighboring blocks is determined from the phase-potential difference, defining the upstream and downstream points. Then, for each interval, M_{ox} (or M_{oy}) is given the value of $k_{ro}/B_o\mu_o$ at the upstream-block center point (the point with the highest oil-phase potential), ignoring completely the value of the mobility at the downstream point.

Fig. C.1 shows that the solutions obtained by Huppler using upstream weighting are superior to those obtained using midpoint weighting. The numerical solution is smeared somewhat, compared with the sharp front expected for the exact solution; this smearing is referred to as numerical dispersion, which has been treated in considerable detail by Lantz[3] and Peaceman,[2] and is discussed in Chaps. 2, 5, and 6.

Upstream weighting has a simple physical interpretation. In accord with the conservation-of-mass equations from which the difference equations (Eqs. C.1 and C.2) were derived, the mobility used should be the average mobility of the fluid flowing between blocks during the timestep. By Darcy's law for each phase, this fluid comes from the block with larger phase potential. The upstream-weighting scheme is based on the assumption that the upstream block is a "stirred tank," so that the mobility of the fluid going across the interface is the same as the mobility of the fluid at the block center.

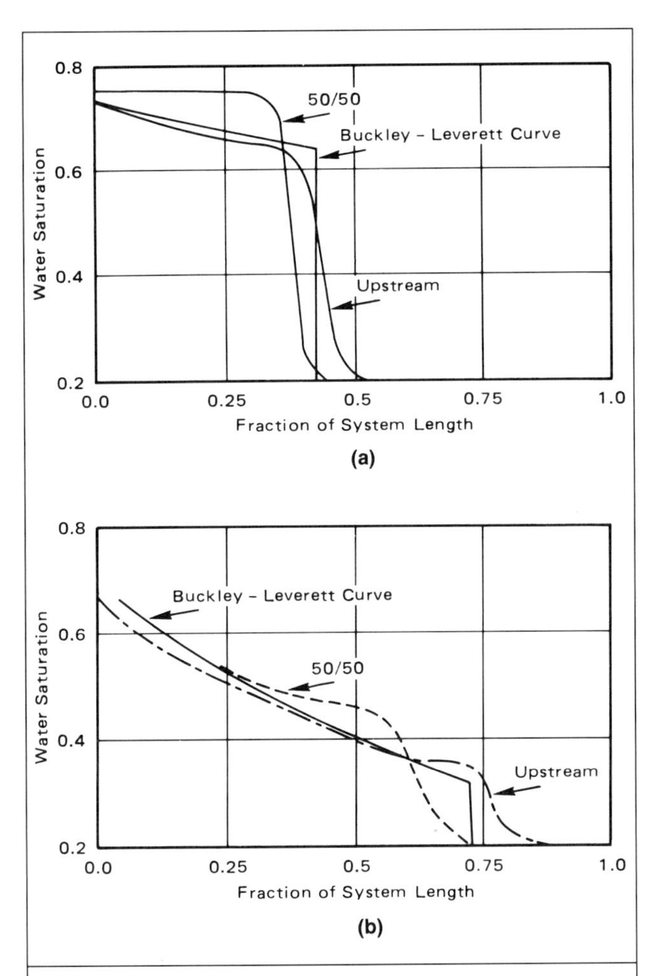

Fig. C.1—Waterflood saturation profiles computed with different mobility-weighting schemes[1]: (a) favorable mobility ratio and (b) unfavorable mobility ratio.

The stirred-tank analogy also helps explain numerical dispersion: after blocks are "stirred," sharp fronts within blocks are smeared.

A number of "higher-order" schemes have been proposed to reduce the numerical dispersion associated with upstream weighting while the oscillations and instabilities of midpoint weighting are avoided (see Bech's[4] literature survey). Many of these can be viewed as variants of the "two-point" upstream-weighting method.[5-8] The basic idea is to allow a more accurate nonuniform distribution of fluid (or mobility) in the upstream block. The distribution often varies linearly with position in the block, subject to constraints that the distribution is "physical"—e.g., it avoids artificial maxima or minima. Development of higher-order schemes is still an active area of research.

C.2 Completely Explicit Formulation

In the previous section, we discussed how the choice of mobility weighting affects the evaluation of the transmissibilities and mobilities for each gridblock boundary. We have not yet dealt with the choice of the timestep levels to use in evaluating the spatial differences. As was pointed out, this choice of timestep levels plays an important role in distinguishing among the various numerical procedures for solving multiphase flow problems.

In this section, we consider the most obvious choice. We simply evaluate all quantities in the spatial differences at the old time level, t^n. From Eqs. C.1 and C.2, we see that this gives rise to the following *explicit* finite-difference equations:

$$\Delta T\cdot[M_o^n\Delta(p_o)_{i,j}^n]+(q_o)_{i,j}^n=\frac{V_{i,j}}{\Delta t}\left[\left(\frac{\phi S_o}{B_o}\right)_{i,j}^{n+1}-\left(\frac{\phi S_o}{B_o}\right)_{i,j}^{n}\right] \quad \text{(C.9)}$$

and

$$\Delta T\cdot[M_g^n\Delta(p_g)_{i,j}^n]+(q_g)_{i,j}^n=\frac{V_{i,j}}{\Delta t}\left[\left(\frac{\phi S_g}{B_g}\right)_{i,j}^{n+1}-\left(\frac{\phi S_g}{B_g}\right)_{i,j}^{n}\right]. \quad \text{(C.10)}$$

Because everything on the left side is known, this pair of equations is very easy to solve at each gridpoint for the two quantities

$$\left(\frac{\phi S_o}{B_o}\right)_{i,j}^{n+1}$$

and

$$\left(\frac{\phi S_g}{B_g}\right)_{i,j}^{n+1}.$$

Use of the following auxiliary relationships then permits solution for the new saturations and pressures in each gridblock:

$$S_o+S_g=1, \quad \text{(C.11)}$$

$$\phi=\phi(p_o), \quad \text{(C.12)}$$

$$B_o=B_o(p_o), \quad \text{(C.13)}$$

$$B_g=B_g(p_g), \quad \text{(C.14)}$$

and

$$p_g-p_o=P_c(S_g). \quad \text{(C.15)}$$

We refer to this as an explicit method because no unknowns at neighboring blocks are involved. Unfortunately, use of Eqs. C.9 and C.10 will usually produce nonsense for answers, unless compressibilities are very large or timesteps are very small. Otherwise, these equations are unstable. An unstable difference equation or set of equations is one in which errors from any source become magnified each timestep.

One of the major objectives of numerical analysis is prediction of the stability of a set of difference equations. To explore the concept of stability, in the next section we consider a simpler problem, the single-phase version of Eqs. C.9 and C.10.

C.3 Explicit Solution for Single-Phase Pressure

We first examine a 1D, single-phase version of Eqs. C.9 and C.10. If the single phase is oil, then $S_o=1$ and $S_g=0$. Further, let us assume uniform permeability, porosity, viscosity, and grid spacing. Eq. C.9 then becomes

$$\frac{hk}{\mu_o}\frac{\Delta y}{\Delta x}\left[\frac{(p_o)_{i+1}^n-(p_o)_i^n}{(B_o)_{i+1/2}^n}-\frac{(p_o)_i^n-(p_o)_{i-1}^n}{(B_o)_{i-1/2}^n}\right]$$

$$=\frac{\phi h\Delta x\Delta y}{\Delta t}\left[\left(\frac{1}{B_o}\right)_i^{n+1}-\left(\frac{1}{B_o}\right)_i^{n}\right]. \quad \text{(C.16)}$$

The compressibility of oil, c_o, may be defined by

$$c_o=B_o\frac{d(1/B_o)}{d(p_o)}.$$

Then when c_o is very small, ignoring higher-order powers of c_o,

$$\frac{1}{B_o}=\left(\frac{1}{B_o}\right)^{ref}+\left(\frac{c_o}{B_o}\right)^{ref}[p_o-(p_o)^{ref}].$$

Plugging this result into Eq. C.16, ignoring spatial variation in B_o, and multiplying through by B_o^{ref} produces the following approximation of Eq. C.16:

$$\frac{k}{\mu_o \Delta x^2}[(p_o)_{i+1}^n - 2(p_o)_i^n + (p_o)_{i-1}^n] = \frac{\phi c_o}{\Delta t}[(p_o)_i^{n+1} - (p_o)_i^n]. \quad \text{(C.17)}$$

This is an *explicit*-difference equation that approximates the differential equation

$$\frac{\partial^2 p_o}{\partial x^2} = \frac{\phi \mu_o c_o}{k}\frac{\partial p_o}{\partial t}. \quad \text{(C.18)}$$

Eq. C.18 has exactly the same form as the heat flow (or heat conduction) equation that describes temperature distribution in a 1D rod. Note that Eq. C.18 is *linear*; its coefficient $\phi\mu_o c_o/k$ does not depend on p_o. Standard sources on numerical analysis[2,9,10] show that Eq. C.17 is stable if

$$\frac{k\Delta t}{\phi \mu_o c_o \Delta x^2} \le ½. \quad \text{(C.19)}$$

This condition can be met only if the timestep, Δt, is kept sufficiently small. Otherwise, the solution rapidly diverges and becomes quite meaningless.

It can be shown (Ref. 2, Page 144) that similar stability considerations hold for the solution of multiphase flow problems and that, in the absence of compressibility, Eqs. C.9 and C.10 are unstable for *any* size timestep. Hence, there is no point in even trying an explicit method for solving incompressible multiphase flow problems. Where there is compressibility, an explicit method is stable for a small enough value of Δt, but an unreasonable number of timesteps may be necessary.

C.4 Implicit Solution for Single-Phase Pressure

Numerical analysis indicates that a stable difference equation can be obtained for solving Eq. C.18 by using *new* values for pressures on the left side of Eq. C.17. It can be shown[2,9,10] that the resultant difference equation,

$$\frac{k}{\mu_o \Delta x^2}[(p_o)_{i+1}^{n+1} - 2(p_o)_i^{n+1} + (p_o)_{i-1}^{n+1}]$$

$$= \frac{\phi c_o}{\Delta t}[(p_o)_i^{n+1} - (p_o)_i^n], \quad \text{(C.20)}$$

is stable for any size timestep. This equation is referred to as *implicit* because there is an implicit relationship between the unknown pressures at Points $i-1$, i, and $i+1$. To express the problem completely, Eq. C.20 must be written I times, once for each Gridpoint i, and all I equations must be solved simultaneously.

Consider a 1D case where there are six interior nodes, with the pressure fixed at p_1 at the left end and at p_8 at the right end. Let

$$\alpha = \frac{\phi c_o \mu_o \Delta x^2}{k \Delta t},$$

and drop Subscript o from the pressure. Then the simultaneous equations that have to be solved each timestep are

$$(2+\alpha)p_2^{n+1} - p_3^{n+1} = \alpha p_2^n + p_1,$$

$$-p_2^{n+1} + (2+\alpha)p_3^{n+1} - p_4^{n+1} = \alpha p_3^n,$$

$$-p_3^{n+1} + (2+\alpha)p_4^{n+1} - p_5^{n+1} = \alpha p_4^n,$$

$$-p_4^{n+1} + (2+\alpha)p_5^{n+1} - p_6^{n+1} = \alpha p_5^n,$$

$$-p_5^{n+1} + (2+\alpha)p_6^{n+1} - p_7^{n+1} = \alpha p_6^n, \text{ and}$$

$$-p_6^{n+1} + (2+\alpha)p_7^{n+1} = \alpha p_7^n + p_8.$$

The right side of these equations contains only known values of the pressure (i.e., they are known after the previous timestep has been solved), as well as Boundary Pressures p_1 and p_8. The left side involves the unknown values of p_i^{n+1}, which are related to each other implicitly through these simultaneous equations.

It is useful to consider these same equations in a matrix format:

$$\begin{bmatrix} (2+\alpha) & -1 & 0 & 0 & 0 & 0 \\ -1 & (2+\alpha) & -1 & 0 & 0 & 0 \\ 0 & -1 & (2+\alpha) & -1 & 0 & 0 \\ 0 & 0 & -1 & (2+\alpha) & -1 & 0 \\ 0 & 0 & 0 & -1 & (2+\alpha) & -1 \\ 0 & 0 & 0 & 0 & -1 & (2+\alpha) \end{bmatrix} \begin{bmatrix} p_2^{n+1} \\ p_3^{n+1} \\ p_4^{n+1} \\ p_5^{n+1} \\ p_6^{n+1} \\ p_7^{n+1} \end{bmatrix}$$

$$= \alpha \begin{bmatrix} p_2^n \\ p_3^n \\ p_4^n \\ p_5^n \\ p_6^n \\ p_7^n \end{bmatrix} + \begin{bmatrix} p_1 \\ 0 \\ 0 \\ 0 \\ 0 \\ p_8 \end{bmatrix}, \quad \text{(C.21)}$$

which can be abbreviated to

$$Ap^{n+1} = \alpha p^n + b, \quad \text{(C.22)}$$

where A is the coefficient matrix, p^n contains the old, known, pressures, p^{n+1} contains the new, unknown, pressures, and b contains the boundary information. p^n, p^{n+1}, and b are column matrices.

The structure of this particular coefficient matrix is very simple: each row has only three nonzero terms: $(2+\alpha)$ on the main diagonal, and -1 on the two diagonals adjacent to the main diagonal. This is a particular case of tridiagonal coefficient matrices. 1D problems with a single variable at each gridpoint characteristically lead to sets of simultaneous equations with tridiagonal coefficient matrices. This is particularly fortunate because simultaneous equations having this form are very easy to solve with the "tridiagonal" algorithm. This algorithm, which is presented in Sec. C.9.1, is simply a direct-solution method based on Gaussian elimination. Because this algorithm takes advantage of all the zeros outside the three diagonals, the amount of computing work required to solve a tridiagonal system of equations is directly proportional to the number of equations. This is in contrast to the situation with a full coefficient matrix; the computing time for direct solution by elimination for a full matrix is proportional to the *cube* of the number of equations.

Unfortunately, implicit difference equations in two or three dimensions are not so easy to solve. Consider the two-dimensional (2D) version of the differential equation (Eq. C.18):

$$k_x\frac{\partial^2 p_o}{\partial x^2} + k_y\frac{\partial^2 p_o}{\partial y^2} = \phi\mu_o c_o\frac{\partial p_o}{\partial t}. \quad \text{(C.23)}$$

By analogy with Eq. C.20, the 2D *implicit* difference equation is

$$\frac{k_x}{\mu_o \Delta x^2}[(p_o)_{i+1,j}^{n+1} - 2(p_o)_{i,j}^{n+1} + (p_o)_{i-1,j}^{n+1}] + \frac{k_y}{\mu_o \Delta y^2}[(p_o)_{i,j+1}^{n+1}$$

$$-2(p_o)_{i,j}^{n+1} + (p_o)_{i,j-1}^{n+1}] = \frac{\phi c_o}{\Delta t}[(p_o)_{i,j}^{n+1} - (p_o)_{i,j}^n]. \quad \text{(C.24)}$$

Like Eq. C.20, this equation is also stable for any size timestep. The structure of the coefficient matrix, however, is not as simple

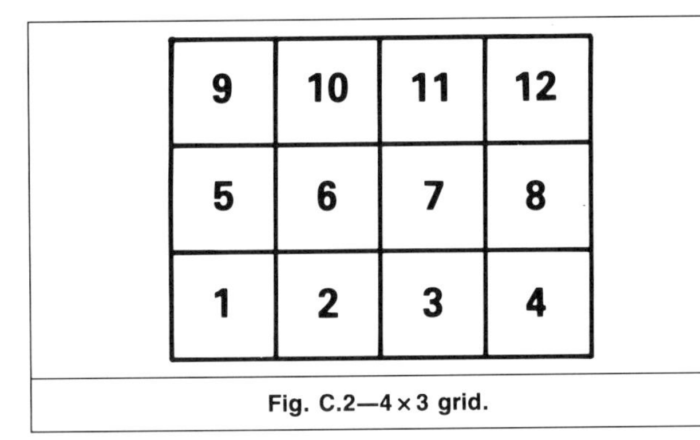

Fig. C.2—4×3 grid.

as that shown in Eq. C.21. As an example, consider the rectangular grid shown in Fig. C.2, having four blocks in the x direction and three blocks in the y direction.

Suppose the grid is bounded on all four sides by blocks in which the pressures are known, analogous to Blocks 1 and 8 in the 1D case. Then consider the coefficient matrix in Fig. C.3 (with the zero terms omitted).

$$\begin{bmatrix}
(4+\alpha) & -1 & & & -1 & & & & & & & \\
-1 & (4+\alpha) & -1 & & & -1 & & & & & & \\
 & -1 & (4+\alpha) & -1 & & & -1 & & & & & \\
 & & -1 & (4+\alpha) & & & & -1 & & & & \\
-1 & & & & (4+\alpha) & -1 & & & -1 & & & \\
 & -1 & & & -1 & (4+\alpha) & -1 & & & -1 & & \\
 & & -1 & & & -1 & (4+\alpha) & -1 & & & -1 & \\
 & & & -1 & & & -1 & (4+\alpha) & & & & -1 \\
 & & & & -1 & & & & (4+\alpha) & -1 & & \\
 & & & & & -1 & & & -1 & (4+\alpha) & -1 & \\
 & & & & & & -1 & & & -1 & (4+\alpha) & -1 \\
 & & & & & & & -1 & & & -1 & (4+\alpha)
\end{bmatrix}$$

Fig. C.3—Coefficient matrix.

There are now five nonzero diagonals, but the two outer diagonals are not adjacent to the three inner diagonals. This is an example of a band matrix, which is a matrix having zero coefficients on all diagonals outside a band of width w. Direct algorithms for solving N_{eq} equations with a coefficient matrix with a bandwidth w require computing work proportional to $w^2 N_{eq}$. (The detailed steps for using direct elimination to solve band equations are given, for example, by Peaceman.[2])

When blocks are ordered as in the simple grid, then $w=2I+1$ and $N_{eq}=IJ$, so that the computing work for 2D problems is roughly proportional to I^3J.

For three-dimensional (3D) problems, the work is proportional to I^3J^3K.

Use of the nested-dissection method, as well as other sparse matrix techniques,[11-13] has reduced these work estimates somewhat. Still, direct methods are not routinely applied to any but the smallest 3D problems.

Because direct methods are not practical for solving very large systems of simultaneous equations, iterative methods must be used. These involve starting with some initial guess for the unknown pressures (usually their values at the old time level) and applying some repetitive calculation to improve the guess until, after a sufficient number of iterations, the simultaneous equations are satisfied to within some tolerance. Each iteration requires a fixed amount of computing work for each gridpoint, so the amount of computing work is proportional to the number of gridpoints times the number of iterations. There are a number of iterative methods for solving the simultaneous equations occurring in reservoir simulation; these are discussed in more detail at the end of this appendix.

This section and the last have indicated that explicit solution of the linear pressure equation is unstable unless the timestep is very small, but implicit solution is stable for any timestep. Experience has shown that these stability considerations usually carry over to the full nonlinear case.

C.5 Multiphase Implicit Pressure, Explicit Saturation (IMPES) Approach

Several options exist for picking the dependent variables in multiphase problems. In three-phase problems, the most common option is to solve for one phase pressure (usually p_o) and two saturations. As we will show later, this choice leads to the IMPES procedure, which involves solving first implicitly (as required for stability) for the oil pressure at each point and then solving explicitly for the saturations. Its appeal is a result of greatly reduced computing requirements, because it avoids the simultaneous implicit solution for several unknowns at each gridpoint.

To simplify the discussion for multiphase problems without neglecting their essential nonlinearity, we will assume that the fluids and the rock are incompressible. Practical reservoir simulations should, of course, include compressibility. Including compressibility increases the complexity of the algebra but, as indicated in Sec. C.3, it also makes numerical solutions easier to obtain. Conversely, incompressible problems, while leading to simpler equations, are more difficult to solve from a numerical point of view. Consequently, for the remainder of this appendix, it should be adequate to consider only incompressible problems to convey the main ideas for dealing with nonlinearity.

The IMPES procedure is described here for the two-phase, incompressible case. With the assumption of incompressibility, Eqs. C.1 and C.2 become

$$\Delta T\cdot[M_o^n\Delta(p_o)_{i,j}^{n+1}]+(q_o)_{i,j}^n=(V_{i,j}\phi/B_o\Delta t)[(S_o)_{i,j}^{n+1}-(S_o)_{i,j}^n] \quad \text{(C.25)}$$

and

$$\Delta T\cdot[M_g^n\Delta(p_g)_{i,j}^{n+1}]+(q_g)_{i,j}^n=(V_{i,j}\phi/B_g\Delta t)[(S_g)_{i,j}^{n+1}-(S_g)_{i,j}^n]. \quad \text{(C.26)}$$

A pressure equation is obtained by combining Eqs. C.25 and C.26 in such a way that the saturation accumulation terms cancel out. This may be done by multiplying Eq. C.25 by B_o, multiplying Eq. C.26 by B_g, and adding them together to obtain

$$B_o\Delta T\cdot[M_o^n\Delta(p_o)_{i,j}^{n+1}]+B_g\Delta T\cdot[M_g^n\Delta(p_g)_{i,j}^{n+1}]$$
$$+(B_oq_o+B_gq_g)_{i,j}^n=0.$$

To obtain an equation in p_o alone, we take

$$(p_g)_{i,j}^{n+1}=(p_o)_{i,j}^{n+1}+(P_c)_{i,j}^n. \quad \text{(C.27)}$$

Noting that because the fluids are incompressible, $B_o=B_g=1$, we obtain

$$\Delta T\cdot[(M_o^n+M_g^n)\Delta(p_o)_{i,j}^{n+1}]+\Delta T\cdot[M_g^n\Delta(P_c)_{i,j}^n]+(q_o+q_g)_{i,j}^n=0. \quad \text{(C.28)}$$

For the compressible case, as well as the three-phase case, the situation is somewhat more complicated, but the two or three equations can still be combined in such a way as to eliminate the saturation accumulation terms. See, for example, Stone and Garder[14] or Breitenbach *et al.*[15]

Note that the old value of capillary pressure is used in Eq. C.28 to avoid having more than the one unknown, p_o, at each gridpoint. This then gives a set of linear equations, with the same structure as Eq. C.24, that can be solved by direct or iterative methods.

The value of $(p_o)_{i,j}^{n+1}$ thus obtained can then be substituted directly into the left side of Eq. C.25, and values of $(S_o)_{i,j}^{n+1}$ can be obtained explicitly point by point.

The IMPES procedure was first proposed by Stone and Garder[14] for 1D problems and by Sheldon *et al.*[16] for 2D problems; in both cases, capillary pressure was assumed to be zero. Applications to problems including capillary pressure are given by Breitenbach *et al.*[15] and MacDonald and Coats.[17] The method is frequently subject to stability problems, however, which restrict the allowable timestep. A common restriction on IMPES resulting from saturation being handled explicitly is that no more than 1 gridblock PV throughput is allowed per timestep. This restriction can be severe when gridblocks are very small, as in coning models.

IMPES methods can be useful. Their advantage is their relatively small computing requirement per timestep. Their disadvantage is their stability limitation. They continue to be used widely, despite the recent trend toward simultaneous methods that solve implicitly for more than one unknown in each gridblock. In the next section, however, we describe another sequential procedure that retains the speed advantage of IMPES while avoiding its stability limitation.

C.6 Sequential Solution With Total Velocity

The IMPES procedure is one of a family of methods known as sequential solution methods. All of them involve, at each timestep, solving in sequence first for a pressure and then for one or two saturations. Spillette *et al.*[18] proposed a sequential solution method that retains the advantage of reduced computation per timestep but possesses much greater stability than the IMPES procedure. The first step of the sequence is exactly the same as for the IMPES procedure; Eq. C.28 is used to solve for the oil pressure in each gridblock. The significant difference is in the second step of the sequence, where the so-called Buckley-Leverett form of the saturation equation is used to solve for the one or two saturations in each gridblock. The Buckley-Leverett form of the saturation equation differs from the oil equation (Eq. C.25) used in the IMPES procedure in that it requires a total velocity to be derived from the oil pressures obtained in the first step of the sequence.

We go back to the differential equations (Eqs. B.10 through B.12) to derive the Buckley-Leverett form of the saturation differential equation. For two-phase, incompressible, horizontal flow, Eqs. B.10 and B.12 simplify to

$$-\nabla\cdot\vec{v}_o=\phi\frac{\partial S_o}{\partial t} \quad \text{(C.29)}$$

and

$$-\nabla\cdot\vec{v}_g=\phi\frac{\partial S_g}{\partial t}, \quad \text{(C.30)}$$

where

$$\vec{v}_o=-\lambda_o\nabla p_o \quad \text{(C.31)}$$

and

$$\vec{v}_g=-\lambda_g\nabla p_g \quad \text{(C.32)}$$

are the Darcy velocities for each phase, and

$$\lambda_o=\frac{kk_{ro}}{\mu_o}$$

and

$$\lambda_g=\frac{kk_{rg}}{\mu_g}$$

are the phase mobilities. Total velocity is defined by

$$\vec{v}_t=\vec{v}_o+\vec{v}_g. \quad \text{(C.33)}$$

From the definition of capillary pressure, we have

$$\begin{aligned}\nabla P_c&=\nabla p_g-\nabla p_o\\&=-(\vec{v}_g/\lambda_g)+(\vec{v}_o/\lambda_o)\\&=(\lambda_g\vec{v}_o-\lambda_o\vec{v}_g)/\lambda_o\lambda_g\\&=[\lambda_g\vec{v}_o-\lambda_o(\vec{v}_t-\vec{v}_o)]/\lambda_o\lambda_g.\end{aligned}$$

Then

$$\vec{v}_o=f_o\vec{v}_t+\lambda_g f_o\nabla P_c, \quad \text{(C.34)}$$

where the fractional flow of oil is given by

$$f_o=\frac{\lambda_o}{\lambda_o+\lambda_g}. \quad \text{(C.35)}$$

Substitution of Eq. C.34 into C.29 then gives the Buckley-Leverett form of the saturation equation:

$$-\nabla\cdot(\lambda_g f_o\nabla P_c)-\nabla\cdot(f_o\vec{v}_t)=\phi\frac{\partial S_o}{\partial t}. \quad \text{(C.36)}$$

For the finite-difference form of this equation, see Peaceman.[2]

After the solution for the oil pressure, x and y components of the oil velocity may be obtained by the finite-difference form of Eq. C.31, which is

$$(v_{ox})_{i+½,j}=-(\lambda_o)^n_{i+½,j}[(p_o)^{n+1}_{i+1,j}-(p_o)^{n+1}_{i,j}]/\Delta x_{i+½} \quad \text{(C.37)}$$

and

$$(v_{oy})_{i,j+½}=-(\lambda_o)^n_{i,j+½}[(p_o)^{n+1}_{i,j+1}-(p_o)^{n+1}_{i,j}]/\Delta y_{j+½}. \quad \text{(C.38)}$$

As indicated by Eq. C.27, new gas pressures are obtained by adding, at each point, the old capillary pressure to the new oil pressure. These values of $(p_g)^{n+1}_{i,j}$ are then substituted into equations similar to Eqs. C.37 and C.38 to obtain the x and y components of the gas velocity. Finally, the components of the total velocity are obtained by

$$(v_{tx})_{i+½,j}=(v_{ox})_{i+½,j}+(v_{gx})_{i+½,j} \quad \text{(C.39)}$$

and

$$(v_{ty})_{i,j+½}=(v_{oy})_{i,j+½}+(v_{gy})_{i,j+½}. \quad \text{(C.40)}$$

As pointed out by Spillette *et al.*,[18] for an incompressible model, the total velocities obtained this way are independent of the time level at which P_c is evaluated in Eq. C.27. It is also true that the time level chosen for the mobilities used in solving for the pressures and then the velocities has little effect on the total velocity. This indicates the fundamental role played by total velocity in multiphase flow behavior. It also shows why use of the Buckley-Leverett form of the saturation equation is superior to the IMPES procedure; the latter uses the oil velocity in the saturation equation, and the oil velocity is much more sensitive to the time level chosen for capillary pressure and mobilities.

In setting up the finite-difference analog of the saturation equation, Spillette *et al.*[18] recommend that capillary pressure be treated in a semi-implicit way (to be discussed later). This gives rise to an implicit difference equation that is linear in saturation. For two-phase problems, one saturation is solved for at each point as the second step of the sequential solution method; for three-phase problems, two saturations are solved for at each point. Again, either direct or iterative methods may be used to solve these linear simultaneous equations.

The finite-difference implementation of the sequential solution method, using total velocity in the saturation equation, was first discussed by Spillette *et al.*[18] and is elaborated upon by Peaceman[2] and Weinstein *et al.*[19] Spivak[20] discussed the Buckley-Leverett form of the saturation equation in his appendix, but did not formulate a numerical solution for it. Spivak *et al.*[21] present a similar sequential variational method that uses at each timestep a Galerkin (rather than finite-difference) solution for pressure followed by a Galerkin solution for the total velocity form of the saturation equation.

C.7 Fully Implicit Formulation

Both methods described so far in this appendix use an explicit mobility factor—i.e., the functions of saturation that appear in the spatial differences are evaluated at the old time level, t^n. Simulators based on explicit mobility are satisfactory for a great variety of field problems, but there are two particular types of problems where they fail badly. One is the coning problem, which involves converging radial flow into a well, with small radial intervals near the boundary that represents the well. The second is the gas-percolation problem, in which gas comes out of solution and flows vertically. Both types of problems involve high velocity in one or both phases. In the coning problem, the high velocity is a result of the converging flow. In the gas-percolation problem, high gas velocity is a result of the large density difference between oil and gas combined with the low viscosity of gas. In both cases, very small timesteps are required to prevent large oscillations in the saturations calculated in the high-velocity regions.

It was stated earlier that under certain restrictive assumptions, equations implicit in pressure can be shown to be stable for any size timestep. When more than one phase is present, however, stability restrictions on the saturation equations also apply. Stability analyses for saturation equations under various assumptions can be carried out.[2,17,22,23] For the 1D version of the Buckley-Leverett equation (Eq. C.36) with no capillary pressure, using upstream explicit mobility, the timestep must satisfy the inequality

$$\Delta t \leq \frac{\phi \Delta x}{v_t(\max|\mathrm{d}f_o/\mathrm{d}S_o|)} \quad \text{(C.41)}$$

for stability. This condition ensures that no more than 1 gridblock PV throughput can be allowed per timestep, and is equivalent to the well-known "CFL condition"[9,10] for hyperbolic equations. It shows clearly why the timestep must be very small when the velocity becomes very large to prevent oscillatory solutions for saturation.

The same stability analyses show that use of an implicit mobility will make the difference equations stable for any size timestep. Thus, Eqs. C.1 and C.2 could then result in the following completely implicit difference equations:

$$\Delta T\cdot[M_o^{n+1}\Delta(p_o)_{i,j}^{n+1}]+(q_o)_{i,j}^{n+1}$$

$$=\frac{V_{i,j}}{\Delta t}\left[\left(\frac{\phi S_o}{B_o}\right)_{i,j}^{n+1}-\left(\frac{\phi S_o}{B_o}\right)_{i,j}^{n}\right] \quad \text{(C.42)}$$

and

$$\Delta T\cdot[M_g^{n+1}\Delta(p_g)_{i,j}^{n+1}]+(q_g)_{i,j}^{n+1}$$

$$=\frac{V_{i,j}}{\Delta t}\left[\left(\frac{\phi S_g}{B_g}\right)_{i,j}^{n+1}-\left(\frac{\phi S_g}{B_g}\right)_{i,j}^{n}\right]. \quad \text{(C.43)}$$

Note that the well flow terms should also be evaluated at the new time level.

Blair and Weinaug[24] were the first to propose use of such a fully implicit simulator. It can be shown that if the mobility factors are simply updated each iteration, the resultant iteration will not converge for any timestep that violates Eq. C.41. Blair and Weinaug found it necessary to use Newtonian iteration; this made it possible to take much larger timesteps.

Newtonian iteration is a method of more general utility than direct substitution for dealing with nonlinear simultaneous equations. The general description of Newtonian iteration is as follows. Suppose there are N equations in N variables:

$$f_1(p_1,p_2\ldots p_N)=0,$$

$$f_2(p_1,p_2\ldots p_N)=0$$

$$\vdots$$

$$f_N(p_1,p_2\ldots p_N)=0.$$

The function f is linearized around the current guess p^k and set to zero. The resultant iteration consists of solving the following *linear* simultaneous equations for p^{k+1}.

$$\left(\frac{\partial f_1}{\partial p_1}\right)^k(p_1^{k+1}-p_1^k)+\left(\frac{\partial f_1}{\partial p_2}\right)^k(p_2^{k+1}-p_2^k)+\ldots$$

$$+\left(\frac{\partial f_1}{\partial p_N}\right)^k(p_N^{k+1}-p_N^k)=-f_1^k,$$

$$\left(\frac{\partial f_2}{\partial p_1}\right)^k(p_1^{k+1}-p_1^k)+\left(\frac{\partial f_2}{\partial p_2}\right)^k(p_2^{k+1}-p_2^k)+\ldots$$

$$+\left(\frac{\partial f_2}{\partial p_N}\right)^k(p_N^{k+1}-p_N^k)=-f_2^k,$$

$$\vdots$$

$$\left(\frac{\partial f_N}{\partial p_1}\right)^k(p_1^{k+1}-p_1^k)+\left(\frac{\partial f_N}{\partial p_2}\right)^k(p_2^{k+1}-p_2^k)+\ldots$$

$$+\left(\frac{\partial f_N}{\partial p_N}\right)^k(p_N^{k+1}-p_N^k)=-f_N^k.$$

In the current case, $N=2IJ$ because there are two equations and two unknowns (e.g., p_o and S_o) for each gridblock. The entries in f^k are of the form

$$\frac{V_{i,j}}{\Delta t}\left[\left(\frac{\phi S_o}{B_o}\right)_{i,j}^{n+1,k}-\left(\frac{\phi S_o}{B_o}\right)_{i,j}^{n}\right]$$

$$-\Delta T\cdot[M_o^{n+1,k}\Delta(p_o)_{i,j}^{n+1,k}]-(q_o)_{i,j}^{n+1,k}$$

and

$$\frac{V_{i,j}}{\Delta t}\left[\left(\frac{\phi S_g}{B_g}\right)_{i,j}^{n+1,k}-\left(\frac{\phi S_g}{B_g}\right)_{i,j}^{n}\right]$$

$$-\Delta T\cdot[M_g^{n+1,k}\Delta(p_g)_{i,j}^{n+1,k}]-(q_g)_{i,j}^{n+1,k},$$

corresponding to the residuals* (i.e., errors after k iterations) of Eqs. C.42 and C.43. The resultant linear equations in the unknown $(p_o)_{i,j}^{n+1,k+1}$ and $(S_g)_{i,j}^{n+1,k+1}$ have the same general structure as the pressure equation in Sec. C.4.

*See Chap. 6.

When f is very nonlinear, Newton's method may not converge. In effect, this results in timestep restrictions tied to the nonlinearities in the model. These restrictions, however, are usually much less stringent than for less-implicit methods.

Many other workers have constructed fully implicit simulators.[25-33] All use Newtonian iteration, with perhaps some minor variations, and claim a high degree of stability that permits taking adequately large timesteps. While the use of Newtonian iteration increases the work per timestep considerably compared with the use of explicit mobility, this is more than compensated for by the ability to take practical size timesteps in coning, gas percolation, steamflooding, fracture, and other problems with large gridblock PV throughputs.

Attempts have been made to use implicit methods adaptively.[34-36] In this approach, gridblocks are labeled implicit or explicit as needed to maintain stability. Implicitness labels are adaptively updated by the simulator on the basis of user-input parameters. This approach can result in significant reduction in computer time and storage compared with fully implicit methods, but it requires more-complicated data structures and special solvers to handle the resultant linear systems.

C.8 Semi-Implicit Formulations

Another approach that can overcome the timestep restriction without increasing the computational effort much beyond that required for explicit mobilities is the use of semi-implicit mobilities. In this approach, the mobility factors (and capillary pressures) at the new time level are estimated by extrapolation. For example, relative permeabilities at the new time level are estimated as follows:

$$(k_{ro})_{i,j}^{n+1}=(k_{ro})_{i,j}^{n}+\left(\frac{dk_{ro}}{dS_o}\right)_{i,j}^{n}[(S_o)_{i,j}^{n+1}-(S_o)_{i,j}^{n}]. \quad \text{(C.44)}$$

Note that the derivative of relative permeability is evaluated at the old time level.

Similarly, capillary pressure at the new level can be estimated by the equation

$$(P_c)_{i,j}^{n+1}=(P_c)_{i,j}^{n}+\left(\frac{dP_c}{dS_o}\right)_{i,j}^{n}[(S_o)_{i,j}^{n+1}-(S_o)_{i,j}^{n}]. \quad \text{(C.45)}$$

These estimates for new values of relative permeabilities (or mobilities) and capillary pressure should be carefully distinguished from the fully implicit mobilities and capillary pressures referred to in the previous section. They are referred to as semi-implicit.

MacDonald and Coats[17] and Letkeman and Ridings[37] first implemented semi-implicit mobilities and capillary pressures in simulators designed to perform coning calculations. It can be shown[38] that their formulations are equivalent to taking just one step of a Newtonian iteration. Products of the differences $S_{i,j}^{n+1}-S_{i,j}^{n}$ and $p_{i,j}^{n+1}-p_{i,j}^{n}$ are dropped to keep the equations more nearly linear. Nolen and Berry[38] also implemented a semi-implicit simulator, but they avoided the need to drop these product terms by using a Newtonian iteration to solve the resultant nonlinear equations. In this case, the use of Newtonian iteration did not add significantly to the computational work. Nolen and Berry point out that large material-balance errors can result for dissolved gas systems if these product terms are neglected.

Semi-implicit mobilities can also be used in the sequential solution approach with total velocity described by Spillette *et al.*[18] Both Nolen and Berry[38] and Spillette provide for the use of a "chord slope" for the derivative in Eq. C.44—i.e.,

$$\left(\frac{dk_{ro}}{dS_o}\right)_{i,j}=\frac{k_{ro}(S_{o_{i,j}}^{n}+\Delta S)-k_{ro}(S_{o_{i,j}})}{\Delta S}, \quad \text{(C.46)}$$

where ΔS is a preselected, arbitrary increment of saturation. They suggest that ΔS should be slightly larger in absolute value than the maximum saturation change expected to occur over the timestep. This maximum saturation change is frequently known when automatic timestep control is used (see Chap. 5).

18	8	22	11	24	12
4	17	7	21	10	23
14	3	16	6	20	9
1	13	2	15	5	19

Fig. C.4—D4 ordering of gridblocks.

Note that for production wells, the flow terms $(q_o)_{i,j}^{n+1}$ and $(q_g)_{i,j}^{n+1}$ in Eqs. C.42 and C.43 must also be evaluated in a semi-implicit fashion using extrapolated values of mobilities in the wellblocks. Where the well penetrates several wellblocks and the total flow for the well is specified, the situation is more complicated. Nolen and Berry[38] discuss in considerable detail the formulation of semi-implicit well production rates.

Along with the fully implicit approach, the semi-implicit approach has gained wide use throughout the industry.[18,19,25,39,40] Peaceman's[23] analysis of the stability of difference equations with semi-implicit mobility shows a mild restriction on the allowable saturation change over the timestep. The resultant timestep sizes are acceptably large for most field-scale reservoir simulation models.

While these improvements in the stability of the difference equation permit use of larger timesteps, the problem of time truncation error still remains; with semi-implicit and fully implicit methods, the larger the timestep, the larger will be the error. Jensen[41] and Sammon and Rubin[42] describe estimates of the time truncation error, which can be used to estimate acceptable timestep sizes. Most simulators, however, simply choose timestep sizes on the basis of user-defined allowable pressure and saturation changes over the step.

C.9 Solution Algorithms

The emphasis in this appendix has been on the distinction between various finite-difference equations for approximating the partial differential equations that describe multidimensional multiphase flow. Nonlinearities have been treated in such a way that the difference equations reduce to sets of simultaneous linear equations. It remains now to discuss the variety of methods that exist for solving these simultaneous equations.

The choice of the difference method is of primary importance in determining the quality of the solution; in a certain sense it should not matter what method is used to solve the linear simultaneous equations. The same answer should be obtained whether one uses a direct solution method or carries out any convergent iterative procedure sufficiently long to reduce the error to a negligible value. The choice of the solution method is of practical significance, however, because it affects the computational labor required for each timestep. Furthermore, when iteration is used, the choice of the method has an indirect effect on the quality of the solution because the rapidity with which it converges, as well as the computational work per iteration, has an influence on how large an error the user will tolerate at the conclusion of each timestep.

C.9.1 Direct Methods. Direct methods have already been discussed to some extent in Chap. 6 and in Sec. C.4. As pointed out, for 2D problems, the most straightforward direct method is to number the grid in row sequence with the rows oriented along the direction having the smallest number of gridblocks. With this ordering, the coefficient matrix has a band structure, and the band algorithm can be used to solve the system of equations with work proportional to I^3J. Price and Coats[11] have proposed a number of nonstandard orderings, the best one being the alternate diagonal, or D4, ordering illustrated in Fig. C.4 and discussed in Chap. 6.

While the work is still roughly proportional to I^3J for 2D problems and I^3J^3K for 3D problems, a reduction of work by a factor of two to six has been achieved for a number of practical problems. McDonald and Trimble[12] have proposed another nonstandard ordering, called the alternating column (or zebra) ordering, which is faster than the alternate-diagonal ordering for large grids ($I=J>18$). Yet another approach is the nested-dissection scheme proposed by George[13] that uses a rather complicated "divide-and-conquer" ordering scheme. It has a computational work requirement (for a square grid) that is roughly proportional to only I^2J. Its superiority becomes most evident for large grids. McDonald and Trimble[12] report that for square grids, nested dissection is faster than their zebra ordering for $I=J>30$, but that it becomes inefficient for nonsquare grids. For example, if $I=2J$, nested dissection is slower than zebra ordering up to $J=73$ (which is a very large grid indeed). Sherman[43] provides a recent discussion of the application of nested dissection to reservoir simulation.

While a detailed description of a direct-solution method for 2D or 3D problems is beyond the scope of this discussion, it is useful to consider the tridiagonal algorithm in detail. It is the simplest example of a direct-solution algorithm. As we have already pointed out, it is used for 1D problems with one unknown per gridpoint; later, we shall see that it is also used as part of some iteration methods for 2D and 3D problems.

The coefficient matrix for a tridiagonal system of equations is one of the simplest examples of a band matrix, having a bandwidth, w, equal to 3. A general tridiagonal system of N_{eq} equations may be written as follows:

$$B_1p_1 + C_1p_2 = D_1,$$

$$A_ip_{i-1} + B_ip_i + C_ip_{i+1} = D_i \quad (2 \le i \le N_{eq}-1), \text{ and}$$

$$A_{N_{eq}}p_{N_{eq}-1} + B_{N_{eq}}p_{N_{eq}} = D_{N_{eq}}.$$

A straightforward algorithm to solve this system consists of successively eliminating each unknown p_i from the $(i+1)$st equation. After dividing by B_1, the first equation becomes

$$p_1 + \Omega_1 p_2 = \gamma_1,$$

where $\Omega_1 = C_1/B_1$ and $\gamma_1 = D_1/B_1$. Subtracting A_2 times this new equation from the second equation yields

$$(B_2 - A_2\Omega_1)p_2 + C_2p_3 = D_2 - A_2\gamma_1.$$

After this new second equation is divided by $\beta_2 = (B_2 - A_2\Omega_1)$, it becomes

$$p_2 + \Omega_2 p_3 = \gamma_2,$$

where $\Omega_2 = C_2/\beta_2$ and $\gamma_2 = (D_2 - A_2\gamma_1)/\beta_2$. p_2 can now be eliminated from the third equation. Proceeding in this way, the final equation becomes

$$p_{N_{eq}} = \gamma_{N_{eq}},$$

and $p_{N_{eq}-1}$ can now be computed from

$$p_{N_{eq}-1} = \gamma_{N_{eq}-1} - \Omega_{N_{eq}-1}p_{N_{eq}}$$

and so on back to p_1.

Writing the complete algorithm out in detail, the forward solution proceeds in order of increasing i. For the first $i=1$,

$$\beta_1 = B_1,$$

$$\Omega_1 = C_1/B_1,$$

and

$$\gamma_1 = D_1/B_1.$$

For each succeeding i $(2 \le i \le N_{eq})$,

$$\beta_i = B_i - A_i\Omega_{i-1},$$

$$\Omega_i = C_i/\beta_i,$$

and

$$\gamma_i = (D_i - A_i\gamma_{i-1})/\beta_i.$$

The back solution proceeds in order of decreasing i. First,

$$p_{N_{eq}} = \gamma_{N_{eq}}.$$

Then for each i, in decreasing sequence $(N_{eq}-1 \ge i \ge 1)$,

$$p_i = \gamma_i - \Omega_i p_{i+1}.$$

Presentations of this algorithm may be found in a number of references.[2,10,44] It is sometimes referred to as the Thomas algorithm.

Like all direct methods, it requires a fixed number of operations to solve the simultaneous equations. It requires $2+8(N_{eq}-1)$ operations, so that the amount of work is almost directly proportional to the number of equations. For more general band equations, with a bandwidth w, the work is almost directly proportional to w^2N_{eq}.

C.9.2 Iterative Methods. We have seen that the work requirement for direct methods increases very rapidly as the size of the grid increases, so that for reservoir models with a large number of gridblocks, direct methods may simply be too expensive to be practical. Iterative methods provide an alternative. In general, the work requirement per iteration is directly proportional to the number of gridblocks. Hence, if L is the number of iterations per timestep, the work requirement per timestep is proportional to LIJ for 2D problems, and proportional to $LIJK$ for 3D problems. Depending on the iterative method, the number of iterations usually increases much less rapidly than the number of gridblocks.

The number of iterations per timestep depends on many factors: the choice of iteration method, the number of gridblocks, the nature of the problem itself, and finally, the accuracy required. While one can say that direct methods are suitable for small problems and iterative methods are necessary for large ones, it is not possible to give a general answer to the question of where the crossover point is. Many simulators provide several options for the solution method, including both direct and iterative methods. For a given problem and grid spacing, the user may have to try several methods to decide which to use.

We will discuss several of the best iterative methods currently used in reservoir simulation: (corrected) line-successive overrelaxation (LSOR), the strongly implicit procedure (SIP), and nested-factorization/preconditioned orthomin. Their use will be illustrated for the solution of the equation

$$E_{i,j}p_{i,j} - D_{i,j}p_{i-1,j} - F_{i,j}p_{i+1,j} - B_{i,j}p_{i,j-1} - H_{i,j}p_{i,j+1} = q_{i,j}. \quad \text{(C.47)}$$

This is the most general form of the five-point difference equation for solving problems involving one dependent variable per gridblock in a 2D grid. It includes both the implicit difference equation for single-phase pressure, Eq. C.24, and the pressure equation arising in sequential solution methods, Eq. C.28.

Note that $E_{i,j}$ is the coefficient that lies on the main diagonal of the coefficient matrix. It turns out that, for reservoir problems, Eq. C.47 is diagonally dominant; i.e., the magnitude of the diagonal coefficient is greater than or equal to the sum of the magnitudes of the off-diagonal coefficients.

$$|E_{i,j}| \ge |D_{i,j}| + |F_{i,j}| + |B_{i,j}| + |H_{i,j}|. \quad \text{(C.48)}$$

This condition is essential to the convergence of the various iterative procedures.

Some additional general observations about iterative methods can now be made. First, all iterative methods involve making some initial guess for the pressures, $p_{i,j}$. This initial guess is usually the value of the pressure at the old time, $(p_o)^n_{i,j}$. Some method is then used to improve the guess with each iteration until, after a sufficient number of iterations, the simultaneous equations are satisfied to within some tolerance. Several criteria are in use for deciding when to stop the iteration. The first involves the use of residuals, which are a measure of the degree to which equations are not satisfied. In the case of Eq. C.47, the residual would be defined by

$$R^k_{i,j}=q_{i,j}-E_{i,j}p^k_{i,j}+D_{i,j}p^k_{i-1,j}+F_{i,j}p^k_{i+1,j}$$
$$+B_{i,j}p^k_{i,j-1}+H_{i,j}p^k_{i,j+1}. \quad \text{(C.49)}$$

Superscript k refers to the iteration count, so that $p^k_{i,j}$ is the kth iterate for the unknown pressure in Block (i,j). The residual, $R^k_{i,j}$, obviously is zero when Eq. C.47 is satisfied.

As the iteration proceeds, if the pressures are converging to the correct solution of the simultaneous equations, then the residuals get smaller and smaller. Hence, they can be used to monitor the iteration. When they reach an acceptably small value, the iteration may be terminated.

Another criterion that is frequently used is the change in pressure from one iteration to the next—i.e.,

$$|p^k_{i,j}-p^{k-1}_{i,j}|.$$

As the iteration converges, this change should get smaller and can be used to monitor the iteration. (This criterion should be used with caution, because a small value of the change can also mean that the iteration is converging very slowly.)

Finally, iterative methods require various iteration parameters. One of the great problems a user faces is the proper choice of these parameters so as to obtain the most rapid convergence. Unfortunately, the optimum parameter choice is a strong function of the nature of the problem being solved. Relaxation methods require choosing only one parameter, but the speed of convergence is critically dependent on finding the optimum value. SIP requires a sequence of parameters; this sequence is used repeatedly until convergence is achieved. Nested factorization does not require any parameters, and orthomin requires one integer parameter.

Brief descriptions of the methods follow.

C.9.2.1 Point Relaxation. The simplest relaxation scheme is simply to solve for the unknown pressure in each block in terms of the old iterate at the neighboring blocks. Thus, from Eq. C.47, we have

$$p^{k+1}_{i,j}=(q_{i,j}+D_{i,j}p^k_{i-1,j}+F_{i,j}p^k_{i+1,j}$$
$$+B_{i,j}p^k_{i,j-1}+H_{i,j}p^k_{i,j+1})/E_{i,j}. \quad \text{(C.50)}$$

(Note that here "old" iterate means the previous iterate, not to be confused with pressure from the previous timestep—i.e., p^n.) This is known as the Jacobi method, or the method of simultaneous displacements.

Eq. C.50 is applied to each block in the grid in some arbitrary, but fixed, order. For instance, the blocks can be taken in each row in order of increasing i, and then the rows taken in order of increasing j. After all the blocks are traversed, the computation starts over again at the first block. A complete iteration consists of one trip through all the blocks. The order in which the blocks are taken is immaterial in the Jacobi method, however, because the "new" iterate is not used until the start of the next iteration.

The rate of convergence (for a precise definition of rate of convergence, see Refs. 2, 45, and 46) can be doubled[2,10] by using new iterates in Eq. C.50 as soon as they are calculated. In calculating $p^{k+1}_{i,j}$ when traversing the grid, $p^{k+1}_{i-1,j}$ and $p^{k+1}_{i,j-1}$ will have been calculated and are available, but $p^{k+1}_{i+1,j}$ and $p^{k+1}_{i,j+1}$ will not yet have been calculated, so $p^k_{i+1,j}$ and $p^k_{i,j+1}$ must be used. Thus the iteration equation becomes

$$p^{k+1}_{i,j}=(q_{i,j}+D_{i,j}p^{k+1}_{i-1,j}+F_{i,j}p^k_{i+1,j}$$
$$+B_{i,j}p^{k+1}_{i,j-1}+H_{i,j}p^k_{i,j+1})/E_{i,j}. \quad \text{(C.51)}$$

This iterative method is known by various names: the Gauss-Seidel method, the method of successive displacements, or ordinary relaxation. The term relaxation comes from the idea that the residual, just before application of Eq. C.51 for Block (i,j), has the value

$$R^k_{i,j}=q_{i,j}-E_{i,j}p^k_{i,j}+D_{i,j}p^{k+1}_{i-1,j}+F_{i,j}p^k_{i+1,j}$$
$$+B_{i,j}p^{k+1}_{i,j-1}+H_{i,j}p^k_{i,j+1}, \quad \text{(C.52)}$$

but after application of Eq. C.51, the residual is "relaxed" to zero. That is,

$$R^{k+1}_{i,j}=q_{i,j}-E_{i,j}p^{k+1}_{i,j}+D_{i,j}p^{k+1}_{i-1,j}+F_{i,j}p^k_{i+1,j}$$
$$+B_{i,j}p^{k+1}_{i,j-1}+H_{i,j}p^k_{i,j+1}=0.$$

Note that the residual for Block (i,j) does not stay zero, but becomes nonzero as soon as Eq. C.51 is applied to the next block, $(i+1,j)$, and a new value of $p_{i+1,j}$ is calculated.

The convergence of this iteration can be speeded up by *overrelaxing*—i.e., after finding the change in $p_{i,j}$ that would reduce the residual for that block to zero, one deliberately goes further and makes an even greater change in $p_{i,j}$. Thus, in ordinary relaxation, we have

$$p^{k+1}_{i,j}=p^k_{i,j}+(R^k_{i,j}/E_{i,j}),$$

while in successive overrelaxation (SOR) we have

$$p^{k+1}_{i,j}=p^k_{i,j}+\omega(R^k_{i,j}/E_{i,j}), \quad \text{(C.53)}$$

where $\omega>1$.

Because Eqs. C.52 and C.53 are applied point by point, this procedure is referred to as point SOR.

It can be shown[2,10,45,47] that the optimum value of the relaxation parameter, ω, lies between 1.0 and 2.0. For so-called "ideal problems" involving uniform grid spacing and uniform values of k_x and k_y, the optimum parameter can be derived analytically, but most reservoir problems are nonideal. Some discussion on how to choose the optimum ω for nonideal problems is given by Young[45,48] and by Forsythe and Wasow.[46]

C.9.2.2 LSOR. Still further increase in the rate of convergence can be obtained by relaxing not one residual at a time, but a whole line of residuals at a time. The line can be either a row or a column in the grid. If it is a row, then the I residuals, defined by

$$R^{k+1,\text{new}}_{i,j}=q_{i,j}-E_{i,j}p^{k+1,\text{new}}_{i,j}+D_{i,j}p^{k+1,\text{new}}_{i-1,j}+F_{i,j}p^{k+1,\text{new}}_{i+1,j}$$
$$+B_{i,j}p^{k+1}_{i,j-1}+H_{i,j}p^k_{i,j+1}, \quad \text{(C.54)}$$

are all reduced to zero simultaneously. This leads to a tridiagonal system of equations that, as we have already noted, is very easy to solve.

Note that the only old iterate used in this calculation is $p^k_{i,j+1}$, corresponding to the next line (row), which has yet to be calculated.

Overrelaxation is then applied by taking the change in the pressure so calculated, $p^{k+1,\text{new}}_{i,j}-p^k_{i,j}$, and multiplying it by the relaxation parameter, ω, to obtain the final value of the new iterate:

$$p^{k+1}_{i,j}=p^k_{i,j}+\omega(p^{k+1,\text{new}}_{i,j}-p^k_{i,j}). \quad \text{(C.55)}$$

This extrapolation is applied to each block in the line, after solution of the tridiagonal equations and before proceeding to the next line of the iteration. The method is referred to as LSOR. For uniform isotropic problems, LSOR can be shown[2,45] to converge faster than SOR by a factor of $\sqrt{2}$, provided optimum values of ω are used. For uniform anisotropic problems (i.e., where $k_x\Delta y/\Delta x$ and $k_y\Delta x/\Delta y$ are constant but not equal to each other), and with no-flow boundary conditions at the edges of the computing rectangle, LSOR has the same advantage over SOR, provided that (1) columns are used for the lines if $k_y\Delta x/\Delta y>k_x\Delta y/\Delta x$ and (2) rows are used for the lines if $k_x\Delta y/\Delta x>k_y\Delta x/\Delta y$.

When the reservoir problem is anisotropic, as is frequently the case for cross sections, an even greater increase in convergence rate can be obtained by use of a correction procedure devised by Watts,[49,50] whose method of additive corrections is applied between LSOR iterations and consists of adding to each pressure in a column a constant, β, so that a "corrected" value of pressure, $p_{i,j}^{k+1,c}$, is used as the starting point for the next iteration. Thus,

$$p_{i,j}^{k+1,c}=p_{i,j}^{k+1}+\beta_i.$$

The β's are chosen so that the *sum* of the residuals for each column is reduced to zero. This leads to a tridiagonal system of equations for the β's, which is easily solved. The procedure is called "line-corrected LSOR" (LSORC); for uniform anisotropic problems, it can be shown[2,50] to be faster than LSOR by a factor of $(\Delta x/\Delta y)\sqrt{k_y/k_x}$, provided that optimum values of ω are used.

LSOR and LSORC are among the most popular iterative methods in reservoir simulation and are used in many simulators described in the literature.

C.9.2.3 SIP. One of the best iterative methods currently available for certain types of problems is SIP, proposed by Stone.[51] It is a member of a class of iterative methods that use approximate factorization. Instead of solving the problem

$$Ap=q, \quad \text{(C.56)}$$

the coefficient matrix, A, is approximated by another matrix, A', that is easy to factor; further, the factors are very simple in form, having only three coefficients in each row. The iteration equation can be written

$$L'U'(p^{k+1}-p^k)=q-Ap^k, \quad \text{(C.57)}$$

where L' and U' are the easily obtained factors of the approximate coefficient matrix, A'. Let

$$v^k=U'(p^{k+1}-p^k) \quad \text{(C.58)}$$

be an intermediate column matrix, obtained by solving the system of equations

$$L'v^k=q-Ap^k=R^k. \quad \text{(C.59)}$$

Eq. C.59 is the forward solution and corresponds to the following simple equation for each gridpoint:

$$b_{i,j}v_{i,j-1}^k+c_{i,j}v_{i-1,j}^k+d_{i,j}v_{i,j}^k=R_{i,j}^k, \quad \text{(C.60)}$$

where $b_{i,j}$, $c_{i,j}$, and $d_{i,j}$ are coefficients (of the L' matrix) yet to be determined. This equation can easily be solved for successive values of $v_{i,j}^k$ in order of increasing i and increasing j.

Eq. C.58 is the back solution and corresponds to the following equation for each gridpoint:

$$\delta_{i,j}^k+e_{i,j}\delta_{i+1,j}^k+f_{i,j}\delta_{i,j+1}^k=v_{i,j}^k, \quad \text{(C.61)}$$

where

$$\delta_{i,j}^k=p_{i,j}^{k+1}-p_{i,j}^k. \quad \text{(C.62)}$$

Eq. C.61 can easily be solved for successive values of $\delta_{i,j}^k$ (and then $p_{i,j}^{k+1}$), but this time in order of decreasing i and decreasing j.

By multiplying the two factors L' and U' together, it can be shown[2,51] that the approximate equation $A'p=L'U'p=q$ corresponds to the difference equation

$$b_{i,j}p_{i,j-1}+b_{i,j}e_{i,j-1}p_{i+1,j-1}+c_{i,j}p_{i-1,j}+(b_{i,j}f_{i,j-1}$$
$$+c_{i,j}e_{i-1,j}+d_{i,j})p_{i,j}+d_{i,j}e_{i,j}p_{i+1,j}$$
$$+c_{i,j}f_{i-1,j}p_{i-1,j+1}+d_{i,j}f_{i,j}p_{i,j+1}=q_{i,j}. \quad \text{(C.63)}$$

Comparing this with Eq. C.47, which we rewrite as

$$-B_{i,j}p_{i,j-1}-D_{i,j}p_{i-1,j}+E_{i,j}p_{i,j}-F_{i,j}p_{i+1,j}$$
$$-H_{i,j}p_{i,j+1}=q_{i,j}, \quad \text{(C.64)}$$

we see that two additional terms have appeared, involving pressures in Gridblocks $(i+1,j-1)$ and $(i-1,j+1)$. One cannot avoid these terms and still maintain easy factorability of the approximate coefficient matrix. To reduce the effect of these additional terms, and thereby to speed up convergence, Stone noted that for smoothly varying p,

$$p_{i+1,j-1}\sim p_{i+1,j}+p_{i,j-1}-p_{i,j}$$

and

$$p_{i-1,j+1}\sim p_{i-1,j}+p_{i,j+1}-p_{i,j},$$

and subtracted these expressions in the following approximation to Eq. C.64:

$$-B_{i,j}p_{i,j-1}+b_{i,j}e_{i,j-1}[p_{i+1,j-1}-\alpha_k(p_{i+1,j}+p_{i,j-1}-p_{i,j})]$$
$$-D_{i,j}p_{i-1,j}+E_{i,j}p_{i,j}-F_{i,j}p_{i+1,j}+c_{i,j}f_{i-1,j}[p_{i-1,j+1}$$
$$-\alpha_k(p_{i-1,j}+p_{i,j+1}-p_{i,j})]-H_{i,j}p_{i,j+1}=q_{i,j}, \quad \text{(C.65)}$$

where α_k is an iteration parameter added to accelerate convergence. Subscript k on α indicates that the parameter changes each iteration. Comparing Eqs. C.63 and C.65 and setting coefficients of corresponding p's equal then gives the following algorithm for evaluating the coefficients of the factors:

$$b_{i,j}=-B_{i,j}/(1+\alpha_k e_{i,j-1}), \quad \text{(C.66)}$$

$$c_{i,j}=-D_{i,j}/(1+\alpha_k f_{i-1,j}), \quad \text{(C.67)}$$

$$d_{i,j}=E_{i,j}+\alpha_k b_{i,j}e_{i,j-1}+\alpha_k c_{i,j}f_{i-1,j}-b_{i,j}f_{i,j-1}-c_{i,j}e_{i-1,j}, \quad \text{(C.68)}$$

$$e_{i,j}=-(F_{i,j}+\alpha_k b_{i,j}e_{i,j-1})/d_{i,j}, \quad \text{(C.69)}$$

and

$$f_{i,j}=-(H_{i,j}+\alpha_k c_{i,j}f_{i-1,j})/d_{i,j}. \quad \text{(C.70)}$$

These five equations can be solved in order for each block, if the blocks are taken in order of increasing i and increasing j.

To summarize, at each gridblock in order of increasing i and j, evaluate Eqs. C.66 through C.70 and C.60, saving all values of $e_{i,j}$, $f_{i,j}$, and $v_{i,j}^k$. Then, in reverse order, use Eqs. C.61 and C.62 to solve for $\delta_{i,j}^k$ and $p_{i,j}^{k+1}$.

Stone found that changing the order of blocks in alternate iterations greatly improves the speed of convergence—i.e., in every second iteration, the factorization and forward solution should proceed in the order of decreasing j and increasing i, while the back solution proceeds in the order of increasing j and decreasing i. This has the effect of bringing Blocks $(i-1,j-1)$ and $(i+1,j+1)$ into Eq. C.63, instead of Blocks $(i+1,j-1)$ and $(i-1,j+1)$.

Stone used a heuristic argument, backed by empirical tests, to develop the strategy for picking SIP parameters. It is extremely important that α_k be varied through a cycle of values; the minimum value of α_k is not critical and may be taken to be zero; however, the maximum value is more critical. It has been found satisfactory in many cases to compute $(1-\alpha_k)$ as a geometric sequence, with

$$1-\alpha_{max}=\min\left[\frac{\pi^2}{2I^2\left(1+\dfrac{k_y\Delta x^2}{k_x\Delta y^2}\right)},\frac{\pi^2}{2J^2\left(1+\dfrac{k_x\Delta y^2}{k_y\Delta x^2}\right)}\right].$$

Thus,

$$1-\alpha_k=(1-\alpha_{max})^{(k-1)/(s-1)},$$

where s is the number of parameters in the cycle. For difficult problems, it may be necessary to increase or decrease $1-\alpha_{max}$ by trial and error.

The SIP algorithm presented here is for the solution of 2D problems, with one unknown per gridblock. Weinstein *et al.*[52,53] have extended this algorithm to three dimensions and also to problems with two or three unknowns per gridblock. Schneider and Zedan[54] modified it to include more diagonals in L' and U'.

C.9.2.4 Nested Factorization. One of the most robust of the currently available iterative methods is the nested-factorization approach of Appleyard *et al.*[55,56] Nested factorization is a preconditioning for the conjugate gradient and orthomin[57] procedures. Nested-factorization/preconditioned orthomin is currently competitive in efficiency with all other available methods for many problems. We begin the presentation of this method by discussing preconditioned orthomin methods.

Suppose solving the system $Ap=q$ for pressure, p, is expensive. Then if we can find a "preconditioning" matrix A' that is an approximation to A, for which it is cheap to solve systems of the form $A's=r$, we can use the following simple iteration to compute p.

Take an initial guess p_1. Solve $A's_1=r_1=q-Ap_1$ and add $p_1+s_1=p_2$. Continue in this way, generating p_3, p_4, etc., until convergence is acceptable.

This is certainly a reasonable approach if A' is very close to A; if A' exactly equals A, $p_2=p$.

A problem with the above iteration is that it tends to get stuck, with the r_k's being near-multiples of each other. The idea in orthomin is to modify r_k so that r_k^{new} is as far from being a multiple of r_{k-1} as possible—i.e., r_k^{new} is made orthogonal to r_{k-1},

$$(r_k^{new})^T r_{k-1}=0,$$

using the formula

$$r_k^{new}=r_k-\frac{r_k^T r_{k-1}}{r_{k-1}^T r_{k-1}}r_{k-1}.$$

Unfortunately, r_k^{new} may still be close to a multiple of r_{k-2}. In general, r_k^{new} is forced to be orthogonal to a specified number, n, of previous residuals $r_{k-1}\ldots r_{k-n}$, with n often set in the 5-to-10 range.

If orthogonalization is to succeed in making all the r_k's very different, the iteration must do a very good job of dealing with each r_k. This can be achieved by changing the addition step in the basic iteration to $p_{k+1}=p_k+\alpha_k s_k$, where the scalar multiplier α_k is chosen so that

$$r_{k+1}^T r_{k+1}=[q-A(p_k+\alpha_k s_k)]^T[q-A(p_k+\alpha_k s_k)]$$

is minimized with respect to α_k.

The resultant solution methods, combining the *preconditioning* matrix A', *orthogonalization* of the r_k's, and *minimization* of $r_{k+1}{}^T r_{k+1}$, are called preconditioned orthomin methods.[57] These methods are widely used in reservoir simulation. In certain cases, however, alternatives to orthomin are preferable. For instance, when A is symmetric ($A=A^T$), the conjugate gradient method[58] is cheaper. Also, when n is large, the generalized minimum-residual method[59] requires somewhat less storage than orthomin.

The term "nested factorization" refers to a particular choice for the preconditioning matrix, A'. The following brief outline focuses on the unique aspects of nested factorization.

Consider the matrix for a 1D problem with three gridblocks:

$$A=\begin{bmatrix} d_1 & u_1 & 0 \\ \ell_2 & d_2 & u_2 \\ 0 & \ell_3 & d_3 \end{bmatrix}.$$

To solve the equation $Ap=q$ for pressures p, we can use a variant of the tridiagonal algorithm, factoring $A=LDU$, where L, D, and U are the "factors" of A:

$$L=\begin{bmatrix} m_1 & 0 & 0 \\ \ell_2 & m_2 & 0_3 \\ 0 & \ell_3 & m_3 \end{bmatrix},$$

$$D=\begin{bmatrix} m_1^{-1} & 0 & 0 \\ 0 & m_2^{-1} & 0 \\ 0 & 0 & m_3^{-1} \end{bmatrix},$$

and

$$U=\begin{bmatrix} m_1 & u_1 & 0 \\ 0 & m_2 & u_2 \\ 0 & 0 & m_3 \end{bmatrix}.$$

In a "forward sweep," we solve $Lx=q$ for x, solve $Dy=x$ for y, and finally in a "backward sweep" solve $Up=y$ for p. The new quantities m_1, m_2, and m_3 are computed by

$$m_1=d_1,$$

$$m_2=d_2-\ell_2 m_1^{-1}u_1,$$

and

$$m_3=d_3-\ell_3 m_2^{-1}u_2.$$

Now, consider the matrix for a 2D problem with three rows of gridblocks,

$$A=\begin{bmatrix} D_1 & U_1 & 0 \\ L_2 & D_2 & U_2 \\ 0 & L_3 & D_3 \end{bmatrix}.$$

Here, each D_1, U_1, L_2, etc., is itself a tridiagonal or diagonal matrix containing entries for one entire row of gridblocks. Applying *LDU* factorization to this matrix, $A=LDU$, where

$$L=\begin{bmatrix} M_1 & 0 & 0 \\ L_2 & M_2 & 0 \\ 0 & L_3 & M_3 \end{bmatrix},$$

$$D=\begin{bmatrix} M_1^{-1} & 0 & 0 \\ 0 & M_2^{-1} & 0 \\ 0 & 0 & M_3^{-1} \end{bmatrix},$$

and

$$U=\begin{bmatrix} M_1 & U_1 & 0 \\ 0 & M_2 & U_2 \\ 0 & 0 & M_3 \end{bmatrix},$$

and

$$M_1=D_1,$$

$$M_2=D_2-L_2 M_1^{-1}U_1,$$

and

$$M_3=D_3-L_3 M_2^{-1}U_2.$$

M_i^{-1} is the inverse of Matrix M_i (see Chap. 6).

Unfortunately, *LDU* factorization is very expensive because M_2 and M_3 are now full of nonzeroes. Even though M_1 has very few nonzeroes, M_1^{-1} is full of nonzeroes, so that $L_2M_1^{-1}U_1$ is full and so is M_2.

The key idea of nested factorization is to *approximate* M_2 and M_3 by other matrices that are similar, but that are not full of nonzeroes. These other matrices are themselves represented and used in factored form; this is where the name "nested factorization" comes from.

The part of M_2 that makes it full is the $L_2 M_1^{-1} U_1$ term. Nested factorization approximates this full matrix by the diagonal matrix, $C_{sum}(L_2 M_1^{-1} U_1)$, which *sums* all the entries in each *column* onto the main diagonal. For example,

$$C_{sum}\begin{bmatrix} a & b & c \\ d & e & f \\ g & h & i \end{bmatrix} = \begin{bmatrix} a+d+g & 0 & 0 \\ 0 & b+e+h & 0 \\ 0 & 0 & c+f+i \end{bmatrix}.$$

The resultant nested-factorization approximation to A is $A'=L'D'U'$, where

$$L' = \begin{bmatrix} M'_1 & 0 & 0 \\ L_2 & M'_2 & 0 \\ 0 & L_3 & M'_3 \end{bmatrix},$$

$$D' = \begin{bmatrix} (M'_1)^{-1} & 0 & 0 \\ 0 & (M'_2)^{-1} & 0 \\ 0 & 0 & (M'_3)^{-1} \end{bmatrix},$$

$$U' = \begin{bmatrix} M'_1 & U_1 & 0 \\ 0 & M'_2 & U_2 \\ 0 & 0 & M'_3 \end{bmatrix},$$

and

$$M'_1 = D_1,$$

$$M'_2 = D_2 - C_{sum}[L_2(M'_1)^{-1}U_1],$$

and

$$M'_3 = D_3 - C_{sum}[L_3(M'_2)^{-1}U_2].$$

As mentioned, M'_1, M'_2, and M'_3 are used in factored form, so the full matrices $(M'_1)^{-1}$, $(M'_2)^{-1}$, and $(M'_3)^{-1}$ are never explicitly needed.

For 3D problems, the nested-factorization approach proceeds similarly; all terms in the *LDU* factorization that would be full are approximated by their diagonal C_{sum}.

Experience has shown that A' is usually a very good approximation to A, and few convergence iterations are needed. This is especially true when transmissibilities are much greater within rows than between rows: the only approximations being made in the tridiagonal algorithms are for terms with small entries (L_2, U_1, L_3, and U_2).

It can also be shown that the nested-factorization A' satisfies $C_{sum}(A')=C_{sum}(A)$. Then if we approximate the solution p of $Ap=q$ by the solution p' of $A'p'=q$, we have

$$C_{sum}(Ap') = C_{sum}(A'p') = C_{sum}(q)$$

or

$$C_{sum}(q - Ap') = 0.$$

For the pressure equation, in physical terms this says that for the reservoir as a whole, exact material balance is satisfied at every iteration.

C.9.2.5 Other Iterative Methods. A number of iterative methods are finding application in reservoir simulation. Promising candidates include other incomplete *LU* or *LDU* factorization methods,[60-63] special iterative techniques for fully implicit formulations,[64,65] multigrid methods,[66] and other minimization techniques.[61] We expect that because of the impact of new vector and parallel computer architectures, development of iterative methods will continue to be a very active area of research.

Nomenclature

A = coefficient matrix
A' = preconditioning matrix
b = column matrix of boundary information
B = FVF, res m³/stock-tank m³
c = compressibility, Pa^{-1}
C_{sum} = diagonal matrix containing column sums
f = fractional flow, dimensionless
h = thickness, m
I = number of gridblocks in x direction
J = number of gridblocks in y direction
k = permeability, m^2
k_r = relative permeability, dimensionless
k_x, k_y = permeability in x and y directions, respectively, m^2
K = number of gridblocks in z direction
M = mobility factor, stock-tank m^3/res $\text{m}^3\cdot\text{s}\cdot\text{Pa}$
M_x, M_y = mobility factor in x and y directions, respectively, stock-tank m^3/res $\text{m}^3\cdot\text{s}\cdot\text{Pa}$
N_{eq} = number of equations
p = pressure, Pa
p^n, p^{n+1} = column matrices of pressures, Pa
P_c = capillary pressure, Pa
q = standard volume flow rate, stock-tank m^3/s
r_k = orthomin residual column matrix
R = residual column matrix
S = saturation, fraction
ΔS = saturation increment, fraction
t = time, seconds
Δt = timestep, seconds
T_x, T_y = single-phase transmissibility factor in x and y directions, respectively, m^3
v = velocity, m/s
v_t = total velocity, m/s
V = volume, m^3
w = coefficient matrix bandwidth
x, y = space dimensions
$\Delta x, \Delta y$ = block length in x and y directions, respectively, m
α = normalized compressibility coefficient
α_k = iteration parameters
λ = phase mobility, $\text{m}^2/\text{Pa}\cdot\text{s}$
μ = viscosity, Pa·s
ϕ = porosity, fraction
Δ = difference operator
ω = SOR relaxation parameter

Subscripts

g = gas
i = gridblock number in x direction
j = gridblock number in y direction
max = maximum
o = oil
x, y = space dimensions

Superscripts

k = current iteration
$k+1$ = next iteration
n = last timestep taken
$n+1$ = next timestep
new = new estimate
ref = reference conditions
T = transpose

References

1. Huppler, J.D.: "Numerical Investigation of the Effects of Core Heterogeneities on Waterflood Relative Permeabilities," *SPEJ* (Dec. 1970) 381–92; *Trans.*, AIME, **249**.

2. Peaceman, D.W.: *Fundamentals of Numerical Reservoir Simulation,* Elsevier Scientific Publishing Co., Amsterdam (1977).
3. Lantz, R.B.: "Quantitative Evaluation of Numerical Diffusion (Truncation Error)," *SPEJ* (Sept. 1971) 315–20; *Trans.,* AIME, **251.**
4. Bech, N.: "Classification of Reservoir Simulators," Energiministeriets Energiforskningsprogram, Olie- og gasreservoirmodeller, Report No. 6, Riso-M-2421, Riso Natl. Laboratory, Roskilde, Denmark (1984).
5. Todd, M.R., O'Dell, P.M., and Hirasaki, G.J.: "Methods for Increased Accuracy in Numerical Reservoir Simulators," *SPEJ* (Dec. 1972) 515–30; *Trans.,* AIME, **253.**
6. Bell, J.B. and Shubin, G.R.: "Higher-Order Godunov Methods for Reducing Numerical Dispersion in Reservoir Simulation," paper SPE 13514 presented at the 1985 SPE Symposium on Reservoir Simulation, Dallas, Feb. 10–13.
7. Ko, S.C.M., Buchanan, W.L., and Vinsome, P.K.W.: "A Critical Comparison of Finite Difference Interblock Mobility Approximations in Numerical Reservoir Simulation," *Proc.,* Annual Meeting of Pet. Soc. of CIM, Calgary, Alta. (May 3–6, 1981).
8. Taggart, I.J. and Pinczewski, W.V.: "The Use of Higher-Order Differencing Techniques in Reservoir Simulation," *SPERE* (Aug. 1987) 360–72.
9. Richtmyer, R.D. and Morton, K.W.: *Difference Methods for Initial Value Problems,* second edition, Wiley-Interscience, New York City (1967).
10. Ames, W.F.: *Numerical Methods for Partial Differential Equations,* second edition, Academic Press, New York City (1977).
11. Price, H.S. and Coats, K.H.: "Direct Methods in Reservoir Simulation," *SPEJ* (June 1974) 295–308; *Trans.,* AIME, **257.**
12. McDonald, A.E. and Trimble, R.H.: "Efficient Use of Mass Storage During Elimination for Sparse Sets of Simultaneous Equations," *SPEJ* (Aug. 1977) 300–16.
13. George, J.A.: "Nested Dissection of a Regular Finite Element Mesh," *SIAM J. Numer. Anal.* (April 1973) 345–63.
14. Stone, H.L. and Garder, A.O. Jr.: "Analysis of Gas-Cap or Dissolved-Gas Drive Reservoirs," *SPEJ* (June 1961) 91–102.
15. Breitenbach, E.A., Thurnau, D.H., and van Poollen, H.K.: "The Fluid Flow Simulation Equations," paper SPE 2020 presented at the 1968 SPE Symposium on Numerical Simulation of Reservoir Performance, Dallas, April 22–23.
16. Sheldon, J.W., Harris, C.D., and Bavly, D.: "A Method for General Reservoir Behavior Simulation on Digital Computers," paper 1521-G presented at the 1960 SPE Annual Meeting, Denver, Oct. 2–5.
17. MacDonald, R.C. and Coats, K.H.: "Methods for Numerical Simulation of Water and Gas Coning," *SPEJ* (Dec. 1970) 425–35; *Trans.,* AIME, **249.**
18. Spillette, A.G., Hillestad, J.G., and Stone, H.L.: "A High-Stability Sequential Solution Approach to Reservoir Simulation," paper SPE 4542 presented at the 1973 SPE Annual Meeting, Las Vegas, Sept. 30–Oct. 3.
19. Weinstein, H.G., Wheeler, J.A., and Woods, E.G.: "Numerical Model for Thermal Processes," *SPEJ* (Feb. 1977) 65–78; *Trans.,* AIME, **263.**
20. Spivak, A.: "Gravity Segregation in Two-Phase Displacement Processes," *SPEJ* (Dec. 1974) 419–32; *Trans.,* AIME, **257.**
21. Spivak, A., Price, H.S., and Settari, A.: "Solution of the Equations for Multidimensional, Two-Phase, Immiscible Flow by Variational Methods," *SPEJ* (Feb. 1977) 27–41.
22. Peaceman, D.W.: "Numerical Solution of the Nonlinear Equations for Two-Phase Flow Through Porous Media," *Nonlinear Partial Differential Equations—A Symposium on Methods of Solution,* W.F. Ames (ed.), Academic Press Inc., New York City (1967) 171–91.
23. Peaceman, D.W.: "A Nonlinear Stability Analysis for Difference Equations Using Semi-Implicit Mobility," *SPEJ* (Feb. 1977) 79–91; *Trans.,* AIME, **263.**
24. Blair, P.M. and Weinaug, C.F.: "Solution of Two-Phase Flow Problems Using Implicit Difference Equations," *SPEJ* (Dec. 1969) 417–24; *Trans.,* AIME, **246.**
25. Sonier, F., Besset, P., and Ombret, O.: "A Numerical Model of Multiphase Flow Around a Well," *SPEJ* (Dec. 1973) 311–20.
26. Sonier, F. and Chaumet, P.: "A Fully Implicit Three-Dimensional Model in Curvilinear Coordinates," *SPEJ* (Aug. 1974) 361–70; *Trans.,* AIME, **257.**
27. Trimble, R.H. and McDonald, A.E.: "A Strongly-Coupled, Fully Implicit Three-Dimensional, Three Phase Well Coning Model," *SPEJ* (Aug. 1981) 454–58.
28. Coats, K.H.: "A Highly Implicit Steamflood Model," *SPEJ* (Oct. 1978) 369–83.
29. Bansal, P.P. *et al.*: "A Strongly Coupled, Fully Implicit, Three Dimensional, Three Phase Reservoir Simulator," paper SPE 8329 presented at the 1979 SPE Annual Technical Conference and Exhibition, Las Vegas, Sept. 23–26.
30. Cheshire, I.M. *et al.*: "An Efficient Fully Implicit Simulator," paper EUR 179 presented at the 1980 European Offshore Petroleum Conference and Exhibition, London, Oct. 21–24.
31. Chien, M.C.H., Lee, S.T., and Chen, W.H.: "A New Fully Implicit Compositional Simulator," paper SPE 13385 presented at the 1985 SPE Symposium on Reservoir Simulation, Dallas, Feb. 10–13.
32. Grabowski, J.W. *et al.*: "A Fully Implicit General Purpose Finite Difference Thermal Model for In-Situ Combustion and Steam," paper SPE 8396 presented at the 1979 SPE Annual Technical Conference and Exhibition, Las Vegas, Sept. 23–26.
33. Au, A.D.K. *et al.*: "Techniques for Fully Implicit Reservoir Simulation," paper SPE 9302 presented at the 1980 SPE Annual Technical Conference and Exhibition, Dallas, Sept. 21–24.
34. Thomas, G.W. and Thurman, D.H.: "Reservoir Simulation Using an Adaptive Implicit Method," *SPEJ* (Oct. 1983) 759–68.
35. Forsyth, P.A. and Sammon, P.H.: "Practical Considerations for Adaptive Implicit Methods in Reservoir Simulation," *J. Comp. Phys.* (1986) **62,** 265–81.
36. Hwang, M.K., Jones, W.R., and Odeh, A.S.: "An In-Situ Combustion Process Simulator With a Moving-Front Representation," *SPEJ* (April 1982) 271–79.
37. Letkeman, J.P. and Ridings, R.L.: "A Numerical Coning Model," *SPEJ* (Dec. 1970) 418–24; *Trans.,* AIME, **249.**
38. Nolen, J.S. and Berry, D.W.: "Tests of the Stability and Time-Step Sensitivity of Semi-Implicit Reservoir Simulation Techniques," *SPEJ* (June 1972) 253–66; *Trans.,* AIME, **253.**
39. Coats, K.H. *et al.*: "Three-Dimensional Simulation of Steamflooding," *SPEJ* (Dec. 1974) 573–92; *Trans.,* AIME, **257.**
40. Chappelear, J.E. and Rogers, W.L.: "Some Practical Considerations in the Construction of a Semi-Implicit Simulator," *SPEJ* (June 1974) 216–20.
41. Jensen, O.K.: "An Automatic Timestep Selection Scheme for Reservoir Simulation," paper SPE 9373 presented at the 1980 SPE Annual Technical Conference and Exhibition, Dallas, Sept. 21–24.
42. Sammon, P.H. and Rubin, B.: "Practical Control of Timestep Selection in Thermal Simulation," *SPERE* (March 1986) 163–70.
43. Sherman, A.H.: "Sparse Gaussian Elimination for Complex Reservoir Models," paper SPE 13537 presented at the 1985 SPE Symposium on Reservoir Simulation, Dallas, Feb. 10–13.
44. Carnahan, B., Luther, H.A., and Wilkes, J.O.: *Applied Numerical Methods,* John Wiley Publishing Co., New York City (1969).
45. Young, D.M.: *Iterative Solution of Large Linear Systems,* Academic Press, New York City (1971).
46. Forsythe, G.E. and Wasow, W.R.: *Finite-Difference Methods for Partial Differential Equations,* John Wiley Publishing Co., New York City (1960).
47. Varga, R.S.: *Matrix Iterative Analysis,* Prentice-Hall Inc., Englewood Cliffs, NJ (1962).
48. Young, D.M.: "The Numerical Solution of Elliptic and Parabolic Partial Differential Equations," *Survey of Numerical Analysis,* J. Todd (ed.), McGraw-Hill Book Co., New York City (1962) 380–438.
49. Watts, J.W.: "An Iterative Matrix Solution Method Suitable for Anisotropic Problems," *SPEJ* (March 1971) 47–51; *Trans.,* AIME, **251.**
50. Watts, J.W.: "A Method for Improving Line Successive Over-relaxation in Anisotropic Problems—A Theoretical Analysis," *SPEJ* (April 1973) 105–18; *Trans.,* AIME, **255.**
51. Stone, H.L.: "Iterative Solution of Implicit Approximations of Multidimensional Partial Differential Equations," *SIAM J. Numer. Anal.* (1968) **5,** 530–58.
52. Weinstein, H.G., Stone, H.L., and Kwan, T.V.: "Simultaneous Solution of Multiphase Reservoir Flow Equations," *SPEJ* (June 1970) 99–110.
53. Weinstein, H.G., Stone, H.L., and Kwan, T.V.: "An Iterative Procedure for Solution of Systems of Parabolic and Elliptic Equations in Three Dimensions," *Ind. Eng. Chem. Fund.* (1969) **8,** 281–87.
54. Schneider, G.E. and Zedan, M.: "A Modified Strongly Implicit Procedure for the Numerical Solution of Field Problems," *Numerical Heat Transfer* (1981) **4,** 1–19.
55. Appleyard, J.R., Cheshire, L.M., and Pollard, R.K.: "Special Techniques for Fully Implicit Simulators," *Proc.,* European Symposium on Enhanced Oil Recovery, Bournemouth, England (1981) 395–408.
56. Appleyard, J.R. and Cheshire, L.M.: "Nested Factorization," paper SPE 12264 presented at the 1983 SPE Symposium on Reservoir Simulation, San Francisco, Nov. 15–18.
57. Vinsome, P.K.W.: "Orthomin, an Iterative Method for Solving Sparse Sets of Simultaneous Linear Equations," paper SPE 5729 presented at the 1976 SPE Symposium on Numerical Simulation of Reservoir Performance, Los Angeles, Feb. 19–20.
58. Golub, G.H. and Van Loan, C.F.: *Matrix Computations,* Johns Hopkins U. Press, Baltimore (1983).
59. Saad, Y. and Schultz, M.H.: "GMRES: A Generalized Minimal Residual Algorithm for Solving Nonsymmetric Linear Systems," *SIAM J. Sci. Stat. Comput.* (July 1986) 856–69.

60. Watts, J.W.: "A Conjugate Gradient-Truncated Direct Method for the Iterative Solution of the Reservoir Simulation Pressure Equation," *SPEJ* (June 1981) 345-53; *Trans.*, AIME, **271.**
61. Tan, T.B.S. and Letkeman, J.P.: "Application of D4 Ordering and Minimization in an Effective Partial Matrix Inverse Iterative Method," paper SPE 10493 presented at the 1982 SPE Symposium on Reservoir Simulation, New Orleans, Jan. 31-Feb. 3.
62. Wallis, J.R.: "Incomplete Gaussian Elimination as a Preconditioning for Generalized Conjugate Gradient Acceleration," paper SPE 12265 presented at the 1983 SPE Symposium on Reservoir Simulation, San Francisco, Nov. 15-18.
63. Eisenstat, S.C., Elman, H.C., and Schultz, M.H.: "Block-Preconditioned Conjugate-Gradient-Like Methods for Numerical Reservoir Simulation," *SPERE* (Feb. 1988) 307-12.
64. Wallis, J.R., Kendall, R.P., and Little, T.E.: "Constrained Residual Acceleration of Conjugate Residual Methods," paper SPE 13536 presented at the 1985 SPE Symposium on Reservoir Simulation, Dallas, Feb. 10-13.
65. Behie, A. and Vinsome, P.K.W.: "Block Iterative Methods for Fully Implicit Reservoir Simulation," *SPEJ* (Oct. 1982) 658-68.
66. Behie, A. and Forsyth, P.A.: "Multigrid Solution of the Pressure Equation in Reservoir Simulation," *SPEJ* (Aug. 1983) 623-32.

Appendix D
Regression Analysis in Automatic History Matching

This appendix reviews the types of regression analyses used for automatic matching of reservoir simulation model results with field performance history. Regression techniques have been found to be effective in a variety of areas throughout the scientific world. The focus here is on application of those techniques to estimation of optimal values of reservoir properties to assign to a reservoir model.*

As discussed in Chap. 4, a reservoir simulator must be supplied with a description of the reservoir. After the reservoir model is constructed with this description, boundary conditions are applied and the pressure and saturation behavior of the reservoir is calculated as a function of time.

Simulation to improve reservoir description is, in a sense, the "inverse" of simulation to predict performance. The approach generally adopted is to search for the set of properties that defines a reservoir model so that a simulation based on this model will produce calculated reservoir behavior that represents the closest match to the observed behavior. Examples of properties included in the search are permeabilities, porosities, compressibilities, and reservoir boundaries. Field data could include pressures, water/oil ratios (WOR's), gas/oil ratios (GOR's), or produced fluid volumes.

This search is often referred to as "history matching." Reservoir engineers have been history matching in one form or another for as many years as there have been reservoir models. By far the largest fraction of this modeling is performed "manually"—i.e., by running a number of simulations and altering the model between successive simulations as needed to obtain an improved match to observed data. Efficient selection of the appropriate model adjustments requires experience and an understanding of the effects of various properties on performance. Because success depends heavily on the skill of the engineer, there is some incentive to provide an automated version of the process. Attempts to accomplish this have produced numerous algorithms, many of which will be discussed here briefly. For more detail on a particular algorithm or method, see the references.

Some algorithms adjust the model parameters according to predetermined guidelines. The quality of the match is quantified in terms of an objective function, a relationship that reflects the difference between observed and calculated reservoir behavior. The goal is to find the reservoir model that will optimize this objective function. The process is generally referred to as "automatic history matching" or "inverse simulation." The principal advantages of the approach are that it can significantly reduce the time necessary to obtain a history match and that it can remove some of the dependence on the experience of the engineer.

The most common objective function is the sum of squares of the differences between observed and calculated data, e.g., pressure. Define these differences as residuals, R_k, so that

$$R_k=F_{s_k}(p_k^o-p_k^c), \quad \text{(D.1)}$$

*In this appendix we use a consistent set of units and do not provide the equivalent oilfield units.

where

p_k^o = pressure observed at a given position in the reservoir at some given time,

p_k^c = pressure calculated by reservoir simulation for that position at that time, and

F_{s_k} = a weighting factor.

Then R_k, the "kth residual," will be a measure of the closeness of the match on that particular pressure measurement. If the R_k are combined so that

$$Q=\sum_k^{N_r} R_k^2, \quad \text{(D.2)}$$

where N_r=number of residuals, then function Q is a measure of the overall quality of the match between the simulation and the observed history. If $Q=0$, the observed and calculated data match exactly.

The residuals can also be defined as differences between observed and calculated GOR's, WOR's, produced fluid volumes, or any other data characteristic of the reservoir behavior. Then by using appropriate values for F_{s_k}, these types of data can be combined to yield an overall objective function that includes all the observed field data.

The reservoir description can be represented as a collection of parameters to be determined—i.e., porosities and permeabilities. If X_j, where $j=1,n$ are defined to be those parameters, the problem becomes a search for the set of X_j that results in a minimum objective function Q.

Because the expense involved in reaching a solution generally increases rapidly with the number of parameters to be determined, it usually is necessary to limit the number of properties that can be altered. Any properties that are well-known are usually fixed at their input values. In addition, other groups of properties may be combined and related through a single parameter. For example, all porosities in one region of the field might be described with the relationship

$$\phi(i,j)=X_j\phi_o(i,j),\ a<i<b,\ c<j<d, \quad \text{(D.3)}$$

where $\phi(i,j)$ is the porosity at any location in the region bounded by $i=a$, $i=b$, $j=c$, and $j=d$; $\phi_o(i,j)$ is the input value for that porosity, and X_j is the jth parameter. Modification to X_j then would amount to increases or decreases in all the porosities in the corresponding region. Other parameters could be used to adjust properties in other regions in a similar way.

Because the number of field measurements may not be large and because of the large number of possible combinations of properties, the resultant set of parameters that minimizes Q may not be unique—i.e., there may be some other sets of parameters that would give just as low a value for Q. In addition, the valley of Q is often very shallow in reservoir simulation problems. That means that small changes in Q may result from large changes in the set of X_j. The result is that some methods of minimizing Q may run into difficulty near the solution. In particular, some minimization methods may tend to zigzag close to the solution.

D.1 Direct Method

A variety of methods for automatic history matching have been proposed. One simple method is the "direct method" presented by Veatch and Thomas.[1] The two-dimensional equation that we will use in this discussion is

$$\phi\frac{\partial}{\partial t}(S_p/B_p)=\frac{\partial}{\partial x}\left(\frac{k_x k_{rp}}{\mu_p B_p}\right)\frac{\partial \Phi_p}{\partial x}+\frac{\partial}{\partial y}\left(\frac{k_y k_{rp}}{\mu_p B_p}\right)\frac{\partial \Phi_p}{\partial y}+q_p, \quad \text{(D.4)}$$

for each fluid phase, p, where

B_p = FVF,
k_{rp} = relative permeability,
μ_p = viscosity,
q_p = source or sink term for Phase p, and
Φ_p = potential for Phase p.

The finite-difference form will be

$$\phi\frac{\partial}{\partial t}(S_p/B_p)\Delta x\Delta yh=\Delta_x k_x\left(\frac{k_{rp}}{\mu_p B_p}\Delta_x\Phi_p\right)\frac{\Delta yh}{\Delta x}$$

$$+\Delta_y k_y\left(\frac{k_{rp}}{\mu_p B_p}\Delta_y\Phi_p\right)\frac{\Delta xh}{\Delta y}+q_p. \quad \text{(D.5)}$$

In Veatch's direct method, the difference operator is defined as

$$\Delta_x A\Delta_x\Phi=A_{i+½}(\Phi_{i+1}-\Phi_i)-A_{i-½}(\Phi_i-\Phi_{i-1}). \quad \text{(D.6)}$$

Then the equations can be written as functions of k_x, k_y, and ϕ. The form of the equation is for each gridblock

$$\alpha_1 k_{x_{i+½,j}}-\alpha_2 k_{x_{i-½,j}}+\alpha_3 k_{y_{i,j+½}}-\alpha_4 k_{y_{i,j-½}}-\beta\phi=q_p, \quad \text{(D.7)}$$

where α and β are known quantities dependent on the pressures and saturations in the gridblock and in adjacent blocks. If the pressure profile and the saturation profile are known at n different times, the method can be used to solve directly for n values of ϕ and k.

This method has the advantage of simplicity and does not require the calculation of any derivatives, $\partial Q/\partial k_j$, which can be a time-consuming operation. The principal disadvantage is that it requires pressure and saturation functions at every grid location at several times. In practical situations, that quantity of field data is not usually available. In addition, the solution is required to fit all the pressure and saturation data exactly. As a result, the method can be inaccurate or can yield physically unrealistic results if measurement errors occur.

D.2 Influence Coefficient Methods

Several authors have developed solutions to the inverse simulation problems that are based on influence coefficients, C_I, defined in Refs. 2 and 3 as

$$C_{I_j}=\frac{\partial Q}{\partial X_j} \text{ or } C_{I_{k,j}}=\frac{\partial R_k}{\partial X_j}. \quad \text{(D.8)}$$

Jacquard and Jain[2] applied the methods of electronic analyzers to develop a solution algorithm. The influence coefficients are determined numerically by perturbing each variable one at a time and performing a new simulation after each perturbation. The effect of the change in each parameter, ΔX_j, on each residual is used to calculate the sensitivity coefficients. Carter *et al.*[3] rely on linear programming to minimize an error function, e, defined in terms of the influence coefficients:

$$e=A\Delta X-b, \quad \text{(D.9)}$$

where A is a matrix of influence coefficients, ΔX is a column matrix of the ΔX_j, and b is a column matrix of differences $p_k^o-p_k^c$. These can be very effective methods. They require only first derivatives and are easy to apply. The principal drawbacks are that the behavior near the solution may become less efficient and that the final distribution may be unrealistic.

Hirasaki[4] provides tools similar to influence coefficients for adjusting reservoir properties of simple models based on differences between observed and calculated oil recoveries. Hirasaki analyzed one-dimensional models to develop relationships between "sensitivity coefficients" and dimensionless fluid production. The sensitivity coefficients are defined as the derivatives of cumulative oil production with respect to several reservoir properties—e.g., permeability and porosity. Graphs of the sensitivity-coefficient relationships are used to help estimate the amount to change reservoir properties to match oil recovery.

Hirasaki's method is very easy to apply and actually is closer to a hand adjustment than an automatic method. For very simple systems, when only oil production is to be matched, this approach can be useful. More complex reservoirs with pressures and well data to be matched require more-sophisticated methods.

Slater and Durrer[5] proposed a modification to Jacquard and Jain's method that reduces the time required to obtain a solution. Slater and Durrer's method also computes the change in each residual, which they define as a set of differences between observed pressures and calculated pressures, all in a given region of the reservoir, as a result of a perturbation in the reservoir properties in that region. The effect of perturbations on residuals is used to determine whether the perturbation was in the correct direction. Once the direction of change for each property has been determined, a step in that direction is taken and another simulation is run.

This method differs from Jacquard and Jain's method in that it is not necessary to run another set of simulations at each iteration to obtain sensitivity coefficients.

D.3 Regression Methods

Many of the methods discussed up to this point do not calculate derivatives of the objective function, Q. This approach saves time but may also reduce the effectiveness of the methods because it does not include a mechanism for using information about the effect of changes in a variable in one area of a reservoir on pressures in other regions of the reservoir. Derivation and use of such information require a more-sophisticated approach—e.g., regression. In a regression method, the derivatives of the objective function with respect to each variable are analyzed concurrently to determine the optimum direction for the parameters ΔX_j. The effects of all variables on each residual are included simultaneously.

The most popular regression approaches are gradient methods. All gradient methods start from a base case constituting the best initial guess for each of the reservoir parameters, X_j^i. These parameters are then combined to form a column matrix

$$X^i=(X_1^i,X_2^i\ldots X_n^i)^T. \quad \text{(D.10)}$$

The value of the objective function Q at X^i is $Q(X^i)$. Another X is selected so that

$$X=X^i+\Delta X=(X_1^i+\Delta X_1,X_2^i+\Delta X_2\ldots X_n^i+\Delta X_n)^T \quad \text{(D.11)}$$

and a new value of $Q(X)$ is obtained. If $Q(X)<Q(X^i)$, the change of parameters from X^i to X will move Q closer to a minimum. Gradient methods seek to use the rate of change of Q for different selections of ΔX to select a particular ΔX that will move Q toward its minimum.

This can be seen more clearly by considering a model with two parameters, X_1 and X_2. Q can then be thought of as a surface over Plane X_1, X_2, as illustrated in Fig. D.1, which shows contours of equal Q with a minimum Q at X_1', X_2'. Also shown is an initial guess for X^i and one possible selection for ΔX. Gradient methods use the rate of change of Q in the vicinity of X^i to select the optimum direction and magnitude for ΔX.

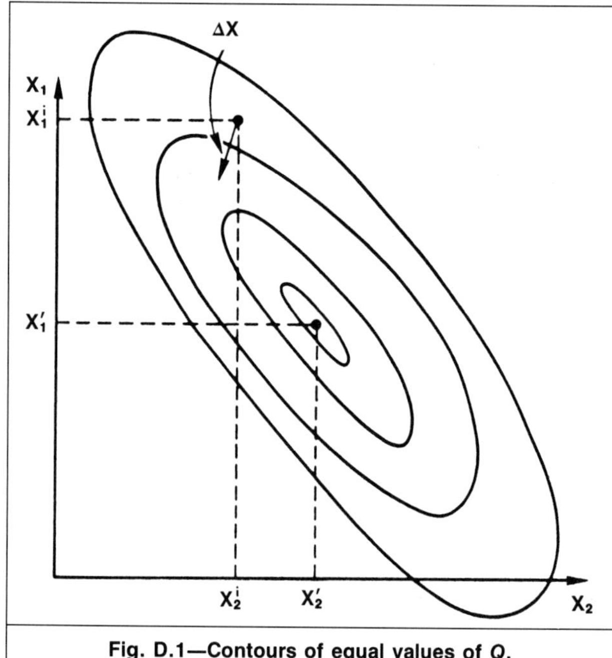

Fig. D.1—Contours of equal values of Q.

D.4 Gauss-Newton Method

One regression approach that uses first derivatives is the Gauss-Newton method, which was applied to reservoir history matching by Jahns[6] and Thomas *et al.*[7]

Once again the objective function, Q, is defined as a sum of squares of a set of residuals:

$$Q=\sum_{k=1}^{N_r} R_k^2(X_1,X_2,X_3\ldots X_n), \quad \text{(D.12)}$$

where $R_k(X_1\ldots X_n)=F_{sk}(p_k^o-p_k^c)$ and F_{sk} is the weighting factor applied to the kth pressure error.

For Q to be a minimum at $X^i+\Delta X$, the following equation must be satisfied:

$$\frac{\partial Q}{\partial X_i}=2\sum_{k=1}^{N_r} R_k(X^i+\Delta X)\frac{\partial R_k(X^i+\Delta X)}{\partial X_i}=0 \quad \text{(D.13)}$$

for $i=1,2\ldots n$.

A Taylor-series expansion about X^i including only the first derivative gives

$$R_k(X^i+\Delta X)=R_k(X^i)+\sum_{j=1}^{n}\Delta X_j\frac{\partial R_k(X^i)}{\partial X_j}. \quad \text{(D.14)}$$

Upon substituting, the result is

$$\sum_{k=1}^{N_r}\left[R_k(X^i)+\sum_{j=1}^{n}\Delta X_j\frac{\partial R_k(X^i)}{\partial X_j}\right]\frac{\partial R_k(X^i+\Delta X)}{\partial X_i}=0, \quad \text{(D.15)}$$

for $i=1,2\ldots n$. If

$$\frac{\partial R_k(X^i+\Delta X)}{\partial X_i}\simeq\frac{\partial R_k(X^i)}{\partial X_i},$$

rearrangement gives

$$\sum_{j=1}^{n}\sum_{k=1}^{N_r}\frac{\partial R_k}{\partial X_i}\frac{\partial R_k}{\partial X_j}\Delta X_j=-\sum_{k=1}^{N_r}R_k(X^i)\frac{\partial R_k}{\partial X_i} \quad \text{(D.16)}$$

for $i=1\ldots n$ and where all derivatives are evaluated at X^i.

This has the form

$$A\Delta X=b, \quad \text{(D.17)}$$

where

$$A_{i,j}=\sum_{k=1}^{N_r}\frac{\partial R_k}{\partial X_i}\frac{\partial R_k}{\partial X_j},\ 1\le i\le n,\ 1\le j\le n$$

and

$$b_i=-\sum_{k=1}^{N_r}R_k(X^i)\frac{\partial R_k}{\partial X_i},\ 1\le i\le n.$$

The first derivatives are obtained by perturbing the variables X_i one at a time while holding the other variables constant and computing the effects on each residual R_k. The equation can be solved for ΔX by any one of a number of solution algorithms. ΔX is the direction for change in X in Thomas *et al.*'s algorithm. The magnitude of ΔX is then determined from a quadratic search along the search direction. Function Q is evaluated at two points in the search direction along with the base point. If Q_a, Q_b, and Q_d are the values of the objective function at Distances a, b, and d along ΔX, then

$$Q_a=c_1a^2+c_2a+c_3, \quad \text{(D.18a)}$$

$$Q_b=c_1b^2+c_2b+c_3, \quad \text{(D.18b)}$$

and

$$Q_d=c_1d^2+c_2d+c_3. \quad \text{(D.18c)}$$

Thomas *et al.* show that the minimum value for Q will occur at

$$|\Delta X|=\frac{c_2}{2c_1}. \quad \text{(D.19)}$$

Application of the algorithm is straightforward. The steps are as follows.

1. Specify X^i as the best guess of reservoir properties.
2. Calculate $\partial R_k/\partial X_j$ for all k and j numerically. This involves $n+1$ simulations of the history period for n variables. Compute A and b.
3. Solve $A\Delta X=b$ for ΔX.
4. Determine distance along the search vector by quadratic search with $|\Delta X|=c_2/2c_1$.
5. Evaluate Q at $X^i+\Delta X$.
6. Repeat if Q is not small enough or if ΔQ is still large.

This method is more expensive than simpler methods, but it is still less expensive than the second-derivative method discussed later. It is easy to apply and generally results in reductions in the objective function, Q. It is also more effective than simpler methods but still may take many iterations to converge to a minimum. In addition, Matrix A may be ill-conditioned and Step 3 may be difficult to solve. The principal advantage of the method is that it has been tested on reservoir problems and generally improves the accuracy of the history match.

D.5 Newton's Method

The Gauss-Newton method uses only the first-derivative term in the Taylor expansion of each residual R_k. Greater efficiency in the solution of the direction for ΔX can be achieved if the second derivatives, $\partial^2 Q/\partial X_i \partial X_j$, are included.[8-10] Newton's method uses the second derivatives in a Taylor expansion of $\partial Q/\partial X_i$ around X^i, shown by

$$\frac{\partial Q}{\partial X_i}(X^i+\Delta X)=\frac{\partial Q}{\partial X_i}(X^i)+\sum_{j=1}^{n}\frac{\partial^2 Q}{\partial X_j \partial X_i}\Delta X_j=0,\ 1\le i\le n. \quad \text{(D.20)}$$

But

$$\frac{\partial Q}{\partial X_i}(X)=2\sum_{k=1}^{N_r} R_k(X)\frac{\partial R_k}{\partial X_i} \quad \text{(D.21)}$$

and

$$\frac{\partial^2 Q}{\partial X_j \partial X_i}=2\sum_{k=1}^{N_r}\frac{\partial R_k}{\partial X_j}\frac{\partial R_k}{\partial X_i}+2\sum_{k=1}^{N_r} R_k(X)\frac{\partial^2 R_k}{\partial X_j \partial X_i}. \quad \text{(D.22)}$$

Therefore,

$$\sum_{k=1}^{N_r} R_k(X^i)\frac{\partial R_k}{\partial X_i}=-\sum_{j=1}^{n}\sum_{k=1}^{N_r}\left[\frac{\partial R_k}{\partial X_j}\frac{\partial R_k}{\partial X_i}+R_k(X^i)\frac{\partial^2 R_k}{\partial X_j \partial X_i}\Delta X_j\right],\ 1\le i\le n \quad \text{(D.23)}$$

or in matrix form, $b=A\Delta X$.

The method is applied as follows.

1. Select X^i with best guess of reservoir properties and perform base-case simulation.
2. Determine the $\partial R_k/\partial X_i$ by performing simulations, each with a perturbation in one of the parameters.
3. Calculate sensitivity coefficients, $\partial Q/\partial X_i$, and second derivatives, $\partial^2 Q/\partial X_i \partial X_j$, with use of Eqs. D.21 and D.22.
4. Create b and A.
5. Solve for ΔX.
6. Perform simulation with $X^i+\Delta X$.
7. Repeat previous steps if convergence criteria are not met.

The approach is more effective than first-derivative methods in determining an optimum ΔX, but it can use large amounts of computer time calculating second derivatives. Bishop *et al.*[8] estimate the computer-time expenditures for calculation of second derivatives in their approach as $1+(n^2+n-2)/(n_G+2)$, where n is the number of variables and n_G is the number of gridblocks.

In some cases, the second-derivative matrix, A, may be singular, or the solution in Step 4 may fail to converge for other reasons. Bishop *et al.*[8] and Breit *et al.*[9] replaced Steps 3 and 4 with a "pattern-search" algorithm.[10] This approach has fewer potential numerical difficulties but may not converge to a minimum Q as rapidly.

The transformational discrimination approach is another second-derivative method that has been successfully applied to very simple tank-type reservoir models in Rossen's[11] and Lutes *et al.*'s[12] algorithms, but for more-sophisticated models, the time requirements can be exorbitant. The algorithm is described in more detail in Ref. 13.

A recent approach to reduction of the time required to obtain second derivatives of the objective function is worth mentioning. If the process has progressed to the point where X is close to X'—i.e., Q is near a minimum—it is reasonable to assume that the individual residuals, R_k, are random in size and that they are small. If the term

$$\sum_{k=1}^{N_r} R_k(X)\frac{\partial^2 R_k}{\partial X_j \partial X_i}$$

is assumed to be negligible, the second derivative of Q becomes

$$\frac{\partial^2 Q}{\partial X_j \partial X_i}=2\sum_{k=1}^{N_r}\frac{\partial R_k}{\partial X_j}\frac{\partial R_k}{\partial X_i}, \quad \text{(D.24)}$$

and only first-derivative simulations are needed. The sensitivity coefficients alone would be sufficient to estimate the second derivatives of the objective function. For reservoir problems, this assumption appears to be valid and significant savings in computer time can be achieved.

To reduce further the number of simulations required, some researchers have assumed that the sensitivity coefficients, $\partial R_k/\partial X_i$, are constant over some region around X^i. Therefore, $\partial R_k/\partial X_i$ would not need to be recalculated at each iteration. $\partial Q/\partial X_i$ would change as X changes, because the residuals $R_k(X)$ would change. Using this assumption, several ΔX steps could be taken before recalculation of the derivatives. The approximation of derivatives and the linearity assumption were both used in a simulation of a large three-dimensional reservoir by Boberg *et al.*[14]

For a single-phase model, Bishop *et al.*[8] have shown that the equations for the derivatives of pressure with respect to reservoir properties, $\partial p_k/\partial X_i$, can be calculated with an equation that is very similar to the pressure equation itself—i.e., if

$$Ap=b \quad \text{(D.25)}$$

is the pressure equation at a given time during a simulation, then

$$A\frac{\partial p}{\partial X_i}=b_i,\ i=1,2\ldots n \quad \text{(D.26)}$$

can be solved for the derivatives at the same time. If the residuals are defined as pressure errors,

$$R_k=F_{sk}(p_k^o-p_k^c), \quad \text{(D.27)}$$

then the derivatives can be calculated analytically instead of numerically. Because Matrix A is identical in all the equations, the work required to solve for the derivatives is significantly less than the work required to perform $n+1$ simulations to calculate the derivatives numerically. This approach is applicable only to single-phase systems.

D.6 Optimal-Control Methods

A major advance in automatic history matching is the application of optimal-control methods. Chen *et al.*[15] and Chavent *et al.*[16] simultaneously published algorithms that used this approach. Both papers restrict their analyses to single-phase systems.

In optimal-control theory,[17] the matrix equation to be solved is

$$\frac{\partial p(t)}{\partial t}=f[p(t),\ u(t)], \quad \text{(D.28)}$$

where $p(t)$ is the "state" variable—e.g., pressure—and $u(t)$ is a "forcing" variable—e.g., permeabilities. It can be linearized to

$$\frac{\partial p(t)}{\partial t}=Ap(t)+Bu(t). \quad \text{(D.29)}$$

One possible objective function to be minimized is

$$Q[p(0),t_f]=\int_0^{t_f} f[p(t),\ u(t)]dt, \quad \text{(D.30)}$$

where t_f is the final time. Lapidus[17] shows that we can define a set of adjoint variables,

$$\psi=(\psi_1,\ \psi_2,\ \psi_3\ldots\psi_n)^T, \quad \text{(D.31)}$$

so that the complete set of equations to be solved becomes

$$\frac{\partial p(t)}{\partial t}=Ap(t), \quad \text{(D.32a)}$$

$$p(0)=p^i, \quad \text{(D.32b)}$$

$$\frac{\partial \psi(t)}{\partial t}=-A\psi(t), \quad \text{(D.33a)}$$

and

$$\psi(t_f)=0. \quad \text{(D.33b)}$$

The change in the objective function resulting from change in $u(t)$ becomes

$$\Delta Q=\psi^T(0)\Delta p(0)+\int_0^{t_f}\psi^T(t)B(t)\Delta u(t)\mathrm{d}t. \quad \text{(D.34)}$$

The equations are then solved forward in time to obtain $p(t)$ and backward in time to obtain $\psi(t)$. The effect of any change in the variables contained in $u(t)$ on the objective function, Q, can then be determined.

In reservoir simulation, the pressure equation, in matrix form, is

$$\frac{\partial p}{\partial t}=\nabla\cdot[\eta(x,y)\nabla p], \quad \text{(D.35)}$$

if gravity is neglected. The initial condition is $p(0)=p^i$, where $\eta(x,y)$ is the hydraulic diffusivity, $k/\phi\mu c$, at a point (x,y). Chen *et al.* show that there is an adjoint function, ψ, analogous to pressure, such that

$$\frac{\partial \psi}{\partial t}=-\nabla\cdot[\eta(x,y)\nabla\psi], \quad \text{(D.36)}$$

with a final condition

$$\psi(t_f)=0. \quad \text{(D.37)}$$

The optimal change in $\eta(x,y)$ is

$$\delta\eta(x,y)=W(x,y)\int_0^{t_f}[(\nabla\psi)\cdot(\nabla p)]\mathrm{d}t, \quad \text{(D.38)}$$

where $W(x,y)$ is an arbitrary positive function of x,y. Because

$$k(x,y)=\eta(x,y)\phi\mu c, \quad \text{(D.39)}$$

then

$$\delta k(x,y)=\phi\mu c W(x,y)\int_0^{t_f}[(\nabla\psi)\cdot(\nabla p)]\mathrm{d}t. \quad \text{(D.40)}$$

The algorithm is as follows.[15]

1. Estimate $k^i(x,y)$ with the best guess for the permeability distribution. Compute $\eta(x,y)$.
2. Compute $p(t)$ by simulating the history period.
3. Compute $\psi(t)$ by solving Eqs. D.36 and D.37.
4. Compute $\delta k(x,y)$ from Eq. D.40 and update $k^j(x,y)$ by $k^{j+1}(x,y)=k^j(x,y)+\delta k^j(x,y)$.
5. Repeat if not converged.

The optimal-control approach requires only the equivalent of two simulations per iteration and therefore is far less costly than second-derivative methods and can be less costly than first-derivative methods. It also results in parameters that are continuous functions of space, eliminating the need to discretize and lump those variables. Unfortunately, the extension of these methods to multiple phases and multiple dimensions has not been as successful, and use of the methods on real reservoir problems is limited. In addition, limiting the range of parameters to within realistic physical limits is not an easy task in this approach.

Chen and Seinfeld[18] extended the optimal-control approach to the estimation of boundary location for a reservoir. Ref. 19 presents more detail about this solution.

Chen and Seinfeld's algorithm was extended to multiple phases by Wasserman *et al.*[19] Their multidimensional algorithm still matches only pressure data but can handle relative permeabilities and changing saturations. The critical assumption is that saturation-dependent functions calculated in the forward simulation are also applicable in the backward simulations.

D.7 Current Applicability of Regression Methods

The use of automatic history matching in reservoir simulation is still limited by computing requirements. With recent and continuing developments in computing hardware, however, these methods should become more attractive. If used properly, they can greatly reduce the effort required to develop a reasonable reservoir description.

Nomenclature

A = coefficient matrix
b = column matrix of known quantities
B = FVF, res m^3/stock-tank m^3
C = coefficient matrix
F_{sk} = weighting factor
h = thickness, m
k_{rp} = relative permeability to Phase p, fraction
k_x, k_y = permeability in x and y directions, m^2
n = number of parameters to be determined
n_G = number of gridblocks
N_r = number of residuals
p = pressure, kPa
p_k^c = pressure calculated by reservoir simulation for a given position at given time, Pa
p_k^o = pressure observed at a given position in reservoir at given time, Pa
q_p = source or sink term for Phase p, stock-tank m^3/s
Q = objective function
r = radius, m
R_k = kth residual
S = saturation, fraction
t = time, seconds
u = forcing variable
Δx = block length in x direction
X = column matrix of unknown parameters—e.g., porosity or permeability
ΔX = column matrix of changes in reservoir parameters
Δy = block length in y direction
Δ_x, Δ_y = difference operators
η = hydraulic diffusivity, m^2/s
μ = viscosity, Pa·s
ϕ = porosity, fraction
Φ = potential, Pa
ψ = adjoint variable

Subscripts

f = final
p = fluid phase
x,y = x and y directions

Superscripts

c = calculated
i = initial
o = observed
T = transpose of matrix

References

1. Veatch, R.W. Jr. and Thomas, G.W.: "A Direct Approach for History Matching," paper SPE 3515 presented at the 1971 SPE Annual Meeting, New Orleans, Oct. 3-6.
2. Jacquard, P. and Jain, C.: "Permeability Distribution from Field Pressure Data," *SPEJ* (Dec. 1965) 281-94; *Trans.*, AIME, **234.**
3. Carter, R.D. *et al.*: "Performance Matching With Constraints," *SPEJ* (April 1974) 187-92; *Trans.*, AIME, **257.**
4. Hirasaki, G.J.: "Sensitivity Coefficients for History Matching Oil Displacement Processes," *SPEJ* (Feb. 1975) 39-49.
5. Slater, G.E. and Durrer, E.J.: "Adjustment of Reservoir Simulation Models to Match Field Performance," *SPEJ* (Sept. 1971) 295-305; *Trans.*, AIME, **251.**
6. Jahns, H.O.: "A Rapid Method for Obtaining a Two-Dimensional Reservoir Description from Well Pressure Response Data," *SPEJ* (Dec. 1966) 315-27; *Trans.*, AIME, **237.**
7. Thomas, L.K., Hellums, L.J., and Reheis, G.M.: "A Nonlinear Automatic History Matching Technique for Reservoir Simulation Models," *SPEJ* (Dec. 1972) 508-14; *Trans.*, AIME, **253.**
8. Bishop, K.A. *et al.*: "The Application of Sensitivity Analysis to Reservoir Simulation," paper SPE 6102 presented at the 1976 SPE Annual Technical Conference and Exhibition, New Orleans, Oct. 3-6.
9. Breit, V.S. *et al.*: "A Technique for Assessing and Improving the Quality of Reservoir Parameter Estimates Used in Numerical Simulators," paper SPE 4546 presented at the 1973 SPE Annual Meeting, Las Vegas, Sept. 30-Oct. 3.
10. Wilde, D.J. and Beightler, C.S.: *Foundations of Optimization*, Prentice Hall Inc., Englewood Cliffs, NJ (1967) 307-18.
11. Rossen, R.H.: "A Regression Approach To Estimating Gas In Place for Gas Fields," *JPT* (Oct. 1975) 1283-89; *Trans.*, AIME, **259.**
12. Lutes, J.L. *et al.*: "Accelerated Blowdown of a Strong Water Drive Gas Reservoir," *JPT* (Dec. 1977) 1533-38.
13. Fariss, R.H. and Law, V.J.: "Transformational Discrimination for Unconstrained Optimization," *Ind. Chem. Eng. Fund.* (1972) **11,** No. 2, 154-61.
14. Boberg, T.C. *et al.*: "Application of Inverse Simulation to a Complex Multireservoir System," *JPT* (July 1974) 801-08; *Trans.*, AIME, **257.**
15. Chen, W.H. *et al.*: "A New Algorithm for Automatic History Matching," *SPEJ* (Dec. 1974) 593-608; *Trans.*, AIME, **257.**
16. Chavent, G., Dupuy, M., and Lemonnier, P.: "History Matching by Use of Optimal Theory," *SPEJ* (Feb. 1975) 74-86; *Trans.*, AIME, **259.**
17. Lapidus, L.: *Optimal Control of Engineering Processes*, Blaisdell Publishing Co., Waltham, MA (1967).
18. Chen, W.H. and Seinfeld, J.H.: "Estimation of the Location of the Boundary of a Petroleum Reservoir," *SPEJ* (Feb. 1975) 19-38.
19. Wasserman, M.L., Emanuel, A.S., and Seinfeld, J.H.: "Practical Applications of Optimal-Control Theory to History Matching Multiphase Simulator Models," *SPEJ* (Aug. 1975) 347-55; *Trans.*, AIME, **259.**

Author Index

Subject Index

D

E

Q

R

T

U

V

W